CW00418422

THE
GERMAN
OCCUPATION
OF JERSEY

THE
GERMAN OCCUPATION OF JERSEY

AGRICULTURE AND SURVIVAL IN A TIME OF WAR

ANDREW GILSON

AMBERLEY

"The past is never dead. It's not even past."
William Cuthbert Faulkner

First published 2023

Amberley Publishing
The Hill, Stroud
Gloucestershire, GL5 4EP

www.amberley-books.com

British Library Cataloguing in Publication Data.
A catalogue record for this book is available from the British Library.

ISBN 978 1 3981 1841 6 (hardback)
ISBN 978 1 3981 1842 3 (ebook)

1 2 3 4 5 6 7 8 9 10

Typesetting by SJmagic DESIGN SERVICES, India.
Printed in the UK.

Foreword

I am delighted to write a foreword to this important book which, as well as providing the only published record of how agriculture served the population of Jersey during the difficult years of occupation by an armed aggressor, also provides us with lessons relevant to the questions of resilience that are being asked of communities in a modern world.

It was clear from the start of the occupation that active resistance by an unarmed local population, in such a small island, faced with an overwhelming army of occupation would have been futile. Survival was to be the name of the game, and the primary objective of the key actors was to feed the people.

What was so important about agriculture in Jersey? In 1939 there were over 1,800 smallholdings and farms in Jersey on an island of some 45 square miles, and it was the dominant economic activity. The 1931 census shows that 25% of the male population were employed in the sector, which was more than twice the number of the next largest activity.

The industry in Jersey, in addition to providing a considerable proportion of food for the Island, was also of international importance. The agricultural returns for 1939 show that approximately 50% of the land area was dedicated to growing cash crops for export to the UK mainland, mostly potatoes and tomatoes. A further 30% was dedicated to producing forage for the population of Jersey cattle that, due to their ability to produce yields of exceptional-quality milk, were being exported in large numbers to establish breeding populations globally.

What was so extraordinary about the occupation period? The author explores how agriculture in Jersey pivoted, within a matter of months, from being a largely export-focused industry into one primarily dedicated to producing food for local consumption. This became vital as the war went on, particularly after the Island was cut off from the Continent following the Normandy landings.

The book provides a detailed examination into the relationship between the German military government and the Jersey civilian government, who, together with the Royal Jersey Agricultural & Horticultural Society and Jersey Farmers Union, had to work together to ensure the Island's survival through its farming industry. It provides a remarkable insight into how much was achieved by a few key individuals. Much has been written about the occupation, but this is the first time that the efforts of the agricultural community have been properly recognised.

What are the lessons for today? In times of global instability, caused either by war or climate change, governments begin to focus on the resilience of their communities. A large part of this is questioning the ability to provide basic commodities to ensure that society continues to function, which naturally includes the availability of food.

In recent decades, military action in various countries resulted in the collapse of agricultural systems, undermining economies and the ability to feed people. This book provides a case study in how an invading power took a pragmatic approach to working with the local institutions in an attempt to ensure some form of stability in uncertain times.

Andrew Gilson, on his retirement from teaching, approached me with various items of research on the subject that he had undertaken as material for his students of history, and asked if I was interested in them. I found his work fascinating and rather rashly suggested he write them up as book. I am extremely glad that he has, and I congratulate Andrew for completing what undoubtedly will become the main reference on the subject.

Whether you wish to become immersed in the detail of agricultural activity during the occupation, or simply want a flavour of what farming life must have been like, I am confident that readers will be as fascinated as I was. It leaves me wondering how we would cope if confronted with the same challenges today?

James Godfrey
Chief Executive & Secretary
Royal Jersey Agricultural & Horticultural Society

May 2023

Royal
Jersey
AGRICULTURAL
& HORTICULTURAL
Society

Preface

The year 2020 marked the 75th Anniversary of the end of German occupation of Jersey. In early 1945 the Island faced the real possibility that the very existence of its population, way of life and culture would disintegrate after five years of constant pressure and interference from the German authorities. The level of social cohesion amongst the local population was crumbling as different groups, individuals and organisations began to react against those they thought had been too close to the German Military Government or German military forces. It must be understood and accepted that there were varied relationships between locals and occupiers. It was not simply a case of Jersey people ignoring all Germans. A German Staff Officer, when asked about local collaboration, answered that the relationships of locals with Germans was "either as Ghosts or Prostitutes". This was wrong. The evidence is clear that there were many shades of relationships between the differing classes and individuals. If we are to understand these connections, it must be studied with a differentiated empathy approach. The various elements of society – social, political, administrative, professions and trades, town and country – had different experiences with the Germans. The leading class of approximately twenty-five top Jersey farmers had structural relationships that were very different to those of the small tenant farmer.

2020 was an important year as the Island was under another real threat from the Covid-19 pandemic, and it also marked the release of new primary sources of evidence in Jersey and in France. The Channel Islands during the occupation were part of the German government of France, so correspondence concerning local matters from Field Command 515, Jersey, were copied and sent to higher authorities based in Normandy and Paris.

This work was started when I retired as a teacher and Head of History after thirty-five years. I had written and produced several Jersey occupation A-level modules and taught these for eight years. During this period many of my students brought in documentation concerning the German occupation, which I copied and incorporated into these A-levels. It became evident that the information from various occupation secondary sources was simply wrong and, in several instances, historical mistakes had been "copied and pasted" from one secondary source to another. In 2015 I obtained the minutes of meetings of the Jersey Farmers Union (JFU) during the occupation and of the "Joint JFU and RJA&HS Emergency Committee" which had been set up early in 1941. In addition, the minutes of the occupation "Price Advisory Board" were discovered. In view of all these new primary sources, the Royal Jersey Agricultural and Horticultural Society asked me to prepare a description of agriculture during the occupation. The work entailed some 5,000 pages of primary source documents from 300 files and research took 7,500 hours. It also entailed twenty-two interviews over seven years.

I would like to take this opportunity to thank all those islanders who allowed me to interview them and to take notes. Sadly, due to the longevity of the work and the passage of time, several of my interviewees have since passed away. I would especially like to thank Alan Allix, a founder member of the Channel Island Occupation Society, who kindly allowed me the benefit of his personal research on Field Command 515, including details of his interviews with Dr W. Casper and W. Heider, Senior Staff Officers, and Karl Greier, an Austrian civilian seconded as an interpreter between 1940 and 1943. In addition, Mr Allix allowed me the use of his personal archive of occupation photographs, collected during his sixty years of research. It seems difficult to believe that professional historians who have interviewed Mr Allix have in the main ignored his research collected over this period. Mr Allix also accompanied me to Salzburg, Austria, and assisted me in the archives there.

In addition, I would like to thank and acknowledge the assistance and support of Wolfgang Pelz and his brothers in Salzburg who very kindly allowed me access to several of their father's private letters and the family biography. All material handed to me was unredacted with no preconditions for use. I am very appreciative of the time given to me by Josie Day, the daughter of Louis Guillemette, who checked and assisted me on several specific details from her father's secret diary. I also thank Maureen Rondel, who found the JFU occupation minutes, and allowed me to copy them; Robert Germain who allowed me use of his company's occupation tobacco ledger; and the executors of Miss Joyce Le Ruez's will. Joy Le Marquand, Ruth Hayward and Pam Laurens allowed me full access to their aunt's private papers and diaries. I would also acknowledge the assistance of Nicola Hughes, Gillian Margaret Coutanche, Vincent Obbard, Michael Dubras, Christine de la Haye, Arthur Le Blancq, the Pallot family of the Jersey Steam Museum, and the late Dennis Le Flem and Nicholas Le Quesne Blampied.

I also acknowledge the assistance of the RJA&HS, who have sponsored the work, and its personnel. James Godfrey who initially unearthed a large amount of occupation documents (and gave me a crash course on the history of Island cattle breeding); Derrick Frigot MBE who explained the significance and history of the major Island cattle breeders; and David Hambrook, David Cotterell, Jane Harvey, and Rachelle Robinson.

The Jersey Archive personnel who assisted and pointed me to the correct files were Stuart Nicolle, Trudy Foster, Janne White, Emily Le Feuvre, Harry Le Feuvre, Catherine Porter and Toni Wolstenholme. In particular, Toni's work in putting online the agricultural files from the occupation and identifying Hans Egon Pelz's importance in the German Military Government was of great value, with the Archive's files B/A/W31/2 onwards forming the backbone of the work. I thank Dr David Bailiey for all the many hours spent on producing from the original German occupation photographs the excellent-quality prints for this book.

The Jersey Library personnel who assisted me were Julia Grady, Susan Armstrong, Jackie Monticelli and Marco P. Campanini. I would also like to thank: Amanda Bennett, of the Priaulx Library, Guernsey; Olivia Grimes, Office of the Superintendent Registrar, Jersey; and Kaya Camara and Martin Huelin, of the States of Jersey Greffe, who assisted me on the complexities of occupation milk and tobacco legislation. Other colleagues who assisted me with information were Stephen Thompson, Howard Davis Farm; Howard Butlin Baker; Carolyn Labey, who kindly gave me copies of her grandfather's occupation account; Lesley Averty for the 1938 photograph of Touzel Brée; and Cerys Rimmer, of the Hydrographic Office.

From Salzburg, Austria, I acknowledge the assistance of the following: Dr Eva Rinnerthaler and Alfred Höck of the Amt der Salzburger Landesarchiv; Dr Peter Krammel, Stadt Salzburg Magistrat, Stadarchiv und Statistik; and Andreas Riedl, Amt der Salzburger Landesregierung. From Vienna, Tarik Gaafar, Universität für Bodenkultur.

From Freiberg, Germany, Michael Noth of the German Military Archives sent me details of Field Command 515, and from Berlin, the Max Planck Society, detailed reports and papers on the Jersey-German crossbreeding programme. From Dummerstorf, the Research Institute for Farm Animal Biology, FBN, kindly allowed me the use of Dr Lauprecht's 1942 scientific article on Jersey cattle, and information on the cattle shipped to Germany in late 1940 for crossbreeding with German cattle. I am very grateful to Professor Wilfred Brade and Dr Gunther Vierek for giving their time to explain the background of the above to a non-scientist.

I would like to thank Johannes von Heissen, and Uwe Günther, who translated for me detailed German reports, documents, letters and biographies. In addition, Valérie Videt, whose invaluable work on the French material saved me from major errors.

Finally, I would like to thank my long-suffering typist Fiona Gardiner who had to deal with my written scripts for seven years and never complained, and Christine Vibert who not only proofread and edited, but also checked, as far as possible, every Jersey, German and French name, address, and title with the official Jersey Archive record, made constructive and informative suggestions about the work, and prepared the Glossary. In addition, I would like to thank my wife, Yulia, daughter, Sophia, and sons, Jonathan and Sebastian, who had to listen to all my frustrations and accept all the time I took away from home.

Andrew Gilson
December 2022

Contents

STRUCTURAL RELATIONSHIPS: 1940–1945
An Agricultural Model

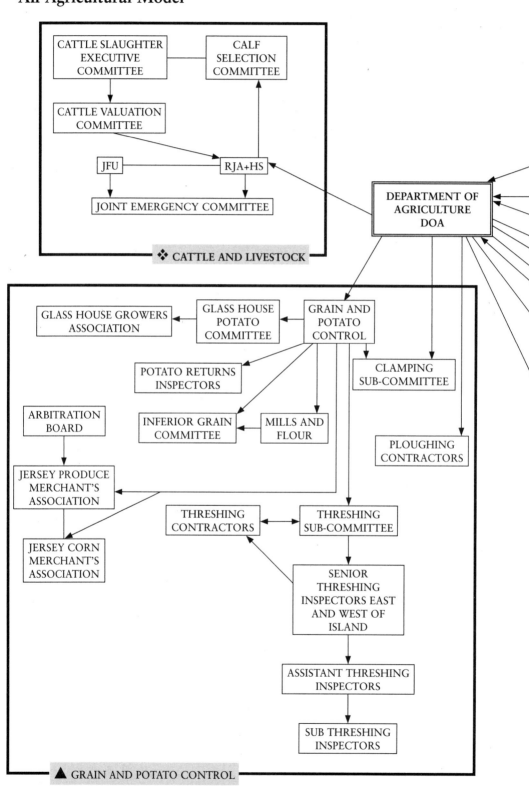

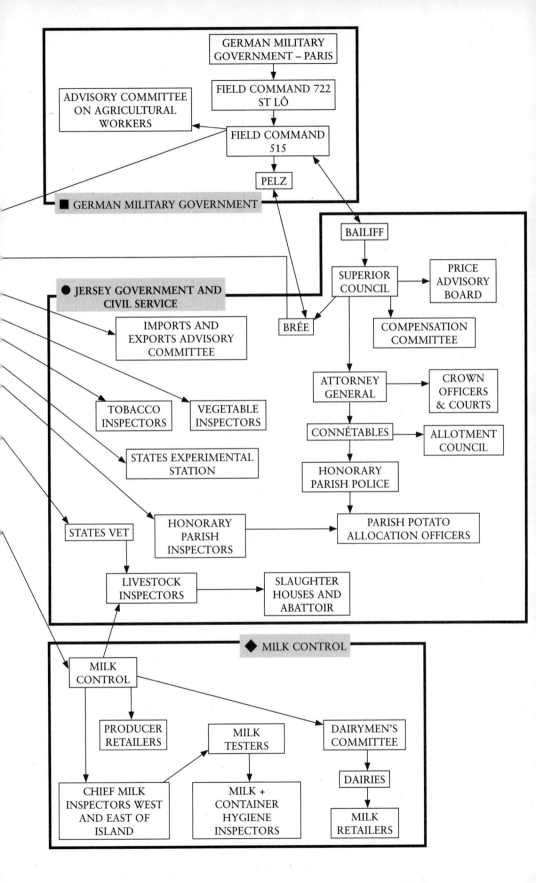

GERMAN MILITARY GOVERNMENT

GERMAN MILITARY GOVERNMENT – PARIS

FIELD COMMAND 722 ST LÔ

FIELD COMMAND 515

ADVISORY COMMITTEE ON AGRICULTURAL WORKERS

PELZ

JERSEY GOVERNMENT AND CIVIL SERVICE

BAILIFF

SUPERIOR COUNCIL

PRICE ADVISORY BOARD

BRÉE

COMPENSATION COMMITTEE

IMPORTS AND EXPORTS ADVISORY COMMITTEE

ATTORNEY GENERAL

CROWN OFFICERS & COURTS

TOBACCO INSPECTORS

VEGETABLE INSPECTORS

CONNÉTABLES

ALLOTMENT COUNCIL

STATES EXPERIMENTAL STATION

HONORARY PARISH POLICE

STATES VET

HONORARY PARISH INSPECTORS

PARISH POTATO ALLOCATION OFFICERS

LIVESTOCK INSPECTORS

SLAUGHTER HOUSES AND ABATTOIR

MILK CONTROL

MILK CONTROL

PRODUCER RETAILERS

MILK TESTERS

DAIRYMEN'S COMMITTEE

DAIRIES

CHIEF MILK INSPECTORS WEST AND EAST OF ISLAND

MILK + CONTAINER HYGIENE INSPECTORS

MILK RETAILERS

The Establishment of a New Agricultural Model, 1940–45

Structural Relationships

"The Little Breton"

The appellation conferred on Touzel John Brée by the Staff Officers of Field Command 515

In 1939 the Island authorities were considering a series of directives which would alter the traditional agricultural model. Previously, farmers had been fiercely independent, growing potatoes and tomatoes for the UK markets, producing dairy products for the local population, and competing to breed pedigree cattle for export. The military occupation in July 1940 changed this model so that it was brought under the control of the States of Jersey. The reasons were: the signing of new contracts with the occupying forces to export produce on its behalf; the immediate necessity to provide agricultural produce to the resident military forces and the civilian population; and the importation of live Continental cattle after 150 years total prohibition. In pre-war times up to 13%, some 1,300 animals, of the Island's cattle population were exported annually. It therefore became of the utmost importance that the German and Island authorities, along with the leading farming community, cooperated to protect their most important asset – Jersey's pedigree cattle herds.

The new agricultural model established and nurtured new and unique "structural relationships" between the German military administrative government (Field Command 515), the civil authorities, led by the Bailiff and the Superior Council, the Department of Agriculture (DOA) and senior civil servants, an inspectorate, and the "elite" class of farmers who formed an important community in both Island politics and the parish honorary system. It resulted in the successful development of a network of these structural relationships, which worked for the mutual benefit of both the civil and military populations.

14

The evidence demonstrates that the German authorities were cognisant of the political, social, and cultural importance of this class of about twenty-five elite farmers and as far as was practical they kept on good terms. Interestingly, the members of this group were the only islanders allowed to formally have licences to keep "hunting rifles", or any weapon, by the German authorities.

The arrival of KVR Hans Egon Pelz, Head of Agriculture and Food Supply for the Channel Islands, was the catalyst for the initial establishment of these structural relationships. On his arrival in Jersey, he immediately set up a balanced working relationship with Touzel John Brée, President of the DOA, whom he describes as his "...civilian counterpart". The question needs to be answered as to why these relationships were successful for almost the entire occupation. The fundamental reason was the role of the individual. Brée and Pelz immediately worked closely to plan, organise, and supervise Island agriculture. Both were highly intelligent, hardworking and conscientious. The latter had completed a long spell of duty in occupied Luxembourg in charge of agriculture. He was fully aware of the problems of supervising the agricultural economy of a conquered territory.

Pelz and Brée met in mid-August 1940, initially to deal with the issue of the German importation of Continental cattle and dogs. This laid the basis for their structural relationship from 1940 to August 1944 (when Pelz left) and paved the way for the Island authorities to be responsible for the agricultural model that it established, along with its 1,800 farmers.

The above facilitated the German Military Government to save its manpower. It could also lay blame at the door of the civilian authorities for any agricultural shortfalls to the resident population. Furthermore, it allowed for the fair distribution of agricultural inputs to farmers, and outputs to the civilians. As Head of Agriculture and Food Supply for the Channel Islands, Pelz could order the Island authorities to provide him with detailed statistics to monitor crop, dairy and meat production. It ensured the German military garrison received its due share, that export contracts on its behalf were correctly carried out, and allowed for secure storage of locally grown agricultural produce. Finally, it was important in checking any excesses in the countryside of the black market. Although this did occur, it was on an individual and small scale and never reached the level it had in occupied France. Island farmers who were discovered to have broken agricultural orders on a regular basis, and who illegally sold produce, were punished. Brée, however, personally preferred giving farmers a formal warning on their future conduct rather than to prosecute.

Much to the credit of Brée the production of milk and dairy products was extremely successful. Every civilian adult and child received throughout the occupation a daily ration of full-fat milk for almost the entire period. Jersey was the only territory in Nazi-occupied Europe where this full-fat ration occurred. In fact, the distribution of milk to children remained until the end of 2010, when the States of Jersey voted to discontinue this allowance to primary school children.

At the apex of this agricultural model, and its resultant structural relationships, was the German Military Government, St Germain, Paris. It issued agricultural directives to all the Field Commands in France. As mentioned, the Field Command in the Channel Islands was 515. During the first three years of the occupation Field Command 515 liaised closely with Field Command 722 at St Lô. They exchanged agricultural produce for each other's mutual benefit and monitored Continental cattle exports from Granville to the Channel Islands. Field Command 515 issued agricultural orders directly to the Bailiff and the Superior Council which, in turn, cascaded down to the DOA, the Grain and Potato and Milk Control Sections. These orders were then issued to all Island farmers with the RJA&HS and the JFU setting up a Joint Emergency Committee which tended to meet in secret, but which worked closely with the DOA when it suited. The final elements of the model were the many and varied groups of agricultural inspectors and sub-committees who kept a close watch on all the agricultural orders. The most important of these were the Honorary Parish Inspectors who were given sweeping powers originating directly from the Royal Court.

When Cultivation Orders were ignored, or not followed to the letter, this was initially dealt with by the DOA and the Honorary Parish Inspectors. Serious infringements and continual disregard of orders were then dealt with by the Attorney General, the Parish Connétables, and the Honorary Parish Police.

This agricultural model could only work by Field Command 515 allowing Inspectors out after curfew, with special passes. It is possible that much of this system of inspection came about as a result of Pelz's own experience working as an Inspector for the Federal State of Salzburg in the 1930s. Finally, we cannot underestimate the value to the population of the personal working relationship between Pelz and Brée. Agricultural matters were discussed between them before directives were issued by the States of Jersey and both men themselves often dealt with problems at grass-roots level. From Pelz's biography it is evident that he visited nearly all the major farms in Jersey and Guernsey and knew the farmers personally.

Chapter 1

Jersey Agriculture 1930–1940

The Arrival of the Colorado Beetle

"Le Doryphore – Peste Malicieuse!"

Président, Union Syndicale des Agriculteurs, St Malo, 1932

The Colorado Beetle originated from Canada and the USA. It first appeared in Europe, in Germany, at the start of the twentieth century and was eventually eradicated after an extensive effort. An outbreak also occurred in 1901 at Tilbury, England, where a number of beetles survived into the following year, before they were all destroyed.[1]

The Colorado Beetle's presence in Europe was subsequently detected in 1922. Its arrival, as a foreign invasive species, most probably occurred at the end of 1918, introduced into France, through imported goods for the war effort either from the USA or Canada.

The first two outbreaks were in 1922 in Gironde and Haute-Vienne. By 1925 it had spread to seven French Departments, nine in 1927, fourteen in 1929 and thirty in 1931. In that year, the Colorado Beetle infestation became a "real national danger". A system of nationwide inspections and spraying of potato plants with lead arsenate and the disinfection of fields with petrol or carbonated sulphur was implemented throughout France.[2]

The main export of Jersey was the Jersey Royal potato. Its export underpinned the entire economy of the Island. The States of Jersey decided on the 7th April 1931 that the risk of the Colorado Beetle spreading from France warranted a total ban on all imported French produce. On the 18th August the French Ambassador in London wrote to the Foreign Office with an official protest. The French government was not protesting about the Jersey embargo of French potatoes, but against "…the universality of the prohibition".[3]

On the 24th August the Bailiff received a letter from the French Ambassador asking for a response to be made to the Home Office, London. The Bailiff's reply on the 28th August was clear and to the point. The Colorado Beetle had been discovered in the Departments of Mayenne and Ille-et-Vilaine which were all within a "zone of protection". In consequence, the export of potatoes and tomatoes grown "inter alia" from Rennes and Dol were no longer permitted from St Malo to England. This gave Jersey full justification for maintaining "an absolute prohibition" on all imports from France.

The Bailiff explained to the Home Office that Jersey scientists had evaluated all "scientific facts" and it was clear that: "Any agricultural or horticultural produce to which particles of soil can be attached may be the medium by which Doryphore[4] can be transported and propagated. And this being so, the absolute prohibition of all agricultural and horticultural produce appears...the only measure under existing conditions". Finally, the Bailiff made it clear to the Home Office that the total embargo was justified. "The question is of vital importance to an island whose main industry is agriculture; and the export of potatoes and tomatoes constitutes its main source of prosperity".

The Colorado Beetle continued to spread along the west coast of France. On the 4th May 1931, the United Kingdom government issued "The Colorado Beetle (Amendment) Order". The ports of Granville and St Malo were added to a 75 kilometre "zone de protection" and agricultural exports were banned.

In view of the proximity of St Malo, a Jersey delegation of farmers visited France and investigated the spread of the Colorado Beetle and its effects on agriculture. The total ban on French imports convinced them that this "... was the only course compatible with the interests of local agriculture". In consequence of the ban a conference was held in London on the 5th and 6th October 1931 between the United Kingdom Minister of Agriculture and a delegation of the most senior French agricultural scientists, together with the French Commercial Attaché. The central issue was the Colorado Beetle and the United Kingdom and Jersey ban on French agricultural imports.

The French government had insisted upon the conference. The meeting was opened by the "Inspector-General for Agriculture" and stated that he was a direct representative for the French Minister of Agriculture who, "very much resented the recent action taken by the Channel Islands in prohibiting all imports of French agricultural and horticultural produce and a formal protest had been made to the Foreign Office". He continued that the official French opinion was that the action taken by the Channel Islands was "a protective measure". Finally, he concluded, the French government would "seek a measure of retaliation".

The meeting became progressively heated. The British Minister of Agriculture stated frankly that advice from scientific experts was that drastic measures were needed to protect both the United Kingdom and the Channel Islands. The French delegation protested that the United Kingdom's and the Channel Island's ban was based on economic and not scientific grounds and the embargo was "purely a political question". The French Attaché added that the embargo was considered by the French government to be "a purely protectionist measure", and the French were "not without means of taking measures of their own to give an answer to such action against French interests". The United Kingdom ban was to allow "a better market" for Channel Island produce. Finally, "the French government...would take what steps they may think necessary in this matter".

On the 15th October the spread of the Colorado Beetle in France and the Channel Islands was raised in the House of Commons as a question to the Minister of Agriculture. He outlined a new and total prohibition of French potatoes, plus a total prohibition of all raw vegetables grown within a 200-kilometre zone of any area where the Colorado Beetle was found.[5]

By the 1st November, the United Kingdom and Jersey governments jointly resolved that "only a complete isolation" from France would be the viable solution to the impending arrival of the invading Colorado Beetle. Both governments were expecting a reprisal by the French, and this appeared on 17th November 1931. The British Consul informed the Foreign Office on the subject of the United Kingdom and Jersey embargo on imported French produce. His report to the Foreign Office stated that thirteen growers in his district had been "especially hard hit by the embargo and, in turn, had threatened reprisals of a somewhat extraordinary nature". The reprisal was "to obtain specimens of the Colorado Beetle and disseminate them amongst the crops of the Channel Islands and United Kingdom". At the same time, the Consul at St Malo reported, "local exporters and farmers are considering reprisals. It has been reported to me by British residents, in whose statements I have every faith, that they have heard the suggestion that the Colorado Beetle should be taken over clandestinely to Jersey, so as to destroy the potato crop in that Island".

The Consul concluded in his Foreign Office report: "It is not obvious by what means the project might be carried out but, having regard to the bigoted character and ignorance of the peasantry of Brittany, it seems highly likely that attempts may be made to bring about this serious mischief".[6]

The Foreign Office in turn forwarded these threats to the Lieutenant-Governor of Jersey. In addition, he received on the 26th November 1931 from the Minister of Agriculture, London, notice of a further threat by French farmers of the establishment of an illegal system for evading the law regarding importation of French produce into the Channel Islands. The threat was to send French potatoes to Southampton and re-ship them to the Channel Islands.

All French "reprisals" were relayed to the Bailiff. He responded to the Home Office that there was very little scope for Jersey to halt the Colorado Beetle next spring if they were "...introduced in quantities by ignorant and bigoted Breton labourers". On the 23rd December the British Consul at Nantes reiterated in a further letter to the Foreign Office that he and the Consul at St Malo were convinced that the threats of reprisals by introducing Colorado Beetles into Jersey should be taken seriously, "...especially on the part of growers in the immediate St Malo area".

The Consul believed that: "The Breton peasant is intensely bigoted and remarkably ignorant and would proceed to any lengths to achieve what he would term 'revenge' and that a great number of Breton agricultural labourers go over to Jersey every year to deal with the potato and tomato crops. It will be, in the highest degree, unsafe for Jersey to continue to employ these men, who could spread the beetle throughout the Island".[7]

On the 16th January 1932 the Home Office informed the Jersey authorities that these threats could not be disregarded and suggested that Jersey should "...substitute British for Breton labour". Members of the Jersey Farmers Union and the Royal Jersey Agricultural & Horticultural Society (RJA&HS) met and unanimously agreed: "That the employment of British labour is essential during the forthcoming potato season, to the exclusion of Breton labour". The decision to employ English labour only for the potato harvest instead of Breton was an experiment that, the following year, was not a success.[8]

The Home Office on the 30th January sent an extremely disturbing letter to the Jersey authorities officially informing the Island that the Ministry of Agriculture, after receiving reports from the Foreign Office, had decided that: "The appearance of Colorado Beetle in the Channel Islands would necessitate an embargo on the admission of Channel Island produce into this country". In addition, the United Kingdom would place an "...immediate embargo... of potatoes".

On the 27th June 2,000 farmers from the St Malo region protested against the Channel Island ban on their agricultural and horticultural produce. They, in addition, made it clear that the Colorado Beetle had not been seen in the region of Ille-et-Vilaine, nor did it exist. Therefore, the idea that the Colorado Beetle was introduced to Jersey from St Malo was an error.[9]

In response to the impending financial ruin to Jersey farmers, the year 1932 witnessed an Island-wide offensive for fighting off the forthcoming Colorado Beetle invasion. The entire agricultural community, led by the States of Jersey, set upon a programme of extensive education and precautionary measures. The Reverend W. G. Tabb lectured extensively, and 2,000 leaflets and 200 posters were obtained from the Ministry of Agriculture and distributed to farmers. Twenty showcases illustrating the life history of the Colorado Beetle were sent to schools. A public exhibition was organised at Springfield, where 120 newly recruited Colorado Beetle Inspectors were lectured and received detailed instructions on combatting the pest by mixing and applying lead arsenate and carbon disulphide. Each Island parish had a store of these chemicals under the care of the Connétable.[10]

On the 1st May 1934 the Jersey authorities, in a further effort to hold back the expected and imminent Colorado Beetle invasion, closed all ports to and from France except St Helier Harbour. All persons, luggage, cargo and ships were to be inspected and, subsequently, disinfected. On the 12th May the ports of Portbail and Carteret were declared infected zones, followed by St Malo, Granville and St Brieuc.

The French government immediately forwarded its objections to these restrictions to the United Kingdom Home Office. The situation continued for another two years until the Home Office wrote to the Jersey authorities on the 23rd March 1936, bluntly informing them that the Ministry of Agriculture had instructed that disinfecting on such a scale was not effective. Each spring, the Colorado Beetle could simply fly the short distance from France to Jersey. The Ministry advised the Jersey authorities to carry out and maintain extensive searches on ships and gear when they entered Island ports.

In preceding years, laws had been enacted by the Jersey government to allow Island-wide spraying of lead arsenate to combat the expected arrival of Colorado Beetle. The dangers of lead arsenate were described in a far-sighted letter, sent on the 26th March 1936 to the Ministry of Health of the United Kingdom, by the Reverend George A. Sexton, DD, FPhS, AMINA (Minister of the New Church, Victoria Street, St Helier). The letter was subsequently forwarded to the Home Office, its central premise being "The dangers of lead arsenate poisoning" prevalent on the Island of Jersey.[11]

The Reverend expressed his real concern regarding the practice of spraying lead arsenate on Jersey potatoes. He wrote: "Owing to panic legislation, Jersey is likely to be deluged in spraying lead arsenate, to frighten away Colorado Beetles which have yet to come to Jersey at all". He furthermore stated that the area of potatoes in Jersey was so large in proportion to the area of the Island, and fields were often mixed with fruit and vegetable gardens, that it would, with certainty, ensure that lead arsenate would also contaminate these crops.

In addition, he envisaged problems with lead arsenate permeating into the water table and affecting drinking water. The dangers to the safety of children and cattle who were near sprayed areas were emphasised, along with the health of those harvesting potatoes and cattle drinking water in the streams that drained directly from sprayed fields.

The question of the effects on the environment by large-scale spraying of lead arsenate was again brought to light on the 1st May 1936. The Island's Agricultural Committee received concerns from a "responsible trading concern in England to a merchant here". The issue was duly debated in the States of Jersey, and the views read out. "I note what you say about Potato Growers not liking to use arsenate of lead. From my own experiments we have found the after-effects on the ground to be injurious. In my own case it has affected and practically made the ground sterile and it took several years before the crops came on as they ought to have done". The Island government, comprising many of the leading farmers, became extremely alarmed and subsequently asked for advice from the Ministry of Agriculture. They responded "On the use of arsenate of lead" on the 11th May.

The Ministry's report concluded: firstly, that arsenical insecticides had been in use extensively since 1859 in the USA and Canada, where, as far as the Ministry was aware, "...there were no records of any damage having been caused to the crops owing to an accumulation of arsenic in the soil". Secondly, potato crops were not customarily sprayed with arsenical compounds in England but in 1933, 2,000 tons were sprayed in Kent and

Essex covering 4,000 acres, with no complaints of any injury to the resulting crops. Finally, fruit trees in England had been sprayed since the beginning of the twentieth century with no evidence of any reduction in the fertility of the soil having occurred as a result of spraying.[12]

In July 1936 a United Kingdom agricultural publication stated, "Practically the whole of France is riddled with this terrible scourge of the potato crop, and it has even reached the Channel Islands".[13] The publication caused immediate consternation amongst the Jersey government and farmers. The Agricultural Department was called to make an immediate report and the possible effects on Jersey's main export of Jersey Royal potatoes.[14] Subsequently the Bailiff wrote to the Home Office insisting that the publication be withdrawn. On the 28th August the Home Office replied: "The false statements regarding the Colorado Beetle have been removed".[15]

On the 16th February 1937 the International Colorado Beetle Conference was held in Berlin under the auspices of the German Ministry for Food and Agriculture and attended by representatives of all European countries where Colorado Beetle outbreaks had occurred. Subsequently the Home Office informed the Jersey authorities that: "The French coast adjacent to the Channel Islands is infected as far as Carteret, with outbreaks in the Department of Manche lying north of a line joining Carteret, Lessay and Carentan". This was in addition to three recent outbreaks in Holland and Belgium.[16]

On the 10th November 1937, the Home Office wrote to the Island government requesting that: "The authorities in the Channel Islands will not take any further extreme action in respect of this pest". On the 12th November the Lieutenant-Governor advised Duret Aubin, the Attorney General, against sending the Bailiff a copy of the Home Office recommendation. Duret Aubin agreed and assured the Lieutenant-Governor that, "No extreme measures are in contemplation here…the matter should drop".[17]

The question arises as to why the Bailiff was not advised of the Home Office request? The answer lies in the fact that had the Bailiff been informed, he would subsequently have had to inform the Agricultural Committee, who in turn would have instigated a new draft of agricultural embargoes leading to a new dispute between the United Kingdom and its Continental neighbours and resulting in the very real threat of reprisals.

On the 14th December the two Crown Officers, the Attorney General and the Solicitor General, wrote to the Lieutenant-Governor and suggested an alternative procedure by which, "We will informally advise the President of the States Agricultural Committee that it might well obtain up-to-date information from the Ministry of Agriculture in relation to the spread of the Colorado Beetle in Europe". He, in turn, would "act upon the advice" and ask for information in the usual manner and receive the "appropriate reply". On the 21st December the Home Office accepted the Crown Officers' "diplomatic method of procedure".

After a particularly pernicious outbreak of the Colorado Beetle in the Netherlands early in 1938, Jersey banned all Dutch produce and on February

3rd declared the country an infected zone. On the 6th April the Chief of Plant Pathological Services and the Agricultural Attaché of the Netherlands met the Jersey Agricultural Committee to discuss the ban and the presence of Colorado Beetle in the Netherlands. The Agricultural Committee agreed to a reduction in the embargo on Dutch imports, and on the 3rd May the Ministry of Agriculture accepted the agreement.

Prior to the German invasion of Jersey on the 1st July 1940, an earlier invasion took place on the 3rd October 1939. The first Colorado Beetle on the Island was discovered by the fourteen-year-old son of Mr A. Minchinton, in a field of just under 5 vergées[18] known as "Les Clos de la Mare", St Ouen. Several adult Colorado Beetles were found before they hibernated. This discovery was extremely fortuitous as it stopped the infestation from spreading to other fields or areas of the Island. The evidence pointed to the beetles being the direct descendants of a single female which had migrated by flight directly from France.

Between the 3rd and 8th October, a total of forty-three Colorado Beetles were discovered. The soil was subsequently fumigated with carbon disulphide and the decayed potato haulms, being first saturated with paraffin, were set alight and burned in pits near the infected area. The potato crops around the infected zone were sprayed with lead arsenate to kill any remaining Colorado Beetles and after two days spraying the work was completed. Three hundred Honorary Colorado Beetle Inspectors then made a meticulous inspection to check the entire Island and, much to the relief of the agricultural community, none were found.[19]

On the 5th January 1940 the Jersey authorities ordered 54 tons of lead arsenate from the company Tomlinson and Hayward in Lincoln. A further order was placed the following month. The decision was made to ship the lead arsenate in separate consignments as firstly, the order was so large there were insufficient containers available; and secondly, in view of the danger of the vessel being sunk by a German U-boat torpedo.[20]

In February the Home Office and the Ministry of Supply gave permission for Tomlinson and Hayward to supply the lead arsenate in 20,000 cartons as the containers of the correct size were found to be unavailable. 17,000 were despatched in March with the remaining 3,000 to follow. There were no further major outbreaks of the Colorado Beetle until 1943.

Potato Blight

An official report stated that 1930 would always be looked upon as: "One of the most disastrous in the annals of the Potato Industry".[21] That year proved a commercial disaster for Jersey farmers. Firstly, prices realised were the lowest for fifty years; secondly, exceptional wet weather in the winter and spring left the ground cold and retarded the growth of early potatoes; thirdly, a severe frost on the 20th March 1930 made the Jersey Royal season very late. Finally, potato blight developed. The report made it clear that, "…so grave are the ravages of the blight on the local potato crop that no practicable step to combat it could be neglected".

The problem of potato blight was a relatively new one. It was made worse by some farmers constantly changing their sprays, some of which were of little value, whilst others sprayed crops as a cure rather than a prevention.

In 1931 Touzel John Brée, Fauvic Farm, Grouville, carried out a series of trials with the States Experimental Station on new techniques to prevent potato blight with home-spraying machines, together with experimental work combining empirical investigations in combatting the disease.[22]

A further outbreak occurred in 1937. Initially 780 gallons of sulphuric acid were sprayed throughout the Island to prevent an epidemic, with a further 5,000 gallons at a later date, in an effort to salvage the remaining crop. 1937 proved to be an important year for farmers. The lesson was truly learnt: an early response had to be implemented whenever blight appeared.[23]

The Potato Eelworm

"The arrival of the "Arran Pilot"

On the 16th March 1940, a meeting of the JFU was convened to discuss an eelworm infestation of 112 vergées of potatoes.[24] Export of these potatoes was prohibited. Mr E. N. Pallot stated that he had traced the first importation of the eelworm to 1931 when it was introduced into Jersey by the "Arran Pilot", a variety of potato which had been imported into the Island in bags which held contaminated soil containing the eelworm, and which subsequently allowed the pest to spread. Mr Pallot was evidently angry with his fellow farmers, affirming that they had ignored his warnings and that eelworm was now prevalent on the Island.[25] The variety "Arran Pilot" referred to by Mr Pallot had arrived in Jersey in 1930 and was delivered to the States Experimental Station to be tested. Seven new potato varieties were received, including one from a Mr Donald MacKelvie, from Arran, Scotland.[26]

In December 1931, Ernest George Ing, a highly skilled horticultural scientist, joined the States Experimental Station. By 1936 he had carried out empirical research on Jersey fruit and vegetable pests and diseases. In addition, Ing was sent to carry out inspections of imported potatoes to check for eelworm. In December 1936 he discovered an infestation in an uncertified potato import.[27] Ing continued his research throughout 1937 and was awarded an increase on an already excellent salary. He, furthermore, published academic papers and articles on Jersey fruit and vegetable pests and diseases, identifying 117, including a newly discovered vegetable eelworm.[28]

In 1938 Ing was given a new contract by the States in respect of his research on combatting the eelworm. His new contract reassigned him from the role of horticulturist to "microbiologist" at the States Experimental Station.[29]

In 1939 an entire crop of 30 vergées[30] of potatoes were destroyed by eelworm at Highview Farm, Mont à L'Abbé. Ing was put in charge of eelworm inspection and assigned to purchase the equipment required to combat the pest.[31] He also collaborated with Dr Thomas Small on the Jersey eelworm problem. They jointly published an article entitled "A Note on Potato Root Worm".

In February 1940, Ing, seeing the extent of the eelworm infestation on the Island, requested an increase in the number of Inspectors who duly discovered, on the 28th March, 130 barrels of imported "Majestic Ware" potatoes from Lincolnshire, all infested with eelworm. The barrels and potatoes were immediately destroyed. By the 22nd May, however, the eelworm had decimated Touzel Brée's entire potato crop. With the potato season in full swing, and with daily exports to England, Dr Small and Ing produced a further report, on the 7th June, on the eelworm problem on Jersey.[32] By the time of the arrival of the German occupying forces in July the eelworm infestation had proved extremely difficult to eliminate. Philip Le Feuvre made the ominous prediction that "If the eelworm was not stamped out, the most valuable land in Jersey would, in a generation, go out of production".[25]

The 1940 Potato Crop

"It was decided to abandon the meeting"

The outbreak of the Second World War in September 1939 left Jersey farmers increasingly concerned and confused as regards which crops to grow and how their main cash crop, the Jersey Royal potato, would be marketed. Certainly, there is no evidence of any cropping plan set up by the Agricultural Committee for 1940. The JFU and the RJA&HS, after asking for guidance from the agricultural authorities, were informed that "Nothing was yet decided upon the control of crops".[33]

There were approximately 1,780 farms and holdings of over 1 vergée in Jersey.[34] The question of the reliance of many Jersey farmers on the early potato crop and its export to the United Kingdom for their income, led to an immense outcry to the States for some form of clarity. The result of this was a meeting convened in February 1940 of States Members, the Attorney General and the Bailiff, together with Mr R. W. Halliday, the United Kingdom's Director of Overseas Food Supply, and Mr R. H. Porter, Assistant Director of Food Transport. The central issue, amongst other problems, was the impending 1940 potato harvest.[35]

The United Kingdom representatives stated that the Ministry of Food's policy was to fix all potato prices. Therefore, the selling price of Jersey potatoes exported to the United Kingdom would have to be fixed and had to cover all shipping and carriage charges which, however, would vary according to the three ports serving the three zones into which England had been divided, and into which Jersey potatoes would be shipped.

Furthermore, it was made clear that under war conditions, shipment of Jersey potatoes would only be allowed to markets within a radius of 30 miles of the port. These ports were: Liverpool and Holyhead in the Northern zone; Cardiff for the Midland zone; and Newhaven for the Southern zone. These three ports would allow a six-week window for a total export of 67,738 tons of potatoes.

The States of Jersey would be the contracting party with the shipping and railway companies. The Auditor met with them and formulated the financial costs of these exports, which subsequently proved to be an extremely difficult task. All parties had to arrive at a formula to cover the various factors involved in exporting Jersey potatoes: unloading lorries, loading onto steamers, stowage, cranage, harbour and pilot dues, and finally, merchants' profits both in Jersey and the mainland. Fixed prices instigated by the Ministry of Food, and the difficulties in computing these factors led, by the 13th June 1940, to a plummeting of the price the Jersey farmer received.

An emergency meeting was immediately announced between the States Accounts Office, representatives of the Great Western Railway and Southern Railway, Cunard, the Ministry of Food and the Solicitor General.

On the 14th June there was a further fall in prices and the marking of farmers' tickets at the weighbridge was stopped. The price decrease was exacerbated, firstly, by distribution problems in the United Kingdom; and secondly, by general uncertainty amongst mainland merchants receiving Jersey potatoes.

The States telephoned the Ministry of Food on the 17th June and the latter agreed to a price reduction on potatoes already imported, on the condition that all further exports were halted.

On the 18th June there was such an oversupply of potatoes in the stores that they were handed to the Connétable of St Helier to distribute amongst the poor and the potato merchants were compensated. On the 25th June, a newly constituted Department of Agriculture met, comprising Touzel Brée, John du Val and Edwin Denize Gibaut. The three met again the next day and ordered that farmers be allowed an export allocation of only 40 cwt. On the 28th June this was again reduced to 20 cwt, which resulted in convoys of lorries, all loaded with potato barrels, parked around St Helier Harbour.[36]

The imposition of fixed prices by the mainland authorities left farmers very angry. Their anger was intensified, as they perceived it, by an unfair arrangement at the weighbridge. The JFU demanded "That the system be modified so that farmers were left free to sell to whom they choose".[25] An emergency meeting was called by the JFU to discuss "The state of affairs caused by the merchants not buying". The JFU did not see fault with the shipping companies for the delay in sending their potatoes to market, but rather with the merchants who purchased their potatoes at a high price but then allowed their stocks to be held in transit. The merchants, in turn, would not purchase any further potatoes until they were able to dispose of those already in their possession.

On 27th June, at a further meeting held by the JFU, Mr J. P. Le Masurier informed his fellow farmers that six potato merchants had refused to pay him. The entire industry was now in crisis and turmoil. The following day a delegation of the JFU met the President of the Jersey Produce Merchants Association (JPMA), Mr J. N. Norman.

The central issue discussed was the refusal of the merchants to pay farmers for their potato tickets, even in cases where the farmers did not owe them money. It was a normal method for farmers to purchase inputs, e. g. seed and fertiliser, from merchants on credit, against the subsequent sale of produce. One merchant, Mr C. Mossop, stated openly that farmers were not paying their accounts. The JFU retorted that the reason for this was that they were simply not receiving due payment from the merchants. But as the merchants understood it, the non-payment by them to the farmers was due to "the allocation" arranged by Brée which prevented farmers from shipping all their potatoes. Therefore, merchants were experiencing difficulties in having their accounts settled.

The President of the JPMA was summoned to discuss the problem with the Crown Officers. He was instructed to explain the current situation between merchants and farmers. Furthermore, he was ordered to prepare a statement covering firstly, the amounts paid out for potato tickets; secondly, the amounts yet to be paid for potato tickets; and finally, what monies were due to the merchants by farmers. The outcome of the meeting was that the States sent a memorandum to the JFU informing them that the Treasury would act as "A clearing house" for the remaining 1940 potato and tomato export season.

A further emergency meeting of the JFU and the RJA&HS was convened to review the clearing house and "The present position of agriculture on the Island".[25] Exports of potatoes had decreased to such an extent "...that there were possibilities that there would be no further exports". Some farmers were laying off agricultural workers, and others "...did not have the cash to harvest their own crops". Carlyle Le Gallais, President of the RJA&HS, suggested sending back all "non-native labour" to ease the unemployment problem.

The agricultural community decided to harvest the entire crop without delay in order to salvage what was left of the export season. Events, however, were to dictate the future course of Jersey agriculture, and the remainder of the potato season. On the evening of the 28th June 1940, the Department of Agriculture (DOA) met to discuss the potato problem. "At...7pm the town was bombed by the Germans and it was decided to abandon the meeting".[35]

Jersey Farmers and Their Response to the War Effort

"Don Des Cultivateurs de L'Île de Jersey"

On the 2nd December 1939, the RJA&HS met to discuss its response to the war effort. The decision was made to purchase an ambulance for the joint Anglo-French armed forces in France. Both the RJA&HS and the JFU would collect donations from all Island farmers. The ambulance would be gifted to the joint forces from "The Farmers of Jersey".[25]

On the 16th December the "Anglo-French Ambulance Corps" accepted the offer and within two weeks donations exceeded the £500 sought and the total figure collected amounted to £590. It was decided to paint an inscription on either side of the ambulance in English and in French with the words "Gift of the Farmers of Jersey" and "Don Des Cultivateurs de L'Île de Jersey".

Two Jersey firms would supply the chassis and one firm would build the body of the ambulance at cost price. Le Gallais collected all the various donations and by April 1940 had instructed the company Messrs Underhill to build the ambulance, forwarding them £385. The ambulance was duly completed, put on show at Springfield and finally sent to the mainland. Its fate thereafter is not recorded. In addition, Le Gallais asked all RJA&HS members to collect waste metal for the use of the "National Service". Each Connétable would organise a collection scheme in their parish.

On the 14th June 1940 a joint RJA&HS and JFU meeting proposed: "To present the British government with a gift of potatoes to His Majesty's Armed Forces".[25] In 1916, Jersey farmers had donated potatoes to the Royal Navy. A letter was read which had been received from Lord Jellicoe on the 17th June 1916, in which he expressed his thanks on behalf of the Royal Navy.[25] The potatoes were collected in June 1940 by the presidents of the two associations and a letter sent to the United Kingdom government to ascertain if the gift of Jersey potatoes for the war effort was acceptable. A list of Jersey farmers who contributed was exhibited at the weighbridge with each parish shown separately. The potatoes were to be put in "clean and sound bags" and labelled "From the Farmers and Growers of the Island".

It was not only farmers who demonstrated their loyalty and generosity to the United Kingdom in its time of need. The States of Jersey made a contribution to the war effort. In March 1940 the Bailiff sent the sum of £100,000 towards war costs, and in April a confidential letter was circulated by the Bailiff to States Members headed "Secret". The letter described, "... as a contribution towards Imperial Defence, the States of Jersey…decided to place all possible facilities at the disposal of the Admiralty for the purposes of flying training of the Fleet Air Arm and to provide or render further assistance in the provision of accommodation for this purpose". The Home Office accepted the offer and replied, "Preliminary arrangements have already been made for the transfer to Jersey Airport of a squadron of Fleet Air Arm aircraft".[37]

References

1. Ministry of Agriculture and Fisheries. Advisory leaflet No 71. HM Stationery Office. London 1931.
2. L'Ouest Éclair. 11th June 1932. "Combatting the Colorado Beetle" Dr Feytaud, Director of the Entomological Station at Bordeaux. Ingénieur Agronome.
3. Jersey Archive. A/D1/A9/3.

4. Colorado Beetle.
5. House of Commons. Statutory Rules and Orders, 1931, No 879. The Colorado Beetle Order of 1931. 15th October 1931.
6. Jersey Archive. A/D1/A9/3. 13194/1147/17/No 57.
7. Jersey Archive. A/D1/A9/3. 14794/1147/17/No 61.
8. RJA&HS Annual Report. 1932. Page 12.
9. Jersey Archive. A/D1/A9/3. Letter to the Governor of Jersey. Union Syndicale des Agriculteurs.
10. The States of Jersey Experimental Station. 1932 Report.
11. Jersey Archive. A/D1/A9/3. 593/980/34.
12. Jersey Archive. A/D1/A9/3. 593/980/42.
13. Cooper, McDuggal and Robertson, Ltd. No 4, Vol 8, July to August 1936. "The Colorado Beetle".
14. Jersey Archive. C/B/A1/3.
15. Jersey Archive. A/D1/A9/3. 593/980/53.
16. Jersey Archive. A/D1/A9/3. 593/980/68.
17. Jersey Archive. A/D1/A9/3.
18. 2.22 vergées to the acre.
19. T. Small, PhD, MSc, ARCS. Report of the Colorado Beetle outbreak in Jersey. The States of Jersey Experimental Station. 6th January 1940.
20. Jersey Archive. C/B/A1/4.
21. The States of Jersey Experimental Station, 'Glenham', Trinity. Rapport de l'analyste officiel du Directeur de la Ferme d'Expériences et de l'Inspecteur en chef des pommes de terre et tomates. 1930.
22. The States of Jersey Experimental Station. 1932 Report.
23. The States of Jersey Experimental Station. 1937 Report.
24. 49.8 acres.
25. Jersey Farmers Union Minute Book. I am grateful to Maureen A. Rondel, former Executive Secretary, for allowing me access to their archives.
26. The States of Jersey Experimental Station, 'Glenham', Trinity. Rapports du Directeur de la Ferme d'Expériences, avec comptes pour l'année 1930.
27. The States of Jersey Experimental Station. 1936 Report.
28. The States of Jersey Experimental Station. 1937 Report.
29. Jersey Archive. C/B/A1/3.
30. 13.3 acres.
31. Jersey Weekly Post. 18th November 1939. "How science helps the Jersey Farmer".
32. Jersey Archive. C/B/A1/4.
33. Jersey Archive. L/D/09/A10.
34. 1 vergée = 4/9 of an acre.
35. Jersey Archive. C/B/A1/5.
36. The notion that experienced Luftwaffe pilots mistook these convoys of potatoes as tanks and bombed them is incorrect.
37. Jersey Archive. C/A5/21.

Chapter 2

The German Military Occupation of Jersey 1940–1945 and the Jersey Pedigree Breed of Cattle

"Cattle must be protected"

KVR Hans Egon Pelz,
German Military Government, Field Command 515,
Head of Agriculture and Food Supply

The German subjugation of Europe demonstrated a propensity for the victorious German scientific community to acquire the valuable agricultural assets of the territories they conquered. It therefore is not surprising that, within two months of the German occupation of Jersey on the 1st July 1940, the German scientific community began arriving to research, record and extract the unique potential of the Island's most valuable and unique asset: the pedigree Jersey cattle breed. The island of Jersey became a repository for the export of pedigree and prize Jersey bulls, cows and heifers by the German scientific community to Germany and Austria. The Kaiser Wilhelm Institute (KWI) in Germany from September 1940 until May 1944 imported Jersey cattle for its extensive short- and long-term research and crossbreeding programmes.

The acquisition of Jersey and its breed of cattle allowed the German occupying forces and visiting cattle scientists to facilitate the export of Jersey cattle to the KWI, Dummerstorf, near Rostock and to make possible and enhance the Institute's crossbreeding programme, by infusing German and Austrian Continental cattle with the qualities of the Jersey breed. German scientists were well aware of the merits of the Jersey breed of cattle, with an unbroken and documented pedigree going back to 1866. They were extremely expeditious in visiting the Island to utilise this library of knowledge for their own empirical research.

Secondly, the German occupation saw Jersey cows become the major provider of milk and butter for the military forces stationed on the Island. Kriegsverwaltungsrat Pelz, Head of Agriculture and Food Supply, Field Command 515, the German Military Government of Jersey and the Channel

Islands, stated under the title, "Cattle must be protected",[1] that it would be a clear policy, in agreement with Jersey's President of Agriculture, Touzel Brée, that they: "Would maintain the protection of cattle so that farmers would not be allowed to slaughter cattle as and how they wished. This was to maintain the supply of milk". KVR Pelz furthermore, and in view of his non-slaughter policy, would therefore import cattle for meat from La Manche, France. The effect of this non-slaughter policy was to lead to an increase in milk and butter production for both the civilian population and German military personnel, almost to the end of the German occupation.

This absolute non-slaughter policy of the Island breed ended on the 10th May 1941, when the Superior Council, Jersey's civilian authority, pronounced that a small number of local cattle would be slaughtered for meat. This modification of policy made it clear that only cattle of an inferior pedigree would be slaughtered and those which produced only low quantities of milk. This would ensure that the milk supply was not prejudiced in any way.

Jersey Cattle Exports to Germany

"The Germans were taking all the cattle away"

Local Jersey residents

The export of Jersey cattle to Germany began in 1887 when Kaiser Wilhelm I appointed the merchant Francis Ernest Balleine with an Imperial Warrant, signed and sealed by Otto von Bismarck, "To promote trade, transport and shipping" with the German Reich.[2]

This was the year of the jubilee of Queen Victoria, the patron of the Royal Jersey Agricultural and Horticultural Society, often referred to as the RJA&HS. It was celebrated with the first public judging of Jersey cattle with buyers from northern Europe present and, consequently, a thriving export market developed. In 1898, a herd of Jersey cows was exported to Würtenburg.[3]

Julius Kühn (1825–1910) imported Jersey cattle for crossbreeding experiments with German cattle at the Institute for Cattle Breeding and Dairying, Halle University, from the turn of the century c. 1900, prior to the First World War.[4]

Gustav Frölich (1879–1940), at the same university between 1925 and 1930, began a series of crossbreeding experiments between the German Holstein and Black Piedmont cattle with the Jersey breed. The research entailed the investigation of crosses of Jersey cattle with German breeds and the resultant analysis of body mass, colour, the amount of milk produced, together with fat content.[5] Frölich's increasing focus of research was "...to increase the fat content of the milk from highly efficient German cattle breeds by means of purposeful crossbreeding".[6]

Between 1937 and 1938 government and scientific pressure within Germany facilitated the establishment of an Institute of Animal Breeding Research, as part of the Kaiser Wilhelm Society for the Advancement of Science. In 1939 the KWI at Dummerstorf was inaugurated as a research facility by Frölich, who was subsequently replaced by Jonas Schmidt (1885–1958). Schmidt resolved that the Jersey and German cattle crossbreeding program would be accelerated with the fundamental aim that German cattle produce milk with a higher fat content. This was to be achieved in the shortest possible time frame by crossbreeding German cattle with Jerseys imported directly from the Island. Schmidt's aim for these crossbreeding experiments was to achieve the "Holy Grail" of German milk production – to breed a cow that would increase its volume of milk produce without decreasing the fat content.

The impetus to produce German milk with a higher fat content was a response to the defeat of Germany in the First World War, in which the "Fettlücke" or "Fat Gap" – a serious deficiency in fats for the German population – was seen as a major factor in its defeat. This dovetailed very neatly with another major aim of the research program at the KWI, that of the principle of "autarky".[7] This was the policy of being self-sufficient in materials and foodstuffs.

On the 28th June 1940 the German Luftwaffe bombed Jersey, resulting in a large number of deaths and casualties. Earlier that morning, a pedigree Jersey calf was born and subsequently named as "Jersey Air Raid" by its owner, Jean Yves Marie Le Flem, and recorded in the Jersey Herd Book.[8]

On the 1st July the German military forces occupied the Island. By early August, some seven weeks after the occupying forces had arrived, Dr Hans Löwe, a former student of Frölich's came to Jersey with a "shopping list" from Germany to purchase pedigree Jersey cows and bulls. Certainly, by the 17th August 1940, "...our visitors are exporting...numbers of prize cattle".[9] These cattle were purchased by Löwe and subsequently shipped to Germany.[10]

Löwe was a senior scientist at the KWI and was in charge of a breeding section.[11] He immediately toured the Island with Connétable John du Val, a member of the civilian Department of Agriculture (DOA), tracking down the very best cattle in each parish. In addition, he was assisted by members of Field Command 515.[12] "Constable du Val came with five Germans to see heifers. Francis went down to a field at St Ouen with them but, fortunately, they did not find the heifers good enough".[13]

Löwe, accompanied by du Val, toured Jersey throughout the rest of August 1940, viewing the best examples of milk-producing cows and prize bulls. On the 19th August the DOA decided that those cattle requisitioned by the German authorities should be valued. J. A. Perrée and a member of the Department of Finance and Economics were instructed to complete the valuations of these pedigree cattle. On the 2nd September, however, a problem arose that slowed down Löwe's purchase of cattle. Field Command 515 wrote to the Bailiff of Jersey[14] and informed him that a Jersey bull had been examined by Dr Löwe, who consequently intended to purchase the animal.

The bull in question, Vinchelez Double Effort, was a superb example of the Jersey breed.[15]

The bull was the property of Mr John H. Roberts, Vinchelez Farm, St Ouen. Roberts was one of the top buyers and breeders of Jersey cattle in the United Kingdom and his herd was of the finest pedigree.[16] It was unsurprising that Löwe demanded the bull. Roberts had evacuated Jersey in June 1940, before the German military occupation, and his property and interests were represented by Advocate J. F. Le Cornu. Much to the chagrin of Field Command 515, Advocate Le Cornu "...absolutely refused, without any reason that can be discovered, to give the animal up". Field Command 515, furthermore, informed the Bailiff that the bull would be exported to Germany with the rest of the cattle selected by Löwe. The Bailiff was ordered by the German authorities to "...cause Advocate Le Cornu to hold the animal ready for shipment in a healthy and undamaged condition".

The advocate additionally was ordered to inform, in writing, the payment required to purchase the bull. The next day the Bailiff replied to Colonel Schumacher, Field Commander of 515, that the matter of the purchase of the bull had been given to the President of the DOA to deal with, Jurat Brée. Brée was horrified at the imminent prospect of such a large number of pedigree indigenous Jersey cattle being sent out of the Island and envisaged that this would be only the beginning of an exodus of Jersey's greatest asset – its breed of cattle.

In an interesting intervention, the Bailiff, an experienced lawyer who was conscious of the legalities of the Hague Convention (a typed copy of which he had at hand) informed Schumacher that, to ensure the purchase of Jersey cattle was expedited in a legal manner, it would be "...better if a formal requisition was made by the Insular Government of all animals required for shipment" to Germany. The Hague Convention established a series of laws and customs which the occupying power must follow.

The solution offered by the Bailiff was excellent news to the lawyers of Field Command 515. The Bailiff's decision effectively meant that the States of Jersey, through the auspices of the Superior Council,[17] would requisition the twenty cows and two bulls, on behalf of the German Military Government, who in turn would ship the cattle to the KWI. Brée was immediately informed by the Bailiff to facilitate the export of the cattle with Field Command 515.[18]

On the 20th September 1940 the DOA wrote to Advocate Le Cornu, instructing him to set a valuation for the bull and to inform Field Command 515. On the same day, the DOA also authorised its secretary, Colin Marie, to send an account to the German Field Command, together with the accounts of Thomas Le Quesne Blampied, FRCVS, the States Veterinary Surgeon, and the RJA&HS for "...services in connection with said purchase".

On the 1st October, twenty Jersey cows and two bulls were exported to Rostock, Germany, via a stopover in Guernsey.[19] On the 24th October, Schumacher informed the Bailiff that the invoice received for "The purchase money and the cost for the twenty-one head of cattle for breeding which were sent to Germany" could be obtained from the Paymaster of Field Command 515. (The records vary between twenty-one and twenty-two animals.) The total cost for the purchase was RM10,109 and 86 pfennigs. Two days later the Bailiff informed Brée that he required details of where the payment should be made, and on the 29th October 1940, the full sum was paid by Field Command 515.[20]

Brée sent Herbert de Gruchy, a Harbour Customs Officer seconded to the DOA, to the Headquarters of Field Command 515, College House, to receive payment for the cattle exported to Rostock. De Gruchy was under the impression, as were many of the Island's population, that the cattle had been sent to Berlin. Once inside College House, de Gruchy was escorted to the Paymaster's Office and given full payment in "...one Deutsche Mark notes", which completely filled his briefcase. De Gruchy particularly noted in his description of the visit to College House that there was no difficulty in conversing with Field Command personnel as "Many of the officers spoke excellent English".[21]

The cattle were taken to the States abattoir, opposite St Helier Harbour, for embarkation to Germany. Their presence in such a large number led to an increasing rumour amongst the Jersey civilian populace that "The Germans were taking all the cattle away".[22]

The exact record of all the Jersey cattle exported to the KWI in Germany is incomplete. The Jersey Herd Book, originating in 1866 and describing the pedigree of every cow and bull designated as a pedigree Jersey, only gives the details of two bulls and two cows of all the animals exported on the 1st October 1940.[23] In addition, also named are a heifer and a cow that were purchased, invoiced and subsequently exported by the German authorities. The invoice is cited at a meeting of the DOA on the 30th October 1940 and comprised the names of a heifer purchased by Field Command 515 directly from the Department of Health called "Eventide of the Lake" at a price of RM 480, and a "Highly Commended" cow named as "Light of Foot's Danube 47th" for RM 384, purchased directly from the DOA. The two animals are officially recorded as being exported on the vessel SS Normand and the latter is cited in the Jersey Herd Book as being "Exported October 1. 1940".[24] Therefore presumably these two animals were with the main shipment of cattle, or additional to, the shipment to the KWI on the 1st October.

The export of twenty Jersey cows and two bulls to Germany did not go unnoticed by the British Military Intelligence Service. Subsequent reports of this export became the inspiration for the successful novel and feature film of 1951, entitled "Appointment with Venus", and the Danish adaptation of the film of 1962 "Venus fra Vestrø".

The accepted interpretation of the origins of the book and films is that it relates to the evacuation of all the indigenous cattle from the island of Alderney during the German occupation of the Channel Islands. This, however, is incorrect. The total evacuation of cattle from Alderney to

Guernsey took place between the 23rd and 26th June 1940, prior to the German occupation of the Channel Islands. This was carried out by Guernsey farmers using two steam ships and the displaced cattle were redistributed amongst the Guernsey herds. Over those four days in June, 224 cows, 150 heifers and 5 bulls were evacuated from Alderney. In addition, all records of the Royal Alderney Agriculture Society were rescued and removed to the parent body in Guernsey. The evacuation of the entire Alderney cattle breed took place whilst Germany Luftwaffe planes flew overhead the two vessels, observing the actions of the Guernsey farmers. The last shipment of Alderney cattle evacuated upon the SS Courier was on or about the 26th June, a full four days before the Germany military occupation of the island of Guernsey.[25]

The arrival of the Jersey herd in Dummerstorf was heralded in a German newspaper on the 10th January 1941 with the headline, "Dummerstorf Schlibet Fettlüke".[26] The sub-title read, "Milchkühe von den Kanalinseln".[27] The article described: "From the Channel Islands the Institute (at Dummerstorf) received valuable animals from the pedigree Jersey breed, who produce a value of 5% and 6% fat in their milk. The calves that crossbreed between the Black Piedmont cattle and the grey brown Jersey bulls, resemble in colour, the coat of a deer".[28] [29]

By December 1941 the KWI crossbreeding experiment between the two Jersey bulls with German cattle was in full operation. A letter dated 5th January 1942 from the Institute for Animal Breeding and Genetics of Domestic Animals, of the Friedrich Wilhelm University, to the Kaiser Wilhelm Society for the Advancement of Science, replied to an order from the Reich Ministry of Food and Agriculture that no further buildings would be constructed for the crossbreeding of German Black and White Lowland and Jersey cattle. The author of the correspondence argued that, in order to make a success of these crossbreeding experiments, more buildings were required as "...crossbreeding needed three generations of calves and the number of cattle would grow".[30] The letter also emphasised and described that there would be an increase in the number of Jersey cattle, especially in view of the fact that there would be an expansion in these crossbreeding experiments. The Institute for Animal Breeding and Genetics of Domestic Animals made it clear to the Kaiser Wilhelm Society that further crossbreeding experiments would "... require additional scientific techniques to increase the percentage of fat in milk", including new artificial insemination scientific procedures. It is interesting to note, and perhaps no coincidence, that the first artificial insemination experiments in dairy cattle in the United Kingdom were also initiated in 1942 at the Cambridge School of Agriculture, by Sir John Hammond.[31]

The aims and objectives of the German and Jersey cattle crossbreeding program were summed up by the Institute for Animal Breeding and Genetics of Domestic Animals, of the Friedrich Wilhelm University.[32] These were to:

1. Make artificial insemination a successful and viable process.
2. Improve the methodology and permanence of the Jersey and German crossbreeding program.
3. Complete a genetic study in "Grossdeutschland" and "Ausland" to identify the most important cattle genes.
4. Pass on the qualities of higher fat content without decreasing milk yields.
5. Provide an educational centre for cattle herdsmen and milk maids.[32]

The Jersey and German cattle breeding program, after the initial experiments, was extended after 1942 to other regional areas. In a letter dated 13th September 1944 from the Chairman of the Farming Union, Linz, Austria, to Professor Dr Jonas Schmidt at the KWI, Rostock, a description summarised a meeting that took place on the 29th August, 1944. The meeting comprised; Professor Dr Schmidt, Director of the KWI, Professor Witt of the Ministry of Agriculture and Food, and Dr Borosky and Josef Dundler of the Mortgage Bank. A description was provided of the crossbreeding program from 1942, monitored by the KWI between, "...a bull from Jersey called Tommy" and native Montafon cattle. The bull in question almost certainly would have been either "La Fontaine Dictator" or "Vinchelez Double Effort".[33] The letter summed up the crucial reasons for the appropriate utilisation of the Jersey bull and emphasised the importance of the Jersey and German crossbreeding program. Finally, Professor Dr Schmidt underlined the importance that he should oversee and scrutinise the analysis of the two cattle breeds and that the Ministry of Agriculture and Food provide financial subsidies, under whose auspices he was responsible.[32]

In the autumn of 1941 Edwin Lauprecht (1897–1987), who was engaged with the German Military Administration in northern France and whose responsibilities included animal breeding in the French occupied territories, visited Jersey. The reasons for his visit were to carry out scientific empirical investigations of the Jersey breed of cattle. Firstly, Lauprecht investigated and published an extensive report on the Island's agricultural system and pedigree cattle stock; secondly, he investigated the Jersey Herd Book; thirdly, he examined milk production records, alongside fat production of leading cattle producers; and finally, observed the special characteristics of the Island's herds.[34]

Lauprecht was billeted with Field Command 515 whilst in Jersey. He was a cattle breeding scientist who had studied with Schmidt in the 1920s, and along with whom he edited scientific journals. He joined the National Socialist German Workers' Party (NSDAP) in 1932 and became a member of the SS the following year.[35]

Whilst in Jersey in late 1941, Lauprecht compiled an extensive and comprehensive report on the Jersey cattle breed. Immediately upon his arrival, he was bestowed an immense store of research data going back to 1866. Lauprecht was certainly in his element; as a research scientist, in an occupied territory, with a full body of empirical investigative material readily at hand, he was given full access to all data he required by the Royal Jersey Agricultural and Horticultural Society. Indeed, Lauprecht felt "Very obliged to the (States of Jersey) Veterinary Surgeon Dr Blampied, as well as the gentlemen of the Jersey Herd Book in St Helier for willingly giving information".[36]

This research expedition to Jersey propelled Lauprecht's scientific career progression. Immediately after his secondment to Jersey in late 1941, he left his position in the Military Government and, on his own request, in early 1942 he joined the KWI at Dummerstorf, to supervise the Jersey and German crossbreeding program. He also published his research after the Second World War.[37] The German occupation of Jersey was an excellent example of foreign conquest facilitating the professional progression of a German scientist. Lauprecht's evaluation and analysis of an entire collection of empirical data, belonging to the Royal Jersey Agricultural and Horticultural Society, basically allowed him to usurp an entire collection of scientific material.

In Lauprecht's acknowledgement of November 1941, whilst in Jersey, he also cited "Special thanks to Kriegsverwaltungsrat Pelz who constantly helped the author during his stay on the Island of Jersey".[38] KVR Hans Egon Pelz (1902–1988) was Head of Agriculture and Food Supply for Field Command 515 for the period 9th August 1940 to early September 1944 with responsibility for the entire Channel Islands. He attended the Universität für Bodenkultur, Vienna, in the 1920s and was an intelligent and successful student. He achieved the degree "Ingenieur" in Agriculture.[39]

In 1930 Pelz joined the Salzburg Department of Cattle Breeding as a junior civil servant and was soon promoted to a Cattle Breeding Inspector, for the Salzburger Kulturrat, with the title, Landestierzuchtinspektoratsadjunkt. In 1938 he was further promoted to the Office of Animal Breeding Director for all Markets and Livestock, "Tierzuchtdirektor für alle Market und den Viehabsatz". During this period Pelz became a prominent member of the Salzburg League Against Cruelty to Animals,[40] and he was also a self-taught classical guitarist.[41]

Pelz's duties between 1930 and 1938 in Austria extended to "The purity, and support for, the improvement of the Austrian cattle breed". He initiated measures to control and regulate Austrian cattle breeding with the establishment of cooperatives and a system of examination and licencing of breed certification, with the purchase of the highest quality pedigree bulls. In addition, Pelz introduced formal records and herd books, whilst working in cooperation with the Ministry of Agriculture, Vienna, under Dr Peter and Dr Eckstein, for the Austrian cattle breeding program.[42]

Pelz volunteered at the outbreak of war in 1939 to enlist in the German army but was informed that his importance to Austrian agriculture made him irreplaceable. In January 1940, however, Pelz was conscripted for military service, and thereafter instructed that he would be involved in "Special Tasks" in line with his expertise.[43]

Pelz's "Special Task", in view of his pre-war skills and competence, was to supervise, administer and moderate the most valuable asset of the island of Jersey: the pedigree herd of cattle. This was in order to extract the breed's potential for the German war effort. As described, it was only a matter of several weeks before the KWI sent a list of the "Commended and Prize" Jersey cattle they wished to purchase. Pelz was allocated to Army Group II and assigned for military administration when Luxembourg was occupied, where he was heralded as a saviour of the beer and brewing industry. His interest in brewing continued throughout his administration in Jersey. Private photographs show he visited Ann Street Brewery, St Helier.

On the 9th August 1940 KVR Pelz, along with the officers of the German Military Government Field Command 515, arrived at low tide, 5.00 p.m., in St Helier Harbour. Pelz records that, to his surprise, he had to climb a 7-metre ladder to the quayside. Immediately upon their arrival the German officers and Pelz, still in military fatigues, were met by Major Demmler and "…were taken to the Hotel Majestic where they had dinner, and the Bailiff, the representative of the Crown, treated the German officers as guests".[44] Pelz's regard for the Bailiff of Jersey was not reciprocated. In his memoirs, the Bailiff referred to Pelz as "…a rather tiresome but very able little German called Dr Pelz".[45]

The dinner at the hotel was described by Pelz as a 'banquet' and along with the Bailiff, "…were also civilian guests dressed in evening gowns and tailcoats". Pelz was particularly struck by the attitude demonstrated by the Bailiff, which he perceived as "A noble gesture". Apart from Pelz's biographical account of the reception held by the Bailiff, Alexander Moncrieff Coutanche (1892–1973), there is not a written record extant for the 9th August 1940 event.

The arrival of the German Military Government, Field Command 515, marked a major change in the organisation of the German authorities in Jersey, as well as the other Channel Islands. Pelz had been well briefed on all matters pertaining to Jersey agriculture, the Jersey cattle breed and the dairy industry. Pelz immediately sought a working relationship with the President of the DOA, Touzel Brée, whom he regarded in his own words as his "counterpart". Within weeks, both men were meeting on a regular basis and discussing all matters agricultural. Approximately some 150 to 200 personnel were sent to Jersey as part of the Military Government of France, in which Jersey and the Channel Islands were included, and Field Command 515 set up its Headquarters at College House, the boarding house for pupils of Victoria College. Initially, the NCOs and ranks were billeted at the Continental Hotel, St Saviour's Road, St Helier, and the officers in buildings of an impressive nature. Pelz was billeted to "Little

Court" in St Lawrence. Many of the Staff Officers – a substantial number of whom had doctorates – were experts in their fields: judicial, industrial, utilities, policing, agricultural, economic, administrative, and logistical.[46]

The large number of Military Government personnel arriving in Jersey as part of Field Command 515 is surprising in view of the size of the Island and its population. They numbered approximately 150 to 200 administrators, many of whom were housed at the Continental Hotel, St Saviour's Road. The reason for these large numbers of highly skilled and qualified German personnel may lie in the revelation, a few weeks after Pelz's arrival, that orders were expected that Hitler was planning to cross the English Channel and "the First Field Command would be 515 on the mainland of Britain". Pelz subsequently was informed that the planned Operation Sealion had been suspended because of the expected high losses in men.[43]

Had Operation Sealion taken place, and England been invaded, then it seems likely that Field Command 515 would have been the first German administrative government in Nazi-occupied Britain.

KVR Pelz, unsurprisingly in view of his qualified experience in Austrian cattle breeding, on his arrival in Jersey was immediately impressed by the beauty and importance of the Jersey breed of cattle. Within weeks, he wrote in a personal letter to a friend in Salzburg: "In the fields the gazelle-like Jersey cows are grazing, pale yellow, like roe deer, which are distinguished and famous for their highest amount of fat in their milk, up to 6.2%".[47] Pelz's detailed personal letter of September 1940, sent to his friend on the subject of his first few weeks in Jersey, offers the unique insight of a senior German officer's private experience and thoughts of Jersey at an early stage of the occupation of the Island.

On his return to post-war Austria, Pelz viewed his role, as Head of Agriculture in occupied Jersey, as instrumental to the survival of the Jersey pedigree cattle breed. Pelz wrote in 1957, in a forthright and candid manner, "I would like to point out that the valuable stock of Jersey cattle got through the time of the occupation unchanged and undiminished. I think I can say that this is due to my special liking of the interest of cattle breeding; which is crucial".[48]

On the 27th June 1944, Pelz was ordered by von Schmettow, Head of Military Forces for the Channel Islands, to the Somme region to administer the repair of communications.[49] However, he did not leave Jersey until late August or early September. In early 1945 he was involved in active service in northern Italy where he was subsequently captured and imprisoned by Italian Partisans. By July 1945, however, Pelz had crossed the Alps and returned to Salzburg. In post-war Austria Pelz went on to achieve a successful career in the cattle industry, as had Lauprecht. In 1949 he became Director of the Salzburg Cattle Marketing Company making,[50] "an extraordinary contribution to the farming community of Salzburg by great knowledge and personal commitment".[51]

The esteem and obvious affection held by Pelz for the Jersey cattle breed was shared by his immediate superior in Jersey, Field Commandant Colonel Friedrich Knackfuss.[52] When Knackfuss was recalled from Jersey in March 1944, he departed the Island after purchasing a Jersey bull and a cow.[53] This certainly ranks as one of the most unique souvenirs of Jersey taken by any German serviceman throughout the entire occupation. It was not until 1946 that a Jersey bull and a cow were discovered in a Normandy village with some documentary evidence that they were indeed the Commandant's souvenirs, presumably abandoned as the German forces retreated, and left in the charge of a villager to await collection.

The purchase of Jersey cattle by German military officers whilst serving on the Island had occurred at an earlier date. A report by Reginald Oswald Weeks, Accountant/Secretary of the DOA's Milk Control Section, on the 20th March 1942, stated that the purchase of a Jersey bull and a heifer had occurred between an Island farmer and a German Military Commander. The transfer of the heifer was made by Mr J. M. Le Brocq, Newlands, St Ouen, to a "Doctor E. Dennisburg" of the German armed forces. The German officer in question was Hauptmann Dannenberg – later described as 'Major Doctor' – who arrived in Jersey in September 1940 to replace Hauptmann Gussek as Inselkommandant until the arrival of Oberst Graf von Schmettow. Dr Dannenberg then became Kommandant of the 1st Kp. MG Battalion 16 for the period 1940 to 1941. A bull calf was also involved in the transaction; however, before Dr Dannenberg could take possession of the calf it was sent to the abattoir for slaughter.[54]

In May 1944 an unknown German officer toured and inspected the Island's herds and was presented by local farmers with examples and at least four breeding bulls. He photographed the animals that farmers were willing to sell to him. On the reverse of one photograph he wrote, "A presentation of a breeding bull in order to buy one". Further photographs were inscribed, "A Jersey cattle shed with Jersey cows. Viewing of this herd in order to buy a breeding bull in May 1944" and "Negotiating to purchase this Jersey bull with a local farmer, May 1944. The invasion wrecked the purchase". There is also a photograph of a Jersey apple crusher which he describes as an "olive oil press". The implication, that D-Day stopped the purchase of the bull, and subsequent export of breeding cattle to Germany, is plausible because by and large sea journeys to Normandy were immediately cut and ceased after August 1944, although air links were maintained. Certainly, there were German purchases of Jersey prize cattle in this period as the transfer of them is recorded in the Jersey Herd Book, and it is possible that three cows were shipped to Germany: Tabor Coronation Lady, Franchise Wonderful's Darling, and Hauteville Marvel, purchased between March 1943 and March 1944.[55]

The German armed forces in Jersey apparently had an ambivalent attitude toward the taste of meat from Jersey cattle. "The Nazis did not like the local meat and when they could, imported beef cattle from Germany and France, as carcasses and on the hoof".[56] In July 1944, a month after D-Day, a French barge of Continental cattle was shipped to Jersey to supplement the meat ration of German troops. These cows were put out to pasture on fields in the parish of St Peter and became a constant attraction for the local civilian population who had never seen large black and white cattle before. A newly born black and white calf became the centre of attraction.[57]

The German occupation of Jersey saw a policy of non-slaughter of Jersey cattle until the 10th May 1941. On the 24th June 1941, Colonel Schumacher, Field Commandant of 515, wrote a letter to the Bailiff entitled: "Import of living animals for slaughter in Jersey". Schumacher made it clear to the Jersey authorities that, due to the increase in the number of German troops,[58] fresh meat was insufficient for their needs. This consequently made it a necessity for the German Military Government to deliver live cattle into Jersey from the Continent. It was common at this time, due to the lack of refrigeration on boats, that cattle were normally imported "on the hoof" for slaughter rather than "on the hook". Hence the proximity of the abattoir to the harbour. The importation of foreign cattle into the Island occurred during the German occupation and they were slaughtered for both the German military and the civilian population. Schumacher was well aware of the consternation that would result amongst the extremely important Island agricultural elite, who comprised many members of the government assembly. Foreign cattle had not been allowed into Jersey since 1763. The leading Jersey farmers saw this as potentially serious which, if not regulated, would jeopardise the integrity of the pedigree Island breed. Schumacher attempted to allay these fears expressing the view, "I am quite aware that these unavoidable measures are dangerous for the local cattle. For military purposes, however, this cannot be avoided".[59]

This order to Jersey farmers to supply their cattle for meat for the Island population (initially farmers were deliberately misinformed that these meat supplies would only be for Island civilians) had both short-term and important long-term consequences. It immediately led to a number of heated discussions between the President of the DOA, Brée, and KVR Pelz. Brée insisted that Jersey cattle had been selectively bred for the beauty of the breed for the show ring, the quality of the milk, with its high fat content, and for the quantity of milk produced. He vehemently disagreed with Pelz that Island cattle would be of any value as meat supplies. Brée, who is often written and described as outwitting Pelz with his guile and cunning arguments, discovered his arguments were a lost cause. The long-term consequence of this decision to use Jersey cattle for meat was that Island farmers immediately began to slaughter cattle that produced poor milk yields, or milk of lower fat content, or were of insufficient quality to enter a show ring. Previously, in the years immediately before the German occupation, inferior Island cattle were sold to unsuspecting mainland dairy farmers by unscrupulous Jersey farmers and agents. This had become an extremely vexatious topic between the English Jersey Cattle Society and the

RJA&HS. A letter to the RJA&HS from the English Jersey Cattle Society just prior to the German occupation plainly accuses Jersey cattle breeders of debasing the entire UK importation of Jersey cattle with a glut of inferior animals. From this period onwards poor-quality calves, heifers, cows and bulls were the first to be culled for meat supplies. In consequence the post-war quality of Jersey cattle for export was of an extraordinarily high level, a fact that was noticed by the world markets which began immediately restocking with new cattle from Jersey.

Three days later, on the 27th June 1941, the States Vet, Blampied, met "… with Herr Pelz who agreed to approach the competent authorities with a view to slaughtering their animals on the Victoria Pier".[59]

The seriousness of the question of German imports of foreign cattle into Jersey became the central issue of an immediate conference and the following attended: Pelz, Brée, Blampied and Henry George Gaudin, described by Field Command 515 as the Managing Director of the Slaughterhouse, or "Schlachthofleiter". The conference delegates decided on altering an existing warehouse into an "emergency slaughterhouse" on Victoria Pier where German-imported cattle could be immediately unloaded, disinfected and slaughtered. The facility would be completely isolated, with no danger of these animals transmitting disease or causing breed contamination of local animals.

The conference was decisive and an interesting example of the many "structural relationships" that were prevalent during the German occupation between government officials and civilians and officers of Field Command 515. It was evident from the DOA records that Brée met on a regular basis with KVR Pelz to discuss all agricultural issues and they formed an extremely close working relationship. In December 1940, Brée gave Pelz an alarm clock for Christmas.[60]

Pelz certainly viewed Brée as "my civilian counterpart, who would consult me".[48] Pelz makes it clear that Henry Gaudin was "my very good friend, often, at the start of my island career, he proudly showed me the rock-hard lumps of meat in the cold storage depot at the harbour".[48]

These structural relationships between the Jersey and German authorities seem to have been whitewashed from the historical record of the German occupation of Jersey, as well as the role of Pelz. An example of this deletion of the historical record can be seen by a conference held at both the States of Jersey Experimental Station, Trinity, and at Little Court, St Lawrence, between the dates 6th to 11th July 1942.

The conference comprised: KVR Pelz; Jurat Brée; Louis Guillemette of the Guernsey Controlling Committee; Ernest George Ing, NDH, Dip.Hort. Sci., an expert on agricultural pests and diseases and especially potatoes; and Michael Wynne Sayer. The latter was an agricultural specialist who accompanied Guillemette from Guernsey and they held a series of meetings with Jersey committees, including this conference for which there are no official records. The aim of the conference was to discuss agricultural problems and to address shortages in food supplies in the Channel Islands. It is interesting to note that the photograph of those attending the conference is a personal one belonging to Pelz and is the only extant photograph of the entire occupation where a senior individual of his rank, and a Staff Officer (he was a major), is not in military uniform. The wearing of a German uniform on all German Military Government interactions with occupied civilians was subject to military law and in standing orders of Field Command 515. What is of even greater importance is that this conference has been entirely omitted from all Island civilian government official records and also from the minutes of the DOA, RJA&HS, JFU and Joint Emergency Committee of the RJA&HS and JFU. The only written record of the conference is Louis Guillemette's private diary.[61.] The photograph was taken by Elsa Brunner, the housemaid at Little Court.

A further point of interest concerning the agricultural conference is that Ing has been positively identified in the photograph by his contemporary work colleague from the States Experimental Station, the late Dr Frank Le Maistre. Ing joined the staff in December 1933, where Le Maistre was already working. Therefore, by the time of the German occupation, Le Maistre would have worked with Ing for six and a half years. The official records demonstrate that Ing was on the Island on 7th June 1940 whilst writing a report on the prevailing potato eelworm infestation and was also carrying out his agricultural and inspection duties.[62] However, he is not mentioned again in any written record whatsoever until the 29th May 1945, twenty days after the Island's liberation. On that day the DOA met to discuss the employment of "Colorado Beetle Staff". It was decided by the DOA that "Dr Thomas Small, the States mycologist, and Mr Ernest G. Ing, *who had both left the Island,* be recalled and re-installed in order that their expert services may be available for dealing with any serious infestation of the Colorado Beetle which may be found on the Island." However, when viewing the written minutes, it is obvious that they were altered to: "Dr Thomas Small, the States mycologist and Mr Ernest G. Ing, *who had both left their posts at the evacuation of the Island in June 1940* be recalled and re-installed in order that their expert services may be available for dealing with any serious infestation of the Colorado Beetle which may be found on the Island."[63]

The very generous sum of £650 was put aside for the two men for the rest of the financial year, and this would equate to approximately double their normal salaries. At the same meeting the Secretary of the DOA, Colin Marie, was instructed to write to Dr Small, asking him whether he would be prepared "immediately to return to the Island to take up his duties with the anticipated danger of infestations of the Colorado Beetle". A number of questions present themselves concerning Ing. Firstly, why is he in Jersey in July 1942 when the official record (amended) states he had already been evacuated in 1940? Secondly, why were the official government record and minutes altered after being written? Finally, why

6

was Marie instructed to write only to Dr Small? On the 12th June 1945, Ing contacted the DOA "regrettably declining the offer of reinstatement on the staff of the States Experimental Station". Dr Small was reinstated by the 11th June 1945.[64]

Colonel Schumacher, in a further letter to the Bailiff on the 2nd July 1941, described the completion of the temporary slaughterhouse on Victoria Pier, which was inspected by Dr Denzilier, the chief German Veterinary Officer from Field Command 722 in St Lô, Normandy, France, and Blampied and Gaudin. The letter also contained an interesting request from Schumacher on the possibility of finding, "...a small establishment in town...fixed up for the production of sausages". Furthermore, he had heard, "Mr Gaudin mentioned the shop of the butcher Chillcot who has evacuated. Mr Gaudin must, if necessary, be in a position to give information in regard to this".[57]

The next day, the Bailiff wrote to Schumacher to inform him that Gaudin was to "...see to the matter of Chillcot's shop". The Bailiff also took the opportunity to request that the emergency slaughterhouse only be used for foreign and not local cattle. On the 17th July, Blampied held a further meeting with Pelz over the final arrangements of the emergency slaughterhouse. Two weeks later, KVR Dr Brosch informed the Bailiff that the emergency slaughterhouse "Had been in operation for several weeks and has proved a success".[57] By the 17th September, OKVR Dr Casper informed the Bailiff that the sausage factory had been so successful that the German troops required a further cold store and Gaudin had been informed that the cold storage at A. E. Smith and Son, 16 Cannon Street, would be sufficient.[65]

"The Jersey breed lived on the edge of a volcano
throughout those years"

H. G. Shepard

Up to May 1941, and whilst the Germans imported Continental cattle, Jersey cattle were only being slaughtered to supplement these meat imports. The Jersey pedigree stock was, to all intents and purposes, left intact to produce milk and butter for the Island civilian and German military populations. This was fundamentally the policy of Pelz. However, by the middle of 1942, this slaughter policy led to an unexpected consequence. The Jersey cattle that were subsequently selected for slaughter at the end of 1941 were carefully chosen by the leading farmers, advised by Robert Wilson Carson, who ensured that only barren heifers and unproductive or low milk-yielding cows were culled and utilised as a meat source. This led in a short period to a significant improvement in the quality of the remaining Jersey breed on the Island. Carson was the leading expert on Jersey pedigree cattle milk production.

On the 17th May 1943 a conference was held between Field Command 515 and Field Command 722 in St Lô. Pelz made detailed analyses of both Jersey's and Guernsey's meat requirements for both the civil and military populations. It was evident to Pelz that Continental meat imports, calculated at 9 tons per month for Jersey and 6 tons for Guernsey, were insufficient. The islands would have to fulfil their meat requirements from their own cattle.[66]

The German Military Government issued a fundamental policy change towards the Jersey cattle breed. The civilian population, as well as the German military contingents, thus far dependent on imported Continental cattle, were ordered to slaughter and rely on the local breed for meat requirements.

There was extreme reluctance amongst the civilian population, leading almost to a refusal, to consume meat from Jersey cattle. Pelz wrote, in a private letter to Dr Kratzer: "the people of the Island successively refused to eat Jersey cattle, their own long-established Island breed".[67] Brée repeatedly justified the error of the German Military Government's policy by explaining, "You cannot eat Jersey cattle, and they only provide milk". Pelz continued his arguments with Brée: "With only great effort and serious admonition did I manage to make Brée supply Jersey cattle for consumption in the context of rationing". Pelz further noted in the letter that, even after the non-slaughter policy was reversed, there was still enough butter and milk for the Island to be self-sufficient.

The reasons for Jersey's self-sufficiency lay not just in the initial non-slaughter policy of Pelz, but also because, between the occupation years 1940 to 1945, the very large numbers of pre-war worldwide Jersey cattle exports ceased. For example, in 1939 exports of sixty heifers in one shipment were not uncommon.[68]

This, combined with the remarkable achievements of the Jersey farmer and the care of his herd during the occupation, resulted in every child on the Island receiving a daily allowance of full-fat, fresh milk for almost the entire period. Jersey was certainly the only German-occupied territory in Europe where children were given a continuous daily supply of fresh milk. There was only an approximately two-week period prior to 23rd April 1945 when farmers appear to have deliberately held back milk supplies as a form of opposition to the German authorities. In consequence, on the 23rd April 1945 Brée wrote to every Jersey farmer with a plea to continue sending their milk through to the dairies. The reason for a number of farmers' hesitancy, and in some cases refusal, to send their milk to the dairies was simple. The German authorities were increasingly requisitioning the majority of the Island's milk supply for their military personnel. In two parishes in particular dairy farmers, as the DOA put it, "sent dirty milk" which often deliberately contaminated an entire days' milk collection.

On the 14th November 1944, Major Heider of Platzkommand had written to the Bailiff a letter entitled "Meat Requirements of the Troops".[69] Heider demanded that "...as from the 10th December 1944, the troops' requirements of meat will have to be covered from the civilian sector". This meat requirement was 7.2 metric tons per week until the 31st January 1945, with an increase to 8.2 metric tons thereafter.[70] Heider, after conferring with Blampied, instructed that meat from local Jersey herds was to be supplied every Thursday. The DOA decided immediately "...that to safeguard, as far as possible, the Island breed", the selection for the German occupying forces be placed in the hands of the "Cattle Slaughter Executive". Between the 18th December 1944 and the 5th May 1945, 1,000 head of cattle were slaughtered, equating to forty a week. In addition, the German Platzkommand commandeered a further 200 head of cattle, which were subsequently sent to Guernsey and Alderney.[71]

On the 10th January 1945 Brée transmitted, through the office of the Bailiff, an invoice for £1,508 for "cattle for slaughter for the requirements of the army of occupation", for the period 18th to 24th December 1944. Brée concluded in his letter accompanying the invoice, "I shall be obliged if you will ask the German authorities to remit the amount to the Treasurer of the States". Accounts for meat supplies had to be made out in kilogrammes and in the German currency and sent in duplicate to the "Verpflegungsausgabestelle" (the building where German troops received their rations or meals), 13/15 Esplanade, and not to the Platzkommand. The German authorities were charged 6d per pound live weight for bulls and cows and 8d per pound live weight for heifers.

By the 27th February the German authorities had yet to pay Jersey farmers for the meat received and they were so advised. On the 20th March the German authorities replied to the DOA that accounts rendered to them would not be accepted as the weights invoiced were in excess of the weights ascertained over the German-controlled weighbridge. Jersey farmers who were now ordered to take their cattle to the Jersey-controlled weighbridge were deliberately given no indication whether the meat was intended for civilian or German military purposes. The accounts were settled by the German authorities to the DOA by the 27th March 1945 based only on the value of cattle weighed on the German weighbridge.

There was therefore a real possibility that, had the German occupation continued for several more months after May 1945, the entire Island of Jersey would have been in danger of losing a number of pedigree herds, even causing "great injury to the Island breed". The RJA&HS was clear: "The Jersey breed lived on the edge of a volcano throughout those years".[72]

The German demand for meat during 1944 also extended to greater demands for butter. On the 11th October 1944, Platzkommand ordered from the DOA a further 5 tons of butter to be delivered to troops in November and December 1944. The DOA met to discuss the demand and "In view of the serious effect which the supplying of these quantities will have upon the stocks of butter for the civilian population..." Brée would "...make energetic representations to the German authorities with a view to securing that these demands for butter shall not exceed a reasonable proportion of the Island's production".[73]

On the 24[74] October Brée reported back to the DOA concerning his interview with the Platzkommandant.[74] The news was not good: "The German authorities had threatened that unless this butter is delivered to them, they will order that the troops are supplied with full cream milk instead of skim milk at the rate of one-half pint per head". The DOA, "under duress", agreed that the supply of butter to German troops would be the lesser of two evils and consequently authorised an increase in the butter supply to the German troops.[72]

On the 25th November the German authorities ordered that an extra 8 tons of butter be produced for December 1944 and January 1945. There was now a real worry and concern amongst the civilian government that this would cause a severe deprivation of milk to young children and persons who were ill. By the 28th November, Platzkommand had commandeered 18½ metric tons of butter from the reserves of the Island. The milk ration to children in primary school and to special groups was subsequently discontinued and resumed again on the 23rd January 1945, although children still received their personal allowance of milk. [72]

The butter so requisitioned was not invoiced to the Platzkommandant directly. Instead, the DOA notified the Department of Finance and Economics of the quantity and the price of the butter delivered which would subsequently be charged against "The cost of the army of occupation".[72]

By the 4th March 1945 the figures demonstrate that German forces stationed on Jersey had consumed: 10,342 pounds weight of butter in January 1945, and 9,587 pounds weight in February. Certainly, butter was a commodity that was in particularly short supply for the German military forces. Between 1943 and 1945, Denmark supplied some one-third of the Wehrmacht's consumption of butter.[75] In 1942 Pelz had sent three tins of Jersey butter to his mother in Austria. She consumed very little of it – in case Pelz was posted away from the Island and could no longer send her further supplies.

The Bailiff, on the 27th October 1944, received a letter from the Platzkommandant requiring that the quantity of milk distributed to civil hospitals and the sick be reduced by half of the quantity sent in September. On the 7th November, the DOA received a further letter from the Platzkommandant, "insisting upon the reduction of the quantity of milk supplied on medical grounds" – in other words, those ill but not in a hospital.

By the 11th November, extra milk was discontinued to nursing mothers and juveniles and, on the 5th December, "In view of certain instructions in a letter dated the 30th November 1944 from the German authorities", the DOA made the following alterations for civilians with special requirements:

1. An Adult Registration Certificate, MR1, was cut to half a pint of milk per day, excluding one day in every seven.
2. A Child and a Juvenile Registration Certificate, MR2 and MR3, was cut to one pint a day.

The Platzkommandant subsequently instructed that, from 15th January 1945, these groups would have their allocation of milk reduced to every three days.

On the 10th February 1945 a further order was received from the Platzkommandant insisting that the Milk Testers give to German troops in control of milk "...such information as the troops require".[72] On the 22nd March, the Platzkommandant wrote to the DOA and ordered that "The supply of liquid milk to the civilian population, with certain conditional exceptions therein specified, shall cease and that, in place of such liquid milk, the members of the civilian population, other than those still entitled to receive liquid milk in virtue of the exceptions aforesaid, shall be issued with ten grams of butter per day provided that the requirements of the army of occupation, in relation to butter requirements first shall have been satisfied". In other words, the German authorities were going to have the first call on the milk supply of the Island. Brée and the DOA were shocked and mortified and the letter was subject to lengthy consideration and discussion. The decision was taken that "As no guarantee exists that any quantity of butter will be available for the civilian population, nor does it appear probable that the supply of milk for children, adolescents, and the sick will be forthcoming, it [the DOA] is not prepared to fulfil the requirements of the German authorities". Brée and the DOA subsequently submitted the following proposition to the Platzkommandant:

1. That the German authorities requisition the Don Street Dairy, the largest of the five dairies.
2. That the DOA will guarantee 4,900 pots of whole milk for the next six months, which would enable the German authorities to manufacture 19 tons of butter each month and would result in 2,250 pots of skim milk and 15 tons of curd for the German troops on the Island.
3. That any deficiency of butter and curd for the German troops shall be made by supplying the German authorities eighty cattle a month in addition to the present quota of cattle required by them.

Brée made it clear to his fellow farmers that "To preserve, as far as possible the Island breed of cattle, no meat whatsoever shall be supplied to the civilian population from the Island cattle".

Brée discussed with the German authorities their demands on the Island's milk supply and energetically explained that the average daily yield per cow over a twelve-month period was "two pots only". The Platzkommandant, however, contested that the real figure was 3 pots. In consequence of the milk production figures that Brée presented, the German authorities agreed to postpone their requirements of the 21st March 1945 until they had carried out an Island-wide trial to ascertain and establish the actual daily milk yield per cow.

The Germans, sensing that milk was being secreted from them, sent their own Inspectors throughout the Island to check on milking and milk production records. Many of these German Inspectors were former farmers from the Eifel region of Germany who served with MG Battalion 16 stationed on the west coast of Jersey. On the 21st March 1945 Platzkommand requisitioned the Don Street Dairy. The DOA met and decided that in view of "The very uncertain position, now prevailing in relation to milk, it is decided to take no action".

The fate of the twenty cows and two bulls exported from Jersey to Dummerstorf in October 1941 for use by the KWI is unclear. Lauprecht, after leaving Jersey in late 1941 to become Head of the Jersey and German crossbreeding program at Dummerstorf, became Associate Professor of Animal Breeding at Rostock University, shortly before the advancing Red Army arrived at Dummerstorf on the 1st May 1945. Lauprecht relocated with fifty-one Jersey crossbreed heifers to Lüneberg, Lower Saxony. In the following weeks after the Russians' arrival at Dummerstorf the entire stock of Jersey cattle, and the scientific research material, was lost.[76]

The remaining Jersey cattle of Dummerstorf were subsequently, "...eaten by the Russian army".[77] The report by the RJA&HS in late 1945, concluded, "In the autumn of 1941, 21 head of cattle were purchased by the Germans and exported to an experimental station on the Baltic Coast for crossing purposes, with what results is not known".[71]

Certainly, one of the most astonishing features of this study has been the opportunity to re-evaluate the importance of Hans Egon Pelz in the occupation history of the Island of Jersey. Pelz was pivotal to many of the structural relationships between Jersey's government, the civil service, farmers and the German armed forces in the Channel Islands. Pelz, however, has been almost totally whitewashed from the entire historical record. He not only worked in close proximity with Touzel Brée, but also with the leading figures of the RJA&HS, with civil servants and he worked in tandem with the abattoirs, checking a fair distribution of meat products for the Island's civil and military populations. Pelz also continually checked the size, the condition, and oversaw how farmers were looking after, their crops. In addition, Pelz worked continuously to supply meat and food products obtained through Field Command 722, St Lô.[78] Every week, Gaudin provided weekly figures of all animals slaughtered, figures consequently verified by the Department of Essential Commodities, the Bailiff and Pelz.[79]

Pelz on his own inclination sought and provided vegetables for the civilian soup kitchens, as well as attending conferences with leading agricultural figures in the Channel Islands to deal with food supply problems. He supervised the Islands cropping plans, checked and monitored cereal harvests and facilitated the importation of agricultural inputs: seed, fertilizer, fuel, machinery and straw from Continental Europe. He allowed the Chief

Veterinary Surgeon of Field Command 515, Dr Kempt, to treat animals belonging to Jersey farmers, and permitted the use of German horses on Island farms.[80]

Pelz, in the course of his Island-wide duties, would inform Brée and the DOA of any infringements by farmers of Cultivation Orders, or illegal stocks of agricultural commodities. Finally, and perhaps the most interesting aspect of Pelz's role, is that whenever the German army on Jersey requested arable land for military purposes, permission had to be given by Field Command 515. On several occasions he did not give consent, reminding the army of the need to conserve arable land. In Pelz's opinion "An area of arable land may be destroyed in real battle, not just for exercise". Pelz made it clear to Field Command 515 that: "The performance of agriculture is just as decisive in war as that of the military".[81] Finally, Pelz noted that, in his opinion, he was central to the survival of the Jersey pedigree breed during the German occupation. This is certainly pertinent, as a close relative to the Jersey breed, the Alderney, never survived and was for all intents and purposes lost.[82]

References

1. Jersey Evening Post, 7th January 1941.
2. Balleine, Francis Ernest. Certificate of Appointment as German Consul by Kaiser Wilhelm I, signed by Otto von Bismarck, dated 14th February 1887. Societé Jersiaise Library. PEO/I/A-E/Balleine, F.
3. RJA&HS Annual Report 1898, p. 14.
4. Lauprecht, E. 1942. Lie Rinderzucht auf der Insel Jersey. Züchtungskunde, Vol 17, p. 382.
5. Brade, Wilfred. Berichte Ülandswirtschaft, 2014. Band 92, Heft 3, pp. 1–24, Kreuzung mit Jersey Rindern und Deren Nutzung in Deutschland aus Historischer Sicht.
6. Frölich, A. 1944, Prof. Gustav Frölich Neuzeitiche Zucht, Haltung und Fütterung der Haustiere Fritz Pfenningstorff, Berlin 1944.
7. The Kaiser Wilhelm Society under National Socialism, 2009, S. Heim, C. Sachse and M. Walker, p. 7.
8. Jersey Herd Book, HBN 51878. She lived a long life and died in 1952.
9. Le Quesne, Deputy Edward, The Personal Diary. The Occupation of Jersey Day by Day. 1999. p. 11.
10. Jersey Archive. B/A/W40/2/1.
11. Kazemi, M. Dahlemer Archivgespräche Herausgeben von Archiv zur Geschighte der Max-Plank-Gesellschaft, 2002, 8, p. 150.
12. Connétables accompanied the KWI scientists in selecting cattle for export to Germany.
13. Le Ruez, N. 1994. Jersey Occupation Diary. p. 21.
14. Head of the Superior Council.
15. Jersey Herd Book, HBN 7475.
16. L. Gordan Tubbs. The Book of the Jersey, 1947, Third Edition, p. 210.

17. The Emergency Governing Committee of the States of Jersey.
18. Jersey Archives. B/A/W40/2/1.
19. Jersey Archives. C/B/A1/5.
20. Jersey Archives. B/A/W40/2/2.
21. Jersey Archives. L/D/25/L/22.
22. H. G. Shepard. 1968, Jersey Farmer and Grower, March, Vol 7, p. 20.
23. The Jersey Herd Books are held by the Royal Jersey Agriculture and Horticultural Society, Trinity, Jersey.
24. Jersey Herd Book. HBN 49625.
25. History of the Royal Guernsey Agricultural and Horticultural Society, 1947, pp. 133–135.
26. Dummerstorf close the Fat Gap.
27. Dairy cows from the Channel Islands.
28. http://buel.bmel.de/index.php/buel/article/viiew/61/brade-92-3-html (1941) Dummerstorf SchliesBt Fettlüke, pdfu.
29. I acknowledge and thank Prof Dr Brade and Dr Gunther Vierek, Fbn-Dummerstorf, for allowing me the use of their documents pertaining to the fat content of milk produced by the crossbreed Jersey and German cattle between 1941 and 1943.
30. Max Planck: Berlin. I: Department 1A, No 2858.
31. Simm, G, 1998. Genetic Improvement of Cattle and Sheep, p. 166.
32. Max Planck: Berlin. I: Department 1A, No 2859.
33. Jersey Herd Book, HBN 7473 and HBN 7475.
34. Lauprecht, E. 1942, Die Rinderzucht auf Insel Jersey. Züchtungskunde. Herausgeben von Der Deutschen Gesellschaft Für Züchtunskunde Unter Mitwirkkung der Tierzuchinstitute an Deutschen Hochschulen. Vol 17, pp. 369–386.
35. Heim, S. 2008. Plant Breeding and Agrarian Research in Kaiser Wilhelm Institutes 1933–1945. Calories, Caoutechouc, Careers, p. 44.
36. The members of the Jersey Herd Book Emergency Committee: President, Carlyle Le Gallais, and Vice Presidents, John Buesnel Michel and Francis Le Boutillier.
37. Schmidt, J 1948/9. Schqarzbunte Niederungskühe und Bullen Kreuzungsver suche und Ihre Bewertung. Züchtungskunde. Vol 20, pp. 29–39.
38. War Administrator.
39. Universitäts-biblothek, Universitaet Fur Bodenkultur. My thanks to Tarik Gaafar for providing details of Pelz's courses and examination results.
40. Salzburg Federal Archive. SLA, Re hrl-brief 1, p. 35.
41. I acknowledge that information on Pelz's pre-war career was obtained visiting Salzburg and I would thank Dr Peter Kramml, Stadt: Salzburg Magistrat, Stadtarchiv und Stadtistik; Dr Eva Rinnerthaler, Amt der Salzburger Landesarchiv and Andreas Riedl, Amt der Salzburger Landesregierung.
42. Private letter from Pelz to Dr Grassberger, referred to as "Court Councellor", dated 10th November 1954. I acknowledge and thank the Pelz family for allowing me access to their father's private correspondence.

43. The biography of Hans Egon Pelz. Damals Erinnerungen. 2015. Compiled and published by the Pelz family.

44. Ibid, Pelz. p. 570. The hotel Pelz describes in Jersey is probably The Grand Hotel, and not the Majestic Hotel. The latter was the headquarters of the Military Government in Paris.

45. Pocock, H. R. S., 1975. The Memoirs of Lord Coutanche, p. 22. Pelz is still referred to in historical publications and reference books with the prefix "Doctor" see: Ginns, M., Jersey Occupied. The German Armed Forces in Jersey, 1940–1945, 2009, p. 45. Pelz never signed himself as "Doctor", 1940–1944, although in 1940 and 1941 he is designated as "Dr Pelz" by the DOA and the JEP. Herbert de Gruchy certainly describes his meeting with "Dr Pelz" when ordered to deliver Cultivation Orders to Island farmers. He, however, seems somewhat confused as to what type of doctorate Pelz had, although he knows it is not a medical qualification. Jersey Archive. L/D/25/L/22.

46. I acknowledge and thank Mr Alan Allix, a founder member of the Channel Island Occupation Society, for allowing me access to his personal information compiled from Major Heider who was present for the entire period, 1940–1945, as a Senior Officer of Field Command 515.

47. Private letter from Pelz to Sepp Bartelt, Salzburg, dated 29th September 1940. The letter was written from "Little Court, St Lawrence, Jersey". Pelz family archive.

48. Private letter to Dr Josef Kratzer, President of the Munich Administrative Court, Munich, dated the 12th February 1957. Pelz family archive.

49. Von Schmettow was the nephew of Field Marshall Gerd von Rundstedt.

50. Salzburger Viehuerwertung.

51. Salzburger Nachrichten, 1988, 24th November.

52. Field Commandant of 515. He arrived in Jersey in October 1941, leaving in either March or April 1944. Knackfuss had close family and kinship ties with Rudolf Schmudt, Hitler's army adjutant, who was injured and subsequently died, following the 1944 bomb plot.

53. Jersey Archive. B/A/W31/2/140.

54. Jersey Archive. C/B/A1/7.

55. Jersey Herd Book. HBN 51861, 51527 and 52083.

56. Earl of Jersey, Chairman, World Jersey Cattle Bureau, T. Le Quesne P, FRCVS, Veterinary Officer to the States of Jersey, 1938–1961. The Jersey Cow and its Island Home, 1965, p. 13. A paper presented at the conference of the WJCB.

57. Lewis, Dr John. A Doctor's Occupation, 1997, p. 199.

58. The number of troops went from approximately 7,500 to 12,000.

59. Jersey Archive. B/A/W70/1.

60. Pelz. op. cit. 42. p. 583.

61. My thanks to Ms Rosie Day, Louis Guillemette's daughter for checking and affirming the dates of the meeting.

62. Jersey Archive. C/B/A1/4.

63. Jersey Archive. C/B/A1/11.
64. Jersey Archive. B/A/L14/9.
65. Dr W. Casper was sent to Copenhagen in March 1943. He was second in command to Dr Werner Best, a Brigadier in the SS Werner Best visited Jersey in 1942 and was an acquaintance of Dr W. Casper.
66. Jersey Archive. BA/W63/35.
67. Private letter from Pelz to Dr Josef Kratzer, President of the Bavarian Administration Court, Munich 22, Ludwigstr, 14, Germany. The letter is dated 12th February 1957. Dr Kratzer served as KVR, Field Command 515, during the German occupation of Jersey. Pelz family archive.
68. Jersey Archive. C/B/A1/3.
69. Major Heider, previously Chief of Staff for Field Command 515.
70. Jersey Archive. B/A/W40/2/3.
71. The figure of 200 cattle taken was modified, in Ralph Mollett's private notes, to 187. Jersey Archive.
72. RJA&HS – Report to the Committee for the years 1940 to 1945, 8th December 1945.
73. Jersey Archive. C/B/A1/10.
74. This was Major W. Heider.
75. Lund, Joachim. (2013) The Wages of Collaboration: the German food crisis 1939–1945 and the supplies from Denmark. Scandinavian Journal of History, 38:4, pp. 480–501.
76. Kazemi, M., op. cit.[11] p. 156.
77. Frigot, D., MBE. 2017. Pioneers of the Jersey Breed, p. 86. The Jersey Herd Book was established in 1866.
78. Jersey Archive. B/A/W63/3.
79. Jersey Archive. B/A/W92/4. File entitled, "Lokale Schlachtungen au Jersey".
80. Dr Kempt made it clear to local farmers that he was very happy to treat animals for free. Farmers subsequently returned to Dr Kempt with sick animals. Interview with Mr Jack Le Sueur, dairy farmer, Clairvale Farm, La Rue de St Mannelier, St Clement, by Mr Alan Allix.
81. Correspondence dated 16th July 1943 by Pelz and Field Command 515. Documents held in a private collection.
82. Crump, F. 1995. The Alderney Cow, p. 26.

Chapter 3

The German Military Importation of Continental Cattle into Occupied Jersey and the Effect on the Jersey Pedigree Breed, 1940–1945

"Interbreeding between Jersey and foreign cattle must not take place"

Field Command 515, The German Military Government

Foreign cattle imports into the Island of Jersey had, since 1783, been prohibited. The purity of the Island stock was closely supervised by the RJA&HS with meticulous records of all Jersey pedigree cattle documented in the Jersey Herd Book. Between 1900 and 1939 an exceptionally lucrative export market developed in North America for purebred Jersey cattle. There was fierce competition amongst Jersey breeders to demonstrate the purity of their stock to their North American customers and in 1939 export consignments of up to sixty heifers were not uncommon.[1]

The purity of the Jersey breed was put in jeopardy in July 1940 by the German occupation of the Island. The military forces immediately began importing live Continental cattle into Jersey. The Jersey government and the leading class of cattle breeders viewed these imports with trepidation and envisaged the impending destruction of over 180 years of selective breeding. The closely recorded and monitored breeding regime had produced a worldwide reputation making the 'Jersey' a pre-eminent breed and an important source of revenue for the agricultural community.

On the 5th August 1940 the High Command informed the States that live cattle would be imported into Jersey from France. The President of the DOA, Brée, in response, requested permission from the German High Command to inspect these cattle and on the same day he asked the Piers and Harbours Committee for permission to inspect them as they arrived on the quayside. Upon their arrival to the Albert Quay, St Helier Harbour, they were taken to the nearby abattoir and numbers of them slaughtered for meat for the German troops. The remaining animals were also used as an additional source of milk for the troops and they soon also became a supply of meat for the civilian population.

Bernard Arthur Baker, an electrical engineer for the Jersey Electricity Company who liaised with Field Command 515 on supplies of electricity and who also repaired installations, obtained an Island-wide permit for a vehicle. He soon observed and stated in his diary: "Quite a number of foreign cattle have been brought over for consumption by both the Germans and civilians and are herded in different parts of the Island. What ugly brutes they are compared to our breed of cows."

On the 12th August 1940 the matter of imported cattle was discussed by the DOA. Brée made clear to his Committee and to the States that he was in no position to take any action in response to the importation of live cattle. The DOA again asked the German High Command, and was granted permission, to inspect these cattle imports on arrival at St Helier Harbour.

These animals were grazed on German military farms such as Don Bridge Farm and the Airport Farm and seemingly were kept separate from the Jersey cattle. Their increasing numbers and obvious appearance in 1940 resulted in a real concern by the Jersey authorities and cattle breeders that they would contaminate, and lead to a degradation of, the pure Island stock. Two months into the occupation of Jersey, the issue of German-imported cattle became a subject of meetings between the States and the German military administrations of both Jersey and France. On the 29th August Field Command 515 published a notification: "NO LIVE CATTLE TO BE IMPORTED". The notice went on to inform all interested groups, "It is learned that live cattle must not now be imported into the Island for slaughter. Instead of live cattle, ready-killed meat is to come instead".[2] On the 30th August the German Military Government held detailed meetings with Brée and addressed many of the concerns of Jersey farmers on the German importation of Continental cattle into the Island.[3]

The situation concerning the halting of live cattle imports, seemingly agreed, soon changed. The German Military Government's head of Agriculture and Food Supplies, KVR Pelz, persuaded his counterpart, Brée, that live meat imports were necessary to feed not only the German garrison but also the civilian population. Pelz did not wish to slaughter Jersey cattle for meat, fully understanding that they were best utilised as a source of milk. On the 7th September, at a States sitting, Brée brought forward a Prospect de Règlement permitting the importation of livestock providing all necessary safeguards were taken. Brée explained to the assembly that the importation of cattle from Europe would be crucial in providing meat supplies for the civilian population, and hence the reason for his Règlement. He endorsed it to a somewhat sceptical meeting. The Connétable of St Ouen, Francis Le Boutillier, himself a leading cattle breeder and Vice President of the RJA&HS, agreed that times were abnormal, but he hoped that the DOA would not allow the importation of cattle which he regarded as "a dangerous procedure". Brée assured him and all others present that cattle landed from

Europe would immediately be taken to the nearby abattoir where all would be safe. The Prospect was agreed and the subsequent law implemented.[4] The Importation of Livestock (Jersey) Regulations 1940 allowed the landing into Jersey of cattle provided they were immediately taken to the abattoir for slaughter. All precautions to prevent the introduction of any contagious or infectious diseases were circulated to all interested parties.

Meetings on the subject continued between Brée and Pelz, the result of the meetings allaying some of the concerns of the Jersey authorities. All live cattle imports were to be kept in specially built stalls at the coastal port of Granville, Normandy and quarantined for ten days prior to sailing, and all would arrive from the one French port. The imported cattle would be shipped in batches of fifty, although in practice numbers could be up to 60 head. On arriving at the Albert Quay, they would be immediately unloaded and taken to the slaughterhouse opposite the quay. Cold storage space was reserved for the carcasses.[3] This was regarded by both parties as the best solution in order to mitigate the chances of these German-imported Continental cattle infecting or mixing with the local Jersey breed.

In reality, this solution did not work so smoothly. Herbert de Gruchy, a Harbour Customs Officer who was seconded to the DOA, provided an eyewitness account of the importation of these animals. They were loaded onto barges at Granville in holds often too small to accommodate them. The numbers could vary between 50 and 60 head. Problems arose when the barges arrived at the Albert Quay. If the tidal conditions did not allow the barges to moor alongside, the cattle were left in the holds in crowded and unhygienic conditions. In addition, they could be left unfed and without water. The box lift from the quay on occasions was unable to be lowered due to a lack of space in the barge hold. In consequence, straps were placed around the animals and their horns and then they were lifted onto the quayside. This resulted in imported cattle sometimes escaping and running around St Helier Harbour. On one such occasion, when Herbert de Gruchy asked a German officer, who was present, why cattle were imported alive, the reply was "Last time we brought them in dead, there were no livers or hearts." [5]

In 1941 the number of German importations of live cattle increased. These cattle were very different in size and colour to the Jerseys and were grazed in fields in St Mary and St Peter. They became an attraction to local sightseers who had never before seen any breed other than the Jersey. Unfortunately, these imported cattle also introduced a new disease into the Island, the warble fly. This again alarmed the Island civilian authorities. Their concerns prompted a joint German Military Government initiative comprising: Field Command 515; Field Command 722, St Lô; the DOA; veterinary surgeons, both from Jersey and France; and Henry George Gaudin, the Managing Director of the Slaughterhouse, or "Schlachthofleiter" as described by Field Command 515. The decision was made to isolate and quarantine all German-imported cattle. The slaughter would take place in a planned and converted warehouse on the Victoria Quay, St Helier Harbour. This would facilitate imported cattle being unloaded directly on arrival and immediately slaughtered. The importance attached to this new facility is demonstrated by the large numbers of Staff Officers and NCOs of Field Command 515, Field Command 722, and Jersey civilian personnel involved in its planning and construction.[6] The new slaughterhouse was within the existing warehouse on the arm of the Victoria Quay running north-south.

Colonel Schumacher of Field Command 515, who represented the German Military Government both in Jersey and the Channel Islands, clearly stated the reasons for the newly constructed facility, even though there was a large and well-established abattoir at the northern end of the main harbour. Firstly, imported cattle were arriving into Jersey in an extremely poor condition. Secondly, the increase in the number of German military personnel into Jersey warranted a new slaughterhouse. Finally, the greater number of imported Continental cattle was increasing the risk of infected cattle spreading disease to Jersey herds. A separate slaughterhouse would lessen the chances of imported cattle mixing with Jersey cattle.[6]

The Victoria Pier slaughterhouse had one real advantage. Unlike the Albert Quay, it had non-drying deepwater berths, which allowed offloading whatever the state of the tide. In addition, it had a 20-ton crane allowing imported cattle to be taken off quickly, and the berth then vacated to allow other vessels to utilise the deepwater berths. The new facility was completed by July 1941 and immediately put into full-scale operation. It was efficient and proved successful. However, its operations abruptly ceased in November 1941. The reasons for its closure are unclear, especially when viewed in terms of the resources put into its planning and construction. One possible explanation was that the aged Colonel Schumacher, described by Major Heider as "...a cross between a bank manager and a headmaster"[7] had been replaced by the more energetic Colonel Knackfuss as Field Commander 515. Knackfuss scrutinised Field Command 515 personnel deployments and logistics and he made the decision to close the slaughterhouse. Why use resources for a secondary abattoir when a perfectly suitable one was nearby? Perhaps a more conceivable reason for its closure could have been the arrival of Dr Fritz Todt to Jersey on the 5th October 1941, when he issued the "Construction Orders" direct from Hitler to fortify the Island.[8] Todt was accompanied by Hitler's Wehrmacht Adjutant, General Schmundt.[9]

Todt made a survey of St Helier Harbour and its tidal conditions. In consequence, Todt would have certainly required the two non-tidal berths and cranes that had previously been requisitioned for the Victoria Quay slaughterhouse, in order to unload fortification materials such as steel, cement and machinery, along with OT workers. Todt was not a man who would allow his ships to be anchored in St Aubin's Bay and open to air attack while there were berths available that were non-tidal. Although Knackfuss had close family and friendship ties with General Schmundt, it would have been impossible for him to refuse orders from two officers who both had direct access to Hitler and, even more so, one armed with a Führer Directive.

The loss of the Victoria Pier slaughterhouse did not affect the number of Continental cattle imported into Jersey. In 1941 up to 78 head of cattle a month were being shipped into the Island.[10] In 1942 imports from France continued to rise with a total of 1,747 animals, of which 1,699 were cows and forty-eight bulls. The monthly live imports were as follows:

January	237
February	89
March	Nil
April	91
May	91
June	192
July	194
August	202
September	202
October	181
November	175
December	123

In May 1943, Field Command 515 issued a fundamental policy change concerning imported Continental cattle. The civilian population, as well as German military contingents, who had been thus far dependent on imported cattle, were ordered to slaughter and rely on the local breed for their meat. On the 17th May a conference was held in St Lô between Field Commands 722 and 515. Pelz made a detailed analysis of the meat requirements for the civil and military populations and, after examining Jersey's and Guernsey's meat production figures in detail, he calculated that French meat imports would need to be 9 metric tonnes, and for Guernsey 6 metric tonnes, per month. Pelz received from the Jersey abattoir precise weekly weights of all slaughtered animals, verified by States Members and by civil servants, which he carefully scrutinised. Both Jersey and Guernsey would now have to fulfil all their meat requirements from their own local cattle.[11]

The German Military and Their Use of Pedigree Jersey Bulls

In the summer of 1943 German military personnel specifically targeted Jersey pedigree bulls to serve their own Continental cattle that grazed on military farms. This was in contravention of standing orders issued by the Military Government on the Island, Field Command 515. All military personnel, when carrying out an agricultural purchase or exchange with a civilian Jersey farmer, had to receive authorisation from Field Command 515. This would entail the issuing of a permit signed by KVR Pelz. This order, however, did not stop attempts to coerce Jersey cattle breeders into allowing their pedigree bulls to serve German-imported foreign cattle.

"A man from the German airport came with one of their cows (an ugly French black and red one!) to mate with one of our bulls. We did not want to, because we could not have used that bull again with Jersey cows. We phoned the Department [the DOA] in town and they said we must refuse and tell the Germans to buy a bull and keep it on their own farm. The man with a cow looked in a horrid temper – said the German Commandant at the airport had sent him. We managed to send him away and hope we won't get into trouble."[12]

In the same week as Nan Le Ruez witnessed the above confrontation, Carlyle Le Gallais, one of Jersey's leading cattle breeders, President of the RJA&HS and the Jersey Herd Book, and "adjoint" member of the DOA, leased his "highly commended Jersey pedigree bull" Roseland Diabolo to another Jersey farmer, Peter Charles Le Bailly, St Brelade, to serve Le Bailly's herd.[13] Subsequently, Le Bailly sub-leased Roseland Diabolo for "...serving animals belonging to the German occupying forces."[14]

The consequences of this illicit union between a pedigree Jersey bull and German-imported Continental cows were met with both fury and consternation by Jersey's elite cattle-breeding farmers. The States expressed the "...fear of any ill effects on the purity of the breed."[14] The purity of the Jersey breed, and documented in the Jersey Herd Book, was a fundamental reason for the high prices that these cattle commanded on the world's markets from c. 1860 to 1940.[15]

Immediately after the news had spread throughout the Island that Roseland Diabolo had been used by the German military forces to serve their imported cattle, Brée reported, "...foreign cattle now in the Island are being taken to bulls of the Jersey breed and, in view of the purity of the Island breed of cattle", he was to make, "energetic representations" to the Field Command. Brée, furthermore, expressed the concern of breeders that this practice, "...would have far reaching and serious repercussions on our breed."[16] Brée decided to consult with Pelz on the matter and to confront the Field Command 515 on the seriousness and possible consequences of Jersey bulls serving imported Continental cattle. Field Command 515 and Pelz promptly notified all German military units that, "Interbreeding between Jersey and foreign cattle must not take place."[17]

Le Gallais and the RJA&HS notified all Jersey breeders that they must not, and in any circumstances, use their bulls to serve foreign cows. In addition, they were advised that if any problems were encountered with German military units forcing them into using their bulls to serve Continental cattle, the military unit be immediately referred to the civilian authority, who in turn would inform Field Command 515 and Pelz.

The RJA&HS wrote to the DOA on the 23rd August 1943 informing them that all Jersey cattle breeders would comply with its orders. The DOA, in the face of increasing Island-wide concern, resolved that the issue had become of paramount importance and must be dealt with. An immediate report was ordered on the possible consequences of the practice of German-imported Continental cattle being served by Jersey bulls. On the 27th August, the States

Vet concluded in his report that, "A Jersey bull will not transmit characteristics of such imported cattle to Jersey cows which it may serve consequently."[17] The report, however, did not in any manner mitigate or convince Jersey's cattle breeders that a degradation in the purity of the Jersey breed would not happen. The DOA was met with demands from this group, who formed an important and powerful lobby, that the offending bull, Roseland Diabolo, be slaughtered. On the 31st August the DOA wrote to Le Gallais, the owner of the bull that, "In view of the interests of the Jersey breed of cattle, it would be advisable to cause the bull in question to be slaughtered."[17] In an attempt to calm down the storm of protest by the Island's cattle breeders, Brée, through his counterpart Pelz, sent out an order from Field Command 515 to all German military units that "Under no circumstances should such services be permitted", and "all owners of stud bulls notified accordingly."[14]

However, evidence appears to demonstrate that the German military attempted to access Jersey bulls to serve their Continental cattle on their farm at Don Bridge, St Brelade, at a much earlier date during the occupation. In an interview with the author on 3rd April 2015, Alfred Vibert clearly recollected that in 1941, as a teenager running his late father's farm at Franc Fief, St Brelade, another Jersey teenager turned up one day with an imported French cow from the farm at Don Bridge. The Jersey youth explained to Mr Vibert that he was to allow his mother's bull, Samarès Golden Spire, to serve the French cow. The bull, leased from Lady Knott in December 1939, was "Highly Commended" and a quality specimen.[18] Mr Vibert had recently been warned by the RJA&HS that under no circumstances should a Jersey bull be used to serve German-imported Continental cattle. The reason given was the threat of the introduction of the warble fly. Mr Vibert recalled, "The Jersey lad and the French cow were sent packing."[19] After a short period, the Jersey youth returned with a German sergeant who again demanded the services of Samarès Golden Spire. The answer was again negative, much to the annoyance of the sergeant who subsequently left. The very same morning a German staff car with two officers and a corporal returned and made the same demand. One of the officers, speaking in perfect French, made it clear that the RJA&HS order was unacceptable. The corporal was ordered to fetch the bull from the farm barn. The bull in question, as the German corporal approached him, bellowed very loudly. The German military officers, not sure of the temper of the bull, decided not to risk using the bull to serve their cow and subsequently left. Samarès Golden Spire was officially reported dead on the 9th September 1941 and a declaration made in the Jersey Herd Book. Therefore, the above incident must have occurred between summer 1940 and before September 1941. This incident was probably the first of the German military trying to use a Jersey bull to serve an imported Continental cow.

The Island-wide clamour by cattle breeders for action to be taken against Roseland Diabolo did not lessen. Therefore, in an attempt to resolve the crisis, a confidential meeting was convened on the 11th September 1943, comprising twenty-seven of Jersey's premier cattle breeders belonging to the two main farming associations – the RJA&HS and the JFU.[20] The meeting was held at the former's main office at 3 Mulcaster Street, St Helier. The issue discussed was the consequences of the crossbreeding that had taken place between Roseland Diabolo and German-imported Continental cattle.

An "Emergency Committee" of the RJA&HS and the JFU had been set up in early 1941 and it met throughout the German occupation. The minutes were kept secret. This evidently was to bypass the orders of Field Command 515, regarding societies, meetings, rules and members.[21] Harold George Shepard, Secretary of the RJA&HS, kept detailed minutes of these meetings which he never circulated, as it was "...not safe to enter into the usual minute books". The meetings were begun in early 1941 and continued well into 1945, even after the liberation in May.[22] The file gives a unique and fascinating insight into what the leading farmers thought and how they interacted with their own authorities and with the German Military Government.

An air of hostility pervaded the meeting which was chaired by Le Gallais. He opened with the central issue which was, "Serving of foreign cattle by Jersey bulls, and especially the recent case where such cattle had been served by his Roseland Diabolo at stud in St Brelade". He informed the meeting that, "In no circumstances were Jersey bulls to be used on imported cattle". After a few general comments Le Gallais stated that he had received "certificates" from the State Vet and from a second veterinary surgeon, E. Messervy, that there was unequivocally, "No danger of telegony". In other words, Le Gallais assured them that a Jersey bull which had previously been used on imported German Continental cows would not produce a crossbreed calf.[22]

The consensus amongst the Island's breeders remained insistent on the slaughter of Roseland Diabolo. Le Gallais tersely responded that, "Other bulls had also served foreign cattle". He subsequently left the room, and the chair was taken by J. B. Rondel, who had advised Le Gallais that the bull should be slaughtered as "a gesture". Le Gallais had retorted he would be willing to do so provided all other Jersey bulls which had served German and foreign cows were similarly killed. One of Jersey's most respected cattle breeders, Eugene Charles Perrédès, intervened. He cited instances in the USA and England when Jersey bulls served other breeds of cattle without any effects on the purity of subsequent progeny. Perrédès proposed that Roseland Diabolo should not be slaughtered, despite the fact he had served German-imported Continental cows. The motion was seconded by Philip Le Feuvre. This, however, was not accepted by all and Harold Le Brocq proposed that all Jersey bulls so used be immediately slaughtered. A deciding vote was taken and Perrédès' proposition was carried. Philip Le Feuvre then drew attention to the dangers to the Jersey breed which might arise from the introduction into Island herds of crossbreed calves, the products of Jersey bulls serving imported cattle. He proposed that the DOA be requested to order such calves to be slaughtered. This proposition was unanimously carried.[22]

The controversy of pedigree Jersey bulls serving German-imported Continental cattle did not end. On the 14th September 1943, the DOA met to discuss a letter from Le Gallais enclosing two certificates from two veterinary surgeons. The letter stated that they had both tested Roseland Diabolo for contagious diseases with negative results. They advised the DOA that a period of one month should elapse between the last service of a German-owned Continental cow, and the serving of local cattle. The veterinary surgeons stated clearly this would ensure, "No danger of the bull transmitting any infectious or contagious disease to local cattle as a result of his having served foreign cattle". The issue now predominating when Jersey bulls served imported cattle was not that just of telegony degrading the pedigree stock of Jersey cattle, but the danger of Continental cattle introducing cattle diseases into Jersey. Continental cattle were now introducing the warble fly into Jersey and these were appearing in Jersey herds. With regard to Le Gallais' letter, the DOA decided to take no further action in relation to his bull, Roseland Diabolo.[14]

In view of the constant Island-wide hostility concerning Roseland Diabolo and other Jersey bulls that had served imported cattle, and the issue remaining unresolved amongst many of the Island's cattle breeders, Le Gallais decided to take the matter in hand, in order to finally draw a line. On the 18th September 1943, as President of the RJA&HS, he wrote to the DOA and suggested that the officials of the Jersey Herd Book should have a meeting with Field Command 515 to discuss the issue. The Field Commander had already, on the 4th September, ordered all German military units not to use Jersey bulls to serve imported Continental cattle. Why, therefore, did Le Gallais ask for a meeting with the German Military Government and what did he hope to achieve? The answer can probably be found in the increasing hostility throughout the Island that bulls so used had not been slaughtered, although the scientific advice offered by the veterinary surgeons confirmed there would be no degradation of the purity of the Island's stock. Roseland Diabolo was extremely valuable and there was no scientific or financial reason to simply slaughter him.

Le Gallais had personal contacts with Pelz and the Staff Officers of Field Command 515. He would now call upon their powerful contacts to reassure the Island's cattle breeders that a line had been drawn under the practice of Jersey pedigree bulls serving imported cattle. Pelz was able and willing to assist him, regarding himself as an expert and guardian of the Jersey cattle breed. [23]

In late 1941 Pelz, Le Gallais and members of the Jersey Herd Book, along with the States Vet Blampied, had assisted Edwin Lauprecht on his research visit to Jersey, examining the Island's herds and carrying out an analysis of milk and fat output from the Jersey Herd Book and the RJA&HS records. In 1942, Lauprecht's research paper was published and he acknowledged and thanked them for their assistance, which he added was "willingly given."[24]

Le Gallais' relationship with Pelz and Staff Officers of Field Command 515 also went back to December 1941, when he supplied fresh milk from his herd at Roseland Farm.[25] The German residences were all within a 1-kilometre radius of Le Gallais' dairy farm. On 25th June 1942 Pelz wrote to Le Gallais, issuing further instructions for the supply of fresh milk to the Staff Officers of the German Military Administration. Pelz wrote "In the supply of milk to the German Field Command, you have so far punctually carried out my instructions regarding the delivery of milk to the quarters of the Field Command. I would request that all accounts for milk so far delivered to these houses be drawn up and sent to the Field Command. Hereafter, as from the 1st July [1942] onwards the milk is to be paid for weekly by the occupants of the above houses".[25]

The residences referred to by Pelz, and to which Le Gallais delivered milk, were Linden Court, White Lodge, Braeside, Newlands and Langford. Linden Court was the residence of Field Commander F. Knackfuss, Chief of Staff W. Heider, and the Adjutant to Knackfuss, First Lieutenant Klob. The residents at White Lodge were: KVR Pelz, KVR von Aufsess, KVR Pokorni and OKVR Dr Casper. Braeside and Newlands were the residences for Staff Officers and Langford was the Kasino, or Officer's Mess, for Field Command 515.

Le Gallais' provision of fresh milk to the Staff Officers of Field Command 515, placed the civilian authorities and the DOA in a dilemma. He was an "adjoint" member of the DOA and appointed as "Agent to take charge of the milk section with full powers and matters of policy to the DOA." [26.] As a milk producer he had also acted as a retailer. He, however, had never applied for a producer-retailer licence, required under the Milk Control (Jersey) Order, 1940. In effect, Le Gallais, as a member of the DOA, was breaking an Order that he was responsible for supervising. Brée and the DOA dealt with this infringement of the law in a unique manner, allowing him to remain within the letter of the order, if not the spirit. In an interesting decision, and the only example throughout the German occupation, the DOA, "In order to regularise Mr Le Gallais in relation to the said Order", issued a backdated producer- retailer licence as from the 12th December 1941, confined to those residences to which Le Gallais delivered fresh milk.[26.]

One of the first cases of an infringement of the Milk Control (Jersey) Order, 1940 occurred on the 21st October 1940. Mr R. O. Weeks, Secretary and Accountant of the Milk Control Section of the DOA, brought up in a meeting the case of A. R. Renouard, St Martin, who had allegedly been selling milk without a licence. It was immediately decided to forward the matter to the Attorney General for appropriate action.

On the 23rd March 1943, the DOA authorised a renewal of Le Gallais' retailer licence for a further twelve months. In effect, he was the supplier of fresh milk to the Field Commander and Staff Officers of Field Command 515, from 21st December 1941 to the 22nd March 1944. [27]

Le Gallais and Pelz subsequently met to resolve the issue of the illicit use of Jersey bulls serving imported Continental cattle, and the resulting progeny. The decisions jointly made were that Pelz and the German Military

Government would ensure that all German-imported Continental cows which had been served by Jersey bulls would be slaughtered, including the two German cows served by Roseland Diabolo. As a gesture of goodwill, the German Military Government, when receiving cattle into Jersey, would replace those slaughtered with animals from the next consignment from France, and Pelz, on behalf of the German Military Government, would select the animals.[17]

Le Gallais, in a statement to Jersey's cattle breeders through the auspices of the RJA&HS, reported with certainty that because his bull (whilst in Mr Le Baillly's custody) had served German-imported cattle, "The German authorities had stated that under no circumstances should such services be permitted and all owners had been notified accordingly".[14]

The Liberation of Jersey and the Fate of German-owned Imported Cattle, May and June 1945

"All cattle which have been in German ownership were slaughtered without exception"

Within days of the German surrender and the liberation of Jersey on the 9th May 1945 the RJA&HS rounded up "All cattle which had been in German ownership and they were slaughtered without exception". Heifers which had passed from German military to private ownership were also purchased and slaughtered.[28] All 200 Jersey cattle which had been requisitioned by the German authorities in 1944 and shipped to Guernsey and Alderney were also slaughtered.

The slaughter of all crossbred Jersey-Continental cattle in May 1945 would seemingly have ended the concerns that the purity of the Jersey breed had been tainted during the German occupation. These concerns, however, were not totally at an end. In an effort to allay the fears of the valuable American export market that a degradation of the Jersey pedigree breed had not occurred, Sir Daniel Cabot, Chief Veterinary Surgeon at the Ministry of Agriculture and Fisheries for the United Kingdom government, immediately came to Jersey to investigate the issue. Cabot's subsequent report, by June 1945, made it clear that there were and never had been any effects on the purity of the Jersey breed by the use of bulls serving German-imported cattle. His report stated that foreign cattle brought to Jersey had, "...all been disposed of", and concluded that there had been, "No risk of the Island stock being damaged by crossbreeding with other animals".[29]

What of the fate of Roseland Diabolo? Sadly, he died in 1944 at the relatively young age of four years. The cause of his death is unknown. In fact, none of the Jersey bulls which had served German-imported cows survived after 1945.

References

1. Jersey Archive. C/B/A1/3.
2. Deutsche Inselzeitung. 29th August 1940.
3. Jersey Archive. B/A/W32/2/4.
4. Deutsche Inselzeitung. 7th September 1940.
5. Jersey Archive. L/D/25/L/22.
6. Jersey Archive. B/A/W70/1.
7. Alan Allix, interview with Heider.
8. Channel Island Occupation Society. Archive Book No 8, August 2006, p. 16.
9. Wood, Alan and Mary. Islands in Danger. The Story of the German Occupation of the Channel Islands, 1940–1945. 1975 Edition, p.119.
10. Jersey Archive. B/A/W63/35.
11. Jersey Archive. B/A/W40/2/3.
12. Le Ruez, N. Jersey Occupation Diary, 1994. 18th August 1943.
13. Jersey Herd Book. HBN 7514.
14. Jersey Archive. L/D/09/A10.
15. Tubbs, L. Gordon. The Book of the Jersey, 1939, pp. 98–111.
16. RJA&HS. Letter dated 20th August 1943 from the DOA to C. Le Gallais, President of the RJA&HS.
17. Jersey Archive. C/B/A1/9.
18. Jersey Herd Book. HBN 7423.
19. Interview with Mr A. Vibert. 3rd April 2015.
20. Jersey Farmers (Trading) Union.
21. JEP. 28th August 1940 and 13th January 1943.
22. RJA&HS and JFU Joint Emergency Committee Minutes.
23. Private Letter from Pelz to Dr Josef Kratzer, President of the Munich Administrative Court. Dated 12th February 1957. Pelz family archive. Kratzer served in Field Command 515 during the occupation of the Channel Islands.
24. Lauprecht, Dr E, 1942. Vol 17, pp. 369–386. Die Rinderzucht auf Insel Jersey: Züchtungskunde. Herausgeben von Der Deutschen Gesellschaft Für Züchtunskunde Unter Mitwirkung der Tierzuchinstitute an Deutschen Hochschulen.
25. Jersey Archive. C/B/A1/7.
26. Jersey Archive. C/B/A1/5.
27. Jersey Archive. C/B/A1/8.
28. RJA&HS. Report of the Committee for the years 1940–1945, 8th December 1945, p. 16.
29. JEP 8th February 1994, p. 13.

Chapter 4

The First Four Months of the German Occupation, July to October 1940

The Island's Milk Supply

"We must ensure a sufficient supply of milk for public needs"

The Milk Control Board

The outbreak of war in September 1939 prompted the first change to agriculture; this was the establishment of a Milk Control Board. It was set up on the 4th September 1939 with the instruction, "To act as a control board to take charge of the arrangement for the collection and distribution of the public milk supply and the manufacture of butter".[1] It was also given full authority to set milk prices. Its initial plan divided the Island's milk supply into a logical system of collection and distribution, in order that there were no overlapping rounds of milk collection resulting in a wastage of petrol or manpower. The Milk Control Board immediately decided to utilise only the larger dairies which dealt with the annual milk production of 2 million gallons.[2] The next day the Board inspected four of the largest dairies. In October, legislation was passed to enact its powers.

On the 3rd November 1939 the Board met with the Island's milk production and distribution industries to ensure, "...a sufficient supply of milk for public needs". The Board laid the basis for the Milk Control (Jersey) Order and the Provisional Prices (Milk) Order to ensure that the milk supply was protected. At its initial meetings the farmers' representatives stressed the importance of "...guaranteeing farmers a better price", in view of the possibility of, "The drastic reduction in herds owing to the heavy costs of production". In other words, farmers wanted a higher payment for their milk otherwise it would be uneconomic to retain large herds for the benefit of the entire Island. The major dairies made it clear that they alone would command the retention and control of all milk supplies. The smaller dairies were not to be included.[1]

The Department of Agriculture – the DOA

The newly constituted DOA met for the first time on the 25th June 1940. The meeting was disrupted by the German bombing of St Helier Harbour. The DOA comprised: the President, Jurat Touzel John Brée, John du Val, Connétable of St Peter, and Edwin Denize Gibaut, Deputy of Trinity.

They met a week later, on 1st July, the first day of the German occupation. Also present were Carlyle Le Gallais, President of the RJA&HS; Philip Le Feuvre, President of the JFU; Wesley Mallet, Deputy of St Mary; and David Simpson, Director of the States of Jersey Experimental Station. Brée reported on "The current political situation" and the German ultimatum of surrender which expired at 7.00 a.m., 2nd July 1940, by which time all principal buildings, "...must be flying the white flag". The meeting discussed the "additional powers" that would be granted to the DOA by the States. Further topics were the problems of storing the huge volume of potatoes which had not been exported, the availability of straw and concentrated animal feed, and the exact location of all the dairy herds.[3] Philip Le Feuvre was delegated to represent the DOA with the Labour Board and to examine rates of pay for agricultural workers. Le Gallais was instructed to investigate the question of milk collection and transport.

The next day, 2nd July, Le Gallais proposed "A new system of collecting milk". All milk collections would be carried out by five dairies: Fairview, Tanguy's, Victoria, Jersey and Don Street and the entire Island-wide scheme rationalised with each dairy collecting only from a prescribed area. All dairy farmers would take their milk to the main road to be collected; no farmer would have to cart their milk more than 1 mile; Don Street Dairy would require an additional lorry, which was subsequently sanctioned by the German Military Commandant. Le Gallais informed the meeting that the entire scheme would be ready within a week. It was subsequently submitted to the States and approved.

On the 5th July, the same day that the first consignment of potatoes was shipped by the Jersey authorities on behalf of the German occupiers, Brée held a meeting with 120 dairy farmers. The meeting was convened to discuss the new Island-wide milk-collection scheme. Brée wasted no time in addressing the farmers, giving a detailed account of "The reorganisation of the milk collection because of the German occupation". The DOA had appointed Le Gallais as its agent, with full powers to take charge of the milk section, but "...with matters of policy to be referred to the DOA". In future DOA meetings he was often given the appellation "an adjoint member". Le Gallais then addressed the meeting. He gave a description of the new milk-collection scheme, its distribution, and his rationale for the pricing of milk.[4] Dairy farmers would receive 8¼ pence per pot, and the dairies 2 pence per pot.[5]

On the 8th July 1940, the new scheme was publicly announced and the dairies designated to collect milk in each area:

Don Street Dairy: The west of the Island and north as far as Rozel.
Jersey Dairies: Part of St Mary, and St Peter.
Victoria Dairy: St Helier and parts of Trinity.
Tanguy's Dairy: Grouville, St Clement and parts of St Saviour.
Fairview Dairy: Parts of St Saviour and Grouville, and St Martin,

Le Gallais stressed that all retail outlets which bought milk from these dairies would only be allowed to trade on payment of weekly cash accounts. On the 9th July, Le Gallais issued a permit for the hospital to receive milk and stated that all public institutions and "...establishments of the forces of occupation", should be treated as depots in the matter of milk supplies. He furthermore stressed that all businesses involved in milk supply and distribution had to agree to his terms. Firstly, only a week's credit was permitted; secondly, payments to dairy farmers would be every four weeks; and finally, all retail dairy transactions would be "cash only", soon after modified to "on a cash basis". All matters of administration, control, allocation and deliveries of milk supplies were under Le Gallais' control.

Within two days problems arose. On the 10th July, Le Gallais raised the question to the DOA of the milk supply to the German garrison at St Peter's Barracks. The garrison was supplied with milk by Mr J. Le Masurier, St Helier. Le Gallais was particularly annoyed as Le Masurier's delivery was "...completely upsetting the milk round arrangements". He concluded that the lorries already collecting milk in that area could conveniently deliver the required quantities of milk to the German military establishments, thus saving unnecessary mileage. Brée, always the pragmatist, decided that an easier and more direct line of communication would yield better results by taking the matter up with the German Military Commandant. He subsequently met the Commandant and was given "...powers to take up with Mr Seymour who was carrying out the catering for the German authorities". Brée interviewed Seymour and the latter agreed that there would be no further deliveries from St Helier to German military establishments. Finally, Brée ordered Seymour that in future he would be allowed to collect milk from only one dairy and, along with all other supplies and catering stores, deliver them himself to the German establishments with which he had a contract.

On the 17th July the DOA and the farming associations agreed that no milk would be collected before 7.30 a.m. and there would be only one collection each day to save petrol. The problem of collecting milk from farmers was never satisfactorily solved by the dairies throughout the German occupation. The fundamental problem facing farmers, with the advent of only one collection a day, was that a number of dairymen kept their cows in "Such a dirty condition that there was a grave risk of milk turning sour". It took only one farmer to leave "dirty milk", subsequently collected by the dairy and mixed with the rest of the day's milk, to spoil an entire load. The problem of "dirty milk" arose continually throughout the German occupation and became worse as dairy farmers found it increasingly difficult to keep their milk from turning sour because of a shortage of power to keep milk cool or to hygienically clean milking equipment. To make matters worse, increasingly later collections by the dairies meant that milk would stand outside in churns for longer than it should have done.

In late July 1940, Le Gallais reported back to the DOA on a problem he had discovered: the Roman Catholic order the Little Sisters of the Poor had been receiving free skim milk every day from the Don Street Dairy. He decided that the religious community, dedicated to looking after old people, should in future have to pay for skim milk at the current price of 1 halfpenny per quart.

On the 27th August, a delegation from Tanguy's, Jersey, Fairview and Victoria Dairies came before the DOA to discuss the question of the price for milk supplied to the German army of occupation and paid for by the Department of Finance and Economics.

The 1940 Tomato Crop

"We did our best to dispose of the very large tomato crop but with our limited facilities and no export market trade, many tons rotted on the plants."

Bernard Ernest Horsfall, Manager of John Terry Limited, one of Jersey's largest agricultural merchants

When the German military occupation took place, on the 1st July 1940, the first and second tomato crops were still growing and were not ready to be harvested. The first crop would not be ready to pick until mid-August and the second not until September. The tomatoes had been planted as soon as the potato season had begun to end. The entire tomato crop for 1940 approximated to some 25,000 tons.

The DOA decided within a week of the German occupation that the first and second tomato crops presently growing would be destroyed and the land cleared for new types of crops. The historical interpretation is summed up in the following report of 1945 which stated:

"Many vergées of tomatoes, both first and second crop, had been planted. With no prospect of marketing the crop, thousands of plants were neglected and permission was eventually given for a proportion to be uprooted allowing the ground to be prepared, in due time, for vital food crops".[6]

The German Military Authority, however, immediately forbade any destruction of the tomato crop. Within two days, the DOA rescinded its order to destroy the crop. The issue as to whether the tomatoes were left to rot, or were destroyed, has been confused by the initial DOA order in early July 1940 to destroy the entire crop, to make land available for cereals or other new crops because the United Kingdom export market had ceased. Cruickshank certainly mentions that "...surplus tomatoes had to be sent to France". He, however, does not state for which year, or the amounts exported to the European mainland.[7]

A personal account of the German occupation by Denis Vibert who escaped from Jersey to England on the 21st September 1941 made the observation, "At the time of the Occupation the farmers had already planted their tomato crops and, realising that there would probably be no market, they wished to plough them up. The States promised, however, they would buy the crop under the compulsion of an order the farmers were obliged to carry on with the growing. The promise was not fulfilled with the result that the farmers were left with the surplus in their fields".[8]

On the 18th May 1945, nine days after the liberation of Jersey, Bernard Ernest Horsfall, manager of John Terry Limited, one of the largest agricultural merchants, wrote a letter to all the company's United Kingdom agricultural importers informing them that the company was back in business and trading. The letter stated that in 1940 "The large tomato crop...with no export trade very many tons rotted on the plants."[9] The notion of 25,000 tons of tomatoes rotting away in the fields of Jersey in August and September 1940, or that all this fruit was deliberately destroyed, certainly does not seem realistic.

The German Military Command on the Island would never have sanctioned the destruction of such a large and valuable crop. On the 5th July 1940, two direct orders were sent to the DOA. The first was the prohibition of any destruction of the 1940 tomato crop; and secondly, the prohibition of the destruction of any potato crop. The DOA immediately complied with these two orders.[10]

This reversal of the DOA's initial order to clear the fields of tomatoes resulted in confusion amongst farmers who had large areas of tomatoes growing successfully. A number of farmers began to actively to clear fields of tomato plants. In addition, some of the more important farmers wrote to the DOA seeking clarification concerning their tomato crops. On the 17th July a meeting of farmers was held under the auspices of the JFU to discuss the issue. Mr J. F. Pallot began the discussion by requesting information as to why farmers had been ordered to preserve the crop with no apparent plan to market the produce. Philip Le Feuvre replied that the order to preserve the tomato crop was, "An order beyond their control". He additionally made it clear that no one could assume that Jersey farmers would not sell their tomatoes.[11]

The 1940 first and second tomato crops were not destroyed in order to clear the fields for other cereal or food crops, and they were not left to rot. The question therefore arises as to what became of the thousands of tons of tomatoes that ripened and were ready for export during the months of August, September and October 1940. The simple answer is that on the 16th August 1940 the German Military Government, Field Command 515, had requisitioned the entire crop. The following day, after requisition of the crop, the DOA recommended to the Superior Council that, "Farmers who might be called to supply tomatoes on requisition for the German authorities, be reimbursed for the cost of labour picking these tomatoes, assembling the containers and delivering to the harbour of St Helier on behalf of the German authorities".[3] At a meeting of the Superior Council on the 17th August, Brée discussed the German requisition. He then communicated the decision of the Superior Council to the DOA, which was: "The DOA was authorised, in the event of tomatoes being requisitioned by the German authorities, to pay the actual labour charges involved".

After the German requisitioning of the tomato crop, a series of meetings were held on the 30th and 31st August 1940. These meetings were attended by: KVR Pelz, Head of Agriculture and Food Supply, Field Command 515; KVR Milkau, Field Command 722, St Lô, Normandy; Touzel Brée, President of the DOA; and Edwin Le Masurier, President of the Department of Essential Commodities. One of the major topics for discussion was the export of the 1940 tomato crop.[12] Pelz unequivocally stated that during the months of September and October 1940 there was to be made available a weekly supply of 80 tons of Jersey tomatoes for export. Milkau had already taken steps to export these tomatoes to French canning factories. In addition, Pelz insisted that Jersey canneries would have to be utilised to their full capacity and, if need be, to work double shifts. The tomatoes would be canned as tomato purée. All surplus tomatoes would be exported to France and sold on the open market through French representatives.

Field Command 722, St Lô, reciprocated its requisition of Jersey tomatoes by supplying the Island with 10,000 tons of butter and tinned milk from the Carentan company the Gloria Dairy. In addition, Pelz established a permanent German Command in Granville whose sole duty was to procure foodstuffs and animal feed for Jersey. This German Command liaised with Field Command 722 and with the Island's Buying Commission. Milkau, in September and October, supplied Jersey with tinned meat from France.

On the 2nd September the Bailiff was informed of the plans to export the Jersey tomato harvest. The next day he acknowledged and confirmed the decisions made during the two-day conference between Brée, Le Masurier and Field Commands 515 and 722.[12] The DOA agreed that payment to farmers for their tomatoes, both first and second crop, would be "One shilling and four pence per twelve pounds nett of tomatoes, including container, packed, ready for shipment. The farmer is to make his own arrangements for packing". The DOA, in consequence, requested a credit of £40,000 from the Department of Finance and Economics but the next day it revoked the request for £40,000 credit and the price it had stated it would pay farmers for their tomatoes.

This apparent confusion on the pricing and reimbursement for their tomatoes annoyed many farmers. Vingtenier P. Le Masurier of St Ouen wrote to the DOA describing the condition of the tomato crop belonging to Mr J. C. Malzard, St Ouen, who had made it evident he wished to destroy his crop.[13] The DOA immediately responded with an Island-wide declaration that it would not allow the destruction of the tomato crop.

By the 2nd September the German authorities had requisitioned all the tomatoes. The DOA, however, had not yet resolved the issue of how much farmers should be paid for these tomatoes. The DOA recommended to the Superior Council that farmers be paid the cost of labour for picking and delivering tomatoes to the quayside at a rate of 1 halfpenny per pound weight, together with the cost of assembling the export containers at a rate of 4 shillings and sixpence per 100 12-pound containers. Its final recommendation was that farmers be paid, "Without prejudice to the claims for the value of the produce and containers". The fundamental problem concerning the payment that should be made to farmers centred around the labour costs involved for tomatoes requisitioned by the German authorities. This, however, appears not to have been resolved. There was an increasing protest from farmers: the remuneration for picking, packing and delivery of tomatoes to the quayside was insufficient to cover their labour costs.

Jersey Tomatoes: Picked, Packed, Delivered to St Helier Harbour and Exported Requisitioned by the German Authorities – September and October 1940

Date of German Requisition	Date of Shipment	Amount of Export	Value of Shipment	Notes of Shipment
2nd & 3rd September	16th September	2,266 trays	£226-12-0	Payment of DOA to farmer 5/6 per ton less for loading onto barges. Invoice to German authorities to be collected by DOA Secretary Colin Marie.
14th & 16th September		4,902 trays	£367-13-0	Marie ordered to collect monies from German authorities and subsequently to pay farmers with the monies collected. The farmers who supplied the shipments were paid at a rate of 2/- per tray, less 5/6 per ton for the cost of loading. The DOA made an allowance of 25% to the German authorities in respect of tomatoes which had arrived at Granville in a "rotten condition".

Date of German Requisition	Date of Shipment	Amount of Export	Value of Shipment	Notes of Shipment
28th September			£401-18-0	Marie ordered to collect monies from German authorities and to pay farmers involved in the supply of tomatoes, 2/- per tray, less 5/6d per ton to cover the cost of loading.
7th October			37 RM 56 Pfennigs	Marie charged with collecting monies, in respect of the loading of tomatoes, from the German authorities.
	11th to 16th October		£134-1-2	Marie to invoice the German authorities for four shipments and to pay farmers 2/6 per tray, less 5/6 per ton for loading.
	18th to 20th October			Marie authorised to collect monies from the German authorities and pay farmers who supplied their tomatoes at 2/6 per tray, less 5/6 per ton for stevedoring charges. The payment to be made to farmers at the rate of exchange current on the date which the German authorities paid for these tomatoes.
	27th October		£35-2-17	Marie to collect monies and pay the farmer who delivered tomatoes for shipment at 2/6 per tray, less 5/6 per ton for stevedoring charges. Payments were made to farmers in Reichsmarks at the rate of exchange current on the date the German authorities pay for the tomatoes.

Date of German Requisition	Date of Shipment	Amount of Export	Value of Shipment	Notes of Shipment
16th/28th September	5th & 8th October		190 RM 44 Pfennigs	Collected by the DOA from German authorities for the cost of handling the tomatoes shipped to the order of the German authorities.
	29th September		£29-0-0	Marie ordered to collect monies from German authorities and on receipt pay the farmers who brought the tomatoes shipped, at 2/6 per tray, less 5/6 per ton for stevedoring charges. Payments to farmers at the rate of exchange on the date which German authorities paid for the tomatoes.

The Resumption of Potato Exports to Mainland Europe

"Transport to the German Commandant of the Island, with the compliments of the department, an offer of the RJA&HS to the said German Commander a gift of two tons of potatoes."

Department of Agriculture's instruction to its secretary, Colin Marie

After the Germans occupied the Island, there were two problems concerning the 1940 potato crop. The first was how to store the Island's very large remaining crop of potatoes which had lost its United Kingdom market. The second was how to assist Jersey farmers who had used resources to grow potatoes which could not be exported and, in many cases, were still in the ground. Immediately after occupation the DOA resolved that it would buy potatoes at a fixed price of between £5 and £6 a ton, but would also allow farmers to sell some of their crop privately, although the price was regulated, thus achieving an income.

On the 5th July 1940, the German Military Command instructed the DOA that it "Wished for the potato market to be opened". In addition, it ordered 300 tons of potatoes to be made available for shipment by 10.00 a.m. the next day.[3] The German delegation requested the DOA to fix the price of these potatoes at £9 a ton FOB.[14]

Brée immediately arranged with the Jersey Produce Merchants Association (the JPMA) for the allocation of potatoes for shipment, on the orders of the German Military Command, from their potato stores. In discussions with Brée the German delegation made it clear that the civilian Harbour Master would not be allowed any inspection of the barges that would be brought in from France to export the potatoes.

On the 6th and 7th July, the first potato exports ordered by the German authorities were shipped to Granville. There was extreme reluctance by the St Helier Harbour workers to load these potatoes into the barges and many men refused to do so when ordered.[15]

Eventually, Arthur Blampied, Mr Huelin and Mr Godfrey were induced with overtime payments to work outside normal working hours and they loaded three barges with 1,080 tons of potatoes. The barges had originally come from Strasbourg and had fled to St Malo after the invasion of France. At St Malo, they had been captured by a German torpedo boat and were pressed into service transporting goods to and from the Channel Islands.

All forthcoming German orders concerning the export of potatoes were processed by the DOA which initiated a parish collection scheme based on an allocation system. When a German order was received by the DOA it was written in duplicate; one copy was forwarded to the States Greffier and the second to the Bailiff to sign, in order to obtain an official sanction from the German Commandant to publish the parish allocation orders for these potatoes.

Brée wasted no time and on the 8th July completed all the collecting arrangements for the parochial quotas to provide the necessary tonnage required by the German Military Command. The Connétables were issued with fifty counterfoil books to record and quantify the potatoes brought to the Weighbridge by farmers from their respective parishes.[16] In addition, every parish had to complete forms to quantify firstly, the amount of potatoes to be dug; secondly, the potatoes held in store; and finally, the quantity of seed potatoes.

Further orders were placed with the DOA and the question now arose of how payment for these potatoes, sold to the German authorities, was to be made. The decision was taken to instruct the Treasury of the States to invoice the "German Commandant of the Island" the sum of £9,502-4-0, "in respect of 1,055 tons 16 cwt of potatoes at £9 a ton FOB". This sum thereafter was posted to the credit of the "Potato Export Fund". Colin Marie was instructed to transmit to the Treasurer of the States a copy of the invoice sent to the German Commandant for information. Marie was also instructed by the DOA "To transport to the German Commandant of the Island, with the compliments of the department, an offer of the RJA&HS to the said German Commander a gift of two tons of potatoes".[3] On the same day, Brée was informed by Mr T. Dorey from Dorey and Company Limited, that 2 tons and 8 hundredweight of potatoes had been commandeered by the German authorities at the Grand Hotel.

On the 18th July the DOA issued a statement that it would purchase from farmers all varieties of potatoes at £2 per ton and proclaimed that all potatoes would be put into store. The Superior Council approved the purchase and, on the 19th July, Brée announced to the DOA that, in consultation with the German authority, the price of potatoes sold to them would be reduced to £7 per ton FOB. By the 22nd July the DOA had purchased the Island's entire crop of early potatoes from Jersey farmers and had immediately put them into store.

On the 26th July, the DOA actioned the allocation of a further 60 tons of potatoes for export. It also issued the Potatoes (Sales) (Jersey) Order, 1940. This law required every grower of potatoes to obtain a licence to sell to retailers outside St Helier.

A substantial number of farmers had become increasingly and openly uncooperative with the DOA because of the continued demands from the authorities to dig up the remainder of their potatoes. Many farmers refused to dig them, with the explanation that there was a lack of labour. Brée, in no uncertain terms, responded that this being the case, their potatoes would be dug by employees of the Department of Labour. This subsequently would mean that these farmers would forfeit any rights to their potatoes. Notices were printed and published to underline the threat, but the problem of uncooperative farmers persisted. In early August 1940 it was evident that a hardcore of farmers were refusing to cultivate their fields, advancing the reason that they no longer wished to farm on behalf of the German military occupiers. The Island's Attorney General, Charles Walter Duret Aubin, in a forthright legal instruction, ordered the DOA to take control of the agricultural land if these farmers remained recalcitrant. In addition, they were threatened with imprisonment.

On the 19th August, the DOA credited the German Military Government with £562-10-0 for 15,000 sacks at 9 pence each. The sum was credited to the next invoice sent to the German authority for the next potato export.

By late August the German Military Government was demanding from the States lower prices for potatoes purchased for export to Europe. The Superior Council and the DOA consequently allocated to Brée, "All the necessary powers to come to an agreement as to the new price to be charged for potatoes shipped to the order of the German authorities as from the 26th August 1940". On the 26th August, Brée met with "Herr Geib", representing the German Military Government. They discussed "The question of the potatoes shipped to the order of the German authorities". Brée was again instructed that he was in charge of these discussions and had the "necessary power" to negotiate. An agreement was concluded: "...between the President of the DOA and Herr Geib that shipments of potatoes, as from the 26th August 1940 should be at a rate of £6 per ton FOB". On the same day the Department of Essential Commodities commandeered 9,000 sacks from the store of the Jersey Trading Company Limited, which was no longer in business and the following day the agreement between Brée and Geib was finalised. An export order was made by Geib for the shipment of 1,940 tons of potatoes to the value of £11,677-10-0 FOB, which included the cost of the sacks. The German authorities were credited with 5,000 sacks together with the 15,000 already received by them in respect of the three shipments made on the 24th, 26th and 27th August 1940.

On the 25th September the DOA made an allowance to the German authorities of 5 shillings per sack of potatoes in respect of 700 which had been shipped on the 14th and 16th September and which had arrived in Granville in a "rotten condition". On the morning of 27th September the DOA summoned George Breuilly, manager of the Country Gentlemen's Association Limited, the company which shipped the potatoes to Granville.[17]

Breuilly was questioned about the exported potatoes and why they were shipped on the 14th and 16th September in "a bad condition". It was made clear to Breuilly that, "an allowance might be discussed" concerning the repayment of monies received by the CGA Limited. The interview was joined by Mr A. V. Godfrey, the DOA's Chief Inspector of Agriculture. Godfrey impressed upon Breuilly that the condition of the potatoes shipped to Granville, to the order of the German authorities, had forced the DOA to make an allowance of £210 to them. Breuilly was instructed to inform the DOA by the following week what "allowance" he was prepared to make towards the loss sustained by the DOA on this shipment. The offer made by Breuilly to the DOA was 7 shillings and sixpence on the 700 sacks of potatoes which had arrived at "Granville in a useless state". The DOA decided not to accept so low an offer and Breuilly was instructed to submit a "better offer" by the following week.

At the subsequent meeting Breuilly offered, by way of an allowance, to replace the 700 sacks of potatoes rejected by the German authorities at Granville. The DOA, however, decided neither to reject nor to accept his offer until it was, "...known whether any complaint was going to be made by the German authorities in respect of potatoes despatched on 28th September 1940". The following week the two parties met again on the subject of "defective potatoes" shipped by the CGA Limited on the 14th and 16th September 1940. An agreement was concluded that the company would reimburse the DOA the sum of 30 shillings per ton on 35 tons of defective potatoes making a total of £52-10-0. The sum was deducted from the next payment made to the CGA Limited in respect of storing and shipping potatoes.

On the 4th October Mr J. M. Norman, President of the JPMA, and Mr Chas Gruchy, Vice President, suggested to the DOA that further potato exports, presumably on the orders of the German authorities, be made from the very large amounts stored by the agricultural merchants. The JPMA rationale was based on the notion that the large quantities of surplus potatoes stored by them would otherwise mean that, "Merchants would treat the potatoes in their stores as abandoned". The DOA advised that no further shipments should be made from these stores, but that the JPMA should supply details of the total quantity of potatoes held in their stores.

In August 1940 the Public Health Department wrote to the DOA requesting that the three hospitals – General, Overdale and Mental – be permitted to purchase potatoes directly from farmers at £2 per ton. The DOA replied that the General and Overdale hospitals would only be allowed to purchase potatoes from licensed merchants at £2-17-6 per ton. The Mental Hospital was instructed to inform the DOA of the quantities it required up to December 1940. It subsequently received supplies at a price of £2 per ton from a potato depot which was opened at Carrefour au Clercq, Grouville.

Jersey Potatoes Delivered to St Helier Harbour and Exported to Europe to the Order of the German Authorities – July to October 1940

Date of German Requisition	Date of Shipment	Amount of Export	Value of Shipment	Notes of Shipment
5th July 1,080 tons	6th & 7th July	1,055 tons 16 cwt	£9,502-4-0	Germans request potato exports be resumed. Price was £9 per ton FOB. Initial reluctance by dockworkers to load potatoes onto barges to Granville. Potatoes taken from stores of potato merchants.
10th July	10th & 11th July	998 tons 10 cwt	£8,980-10-0	Loaded onto the three barges "Pitre Captou 51", "Point à Petre" and "Saigon". Sold at £9 per ton. Marie ordered to send an invoice to the German authorities and a copy to the Treasurer of the States. He also forwards an invoice to the German authorities for £110 in respect of 19 tons of potatoes undercharged on the shipments of the 6th and 7th July.

Date of German Requisition	Date of Shipment	Amount of Export	Value of Shipment	Notes of Shipment
23rd July Two orders		61 tons 16 cwt and 5 tons		Loaded onto "SS Holland" and "SS Oula of Normandy". £9 per ton FOB. Marie forwards the invoices to the German authorities and Treasurer of the States.
	24th to 26th July	1,450 tons	£13,050-15-0	Shipped by five barges. Marie forwards the invoice to the German authorities and a copy to the Treasurer of the States.
31st July to 2nd August		1,542 tons 6 cwt	£10,796-2-0	Marie instructed to deliver the invoice to German authorities and a copy to the Treasurer of the States.
	6th and 7th August	1,427 tons 16 cwt	£9,994-12-0	Marie to forward invoice to the German authorities. Potatoes sold at £7 per ton FOB.
12th, 13th and 14th August	Three shipments – 12th, 13th & 14th August	1,319 tons 10 cwt	£9,233-7-0	Marie instructed to deliver invoice to German authorities and a copy to the Treasurer of the States.
17th August	17th August	30 tons	£210-0-0	Marie instructed to deliver invoice to German authorities and a copy to the Treasurer of the States.
	20th August	1,902 tons	£13,391-4-0	Marie instructed to deliver invoice to German authorities and a copy to the Treasurer of the States.

Date of German Requisition	Date of Shipment	Amount of Export	Value of Shipment	Notes of Shipment
27th August	27th August Three shipments	1,940 tons	£11,677-10-0	German authorities credited with 20,000 sacks in respect of these three shipments, at 9d a sack. Marie instructed to deliver invoice to Herr Geib. New rate of £6 per ton FOB.
	2nd & 3rd September	2,065 tons 8 cwt	£12,392-8-0	Marie instructed to hand invoice to Herr Geib and a copy to the Treasurer of the States.
	5th September	100 tons	£600-0-0	Marie instructed to send invoice to the German authorities and a copy to the Treasurer of the States.
6th September	6th September	98 tons 10 cwt	£591-0-0	Described as: "To the orders of the Field Command".
	14th & 16th September		£11,741-14-0	The amount was posted to the credit of the "Potato Fund Occupation Account". Marie ordered to send invoice to the German authorities and a copy to the Treasurer of the States. 700 sacks of potatoes arrived in Granville in a "rotten condition". An allowance of £210 made by the DOA to the German authorities.
2nd & 3rd October			£2,115-12-0	Invoice sent to the German authorities. The sum to be credited to the "Potato Fund, Occupation Account".

Date of German Requisition	Date of Shipment	Amount of Export	Value of Shipment	Notes of Shipment
3rd October		1,000 tons	£4,000-0-0	"On the request of the German authorities", it was decided to sell a further 1,000 tons of the "Royal" variety at £4 per ton FOB.
	7th & 8th October		£1,086-12-0	Shipped to Guernsey on the SS Holland. Marie ordered to forward invoice to the German authorities and a copy to the Treasurer of the States.
11th October		700 tons	£2,800-0-0	It was decided that a further 700 tons of "Jersey Royal potatoes" should be sold to the "German Forces of Occupation", at a price of £4 per ton FOB.
	12th to 16th October Five shipments		£6,808-4-0	The amount to be credited to the "Potato Fund Occupation Account". Marie to hand invoice to the German authorities and send a copy to the Treasurer of the States.

The total value of all shipments of potatoes sold by the DOA to the German authorities and exported between July and October 1940 was £128,971-14-0. This figure, using the Bank of England inflation rate, would correspond to £7,383,328 in 2020.

Payment to Farmers for Potatoes Exported Prior to the Military Occupation Problems between Agricultural Merchants and Farmers

On the 13th July 1940, the JFU and JPMA met to discuss the non-payment of farmers' potato tickets, issued for produce exported to the United

Kingdom prior to the German military occupation. The problem had arisen that many farmers who held weighbridge tickets confirming the weight and quantity of potatoes which were subsequently exported to the United Kingdom had not been paid by the merchants. This had the knock-on effect that, apart from these farmers not receiving their due remuneration, a substantial minority were in financial hardship because they could not fulfil the payment of their debts to the agricultural merchants. This problem was exacerbated by a group of farmers – several whom leased their land – who had purchased supplies and agricultural inputs from merchants against the following season's crop of potatoes and tomatoes. This form of credit was well established and a recognised feature of agricultural finance.

After the arrival of the German military forces the problem of payments and monies owed by both parties became increasingly difficult to resolve. Brée made the decision that it had to be resolved quickly – he had other problems to contend with. In order to reach a satisfactory compromise Brée, along with the Crown Officers and the Finance Committee, set up a "clearing house" to ensure potato accounts and weighbridge tickets were paid to farmers. The fundamental problem was that due to the "cessation of contact with the mainland" large sums of money were held up.[11] The problem was compounded by cheques which had not been sent to the United Kingdom for banking clearance and were effectively "frozen".

The DOA immediately supported the clearing house scheme by allowing two rooms at its headquarters at Victoria Chambers, Conway Street, to be used as administrative offices. The States underwrote the scheme; however, it would only cover the period of potato exports up to the 30th June 1940. The total amount owed by merchants to farmers was £120,000. This was money which had been held by the merchants and frozen in the United Kingdom or uncleared in many cases in Jersey banks.

On the 24th July 1940, the clearing house scheme was implemented. The JFU and the JPMA met to settle their differences. The States of Jersey advanced a payment of £30,000 against uncleared funds. The merchants were paid between £100,000 and £127,000 for monies owed to them before the 25th June 1940. The actual sum is not clear because of continuing disagreement between merchants and farmers. Furthermore, it was agreed that any further disputes between them would be forwarded to a jointly agreed Arbitration Board with two members from the JFU and two from the JPMA. The Arbitration Board would be adjudicated by an independent Chairman, John A. Perrée. Both merchants and farmers were satisfied with the clearing scheme. The farmers, in particular, were paid the full value of their weighbridge potato tickets. Effectively the problem was solved.

The 1940 Cereal Harvest

"The growing of cereals had been abandoned long ago in the past, simply because it was not an economic proposition when compared with the growing of potatoes."

Lord Coutanche – Baliff of Jersey

Two weeks after the German occupation, on the 15th July 1940, the DOA made the decision to disallow farmers to thresh any cereal crop. Harvesting of cereals would only be permitted with a "threshing permit" granted by the DOA. Brée, in a meeting with farmers over the issue of threshing the 1940 cereal crop and being described at the meeting as "the learned Jurat", explained why the order prohibiting threshing had been issued.[4] One permit had already been issued to John Richard, a threshing contractor. He was supplied with petrol from the Petrol Controller to complete the threshing of a crop in the north of the Island. On the 26th July petrol and paraffin were further authorised to the threshing companies and contractors in order to be ready for the forthcoming harvests of wheat, barley and oats.

Between the 2nd and 7th August Brée worked non-stop to formulate not only the forthcoming law on agriculture – the Cultivation of Lands (Jersey) Order, 1940 – but also the new cropping plan for the 1941 growing season. The most pressing problem, however, was the harvesting of the 1940 cereal crops and, in the midst of all his other commitments, he met Le Gallais on the 20th July to discuss the problem. Le Gallais, in turn, consulted his highly competent secretary, H. G. Shepard. Shepard had joined the RJA&HS in 1917 and had an unparalleled understanding of Jersey's agriculture. In addition, he knew all the Island's threshing contractors and cereal farmers, understanding their problems and needs. Le Gallais and Shepard carefully examined and calculated the area of barley, wheat and oats that remained to be harvested. The figure was 2,500 vergées.[18] Le Gallais informed Brée of the utmost urgency and necessity of obtaining petrol supplies for threshing and Brée immediately met with the Petrol Controller, who granted the necessary fuel to cover the harvest. Le Gallais and Shepard also calculated the fuel needed by threshing contractors and convinced the Petrol Controller of the accuracy of their demands.[3] It was fortuitous that a larger area of cereals than usual had been grown in 1940 and this provided most of the seed for the 1941 crop.

The accepted historical interpretation is that by 1940 potatoes and tomatoes had completely displaced cereal crops. It is, however, interesting to note that throughout the 1930s the official agricultural reports from the States Experimental Station describe a series of experiments on various cereal types on behalf of Jersey farmers. These included experiments with varieties of oats such as "Victory" and "Star". In 1933, two new varieties were trialled, including seed from the Agricultural Experimental Station at Craibstone, Aberdeen. In 1937, 4 vergées of oats were tested.[19]

In 1940, as part of the mixed farming economy, farmers still grew cereal crops, although the areas had greatly decreased. At the end of World War One, the price of agricultural land on the Island had doubled and even trebled. The most fertile and valuable land was changed almost exclusively to the growing of potatoes and tomatoes. In 1919, 2,178 vergées of wheat were grown; in 1930, 1,058 vergées; and in 1938 it had decreased to 169 vergées. In 1919, the area devoted to growing oats was 3,526 vergées and by 1939 it was 943 vergées. In 1938, wheat and oats accounted for 1,112 vergées.[20] In 1932, Shepard made a precise assessment of the areas of cereals grown on the Island. His figures were: wheat, 757¼ vergées; oats, 2,315½ vergées; and barley, 86½ vergées. The total area for growing cereals was 3,159 vergées, which in 1932 accounted for some 6–8% of the total agricultural land use.[21] The notion that in 1940 geriatric farmers in their eighties and nineties were dragged out of their wheelchairs to resurrect cereal growing on the Island is incorrect. In August 1940, Le Gallais and Shepard made a second and more detailed calculation of the area of cereals grown and, in their report, stated that there were 2,800 vergées, approximating to about 5% of agricultural land use.

The Island in 1940 had a well-established network of experienced cereal threshing businesses which, every summer and autumn, were employed around the parishes where they were based. In a meeting of the Advisory Pricing Board on the 11th July 1941, Mr T. G. Le Cappelain, one of the largest established threshing contractors, was asked, "…as to the number of threshing outfits in the Island". Le Cappelain's reply to the question was, "…nine or ten large and five small".[22]

Threshing of cereals normally took place in the latter part of September depending on weather conditions. By August 1940, Brée had yet to acquire fuel for threshing operations. Perhaps of greater necessity, he needed farmers' cooperation in the harvesting of their current cereal crops. A small amount of threshing had been allowed by the issue of a permit to J. Richard, an established contractor. On the 12th August, Richard made a request for 6 gallons of petrol for moving two threshing machines in need of repair. He was immediately informed that no petrol was available and to move the machines by horse traction.

On the 14th August, Brée met with farming representatives from all the parishes. He issued an Island-wide "No Threshing Order". Two farmers refused to comply with this order and were summoned before the DOA. Both men were threatened with the requisition of their land and crops if they persisted in breaking the order.

The first Island-wide cereal threshing order was authorised for the 23rd September; it was to operate for two weeks. Mr J. G. Malzard was appointed by the DOA as "Chief Threshing Officer". In addition, three Threshing Inspectors were hired, at £3 a week, to assist him in supervising and monitoring the distribution of grain at the threshing machines. Farmers were permitted to retain any bags of grain rejected by the Threshing Inspectors as being unfit for milling flour. Each farmer was issued with a voucher informing him of the store to which to transport his grain. The Threshing Inspectors weighed the grain and a ticket was produced. In addition, the farmer was handed an official cereal order which stated: "Any person holding threshed stocks of wheat, oats, barley or rye, or buckwheat must notify the DOA of the quantity of each variety in his possession. Such information to reach the department no later than 28th September 1940".

The new imperative facing Brée and his officials was that, after this initial threshing of the cereals, there was the question of the storage of grain to be dealt with. The Corn Merchants' Association wanted payment for this service and met with the DOA to discuss the issue. The DOA offered the merchants thirty shillings a ton to store grain. The details of the contract between the two parties proved difficult to resolve and necessitated several lengthy meetings which resulted in the following terms of business.

1. The Chief Threshing Inspector will make all decisions as to whether the weather is suitable for threshing. All grain brought into store is to be in a dry condition.
2. All threshing for the first two weeks will be carried out only at the threshing depots.
3. Farmers are to provide their own sacks.
4. A system of carbon copy slips will be arranged for each farmer to present to the merchant for a signature. Only stores allocated by the Chief Inspector are allowed. Weights of grain are to be clearly marked on the carbon slips.
5. Only the number of cereal sacks written on the carbon slip and delivered by the farmer will be accepted at the store.
6. Storage must be only on wooden floors.
7. Payments for storage will be monthly.
8. The official grain depots are listed. The capacity of these is 810 tons.
9. The DOA agrees to pay the corn merchants the sum of 30 shillings per ton to store the grain. This is inclusive of receiving the grain into store, care of grain and turning weekly, bagging, and handling to the millers.

The prices paid to farmers by the DOA for grain delivered to the weighbridge and sent to the stores were:

Wheat	16/10 per cwt
Oats	17/- per cwt
Rye	15/- per cwt
Barley	14/- per cwt

Problems arose with this system of farmers delivering grain to the official stores. Several farmers who had harvested the grain and delivered their sacks had apparent shortages of grain recorded. Brée discussed the problem with the Crown Officers. It was agreed that farmers who delivered to store less grain than was recorded by the Threshing Inspectors would be held to account by legal proceedings against them. One particular farmer was singled out. Mr L. H. Le Vannais, St Helier, had produced fifty-six bags of grain but consistently refused to take the recorded bags to store. Brée, after consultations with the Attorney General, sent the Chief Threshing Inspector with a summons and requisition order to Mr Le Vannais. It was decided that, in the event of any further difficulty "...with this man", the Chief Threshing Inspector would send a report to the Attorney General in order for him to take "appropriate action".

On the 30th September the threshing of wheat commenced. On the 7th October the Chief Threshing Officer was given authority to use his discretion to allow farmers further threshing periods. At the end of October, owners of horse-drawn seed drills were requested to notify the DOA of the type of drill they possessed in order to sow seed in an economical manner.

The question arises as to why occupation histories have stated clearly that cereal growing had ceased before the German occupation? The Bailiff of Jersey, Head of the Superior Council during the occupation, stated in his memoirs that before occupation, "The growing of cereals had been abandoned long ago in the past".[23] Why did Lord Coutanche clearly state that cereals were not being grown on the Island? From Le Gallais and Shepard's calculations, stated in official DOA minutes and meetings, in 1940 there were between 2,500 and 2,800 vergées of cereals on the Island. The answer can be summarised in the contents of a letter written to the United Kingdom's Home Office by the Attorney General, Duret Aubin, in May 1946.[24] All Jersey farmers were individually liable, long before and during the German occupation, to pay specified tithes for growing cereals to the English Crown. These tithes had not been forthcoming between the years 1940 to 1944. After the liberation this became a contentious issue between the States and the Home Office.

Tithes owed for growing cereals were based upon the area grown. This varied between 3 shillings and sixpence and 2 shillings and fourpence per vergée. It also differed as to whether the crop was wheat, oats, barley, or rye. Up to the 1920s the English Crown collected substantial amounts of tax through the implementation of these tithes but in 1939 only £30 in tithes was paid. The actual amount that should have been collected was approximately £380 to £480. Therefore, we can surmise that a number of farmers had, for a number of years, ceased paying their individual tithes to the English Crown.

This shortfall was certainly noticed after the occupation by the UK collecting authority. The reason is clear. In 1941 the DOA's official cropping plan increased cereal production to 20,000 vergées. Therefore, the tithes due to the Crown would have been thousands of pounds in value. Duret Aubin, in his correspondence to the Home Office on the issue, made it clear that, "During the Occupation the whole cultivation plan had of necessity to be radically altered, the survival of the population requiring as great as possible of cereals, and especially wheat, should be grown".[24] The DOA had therefore directed "…every farmer…in the interests of the community" to grow cereals. He furthermore emphasised, "Every farmer was therefore compelled to grow wheat, oats, barley or rye, on land which normally would have been considered unsuitable for that purpose". Duret Aubin also gave the Home Office the area of cereals sown in 1939 as 909 vergées, while Le Gallais and Shepard confirmed this as 2,500 to 2,800 vergées for 1940. Duret Aubin was attempting to mitigate the Island's non-payment of tithes by reducing the stated area planted with cereals, thereby lessening the money owed to the Crown by individual farmers. He was certainly being economical with the true figure.

After the liberation, HM Treasury requested all cereal tithes from 1941 to 1944 be paid to the Crown. Guernsey in 1946 had paid its cereal tithes in full. The invoice forwarded to the States of Jersey was for £8,000. Each year had been calculated at £2,000. The question of tithes remained with the UK Treasury, which insisted upon payment. The best the States could do in this case was to minimise the extent of cereal growing on Jersey before and during the occupation. Therefore, Coutanche's observations on the demise of cereal growing in pre-war Jersey, and that it had ceased, make sense.

The Cropping Plan: 1940

On the 7th August 1940, Brée produced the cropping plan for the following year. It was slightly amended, and with more detail, on the 14th September and was approved by the Superior Council. Three fundamental changes were made to the Island's agricultural system:

1. Cereal crops would increase from 2,500 vergées to 20,500 vergées.
2. The total area for potato cultivation would decrease to 4,430 vergées.
3. The entire Island agricultural land-use area would be drastically cut to 40,000 vergées, losing some 12 to 15,000 vergées of agricultural land.

Brée felt that, with the implementation of the cropping plan, he needed to persuade the Superior Council and impress upon them, "…the urgency of appointing inspectors" to check that the plan, along with Cultivation Orders, were complied with. On the 27th August the DOA published the Cultivation of Lands (Jersey) Order, 1940. This gave the DOA total control of agriculture throughout the occupation. Every farmer who cultivated land had to follow DOA directions on the crops sown, the seed type and cultivation, the allocation of fertilisers and pesticides, harvesting and storage. Farmers had to employ sufficient labour to comply with orders and the DOA had authority for its personnel to be allowed entry into any farm, field, or building to make an inspection.[25]

The amended cropping plan for 1940 included a number of new details:

1. The area for cultivation, 39,880 vergées, would feed the entire Island population.
2. Each farmer would be allocated an exact area for each crop. Every parish would be allocated Honorary Parish Inspectors to check all these on a regular basis.
3. Mangolds would be grown in far greater quantities than in pre-war days to facilitate the production of milk required. (John du Val commented that he was continually bombarded by complaints from farmers about the drastic decrease of potatoes ordered, making the observation: "They were obsessed by the thought of growing potatoes".)
4. The 1940 wheat crop would produce a sufficient yield of seed for the 1941 crop.
5. Petrol would be issued for ploughing in 1941.

On the 3rd September 1940 the Attorney General proclaimed that the Superior Council would acquire the entire 1940 cereal crop. The DOA was charged to implement "The immediate appointment of the Agricultural Marketing Board to fix the prices of produce to be acquired by the DOA". Those appointed by the Superior Council to be members of this Board were J. A. Perée, J. B. Michel, T. Le Marinel, J. M. Norman and S. G. Le Couilliard.

On the 6th September, the Honorary Parish Inspectors were named. In documents and meetings during the occupation they are mostly referred to as "Parish Inspectors". Their power was derived from the Cultivation of Lands (Jersey) Order, 1940. Each was appointed by the Royal Court. These men were highly respected in the agricultural community and most of them owned farms. They became the cornerstone of the inspection regime which grew throughout the occupation and are unsung heroes who worked constantly for the entire period 1940 to 1945 to ensure farmers played their part in feeding the population. Several different types of Inspectors were appointed during the occupation, their respective duties resulting in a confused picture when discussing the inspection of agriculture. The most important of these were the Honorary Parish Inspectors.

Honorary Parish Inspectors

Appointment made in the Royal Court

Parish	Name	Address
St Brelade	J. J. Le Boutillier	Beauvoir, La Moye
St Brelade	H. M. Gibaut	Wheatlands, Pont Marquet
St Clement	J. P. Le Masurier	Jambart, Pontac

Parish	Name	Address
St Clement	Ernest Malzard	Les Tours
St Peter	George Le Rossignol	La Hauteur, Augrez
St Peter	E. N. Egré	The Gables
St Saviour	J. A. Perrée	Oaklands
St Saviour	Charles Quenault	Hamlet Farm
Trinity	C. P. Ahier	La Roulerie
Trinity	A. R. Le Brun	Diélamont
Grouville	S. G. Le Couilliard	La Carrière, Longueville
Grouville	Emile Le Geyt Siouville	Oakborne
St Helier	P. J. Mourant	Mont au Prêtre
St Helier	Philip L. Baudains	Richelieu, Tower Road
St John	J. Gartrell, Deputy	Cedar House
St John	C. Le Couteur	Northdale
St Lawrence	H. W. Maillard	Blanche Pierre Farm
St Lawrence	F. J. Ahier	La Chasserie
St Martin	Philip Ahier, Deputy	Homelea
St Martin	G. Le Masurier	Les Alpes
St Mary	Philip Le Feuvre, Deputy	Perry Farm
St Mary	E. J. Le Ruez	Westfield

The first meeting was held on the 9th September when the Honorary Parish Inspectors were addressed by the Bailiff and by Brée and were sworn in at twelve noon at the Royal Court. They both stressed, "The seriousness of the present food situation of the Island", and further impressed upon them that, "...their duties were of the greatest importance in making the Island, so far as possible, self-supporting". On 11th September Brée informed the DOA of those selected and on the 14th they were brought together and the 1941 Cropping Plan was explained in detail.

The Price Advisory Board appointed by the Superior Council met for the first time on the 11th September.[22] The Board was crucial during the occupation. All the Island's agricultural produce was bought by the DOA. If the Board failed to evaluate a fair price for crops, commensurate to the farmers' inputs, the end result would be a serious decrease in agricultural produce. Jersey farmers therefore had to trust the Board, and the men who decided upon adequate remuneration were well-established Jersey farmers.

The first task of the Board was to fix the price paid to farmers for the 1940 cereals – wheat, oats and barley – and to prepare the basis for the 1941 prices for cereals and potatoes. In addition, the Concentrated Cattle Foods (Jersey) Order, 1940, was prepared, prohibiting the feeding of cattle (with the exception of animals under six months) any type of oats, bran cakes, molasses, seed, or nuts.

On the 1ˢᵗ November 1940, the Restriction of Legal Proceedings (Jersey) Regulations 1940 was approved. This allowed for a list of every farmer and his address to be prepared and made public. On the same day the DOA completed an inventory totalling all the 1941 crops that were expected, based on the figures of the new Cropping Plan. The amount calculated to fund all the 1941 crops was estimated at £550,000. The Superior Council subsequently set this sum aside for funding the 1941 growing season.

The 1940 Potato Crop and the Establishment of Storage Clamps

"The 1940 potato crop was allowed to come to maturity. It was purchased by the Department of Agriculture and clamped, forming a valuable food supply over the ensuing winter."

H. G. Shepard

The DOA, after the arrival of the occupying forces, purchased the entire 1940 potato crop. Brée realised it was imperative to find sufficient storage space for these potatoes. The agricultural merchants could only take 10,000 tons and Brée realised that he would need to find storage for a further 30,000–40,000 tons. He quickly came to the conclusion that the answer lay in the use of clamps – an inexpensive way of storing potatoes. The method favoured by Brée was to construct a shallow depression in a field. The depressions were insulated by straw, the potatoes placed in them, and again covered by straw, and then soil. The clamps were built to a height of 1 metre with drainage ditches dug along either side.

The DOA sent Wesley Mallet (adjoint member) to meet Charles Gibaut who owned various fields at Broadfields, St Lawrence. Gibaut offered to lease to the DOA 10 vergées at £4 per vergée, but eventually accepted £3 per vergée. A tenancy agreement was signed and backdated to the 24ᵗʰ June 1940. Mallet was subsequently put in charge of the construction and upkeep of all potato storage clamps and was given authority to employ a foreman at Broadfields at 10 shillings a day, and five labourers at 7 shillings a day. The working hours were 7.00 a.m. to 6.00 p.m.

Further clamps were established at St Ouen, where a field of 4 vergées was rented at a cost of £5 per vergée, the tenancy also backdated to 24ᵗʰ June 1940. In addition, a playing field was rented from the Department of Public Instruction, opposite Carmel de Hautmont, St Saviour, just behind Heathfield.

By the 23ʳᵈ August 1940, the clamps at Broadfields were full and extra fields were rented in neighbouring areas. Broadfields was designated the Island depot for all the remaining crop and additional staff were employed. In addition to extra fields being rented at Broadfields, 3 vergées of farmland were rented at China Quarries Farm, St Lawrence.

The New Island Agricultural Policy

"A draft proposal policy for agriculture was required quickly"

A. V. Godfray, Chief Agricultural Inspector

The Superior Council, by early August 1940, had been made aware of the problems affecting agriculture on the Island. Brée explained to the Superior Council that the central issue Jersey immediately had to deal with was that the population needed to be fed. Therefore, it was imperative that there was a complete revision of agriculture. One pressing problem, which had not been anticipated, was that the evacuation of the Island in June 1940 had resulted in several large farms being left unoccupied. These included Gouray Lodge Farm, St Martin, and Vicq Farm, Grouville. On the 2nd August Brée met with David Simpson, Head of the States Experimental Station, and Mr Archie Vivian Godfray, Chief Agricultural Inspector. They concluded that "A Draft Proposal Policy for Agriculture for 1941 was required quickly". It was agreed that a new agricultural policy, in response to the German occupation, would be enacted by the 5th August 1940. To prepare the new policy, Brée called upon the services of a remarkable man, who seems to have been overlooked in the history of the German occupation of Jersey, the Secretary of the RJA&HS, H. G. Shepard. Shepard was an extremely competent and highly organised individual. His knowledge of the structure of the Island's agricultural system was unparalleled and he became secretary to many agricultural committees during the occupation and was invited to many important meetings. His long association with Jersey agriculture and his logical and empirical methodology made Shepard second to none. Furthermore, he was trusted by the DOA, the farmers and the merchants. Brée and Shepard worked together very closely with a team from the DOA. This group of experts allowed Shepard to make reliable calculations as to the areas and quantities of inputs required to grow the various crops that were needed. Brée emphasised to Shepard that because of the "present emergency" it was imperative to devise a viable and realistic agricultural policy for 1941.

The subsequent policy was sent to the Attorney General who prepared the necessary legislation, which was then forwarded to the Superior Council for review. The document prepared for scrutiny was entitled: "Recommendations of the DOA in connection with the future organisation of the farming industry during the present emergency". The new policy took Brée and Shepard three days to write and can be summarised as follows.

1. In order that no arable land be left uncultivated every farmer will be ordered to grow certain quantities of essential crops.
2. The quantity of each essential crop the farmer is required to grow will be fixed on a percentage basis to ensure that there is a sufficiency of all essential crops and a surplus of none.

3. The penalty for failure to comply with such orders or to properly tend crops will be prosecution under the Defence Regulations and the requisitioning of the land occupied by the defaulting farmer for an indefinite period not expressly limited to the period of the war. The period of requisition will extend to at least one year and can be easily extended to two or three years.
4. Farmers will be required to employ sufficient labour for the cultivation of the land. If a farmer lacks labour a scheme will be evolved whereby the cost of labour supplied will be the first charge on the produce of the land occupied by the farmer to whom it was supplied.
5. An Agricultural Marketing Board will be set up for the monitoring of agricultural produce.
6. All land will be employed for the growing of essential crops and all produce will be bought by the Marketing Board.
7. Control of prices will be effected by the Marketing Board with power already vested in the DOA to make price-fixing orders.
8. If a farmer has no incentive to work on the land properly the necessary spur will be provided by the threat that the farm will be requisitioned for the period of the war and that he himself will have to live on his savings or seek employment.
9. A rigorous system of inspection to ensure that the orders for planting are executed and that the growing crops properly tended. For this purpose the DOA will submit the names of three men from each parish who are competent to act as Inspectors and the Superior Council will select two men from each parish to act as Inspectors. The Inspectors will be Honorary and appointed before the Royal Court to carry out their duties.
10. Men who refuse to work on farms will not be able to obtain alternative employment through the Department of Labour and will have to accept the consequences of being unemployed.

Signed T. J. Brée, President, 7th August 1940.

There were several further problems that Brée and the DOA had to deal with. Some twenty pedigree Jersey cows and two highly valued bulls were officially requisitioned by the Kaiser Wilhelm Institute and sent to Dummerstorf, near Rostock. The farmers whose cattle had been requisitioned needed to be compensated. On the 19th August the DOA decided that, in order to compensate farmers, cattle valuations would be carried out by Mr J. A. Perrée and a member of the Department of Finance and Economics. The evacuation of several farmers from the Island in June had resulted in livestock being left unattended, the number being between fifty and seventy cows and bulls. A meeting was convened of the RJA&HS and JFU to discuss the problem.[4] Brée attended the meeting and advised the farmers present that, "The best means of distributing surplus cattle throughout the Island was to give them to farmers who have none". The decision was made to allocate all these abandoned cattle on a compulsory basis to farmers, based on the requirements of the Island.

Fertilisers

By mid-September 1940, the DOA had requisitioned the Island's stocks of artificial fertilisers. On the 11th September all Règlements governing the collection of vraic (seaweed used as a fertiliser) were revoked by the DOA. Future imports of artificial fertilisers were increasingly sourced and obtained through the German Military Government, Field Command 515.

The increasing lack of artificial fertilisers throughout the occupation was somewhat of a historical irony. It was a Jerseyman and former pupil of Victoria College, Robert Le Rossignol (1884–1976) who, along with Fritz Haber in 1908, developed the high-pressure device and catalyst needed for the Haber process to produce ammonia for artificial fertilisers. Haber subsequently received the Nobel Prize in 1918. Le Rossignol's importance to the development of the process was acknowledged by Haber, who included his name on the patent.[26] Le Rossignol donated his personal scientific balance to Victoria College where it is displayed in the vestibule of the Science Department.

Farm Evictions

"On s'adresse à Dieu pas aux saints!"

"Why speak to the saints when you can go directly to God."

The German military occupation immediately led to the complete loss of the United Kingdom market for the main cash crops, thereby stopping many farmers' cash income. One group especially badly affected by the loss of their main source of cashflow was tenant farmers, who rented not only their fields but also their accommodation, from landlords. A number of tenant farmers were French who had originally arrived from Normandy and Brittany on a seasonal basis and had subsequently remained on the Island.

These tenant farmers were often in debt to agricultural merchants who advanced them the agricultural inputs required for the following year's crops and offset the debt from the sale of the tenant's potatoes and tomatoes. This model worked well until the dislocation of the United Kingdom markets in the summer of 1940.

The first evictions of tenant farmers began in early September 1940. On the evening of the 6th September, Marcel Francois Moisan, L'Etacq, St Ouen, a French national, was given notice of eviction by his landlord, John Vautier. Moisan informed Vautier he would sell all his farm effects in order to pay his debt. In reply, Vautier suggested to Moisan that he should have his effects valued by an auctioneer, and he would accept the proceeds of the sale in part payment for the rent. Vautier had made no "distraint" or legal seizure on goods, but made it clear he required some form of payment.

The next day Moisan decided to take up the matter of his eviction with those whom he perceived had the real authority on the Island, the "Field Commandant Schumacher Colonel". Moisan, following the French maxim "On s'adresse à Dieu pas aux saints", wrote to the Field Commandant of the German Military Government and pleaded his case directly to Schumacher.

> "Not being able to pay my rent this year for a bit of ground and house, on account of the war, my landlord, a rich man, is going to sell everything I have. I will find myself without a bed for my six children. Please tell me if he can do it as I do not know what to do. Thanking you.
> I remain Dear Sir, Yours Truly, M. Moisan".[27]

On the 11th September, OKVR Dr von Stein, on behalf of Schumacher, wrote to the Bailiff concerning the plight of the sixty-eight-year-old Moisan with the request, "Will you please let me know if any help can be given". On the 13th September, the Connétable of St Ouen, Francis Le Boutillier, along with Centenier Philip Coutanche, visited Moisan. Le Boutillier's subsequent report on the eviction merely stated the current situation with the conclusion that, "If Moisan had been reasonable with him (the landlord), Moisan having a large family he would sympathise with him".

On the 17th September, the Bailiff replied directly to Schumacher on the subject of "Mr Moisan's financial difficulties". In an interesting pointer to the future relationship of the Jersey civil authority and the German Military Government, the Bailiff's answer was at best patronising and at worst demonstrated that Moisan's problems did not merit serious consideration. The Bailiff concluded in his response to Schumacher that the case was being dealt with within the legal framework and that "Mr Moisan will have every opportunity of stating his case in the court".

In the same week another tenant farmer, Alexandre Brèqnouen, Longueville, St Saviour, was given notice of eviction. Brèqnouen also wrote to the German Military Government requesting help. OKVR Dr von Stein wrote directly to the DOA on the subject of his eviction. In addition, he sought legal representation through the advocates Bois and Bois. In an interesting intervention the matter was taken up by the Head of Agriculture, Field Command 515, "Herr Doctor Pelz". Pelz had very quickly forged a close working relationship with the President of the DOA, Touzel Brée. This structural relationship between the two men allowed for quick and pragmatic decisions to be made between the Jersey civilian and German authorities over agricultural matters. After meeting with Pelz, Brée felt it wise to deliver some form of compromise. He set up a sub-committee to look into the matter of evictions comprising Carlyle Le Gallais and Edwin Gibaut.

The Arrival of the German Military Government Field Command 515

The officers arrived and "...were taken to the Hotel Majestic where they had dinner and the Bailiff, the representative of the Crown, treated the German officers as guests."

KVR Hans Egon Pelz describing the arrival, on the first day, of Field Command 515

On the 9th August 1940, at low tide, the Staff Officers of the German Administration, Field Command 515, arrived in Jersey. Included in the Field Command was KVR Hans Egon Pelz, Head of Agriculture and Food Supplies for the Channel Islands. Pelz, on his arrival at St Helier, was immediately struck by the 7-metre climb up a ladder to the quayside at the harbour. Still in his military fatigues he, along with his fellow Staff Officers, "...were taken to the Hotel Majestic where they had dinner, and the Bailiff, the representative of the Crown, treated the German officers as guests". At the hotel, Pelz met Major Demmler, a fellow Staff Officer of Field Command 515, who was already on the Island and in charge of the logistical needs of the German military units occupying Jersey.[28]

Pelz described the dinner as a "banquet". Along with the Bailiff, "...were also civilian guests dressed in evening gowns and tailcoats". He was also struck by the attitude of the Bailiff to the German Staff Officers, whom he regarded as his guests. Pelz interpreted this "As a noble gesture".

On the same day, Colonel Schumacher, Field Command 515, proclaimed he had, "Taken over command of the Channel Islands".[29] In order to clarify the structure of German authority, Hauptmann Gussek, the Island's Military Commander, published on 17th August 1940 the proclamation, "The Field Command 515 have commenced duties at Victoria College School House. All matters relating to civil administration will in future be dealt with by the above. Matters of a military character have to be submitted to me as previously".[30]

Gussek's proclamation would seemingly suggest that Field Command 515 did not have authority over the German military forces. This, however, was only a short-lived split of authority lasting until Gussek left the Island. In future Colonel von Schmettow, his replacement as Military Chief, had to provide sufficient justification to Field Command 515 in order to proceed with the requisitioning of land and property, building of military installations and removal of civilians. There was certainly no dual or parallel authority between the military command and the military administration of Field Command 515. In addition, the notion that the Field Commander and his replacement were nominally merely bureaucrats posted to head the Field Command is incorrect. All Field Commanders in the German Military

Government had to have served in the First World War as Officers and to have been on active duty. They would have all had an excellent understanding of the nature and workings of the German armed forces.

The summer of 1940 saw Field Command 515 carry out a charm offensive with the local civilian population. It organised German military bands to play at West Park Pavilion, a boxing competition and, on the 22nd August 1940, a football match between a German and a Jersey XI. The match was played at College Field and was well attended by both local civilian and German military personnel.[31] Before the match kicked off both teams faced each other on the centre of the football ground, with the German team raising their hand in the Heil Hitler salute.[32]

The arrival of the German Military Government was a turning point in the administration of Jersey during the occupation. It also became crucial in the development of the Island's agricultural policies. Field Command 515 provided the States and the DOA with the overall agricultural policies for Jersey and the rest of the Channel Islands.[33] The Superior Council, the DOA and its civil servants and Inspectors would implement the overall plans of Field Command 515. Several policies were sent directly from St Germain, Paris, to Field Command 515.

Pelz immediately began to call upon Brée, demanding detailed statistics on all aspects of the Island's agriculture. He also spent a great deal of time going from parish to parish scrutinising and checking the sowing, condition and harvesting of crops, milk production and livestock slaughter, and liaising with the Honorary Parish Inspectors over farmers' infringements of Cultivation Orders and deliberate hoarding of produce. Field Command 515's agricultural supervision was indeed an ingenious policy and, perhaps more than anything else, stamped its authority on the Island. It outlined to the States its strategic agricultural policy. The civil authority in turn ran the operational details, and the DOA's civil servants would use their own time, energy and expertise implementing these policies. Any resultant grievances against these policies, by the farmers or the population, would be directed at the States and its civil servants and not at the German Military Government. This system of managing agriculture on the Island worked smoothly. However, it changed in nature in early September 1944 when Pelz was sent to the Somme by von Schmettow, in order to utilise his organisational abilities to repair communications. By the end of November 1944, a number of farmers openly refused to comply with orders issued by the DOA regarding cultivation, storage, milk, and animals.

On the 5th September 1940, Field Command 515 wrote to the Bailiff requiring information on the Island's agriculture. The German authority also detailed its agricultural program. Pelz had put together the facts and statistics he needed to set out his future plans for Jersey. On the 20th September Pelz, through the lines of communication set up between Field Command 515 and the States, demanded additional and extremely detailed information and data concerning the dairy industry. The DOA instructed the head of the

Milk Control Section, R. O. Weeks, to collate the information and this was forwarded on the 27th September. On the same day, "Herr Pelz" wrote to the DOA asking for the number and distribution of all cattle, horses, pigs, and poultry. This request was forwarded by the DOA to the States Vet, Thomas Blampied, to deal with. In addition, Blampied was told to supply additional information on the nature of the Island's cattle diseases which "Dr Pelz of the German Field Command" had requested. He produced a full report and forwarded it to the Bailiff, specifically requesting its "...transmission to answer Dr Pelz".

On the 4th October Blampied reported to the States that animals and a "live boar" had been imported by the Germans into the Island. He immediately wrote to Pelz and impressed upon "Herr Dr Pelz the dangers of uncontrolled livestock coming into the Island from France". On the 7th October, he met with "Herr Dr Pelz of the German Field Command", regarding the dangers of unrestricted importation of dogs and other live animals into the Island from the mainland and reported that "Herr Pelz has undertaken to issue instructions prohibiting such importations by the personnel of the German Forces".

On the 9th October Colonel Schumacher wrote to the DOA regarding the use of horses for agricultural work. The DOA replied that all efforts were being made to use horses for agricultural work and to the greatest possible extent.

In September 1940 several farmers whose land abutted the airport had their farms requisitioned by the German Military Government. All requisitioning of agricultural land and property by the German military forces had to be handled by Field Command 515. Documents concerning the requisition of farms and agricultural land at Egypt, Trinity, and in St Lawrence, clearly demonstrate that the German military had to, firstly, demonstrate the military necessity, and secondly, the extent and use of the land it required, along with detailed maps of the land concerned. The German military was not allowed to arbitrarily seize farms or land but had to make a request to requisition them. This was forwarded to Field Command 515 and KVR Pelz examined the potential loss of farmland and took the decision to allow, modify or stop the requisition. Field Command 515 abided by the Hague Convention.

The requisition of farms around the airport was allowed by Field Command 515. In response the DOA decided that the farmers involved should be accommodated on farms which had been left vacant when their occupants had evacuated in June. The Connétables were instructed to send to the DOA lists of abandoned farms in their parishes.

The Regeneration of Jersey's Watermills

One week after the German military occupation of the Island, Deputy Edward Le Quesne, President of the Department of Labour, toured Jersey, "To find out if some of the old Jersey mills could be used for grinding corn, as we realise that very shortly we may be compelled to be self-supporting as regards many of the necessities of life".[15] On the 13th September 1940 the Superior Council instructed the DOA to take formal control and to supervise the mills. On 16th September the DOA requested the Department of Essential Commodities' permission to requisition the following watermills: Tesson and Gargate in St Peter and Grand Val, also known as Baxter's Mill, in St Saviour. On the same day, Mr Peter Philip Day was appointed to take full charge of the Island's mills and operations. He was allocated a salary of £280 per annum and a weekly allowance of petrol from the Petrol Controller. All mills henceforth would be under the direct control and sole responsibility of the DOA.

The first issue to be resolved in the regeneration of the mills was to ensure there was enough running water to allow the waterwheels to function efficiently. On the 23rd September, Brée and the Director of the Jersey New Waterworks met to discuss in detail the release of sufficient water to make the mills fully operational. The Director assured Brée that the company would allow an adequate supply of water for Tesson Mill with the additional offer of any available equipment that it could supply.

Tesson was the first mill to be renovated and it came into operation on the 26th September. During the First World War, it had been worked "both night and day" to supply the Island with flour. Up to the early 1930s there were still five operational watermills in St Peter's Valley, all receiving their water supply from one stream. It had taken several weeks to restore Tesson. Seventeen men were employed, commencing with the cleaning of the pond, which had last been cleaned in 1915. The pond was 130 feet long, 45 feet wide and 5 feet 5 inches deep. A bonus of cleaning the millpond was the discovery of 130 large eels which were subsequently eaten. Tesson Mill had previously been known as Gilley's Mill because the senior miller had been Edwin Gilley. Suitable staff were quickly appointed for the mills. On the recommendation of Mr Day, Harold Ernest Gilley was appointed as miller for Tesson Mill at £3-0-0 weekly. Mr John Lewis was also employed as a "checker and clerk" at £2-10-0 weekly.

Gargate Mill had been burnt down and rebuilt in 1880. It had a reputation as an easy mill to run. The head miller put in charge at Gargate was Ernest Charles Gilley, brother of Edwin. The waterwheel in 1940 was in almost "perfect condition". Ernest had previously been forced to stop milling there between 1931 and 1932 due to a lack of work. He subsequently survived by finding a little milling from local corn merchants. However, by 1933 this had totally ceased. On resuming employment again, he made an observation about the authorities: "They are running after the millers but a few years ago we could have starved". The millpond at Gargate was fully cleared of silt, which had accumulated over forty-five years, and the millstream was widened. It took fourteen men to complete the task.

The third watermill to be renovated in August 1940 was Grand Val. It was owned and had been worked by Mr William Hunt Baxter and had ground corn up to 1919. Mr Baxter, when surveying the renovation of the mill, stated that it could grind 3 tons a day. The milling stones needed to be re-ground. A former miller's son C. J. M. Ball, who had previously worked for Ronez Quarries, was found to dress the stones – no one else could be found on the Island to accomplish this task. The pond required twenty-four men to clean it and the millstream needed substantial labour. The work was carried out by men from the Department of Labour. In the pond, trout were discovered.[34]

By the end of September up to 10 tons of flour was being released to the Department of Essential Commodities and Brée was delighted with this outcome. Each mill rented by the DOA was on a full tenancy of £52 per annum. By the 3rd October all three had been renovated. All three senior millers – Harold Gilley, Ernest Gilley and William Baxter – were directly employed by the DOA at a weekly wage of £3-0-0. In addition, Frederick Horton was employed as Assistant Miller at Tesson and Samuel Gilley at Gargate on wages of £2-10-0 a week.

At the end of October, Brée sanctioned a further renovation at Le Moulin de Quetivel, St Peter, and on the 7th October he inspected Malassis, Grand Vaux, St Saviour, and decided it had to be brought into working order. On the 11th October the Superior Council approved Brée's suggestion for Malassis and, in order to operate a longer working day, Tesson, Gargate and Grand Val mills were all fitted with lighting.

References

1. RJA&HS – Milk Control Committee Meetings.
2. 9,092,180 litres.
3. Jersey Archive. C/B/A1/5.
4. Jersey Archive. L/D/09/A10.
5. 1 pot = half a gallon or 4 pints or 2.27 litres.
6. RJA&HS. Report of the Committee for the years 1940 to 1945. AGM, December 8th, 1945. p.8.
7. Cruickshank, c. 1999. The German Occupation of the Channel Islands: The Official History of the Occupation Years, p. 118.
8. Private account by Denis Vibert to the late Joyce Le Ruez. I express my thanks to Joyce's family, Pam Laurens, Joy Le Marquand and Ruth Hayward, for allowing me access to Joyce Le Ruez's private correspondence.
9. Letter dated 18th May 1945 from John Terry Limited. My thanks to Diane Daniels for allowing me access to this correspondence.
10. States of Jersey. Defence Regulations No 93 and No 94.
11. JFU Minute Book.
12. Jersey Archive. B/A/W32/2/40.
13. An elected parish official with policing powers.
14. Free On Board, i.e., the potatoes loaded into the barge holds for export.
15. E. Le Quesne, 1999. The Occupation of Jersey Day by Day, p. 3.

16. An elected official who is a member of the States of Jersey, in addition to being head of the civil parish authority and of the parish honorary police.
17. George Le Breuilly also used two other forms of his name. The second form was George Breuilly and the third was George Brailey. His occupation identity card has him entered as George Breuilly.
18. 1,111 acres. 2.25 vergées = 1 acre. 1 vergée = 4/9 of an acre.
19. Rapports du Directeur de la Ferme d'Expériences, "Glenham", Trinité, avec comptes pour l'année 1930, p. 9. Rapports du Directeur de la Ferme d'Expériences "Glenham", Trinité pour l'année, 1933, p. 27. Rapports du Directeur de la Ferme d'Expériences "Howard Davis", Trinité pour l'année 1937, p. 10.
20. The Morning News. 19th June 1939. "Jersey Agricultural Statistics. A review of the changes in thirty years". R. D. Payn.
21. Shepard, H.G. 1934. One Hundred Years of the RJA&HS. 1833 to 1933.
22. RJA&HS. Price Advisory Board Minutes.
23. Pocock H. R. S. 1975. The Memoirs of Lord Coutanche, p. 22.
24. National Archive. HO45/20774.
25. Jersey Evening Post, 27th August 1940.
26. Corbet, L. M., A Biographical Dictionary of Jersey. Vol 2, 1998, pp. 258–259.
27. Jersey Archive. B/A/W48/2.
28. Pelz, Hans Egon. 2015. Damals Erinnerungen. The Biography of Hans Egon Pelz compiled, written and published by the Pelz family. The Hotel Majestic is almost certainly the Grand Hotel. The former was the headquarters of the German Military Government, Paris. See: Brandt, K., Schiller, O. and Ahlgrimm. 1953. Management of Agricultural and Food Supplies in the German occupied and other areas of Fortress Europe. A study on Military Government. p. 503.
29. Jersey Evening Post, 9th August 1940.
30. Jersey Evening Post, 17th August 1940.
31. Jersey Evening Post, 23rd August 1940.
32. Deutsche Inseitung, 23rd August 1940.
33. Jersey Evening Post, 7th January 1940 and 3rd March 1941.
34. Jersey Evening Post, 12th August 1940.

Chapter 5

November 1940 to May 1941

Farmers and the Question of Agricultural Labour

*"Unfortunately, we are not having the cooperation we could expect
from the farming community. I am afraid we shall have to use
compulsory powers to force them to till their ground for the common
good."*

Edward Le Quesne, Department of Labour, Superior Council

The Department of Labour was established soon after the arrival of the
German military forces and its responsibility was to procure employment
for islanders who lost their jobs upon the arrival of the Germans on the
1st July 1940. It was headed by Deputy Edward Le Quesne. On the 30th
June an emergency meeting of the JFU and the RJA&HS was convened to
discuss "The present position of agriculture on the Island". Farmers, who
had been forced to reduce the export of potatoes, laid off a substantial
number of agricultural workers. Philip Le Feuvre, President of the JFU, began
proceedings by stating that the immediate problem was "...to fix the price
of labour first". Carlyle Le Gallais, President of the RJA&HS, suggested
sending back to England and Ireland all "non-native labour" in order to
ease the agricultural unemployment problem. In accordance with Le Feuvre's
suggestions farmers set out the official agricultural minimum wage. This was
fixed at 36/- a week. Men living on the farm and receiving board and meals
were to be paid 20/- a week. Females working, but not living on the farm,
24/- a week. Finally, piece work was set at £3 a vergée.

Ironically, farmers discovered not an oversupply but a serious lack of
agricultural labour. This lasted throughout the entire German occupation.

The occupation led to the immediate cessation of the tourism industry
and widespread unemployment. The fishing industry for all intents and
purposes, because of military restrictions, declined within weeks. The day
after the arrival of the Germans, several thousand men were left with no

employment prospects. "Groups of men could be seen walking about the streets".[1]

Two days later, the States and the Chamber of Commerce were requesting farmers to "Make Work" for the unemployed.[2]

The energetic and resourceful Le Quesne, by the 8th July 1940, had set up a number of work schemes for the unemployed. These included establishing allotments, clearing debris from the Royal Yacht and Pomme d'Or Hotels and clearing the railway track.[3]

On the 11th July 1940 the farming associations again met to discuss the agricultural working week. The States agreed to a uniform working day for their labourers. What farmers did not want was to have different working hours from each other. The two farming associations then decided:

1. Permanent staff on a weekly status would work 7.00 a.m. to 8.00 p.m. including wet weather.
2. Day casual workers would work between 7.00 a.m. and 6.00 p.m. These men to receive a breakfast.
3. Men living on the farms such as milkers who start earlier than 7.00 a.m. to be allowed time for breakfast. On Saturdays they would finish at 5.00 p.m.

On the 13th July the States issued its order on wages and conditions for men on its labour schemes. The rate for manual workers was set at 36/- a week. Married workers were entitled to an additional 5/- a week, with a maximum additional wage of 10/- a week for dependents. Dependents were classed as a wife, and children under sixteen years of age. Le Quesne advised farmers that "In the cases of agricultural workers individual arrangements between the employer and worker may be made".[4]

On the same day, men on the labour schemes received their first wage packets. These schemes were extremely successful. They were not so successful, however, for farmers. On the 17th July, Mr H. W. Gibaut asked his farming association for clarification if the 36/- a week wage was the correct wage for agricultural workers.[5] Gibaut had observed, and made it clear to the meeting, that he was concerned that men employed by the Department of Labour only worked 8.00 a.m. to 5.00 p.m. and received the same pay as his own workers. He stated "That it was already beginning to encourage farm labour to drift into the Labour Exchange". Philip Le Feuvre concluded the meeting by saying that some of the work conditions used by the Department of Labour were "...not equitable and certain changes might have to be made". What was being suggested by Le Feuvre was that men on labour schemes should work from 7.00 a.m. to 8.00 p.m., as did permanent agricultural labourers.

Many young farm labourers had left the Island in the evacuations of June 1940 to enlist in the armed forces, but a substantial number of Irish workers had arrived in Jersey for the 1940 season before the occupation. The JFU had written to the Mayor of Cork and, although the States of Jersey was opposed to Irish labour, the JFU had made representations to the High Commissioner of Eire to obtain labour. In addition, substantial numbers of conscientious military objectors had been sent to Jersey to work. A number of Quakers had also applied to come to the Island. Therefore, there were many men who could be used for agricultural work. However, the relatively generous rates of pay and the forty-five-hour working week offered by the schemes, in combination with the high wages offered by the Germans – sometimes three times the normal rate – caused an abrupt and serious shortage of agricultural workers which lasted throughout the occupation.[6]

As early as the 18th July, 1,600 men employed by the schemes were working productively. However, many of the major farmers, some twenty-five to forty in number, contemptuously sneered at Deputy Le Quesne's labour schemes and in many cases refused to cooperate. To the leading farmers the labour schemes were anathema. On the 18th July Le Quesne noted, after determined efforts by the farmers to change the working hours of his schemes, that "Unfortunately we are not having the cooperation we could expect from the farming community. I am afraid we shall have to use compulsory powers to force them to till their ground for the common good".[7] On 13th July 1940, in an attempt to somewhat appease these farmers Le Quesne published a statement under the auspices of the States of Jersey:

"The Department of Labour notifies all concerned that any man employed on agricultural or farm work, refusing to carry out the reasonable instructions of his employer, will not be entitled to alternative work by the Department. The rate of pay for agricultural or farm workers is 36/- per week as defined in the Order".[8]

This seemingly clear and unambiguous statement did nothing to placate the leading farmers' vehement disdain of Le Quesne and the labour schemes.

On the 2nd August, Le Quesne published a lengthy statement giving a detailed explanation of the "local relief work scheme".[9] He reiterated that agricultural workers had had their wages fixed at 36/- a week, but they received additional benefits such as housing, milk and vegetables. In addition, he recognised the present difficulties farmers faced with the loss of their main crop markets for potatoes and tomatoes, however, in the past the farmers had made excellent profits and that, in the current situation, "The farmer will be as generous as possible to the men employed by him".

On the 22nd August, a deputation of the farmers met with Le Quesne to discuss the question of agricultural workers' wages. Le Quesne, in a positive mood perhaps in order to reconcile farmers' objections, suggested that he recommend to the States that all married men working in an agricultural capacity be granted a States subsidy of 5/- a week. On the same day, at a joint JFU and RJA&HS meeting attended by Le Quesne, John Michel and Francis Le Boutillier pointed out, "The short hours for work had drawn men from the farms". Le Quesne however made it clear that, as far as working hours were concerned, this would be left to individual farmers to make their own arrangements. The meeting accepted the 5/- a week subsidy for married men.

On the 28th August, Le Quesne met with the DOA to discuss the question of labour and the problems faced by farmers. Le Gallais gave Le Quesne a real haranguing over the subject, so much so that Le Quesne retorted: "Mr Carlyle Le Gallais was told a few home truths. Some of his criticisms of labour were so unfair that I was on the point of resigning".[10]

In a concerted attempt to find some form of a definitive answer to the agricultural labour problems, some forty of the most important and influential farmers met. Also present were a number of Connétables and the DOA's representative, Edwin Gibaut. "The meeting was convened primarily to discuss the agricultural labour question". Michel opened the meeting, and along with Le Boutillier, reported on the interview that had taken place with the DOA. Michel made it clear that the Department of Labour's only solution was to offer a States subsidy providing married farm workers 5/- more a week. Following a discussion by the meeting on the details of wages paid to men on the labour schemes, a proposal was passed to ask the Department of Labour for a 10/- a week agricultural subsidy. A second proposition was adopted that a representation be made to the DOA that "...owing to the high costs of labour, the farmer requires higher prices for his produce". This statement of intent was tantamount to a warning to the DOA as to the likely outcome of a negative response to requests for agricultural labour subsidies.

On the 14th September 1940, forty farmers from the JFU and RJA&HS met. Philip Le Feuvre reported that the request to the Department of Labour for the higher 10/- increase weekly for married farm labourers had been turned down; however, the 5/- weekly increase was still open. The meeting recalled its decision of the 31st August 1940 asking for a 10/- increase and voted unanimously for the 5/- weekly subsidy. It seems that Brée would not be swayed by his fellow farmers with threats to demand higher prices for their produce.

By September 1940 the labour schemes had proved a real success. Men who may well have been unemployed and succumbed to German offers of well-paid work had been kept fully occupied rejuvenating and repairing the watermills, ponds and channels, roadbuilding, and establishing a series of Island-wide potato clamps and depots. The clamping of the 1940 potato crop, the brainchild of Brée, saved an entire year's crop and provided a valuable food source up to 1941. Therefore, Brée decided in December 1940 and in view of the above success, to extend the provision of men from labour schemes to facilitate the digging of côtils in order to increase the food production area.[11]

The DOA announced on the 14th December that, "Having taken into consideration the necessity of employing the largest amount of available labour on work of a productive nature, the DOA and Department of Labour have decided to recommend to the States that farmers with côtils may have theirs dug by the Department of Labour men at a charge of 9d per perch[12] provided that the necessary tools are supplied by the farmer and that he will supervise the work". It furthermore was made clear that this undertaking was also dependent upon farmers maintaining their normal workforce in employment.

Subsequently, on the 30th December, J. G. Malzard was put in charge of supervising the digging of côtils by Department of Labour employees. These men were paid £3 a week. It appears, however, that this particular labour scheme was not as successful as previous schemes. By the 2nd February 1941, farmers were complaining that the digging of côtils carried out by the men of the labour scheme was too slow. Farmers stated they "...could not afford to continue paying the weekly wages to these men". The DOA response was that "In view of the very low charge being made to farmers for this service, and the possibility of obtaining assistance under the Agricultural Credits Scheme, nothing further could be done to assist them [the farmers] in this matter".

The lack of an effective and highly paid (in farmers' eyes) labour force was a constant topic of discussion amongst the two major farming associations. Their major complaint often described the behaviour of labour scheme agricultural workers who replaced their previous own farm workers who had left to join the States labour schemes. Ernest G. Mourant, Maison de Haut, St Saviour, employed, "...an Irishman who ceases to work for odd days". Mrs S. de La Haye, Beuvelande, St Martin complained of an Irish employee who had absented himself on numerous occasions. Raymond John Labey, Home Farm, also complained that two Irish employees, one married and one single, had left to work on the States schemes. Mr F. P. Ozouf, Highstead, St Saviour, complained he "...had difficulties in keeping farm labourers owing to the attractive hours of labour schemes". Ozouf subsequently refused to apply any further to the Department of Labour for men, being fearful of who they would send.

Not all farmers' complaints were directed at the Irish. Mr J. R. Le Quesne, St Clement employed a Frenchman, Alain Le Bechée, and his wife. They lived on his premises in furnished rooms and were given milk, wood and occasional meals. Le Bechée attended to the cattle on Sunday mornings; however, on one Sunday he did not appear, leaving the cattle unfed because he was digging a friend's ground. On Monday morning, Le Quesne remonstrated with him for his neglect. Le Bechée replied that if Le Quesne was not happy he would go onto a States labour scheme. Le Bechée was immediately dismissed. A report of the above episode concluded, "Le Bechée now boasts of his position to Mr Le Quesne's other men". Mr P. L. Le Masurier, St Ouen, employed a Jerseyman, Mr Walter Hacquoil. On returning from town, Le Masurier found his cattle neither fed nor milked and that Hacquoil had not worked that afternoon. On the following morning Le Masurier called him to account. Hacquoil's reply was that if Le Masurier was not satisfied, he knew what he could do! Le Masurier dismissed him and endorsed his card "for Neglect of Duty" as the reason for his unemployment. He subsequently went to work on the States labour scheme.[13]

Agricultural workers on labour schemes received £2-10-0 a week. However, the hours of these workers exceeded those on non-agricultural labour schemes. The Department of Labour therefore, on the 14th January

1941, communicated to the DOA this discrepancy even though there was a "subsidy in respect of agricultural wages". The DOA, while accepting the principal involved in the payment of such a subsidy, recommended to Brée that, the Superior Council should not pay a subsidy to agricultural workers who were receiving £2-10-0 or more from their employers. On the 20th January, Brée informed the DOA that the Superior Council had approved the granting of a subsidy in respect of agricultural wages on condition that the total remuneration of any agricultural worker should not exceed £2-10-0 a week and that a subsidy could only be paid to workers employed by farmers cultivating their fields under directions issued under the Cultivation of Lands (Jersey) Order, 1940. Furthermore, sons of farmers directly employed by their parents, and casual workers, were not entitled, but men regularly employed by two farmers were allowed to apply for special consideration.

The DOA noted the decisions of the Superior Council. It was a clarification welcomed by the DOA from the most important authority on the Island. Farmers would have to pay £2-10-0 a week, subsidy or not. It also decided that in cases where a farmer provided a cottage or other accommodation rent-free for its workers, this should be assessed at 5/- a week. Furthermore, where farmers provided free meals, the increase in remuneration should be considered as 2/- a day.

On the 31st January 1941 the Superior Council approved the payment of an "…agricultural wages bonus" and on the 3rd March the DOA received a credit of £5,000 "…to meet the costs involved in the scheme to provide a bonus on agricultural wages". Farmers immediately used the agricultural wages bonus to enhance the existing wages of their labourers up to £2-10-0. A problem, however, soon appeared. On the 10th March the Department of Labour wrote to the DOA regarding "The status of a woman living with a man who is not her husband". The DOA replied, "…it could not recognise such a relationship as constituting a "dependent" for the purposes of the agricultural wages bonus". The matter was referred to the Superior Council to adjudicate.

On the 17th May a meeting of the JFU and RJA&HS was convened to discuss farm labour following the Department of Labour's suggestion that it would release labour for the harvesting of the 1941 crops. A protracted discussion took place. The following policy was consequently agreed by the leading farmers.

1. Farm workers should be paid more than those on labour schemes even with a subsidy and thereby attract back onto the farms those men who had left.
2. Wages paid for labour would be dependent on the price received for the potato crop.
3. The States would organise labour for digging potatoes and harvesting cereals.

4. Men who had withdrawn from farm work to go onto labour schemes should be sent back to work on farms. Their names to be ascertained from farmers who had previously employed them.

5. With regard to harvesting, all mowing machines should be converted to reapers and sent from farm to farm with gangs of men from the labour scheme.

The President of the JFU, Philip Le Feuvre, stated he would meet with the Department of Labour to have discussions concerning these points. He was told by the meeting that he must notify the authorities that, in the opinion of farmers, it was imperative that agricultural labour should be paid more than those on labour schemes and that any differences in wages be paid by a subsidy. Further problems discussed for the 1941 harvest and hay-making sectors was the two-hour difference with Greenwich Mean Time and the need for a twelve-hour working day whilst cereal harvesting.

It was decided to meet again in a week's time and to invite both the President of the Department of Labour and the President of the DOA to discuss the question of labour for the 1941 potato and cereal harvests. Le Gallais ended the meeting by saying that he had "...received formal permission from the German authorities to continue the Society's activities and meetings and Mr Le Feuvre of the JFU had received a similar permission".[5]

On the 24th May the RJA&HS and the JFU met with Le Quesne and Brée. The topic for discussion was agricultural labour and subsidies. The importance of this meeting was clearly demonstrated by the fact that forty-eight of the most important farmers attended, including all the leading cattle-breeding members of the RJA&HS. The meeting was addressed by Le Quesne, who referred to the difficulties and endeavours of the Department of Labour. Le Quesne must have felt that, under the constant criticism he had been receiving from the farming community, some form of compromise was required to appease the extremely powerful farming lobby. During this period Le Quesne stated that he had received, "More and more opposition from farmers whose only outlook seems to be how much they are going to make".[1] He subsequently put the following proposals before the meeting.

"That farmers pay a basic rate of 36/- per week for a 56-hour week and that the Superior Council be asked to authorise a subsidy of 14/- per week, making the weekly wages 50/-.

That employers be urged to supply their workers with a warm midday meal.

That overtime, in excess of 56 hours weekly, be at the rate [which was considered fair] of one shilling per hour".

He suggested that: "When the men are not required for lifting the crop, they be paid at the rate of 36/- weekly or returned to the Labour Department". This may have been owing to digging restrictions.

After long discussions and a good deal of criticism, the suggestions made by Le Quesne on behalf of the Department of Labour were adopted by an almost unanimous vote by the delegates of the two farming associations.

Cultivation Orders

Two farmers were interviewed concerning, "their neglect to carry out orders". As a result of the "unsatisfactory nature of the explanations offered, the two cases were referred to HM Attorney General."

DOA Report

The DOA's powers were far-reaching and encompassed stringent and legally enforceable orders. Therefore, to clarify the extent of these powers, Brée and the DOA decided to hold a discussion with HM Attorney General over the question of these powers which had been granted to them by Article 55, Defence (Jersey) Regulations, 1939. Insofar as the purposes of agriculture, horticulture and the dairy industry were concerned, these powers were transferred to the DOA by the Defence (Transfer of Powers) (Jersey) Regulations, 1940. The DOA received confirmation that all questions concerning agriculture, horticulture and the dairy industry were solely within the competence of the Committee.

On the 6th October 1940 the DOA's budget for 1941 was set at £200,000, plus £13,710 for all marketing of produce during 1941. On the 21st November the DOA and the Superior Council met to discuss the pricing of the 1941 crops, in view of the fact that the majority would not be ready until the autumn of 1941.

On the 11th November Honorary Parish Inspectors reported that a field of 15 vergées belonging to Mr Lionel Coutanche was allegedly seriously overgrown. He was immediately spoken to and instructed to clear the land for cultivation under the Cultivation of Lands (Jersey) Order, 1940.

The next day the DOA received a letter from the Department of Finance and Economics informing them that Mr A. T. Starck, St Saviour, had applied for financial assistance. The DOA was requested to investigate the matter and sent Thomas Blampied and Mr D. Simpson to investigate and write a report. Subsequently, in view of "the unfavourable report", the DOA decided that Brée should bring up the matter with HM Attorney General. On the 23rd December a further report by Le Gallais on Starck's farm demonstrated that it was allegedly in a poor state and all the animals were in a "very neglected condition". The farm was requisitioned and the animals taken to the States Experimental Station, reconditioned, and sent to auction. The sale brought in a total of £43- 10-6.[14]

The DOA had sent a clear message to farmers concerning the standards of husbandry and cultivation that it required. If standards dropped to unacceptable levels, the sanction would be immediate requisition of the farm, animals and farming contents. In effect the farmer and family would lose their livelihood.

On the 9th December the DOA decided to ascertain firstly, the quantity of main crop potatoes, and secondly, cereals in store grown in 1940. H. G. Shepard prepared a detailed list of every farmer who had grown potatoes and cereals. This list was important because it allowed Brée, five days later, to consult with Mr B. L. Clift, the Petrol Controller, in order to allocate petrol to the "ploughing contractors" for the 1941 season.

The twelve ploughing contractors who were each allocated a district were: J. Boucault, P. Blandin, E. Daghorn, W. P. Giot, R. Mallet, E. P. Noel, W. P. Fullern, E. Hidrio, A. E. Prouten, C. G. Le Cappelain, P. Pirouet and A. Buesnel. By the end of January 1941, the first instalment of ploughing fuel had been issued; however it proved to be insufficient. On the 6th April, the petrol allocation was doubled from one half gallon to 1 gallon for every 6 vergées.

On the 13th December a meeting took place between the DOA, the Department of Finance and Economics, the Treasurer of the States and HM Solicitor General. The discussion concerned the position of farmers indebted to the Jersey Produce Merchants Association. The JPMA had decided that it would not supply any agricultural inputs to farmers who were in debt to them. The meeting decided to recommend to the Superior Council the adoption of a plan of financial assistance to farmers and by the 30th December a plan had been set up. The scheme allowed for two cash instalments to be given to farmers, the first in January 1941, being £3-10-0 per vergée; the second payable in June 1941 was £2-10-0 per vergée. All monies paid were on areas where cereals and potatoes were grown, as directed by the DOA, under the provisions of the Cultivation of Lands (Jersey) Order, 1940. The farmer had to sign a bond prepared by the Law Officers of the Crown, all cash advances incurring an interest rate of 3%. The farmer would reimburse the DOA out of the proceeds of the crops he subsequently sold to it. Brée submitted the plan for approval by the Superior Council and he also met up with the Crown's legal officers to exercise protection of "The monetary advances made to farmers by the States".

On the 10th January 1941, Brée ordered that all second and late crop potatoes held by farmers be handed in to the DOA or otherwise requisitioned, as in the case of grain. The following week Mr F. Bechelet, St Ouen, refused to allow two DOA officers to inspect the quantity of his main crop potatoes. On the 2nd February, Bechelet found himself in further trouble after a report from the Connétable of St Ouen to HM Attorney General, stating that he had allegedly made butter from the produce of his cows, although he was not a holder of a butter-maker's licence, and was in breach of the Milk Control (Jersey) Order, 1940.

On the 10th March Brée reported on the case of Mr D. T. Langlois, St Brelade, "The farm, stock, tools and utensils with the exception of the horses, box cart and necessary harness were to be requisitioned". This was due allegedly to

"The unsatisfactory conduct of the farmer tenant, Mr D. T. Langlois".[14] The requisition was immediately carried out with the cattle and equipment placed on an inventory and the farm, along with the goods, placed under "lock and key". The subsequent sale of his goods, including the proceeds of pigs and a cow, "Doreen's Golden Fern", amounted to £56-7-0.

On the 24th March, in pursuance of the policy of controlling the growing and harvesting of crops essential to the maintenance of supplies to the community, the DOA issued an order prohibiting the sale or transfer of any crop grown on land affected by the Cultivation of Lands (Jersey) Order, 1940. Several days later the DOA ordered the requisitioning of cereals held by L. H. Vauvais (probably Le Vannais), E. C. Perrédès and H. L. Green.

On the 9th May the DOA discussed the Island-wide need for wood for fuel for the coming winter. The DOA was extremely concerned and would not allow an Island free-for-all. It therefore set up a panel of experts in each parish to mark trees which were suitable for felling.

On the 12th May, two Honorary Parish Inspectors in St John interviewed Mr Theophilus Hotton, and Mr Alfred J. Le Calvez, concerning allegedly, "Their neglect to carry out the directions" of the DOA. As a result of the explanations offered "The two cases were referred to HM Attorney General. The next day, two more farmers were investigated by the Honorary Parish Inspectors for refusing to cultivate their land. These cases concerned Brée who was determined to forward to the Attorney General all instances of a refusal to comply with Cultivation Orders. It was also around this period that Brée decided to first give offending farmers a verbal warning after calling them for an interview with the DOA.

On the 14th May the DOA wrote to the JPMA informing them that all members who sold agricultural inputs must have a licence under the Agricultural Produce (Crop Control) (Jersey) Order, 1941.

On the 23rd May, the Honorary Parish Inspector of Grouville reported a field of six vergées of wheat, near Grouville Arsenal, in a weedy condition. The owner, Marcel Poulain, was given a week to clear the weeds. The DOA was becoming increasingly proactive in its checks and inspections of farms. This did not go down very well with the independence Jersey farmers had known and was becoming a source of real irritation and conflict between the two parties.

Tomatoes

"After due deliberation the DOA directed Mr Benest to pull up the tomato plants within a week"

DOA order

On the 6th November 1940, the secretary to the DOA was authorised to receive from the German authorities an account in respect of tomatoes shipped to their orders. The first was for tomatoes shipped on the 12th and 16th October 1940 and amounted to £2-10-5. The second shipment was on the 2nd November 1940 and was £23-10-1. The secretary was instructed that on receipt of the sums from the German authorities he was to pay the farmers who brought in the tomatoes at 2/6 a tray. A deduction of 5/6 per ton was to be made in respect of stevedoring charges.

On the 2nd December the DOA decided that, for 1941, tomatoes grown for canning would only be supplied from market gardens. The 1941 cultivation directions had made no allowance for tomatoes. At a meeting of the Potato Advisory Board on the 30th May 1941, Mr Ernest Huelin representing Jersey Canners Limited stated his company could manage to process 300 tons of tomatoes, the product of some 60 vergées. This was the total area envisaged for tomato cultivation in 1941. The canning company paid 1 penny per pound weight. Furthermore, if the spices were available, they could also manufacture a large quantity of tomato sauce. Mr Huelin added that there was a need for urgently lifting the potato crop in the early côtils in order that tomatoes could be planted as a second crop. The Potato Advisory Board agreed that tomatoes could be planted as a second crop on côtils, in order to supply the requirements of the canning factory for local consumption.[15]

On the 19th May 1941 Mr W. Benest, St Brelade, was called in for an interview by the DOA. He had planted tomatoes in defiance of a Cultivation Order. The area was 1½ vergées. "After due deliberation the DOA directed Mr Benest to pull up the tomato plants within a week". The Honorary Parish Inspectors then gave him directions for new crops which were to be planted on his land.

Cereals

"The DOA recommended to the Superior Council that an additional threshing machine be purchased from France, making a total of two."

The 1941 cropping plan designated a total area of 39,850 vergées of land for cultivation with 17,900 vergées for cereals – wheat, oats, rye and barley. This approximated to 44.9% of the Island's cultivatable area. The huge increase in cereal cultivation in 1941 became increasingly important to the DOA and involved the supervision of farmers, merchants who stored grain, and inspections. The sowing of cereals was central to the security of the Island's food supply. In his biography Pelz describes often inspecting these cereal crops.

On the 6th November 1940 a delegation from the Jersey Corn Merchant's Association met to discuss payment by farmers for cereal seed. The corn merchants had refused to sell seed to farmers who did not pay by cash. Another problem was that of inferior grain quality and in November 1940 the first reports reached the DOA of grain which had been threshed but not taken into store. The first farmer to be warned by the Chief Threshing Officer, Mr J. G. Malzard, of his failure to bring into store his threshed grain was Mr H. Greenland, St Saviour. He was immediately informed that if the grain was not forthcoming it would be requisitioned. The same threat was made to another farmer, Mr L. H. Le Vannais, St Helier, who had refused to surrender his grain.

On the 6th December the first wheat seed was imported from France and, on the 20th December, the DOA met with HM Receiver General to discuss "...the question of tithes" applicable to cereals and payable to the monarchy. The topic was quietly dropped by the DOA, the reason being that it felt "...not competent to make any recommendation". On the 23rd December, sixteen sacks of wheat were requisitioned from Mr E. C. Perrédès, after a report from J. G. Malzard that the wheat had been threshed two days previously.

Brée, on the 30th December, brought to attention a problem he had increasingly noticed in which a number of farmers had "...sown their wheat allocations in an extravagant manner and therefore did not have enough seed to sow their total area". Perhaps deciding that Cultivation Orders concerning cereals had deliberately not been followed by these farmers, he insisted that they would be required to obtain the quantity of seed needed to complete the sowing prescribed in their Cultivation Orders. Brée, to underline his point, ordered that the price charged for the additional seed would be double that for the quantity originally supplied.

On the 20th January 1941, Mr L. Green, St Martin, had been caught allegedly feeding oats to his cattle. Law Officers were immediately sent to requisition the grain. On the same day cereal seed imported from France was distributed amongst farmers to fulfil their obligations under the DOA's Cultivation Orders. The seed was obtained by Mr Armand Gay, the local representative of the Maison Vilinarium Andrieux, Paris, and it arrived in the Island in two consignments.

By February 1941 the increased area of cereals necessitated threshing machines, reaper binders and twine, for tying bales of straw after threshing, being ordered from France. The Superior Council immediately approved these purchases. In addition, 2,800 sickles were ordered. On the 13th March the DOA instructed Mr J. L. Jouault, in Granville, to purchase binder twine "without delay". On the 31st March, the DOA recommended to the Superior Council that an additional threshing machine from France be purchased. The following week Thomas Blampied, who had already been to France in February to purchase horses, was sent again to purchase a machine.

Further reports were received by the DOA of unauthorised grain being kept by farmers. Malzard was sent to visit Mr F. E. Luce, St Peter, who was allegedly holding a "...quantity of oats in his possession". He also visited Mrs Moulin, St Ouen, on the 23rd May; she allegedly had between 25 and 30 cwt of unauthorised grain, which should have been delivered to the DOA's stores.

On the 28th April Brée requested the Superior Council to seek permission from KVR Pelz and Field Command 515 that steps be taken to effect the destruction of crow and rook nests, together with eggs and young on a property in St Brelade; the birds were destroying cereal crops over a wide area. The German authorities gave permits for the destruction of the nests on the 14th May 1941.

Horses

By 1941 petrol rationing for agricultural purposes highlighted the serious shortage of horses needed to compensate for the loss of motor power. It was therefore decided by the DOA to purchase horses from France. On the 30th January Brée reported that, in discussions with Pelz and Field Command 515, agreement had been reached for Blampied, and one civilian, to proceed to France with "The object of purchasing as many horses as possible for the requirements of the Island". A credit was opened and Blampied was advanced £50 towards expenses for the journey to France. He was accompanied by Mr Arthur Lionel Le Mière. By the end of February 1941 French horses were on the Island and were put up for auction to farmers, an example of how quickly decisions were made and actions carried out. On the 10th March, the DOA conveyed to Mr Le Mière: "Its appreciation of the public spirit which had prompted this gentleman to proceed to France in order to assist Mr Thomas Le Quesne Blampied in the purchase of horses for the requirements of the Island". It was decided to pay him £10 for "...out of pocket expenses".

On the 24th April Brée requested the Superior Council to make representations to the German Field Command for permission to grant a further fifty French horses. The DOA also requested Mr L. H. Blight, Maufant, to allow his stallion to be used for breeding purposes by local farmers. Blight did so, on a "free of charge" basis. A week before, he had been interviewed by the DOA after a pig inspector had reported him for an infringement of his pig declaration.

Fertilisers

On the 6th October 1940 the DOA had instructed the JPMA to assist in issuing guano to farmers at the rate of:

1. 5 cwt per vergée for early potatoes.
2. 3 cwt per vergée for seed and late potatoes.
3. 2 cwt per vergée for cereals and mangolds.

These supplies were made on the production of the appropriate Land Cultivation Order which had been issued to individual farmers. The JPMA was given an alphabetical list of farmers who already had in their possession one ton and over of artificial fertilisers, with a request that the quantities held by these farmers should be taken into account when issuing further supplies.

On the 27th January the question of petrol supplies for the vraicing contractors was a concern.[16] The DOA decided, that in view of the limited availability of petrol for the ploughing season, it could not be supplied to them. On the 10th March, a discussion between the DOA and JPMA looked into the availability of artificial manures for the 1941 crops. The DOA's technical advisor, Mr E. J. Woodcock, stated, "There were adequate supplies available for the requirements of the 1941 crop". He furthermore made it clear that farmers who needed additional fertilisers could be referred to neighbouring farmers who held stocks declared in accordance with the Fertilisers (Returns) (Jersey) Order, 1940, in excess of their requirements under the Cultivation Orders issued by the DOA.

Pigs

The first official mention of pigs by the DOA was on the 3rd January 1941. A statement was sent out with the object of encouraging pig breeding in the Island. It was decided to recommend to the Superior Council that a bonus of £2 should be paid to each pig breeder in respect of each litter born during the current year to sows of which he is proprietor. The next week the Superior Council refused to endorse Brée's pig bonus. It believed that if the price to pig farmers was increased to ¼ penny per pound, this would achieve a better result in increasing the supply of pork. Brée and the DOA openly disagreed with the Superior Council.

On the 17th January Brée again brought forward the recommendation that a £2 bonus be paid to pig breeders for each litter born in the current year. The Superior Council now agreed that as an experiment it would pay the suggested bonus in respect of litters born between the months of May to July 1941. On the 31st January, delegates of the JFU and the RJA&HS formally requested an increase in the price received by farmers for their pork. On the same day Le Gallais submitted a report to the DOA asking Brée to obtain salt, ostensibly for the treatment of sick animals. Allegations had been made that salt was being used for the pickling of pigs slaughtered by farmers in contravention of the Livestock (Restriction on Slaughtering) (Jersey) Order, 1940. On the 3rd February, Brée reported back to Le Gallais, "...that no more salt should be issued to farmers except upon the production of a certificate of a veterinary surgeon".

The Island-wide availability of pork continued drastically to diminish. By the 3rd March it was felt by the DOA that the illegal killing of pigs had reached such a level that legislation was immediately needed. A new order was announced – farmers had to declare the number of pigs they held. Any alteration in the number had to be notified to the DOA, the death of any pig reported within 24 hours, and the body made available for inspection.

The disposal of the body would be at the discretion of the DOA. Finally, the States Vet would be fully authorised to enter any farm or premises and check on swine kept. In a further attempt to encourage more pig breeding, the DOA on the 19th March informed farmers that they would be allowed to retain for their own use a percentage of any pig sent to the abattoirs for slaughter. However, and for what reason is unclear, the DOA within several days decided that this was not expedient and revoked the order. Instead, the DOA recommended a price increase to farmers and asked the Superior Council. Under the order, a new inspector was appointed on the 24th March – Mr John Wesley Blampied, at a salary of £3 a week.

The next day the DOA wrote to the Superior Council and asked to change the Livestock (Restriction on Slaughtering) (Jersey) Order, 1940 to allow 90% of a carcass to be sold and 10% to remain with the farmer. However, on the 5th May, the Superior Council decided to extend the £2 pig-breeding bonus until August 1941. Within weeks of John Blampied's appointment, reports were received of farmers failing to comply with the laws and, by the end of May, sixteen such reports were examined, most concerning non-declaration of pigs. R. S. Langlois, St Saviour, reported three dead pigs but allegedly provided no carcasses. Also, another farmer, P. Le Feuvre, was interviewed; he kept pigs but allegedly had not declared them. In view of the "unsatisfactory replies" given by him regarding the disposal of four pigs, the matter was forwarded to HM Attorney General for investigation.[14]

On the 19th May, Mr Francois Louis Moisan, St Brelade was formally interviewed by the DOA in connection with the alleged sale of a pig to German troops.[14] As a result of the information supplied by Moisan, the DOA requested Brée to take up the matter with Field Command 515; he discussed it with KVR Pelz, who made it clear that all future German purchases from farmers would only be sanctioned by a permit issued and signed by himself.

Watermills and Milling

When the DOA had been put in charge of mills in September 1940 the plan had been to make the Island self-sufficient in cereals and to produce the flour needed for local bread supplies. In November, Edward Le Quesne wrote to Mr P. P. Day, Supervisor of the Mills, and to Mr C. W. Rice, the States Engineer, to check where his responsibilities as President of the Department of Labour, ended. The mills had now been put back into working order by his department, a significant achievement in a short time. Also, in November the DOA confirmed payments of £1 a week in compensation to the owners of Tesson and Gargate Mills. On the 20th December, Brée announced the appointment of William Henry Hawkins at a salary of £3-5-0 a week, with an allowance for lodgings at £1 a week. His contract stipulated that he would work as directed by the DOA at any of the Island's mills.

On the 23rd December, Day was summoned to the DOA and informed that the mills had to urgently step up the production of flour. The interview concluded with the statement, "The need for speeding up the milling operation and particularly the need for the building of a store of grain was impressed upon him". On the same day the DOA wrote to the Department of Labour suggesting that work on the watermill at Malassis be speeded up.

On the 16th January 1941 Hawkins took over operation of the Grand Val as the miller, Mr William Baxter, was suffering ill health. Baxter was given a week's notice and £1 a week sick pay. Hawkins, however, did not actively take charge until the 17th February.

On the 27th January, Mr Le Gros, St Peter's Valley, complained to the DOA that his meadow had been damaged owing to the overflow of the millponds. The matter was referred to the States Engineer. On the 31st January the DOA decided that, in order to ensure sufficient supplies of grain for the requirements of the Island, they would proceed to put Quetivel Mill in order as soon as work was completed on Malassis Mill.

The clerk of the mills, Mr J. Lewis, had his salary increased from £2-10-0 to £2-15-0 a week. On the 31st January, a report recommended the use of auxiliary steamrollers. Consequently, on the 20th February, the power requirement of the mills was discussed and it was decided that the DOA would make an application to the Department of Labour for "The release of three steam rollers to provide such power for the mills during the summer months when a danger exists that the water power available for driving the mills may be insufficient".

The DOA, on the 3rd March, agreed to take on the lease of Grand Val due to Mr Baxter's ill health. (The lease was not in fact finalised until August.) On the 17th March it was decided that as soon as Malassis had been reconditioned Mr Hawkins, presently employed at Grand Val, would be put in charge and two additional men were employed at Grand Val – Mr P. A. Hervieu and Mr E. F. Josse, at a weekly wage of £2-10-0.

On the 31st March all mill transportation was forthwith undertaken by horses.

The Slaughter of Calves and the Island's Milk Supply

On the 10th January 1941 a meeting was convened concerning the slaughter of calves. The Island's milk supply had seriously worsened, and the reason appeared to have been that dairy farmers had drawn heavily upon their milk supplies in order to feed calves. The DOA decided forthwith that it would encourage the slaughter of calves to ensure a constant milk supply for the population. It was noticeable that since the German occupation the number of calves had increased. The reason was the cessation of the heifer export market to the USA and UK that had occurred prior to July 1940, when a shipment of fifty was not uncommon.[17]

The DOA approved the slaughtering of calves in cases where the animal was not worth keeping. Farmers who wished to destroy calves would, in the first instance, contact Mr H. G. Shepard, Secretary of the RJA&HS. A number of farmers had stopped the delivery of milk to the collecting dairies and were using it to feed their calves. On the 17th January Brée interviewed Mr J. E. Pinel, St John, who had ceased delivering 9 pots of milk to the collecting dairy. Pinel explained that the milk had been kept for his calves. Brée and the DOA accepted his account and told him to do his utmost to deliver the maximum quantity of milk each day to the dairy.

On the 27th January the States Vet was authorised to purchase any cows or heifers which their owners wished to slaughter, but which were, "Too valuable from the breeding point of view to be slaughtered". On the 5th May Brée discussed a report by Le Gallais on arrangements to slaughter two animals a week.

In January 1941 reports appear of "Animals reported dead in error". Two cows, Virginia 27th and Golden Rush 17th, the property of Mr Philip Perchard,[18] had been "Reported dead by him but the cows are still alive...no explanation of error by Mr Perchard". Other animals "Reported dead" were the cow Swithin's Valley,[19] the property of Mr J. H. Le Carré, and the bull, Royal Oak,[20] in the possession of Mr J. O. Arthur. Arthur had signed off the animal "dead" on the 5th November 1940 and had given "No explanation of the error forthcoming".

On the 10th May, the RJA&HS met to report that the Superior Council had accepted their recommendation that cattle chosen for slaughter by the States Vet should be paid for by "live weight". The payment would only be made on presentation of the Jersey Herd Book certificate. After the animal was slaughtered, the certificate was returned, and the animal cancelled from official lists.

The DOA also reported to HM Attorney General that, "Suspicion exists that horned cattle are being slaughtered and to ask the Honorary Police of the Island of this suspicion". The RJA&HS decided to establish a Cattle Slaughter Executive Committee which discussed the classes of cattle that would be allowed to be slaughtered. There were, however, many difficulties encountered in the selection of suitable animals. The Committee met on the 12th May to discuss the States Vet's veto of the slaughter of several animals and to make clear what constituted the guiding principles for future decisions on slaughtering. It was agreed that "The first consideration should be to retain animals likely to provide the Island with milk and butter".[13] The Committee, furthermore, agreed that cows of any age could be selected provided they were not more than five months in calf and not producing, or likely to produce, milk. In simple terms this amounted to a cull of Jersey cattle that were poor milk producers. Also discussed was the selection of bulls for slaughter. It was decided that in the case of aged bulls, their calves should be inspected before a decision was made. It was also agreed to allow the States Vet a greater degree of latitude in the choice of heifers, calves and cows of an inferior nature. Finally, Thomas Blampied was invited to join the Cattle Slaughter Executive Committee as his cooperation would facilitate its work.

On the 17th May, Field Command 515 informed the JFU and the RJA&HS that both organisations could continue their activities and meetings. On the same day the Slaughter Committee approved a recommendation from the DOA that Jersey cattle slaughtered at the abattoirs should be purchased by the Department of Essential Commodities on a "live weight" basis at the following prices:

Cows and bulls	6d per pound
Maiden heifers	8d per pound
Calves	9d per pound

The RJA&HS charged the DOA that under no circumstances should it permit the slaughter of any animal unless it was certified by Blampied as being non-productive and that the DOA should make these decisions known amongst all cattle breeders. It laid down two new rules: firstly, no cow in calf would be passed for slaughter; and secondly no animal under six years of age.

On the 31st May a meeting was held of the Cattle Slaughter Executive Committee comprising C. Le Gallais, J. B. Michel, F. Le Boutillier, G. A. Romeril, E. C. Perrédès and R. W. Carson. They agreed that real progress had been made on the slaughter scheme and that a list of bulls on the Island would be compiled.

On the 7th June the RJA&HS met to discuss the weekly slaughter scheme to supply meat for local needs, as ordered by Field Command 515. Each parish had fulfilled its slaughter quota since the inception of the scheme. A letter was also read from the German Field Command concerning its own requirements for the provision of local meat. As a result, the Committee agreed for continual endeavours to maintain "a weekly quota by voluntary methods". Also, the list of serving bulls was examined and it was decided that, before recommending the slaughter of any of these, the progeny should be inspected. Finally, it was decided to inspect all the younger bulls on the Island.

Milk Control

> *"In order to increase the production of butter in the island to compensate for the shortage of other fats, it was decided to recommend to the Superior Council that steps be taken to ration milk."*

DOA statement

When war broke out in September 1939 there were thirty Island milk retailers. The States immediately stepped in firstly, to control the supply of milk; and secondly to ensure it was sold at a reasonable price. Furthermore, it ordered that all surplus milk be made into butter. The butter factory in Don Street was consequently taken over by the DOA. In an attempt to control the price of milk, retailers were compelled to pay a levy of 2d per pot on their sales to cover the costs of the milk control scheme.[21] On the 13th November 1940 the Superior Council ordered the DOA to reduce the levy to 1d per pot. The Milk Control (Prices and Contribution) (No 2) (Amendment No 3) Jersey Order, 1940, was amended and, as a consequence of the reduction in the milk levy, it was decided to increase the price paid to the producers by 1 penny from 8¼ to 9¼ pence per pot in order to make it more profitable for farmers to produce and sell their milk.

On the 18th November the first report from a States Sanitary Inspector, Mr West, was forwarded to the DOA of milk supplied in a "dirty condition" by Mr A. A. Jeanne, St Saviour. Jeanne's licence as a "producer-retailer" was immediately revoked. Producer-retailers were farmers who kept dairy herds but were licensed by the DOA to sell their milk only to the named individuals on their licence. Adulterated milk, and more importantly "dirty milk", remained a major problem for the Milk Control Section throughout the occupation. "Dirty milk" due to poor hygiene and cleanliness was reported upon by Dr R. N. McKinstry, the Island's Medical Officer of Health, who wrote to the DOA in early December 1940. McKinstry identified the main cause as resulting from the transportation of milk from the countryside to the town. He advised that all milk transported should be filtered and pasteurised. The DOA replied that his recommendations were not feasible but wrote to all farmers to "...press for the highest possible standards of cleanliness".

The problem continued throughout December 1940. On the 25th December the Public Health Department sent a report to the DOA by Mr C. P. Dart, another Inspector, regarding "the dirty condition of the milk supplied by F. G. Mourant, St Saviour".[13] The DOA made the decision that all milk supplied by Mourant should be taken to Don Street Dairy for cleaning. The price the farmer received would be reduced by the cost of cleaning the milk.

McKinstry, in his annual report at the end of 1940, emphasised that, "... continual work has been kept up to keep our milk clean". He emphasised that new milk-testing apparatus had been introduced which provided "very satisfactory" results and allowed for successful prosecutions for the adulteration of milk by adding water and extracting fats, which had now become profitable for some producer-retailers.[22]

By the end of 1940 the DOA decided it would have to put more resources into Milk Control and effect some drastic action. It analysed the shortage of fats for the requirements of the population and decided to recommend to the Superior Council that steps should be taken to ration milk "In order to increase the production of butter in the island to compensate for the shortages of other fats".

Rationing allowed the following quantities of milk on a daily basis:

1. Children of 14 years and under, and invalids: one pint of full milk.
2. All persons over 14 years of age, other than invalids: half of a pint of full milk.

All milk rationing was effected by a system of ration cards. The ration to invalids was supplied only to persons holding a medical certificate advocating that the ration be issued. Skim milk would increase in price from 1d to 2d per pot. The Superior Council instructed the DOA to write to every dairy and producer-retailer, "...asking them to restrict sales to their customers to an average quantity supplied during the week ending the 19th November 1940". On the 29th November the milk ration scheme was implemented.

Don Street Dairy – Sören Jensen

On the 8th July 1940 the DOA appointed Carlyle Le Gallais as their agent to take charge of the milk section with full powers, whilst matters of policy remained with the DOA. After this appointment the Defence Committee assigned Mr R. O. Weeks, the former secretary of the Paragon Motor Garage, as "Secretary Accountant" for the control of milk. His role was to register all milk retailers and to collect the levy on their sales of 1d per pot. Weeks was allocated the board room of the Don Street Dairy as his office.

The manager of the dairy was a Danish national, Sören Jensen, who had come to Jersey in 1908. However, following the appointment of Le Gallais and Weeks, Jensen found himself no longer independent, but under the control of the Defence Committee and the DOA. The dairy, under the auspices of the DOA, effectively had three men who regarded themselves as the overall controller. In response to the increasing interference of Jensen by Weeks, at Don Street Dairy, Jensen made a number of complaints to the DOA. A subsequent meeting of the DOA on the 29th November decided that Jensen would be subordinate to Le Gallais and would provide statistical information to Weeks for accounting purposes.

At a meeting on the 6th December, which Weeks and Jensen attended, the latter was instructed to count the egg stocks instead of estimating them. On the 27th January 1941 Le Gallais was instructed by the Food Control Office to take over, through the Milk Control Office, all duties under the Milk (Registration with Retailers) (Jersey) Order, 1940. This now meant that he was effectively in charge of milk retailing and was Week's immediate superior.

Jensen now found himself squeezed between one very ambitious bureaucrat, Weeks, and Le Gallais, who tolerated no opposing view. The result was that Jensen was continually ordered by both men to carry out audits on the production and sale of butter and further checks on the dairy's use of petrol and oil in the lorries. At meetings Le Gallais made it clear that he was in charge, whilst Weeks would bring up all types of complaints about the management of the dairy. In Jensen's autobiography he commented, "I soon found out that at the factory where I had been in charge for over thirty years, I was like a spare wheel".[23] Furthermore,

Le Gallais made it clear to Jensen that he was to take all instructions from Weeks. Jensen had been exceptionally successful in building up a profitable butter and dairy products factory and some of these products were exported. In addition, he was highly thought of as an engineer and manager.

The working relationship between these men came to a head when Jensen was ordered to grade and count every egg sent in by farmers to Don Street. The German Field Command had ordered the dairy to supply them with eggs and Jensen was now expected to account for supplies to the German authorities. When Jensen spoke to Le Gallais about the difficulties of this egg audit, he was given a "very unpleasant reception". In addition, Le Gallais made it clear to him that: "I was not a person that was worth taking any notice, and that I had been all these years at the dairy because I had been able to show a profit and please one man".[23] Jensen spoke to the Chairman of the dairy J. A Perrée, who had originally employed him, and who advised him that "The best I could do was to resign as things were likely to be worse for me".

On the 24th March 1941 Jensen sent in his resignation letter, effective the 30th April, which was immediately accepted by the DOA. On the 21st April Le Gallais produced a report recommending: firstly, that Weeks be appointed "Manager/Secretary" of the Milk Control Section of the DOA; secondly, Mr A. F. Hamon be appointed overall manager of the Don Street Dairy at an annual salary of £208; and finally, that the present engineer, Mr J. Pluck, be appointed "Engineer in Charge" at a salary of £271-14-0.

Jensen's difficulties with the DOA remained. On the 1st May, Brée requested to the Superior Council that Charles Clement Joseph Hamon, a stoker at the General Hospital, be transferred to the Don Street Dairy as it was imperative that the boiler fires were backed down each night. However, Jensen lived in the flat situated on the premises and the flat was now required for the stoker. HM Attorney General, in an effort to make Jensen leave the flat, reported that Jensen had resigned as manager of Don Street "...of his own free will" and therefore had no claim to compensation; therefore, Jensen had to immediately vacate the flat. The DOA was instructed that it should not assume "...responsibility for any inconvenience or expense in which that resignation will involve Jensen". The DOA ordered Jensen to immediately vacate the flat as it, "Urgently needs the accommodation it affords for a member of its staff".[24]

The dairy had been opened to deal with the problem of unsold milk and the butter factory had been set up by Jensen, very much on the lines of the Danish cooperatives. He installed the machinery and in three years it became a profitable business. Between 1914 and 1918 the factory played an important role in the supply of butter. After the war Jensen set up a thriving export market for canned Jersey cream, which by 1940 was regarded as one of the best products of its kind in the United Kingdom.

The question arises as to why Sören Jensen – a skilled engineer, businessman and manager with thirty-two years of exemplary service to the Island's dairy industry – was treated in such a perfunctory manner by the civil authority. The answer perhaps can be found in Jensen's statement that, in 1940, he received "...a visit from a German officer who was an agricultural expert. I showed him around and had some talk with him in the German language".[25] Jensen was made responsible for the provision of eggs from the Don Street Dairy to the German authority, these being collected every Saturday by German officers. Jensen spoke good German and would speak to the officers each week. Unwittingly, he may have shown himself to have been too close to the German occupiers. Another possible reason was that, in February 1941, Weeks asked for a salary increase which he perceived was in accordance with his status as Secretary/Accountant of the Milk Control Section of the DOA. His request was refused on the 17th February; however, the DOA authorised him to engage an additional typist. On the 21st April, Le Gallais recommended to the DOA that Weeks be promoted to Manager/Secretary of the Don Street Dairy with a commensurate salary increase.

By December 1940, supplies of milk to all the dairies had seriously reduced. On the 6th December all producer-retailers were stopped from drawing additional supplies from Don Street Dairy for their named customers. On the same day, Mr H. A. Bisson, St Brelade, was referred to HM Attorney General for "appropriate action". Although not a holder of a producer-retailer licence he had been allegedly selling milk to persons other than the collecting dairies. On the 18th December, the DOA recommended to the Superior Council that, "In view of the continued decrease in the quantity of milk available......all consumers of milk were to register with one licensed retailer only and licensed retailers would only be permitted to serve registered customers". The Jersey Home for Boys, however, would be an exception, as more than one milk supplier was needed for the institution. A strict record was kept of licensed milk producers and to whom they supplied their milk.

Further detailed checks were made in December 1940 by the Milk Control Section. Mr A. A. Jeanne (whose producer-retailer licence had been revoked on the 18th November due to dirty milk) was still selling milk and was referred to HM Attorney General. Brée went directly to Field Command to ask approval for publication of the Milk (Registration with Retailers) (Jersey) Order, 1940 which was enacted on the 23rd December.

The DOA on the 6th January 1941 began a series of interviews with farmers, concerning allegations that milk had been sold without the possession of a producer-retailer licence as now required by Milk Control. Three farmers were interviewed; all agreed to backpay the levy for past sales and they were granted a licence. No further action was taken.

On the 13th January, in view of the chronic shortage of fresh milk, Brée requested the Department of Essential Commodities to release tinned milk.

A newspaper article of the same day describes an unofficial rationing of milk to the public that would take place, otherwise butter would disappear within the week.[26]

In addition, all dairies and retailers were warned to desist from "Unfairly discriminating in the supply of milk to certain customers". On the 24th January, Le Gallais sent a circular to all producer-retailers requesting them to exercise voluntary rationing of milk to customers, to avoid the necessity of introducing compulsory rationing.

On the same day, Mr F. Bechelet, accompanied by his solicitor, Oliver Mourant, was summoned by the DOA to give information concerning certain alleged misdemeanours over his milk supplies. The matter had been looked into by the Connétable of St Ouen and a report sent to HM Attorney General. His statement that "...two cows only supplied one pot of milk daily between them" was regarded as absurd and he was asked where he had obtained his butter. Subsequently, a letter from the Attorney General endorsed the Connétable's report and made it clear that Bechelet was making butter, although he was not the holder of a butter-maker's licence and was in breach of the Milk Control (Jersey) Order, 1940.

The day after Le Gallais had sent his circular to all producer-retailers of milk, an article appeared in the Jersey Evening Post: *"The Milk Shortage. Control Board's Appeal to Producer-Retailers. Are Farmers Playing the Game?"*

The paper published Le Gallais' circular and made it clear who was responsible for the milk shortage. "The dairymen [the dairies] cooperated whole-heartedly and the general public...the farmer-retailer is not pulling his weight". "The Milk Control Board does not consider the producer-retailer [the farmer selling milk to individual customers] has adequately responded".[27]

On the 27th January Le Gallais reported that the Food Control Office, which had up until then managed all matters relating to rationing under the Milk (Registration with Retailers) (Jersey) Order, 1940, now requested that milk control be taken over by the DOA, and he was given the authority to implement all necessary arrangements.

Giuseppi Retrossi and the Manufacture of Ice Cream

On the 31st January 1941, Brée informed the DOA that the Café Mignon, Esplanade, St Helier had been reported to be "...manufacturing and selling ice-cream to the public". He, furthermore, had sent the matter to the notice of HM Attorney General, "With a view to the proprietor Giuseppi Retrossi being brought before justice for an infraction of the Milk Control (Jersey) Order, 1940". The secretary of the DOA, Colin Marie, wrote to the Attorney General on the 1st February stating that evidence of the allegations came from "Mr Weeks' son and another boy who have, I understand, purchased ice-cream recently at this café".[28]

Marie made it clear to the Attorney General that "The particular importance of this case is to be found in the fact that every effort is, at present, being made to reduce the consumption of milk in order to provide for the manufacture of the essential butter supplies". Marie concluded that a full investigation should be carried out "In order that a stop may be put to what amounts to a waste of milk". In response to the seriousness of Marie's allegation against Retrossi the States Analyst was despatched to the Café Mignon. Samples of ice cream were purchased and analysed. The States Analyst in his subsequent report "...showed that the ice-cream was made with dried milk".

The matter of Retrossi's ice-cream manufacture was not dropped by the Milk Control Section. Weeks, after investigating, reported he had "considerable dissatisfaction" concerning the amount of fresh milk Mr Le Flohic of United Dairies was supplying to Mr Giuseppe Retrossi. He stated that the dairy was supplying "...increased quantities of milk to the Café Iniqnon [*sic*], Esplanade where it has been alleged, ice-cream is being made and sold". In consequence Le Flohic was instructed to appear before the DOA.

Weeks and the Milk Control Board increasingly pursued an unrelenting series of investigations into the retailing of milk. The Milk Control Section increased its workforce and milk producer-retailer licences were subsequently revoked. Farmers' milk records were checked and if a discrepancy was found they were immediately called in for interview. Six farmers were officially warned of infractions. Brée favoured a softer approach by giving verbal warnings rather than prosecuting. Farmers who had illegally sold milk were warned and instructed to backpay any milk levy that they owed.

In April 1941 the DOA reviewed the Milk (Registration with Retailers) Jersey Order, 1940 and Le Gallais decided upon a new form of registration. The decision was made to issue a triplicate form which was to be incorporated into the new issue of ration books for the start of July. The system ensured that all milk purchases were recorded and could be cross-referenced; milk could only be purchased by registering with a retailer or producer-retailer and only with the triplicate forms issued by the Milk Control Board.

Farmers and the Superior Council

The Superior Council and the DOA, for the first six months of the occupation, faced three problems. The first was responsibility for feeding the entire population. Secondly, the planning and implementation of a new agricultural model because of the loss of the United Kingdom market. Finally, it was essential to secure new sources of agricultural inputs. The arrival of Field Command 515 and Pelz also meant dealing with increasing requests and commands. Brée, and the Superior Council, decided that the increasing criticism received from leading farmers had to be confronted. Jersey farmers openly resented the increasing compulsion and inspection regimes.

The Superior Council called a meeting on the 5th December 1940 and summoned representatives of the JFU and the RJA&HS. The Bailiff and Brée wanted to ensure that the leading farmers were made aware of the problems and dilemmas facing the civil authorities and what their responsibilities were under the threat of German orders. Deputy Le Quesne summed up the Bailiff's contribution: "Some plain speaking took place. The Bailiff, departing from his usual calm demeanour, told the farmers that he was disgusted with their attitude of self-seeking and that both he and the Superior Council were fed up with this, and that if a more willing acceptance of the authority they themselves had elected was not forthcoming, he would refuse to further collaborate with them, the result being the Germans taking full control of the farms and possibly conscripting the labour of all farmers and farm workers".[29]

Potatoes

On the 7th February 1941, the DOA decided to carry out experiments in the "...production of flour from potatoes". A credit of £250 was opened. On the 10th March Brée proposed that the full costs of production of potato flour be calculated. The following week a new account, "The Potato Experimental Account", was established with a credit of £280-7-6. On the 19th March the DOA received a letter from Orviss Ltd offering to "...wash potatoes in connection with the potato flour scheme at £4 a ton, on condition that not less than 12 tons of potatoes are supplied to the firm for washing each week". The offer was accepted. On the 14th May a further £408-2-3 was credited to the Potato Flour Account.

On the 8th November 1940, under the Potatoes and Tomatoes (Maximum Prices) (Jersey) Order, 1940, the DOA revised potato prices charged by the merchants to 4/- per cwt wholesale and 5/- per cwt retail. The merchants purchased potatoes from the DOA at £3-15-0 per ton. On the 6th December Brée sold 200 tons of potatoes to Guernsey at £3 a ton. On the 18th December he informed the DOA that France (probably French merchants) had ordered 1,000 tons of potatoes at £5 a ton FOB and that he would obtain the requisite permission from Field Command 515.

On the 6th January 1941, the Superior Council ordered that all potatoes had to be delivered to the DOA stores – potato auctions were forbidden. On the 10th January, Brée confirmed that all second-crop or late potatoes would be purchased by the DOA, as in the case of grain. Farmers were instructed to bring these potatoes into store and, if not forthcoming, they would be requisitioned. Some farmers refused and were summoned for interviews. On the 10th February the DOA revoked the Potatoes (Sales) (Jersey) Order, 1940 and replaced it with a new order for potato sales:

1. No person shall, without sanction of the DOA, sell for human consumption any potatoes other than those of the "Royal Variety".
2. Sales of main crop potatoes are permitted solely for seed purposes and the Secretary is charged to make the necessary arrangements with the Law Officers of the Crown for drafting the proposed Order.

On the 24th March the question of releasing main crop potatoes from the potato clamps was discussed by the DOA. The decision was made not to release these potatoes as the Superior Council had agreed that all Jersey Royal potatoes would be sold at half-price as from the 28th April 1941. On the same day, the DOA issued a statement that the planting of late crop potatoes by farmers would have to be checked by the Honorary Parish Inspectors. Farmers who wished to plant the Jersey Royal variety could obtain the seed at the RJA&HS at 6 pence a tray.

On the 9th May, in accordance with a request from the Superior Council, the DOA set up the Potato Price Advisory Board to advise on prices for the 1941 potato crop. On the same day a discussion was held on the possibility of selling 170 tons of seed potatoes, which were required by the Department de L'Orme in Normandy, from the DOA's potato clamps. It was agreed that the seed potatoes be purchased and that the JPMA would ascertain which stores could bag and ship the potatoes for a price not exceeding 10/- a ton.

The DOA released maincrop potatoes on the 19th May 1941 under the Potatoes (Sales) (Jersey) Order, 1941. The wholesale price was set at £8 a ton and the retail, £9 a ton. On the 30th May the DOA released for sale all maincrop potato seed with preference given to farmers who had brought in their maincrop potatoes to the DOA. It, furthermore, was decided to prohibit the sale of maincrop potatoes other than for seed. Farmers were instructed to obtain their seed by a written application not later than the 7th June 1941.

The Potato Price Advisory Board met on the 21st May to discuss potato prices for 1941. It had representatives from the RJA&HS, JFU, JPMA and Department of Labour. Its initial discussions covered the States purchase of all potatoes, their export, transportation, marketing, spraying, quantities of seed, and containers for the 1941 crop. The meeting was attended by Brée. He described the areas devoted to the 1941 potato crop. Brée's figures given to the Board were exactly the same as the DOA's official areas for the 1941 Island Cropping Plan, a copy of which he had provided to the German Field Command, and which had been scrutinised by Pelz. However, Brée's figures to the Board interestingly assign an extra 1,500 vergées of potato cultivation from areas of less than a quarter of a vergée. This extra 1,500 vergées was not on the official cropping plan in which the area devoted to potatoes was 6,430 vergées. Brée's total area to the Board was 7,930 vergées. Furthermore, he stated that, depending on climatic conditions, the presumed yield for 1941 would not exceed 3 tons per vergée. This totalled an estimated yield for 1941 of 24,000 tons. The official potato yield which the German Field Command would have been given was 19,290 tons. This was a discrepancy of 4,710 tons of potatoes. It is doubtful whether Brée was wrong in his allocation of potatoes grown on smallholdings. It appears he was deliberately manipulating the figures to the Field Command.

In addition, Brée emphasised to the Board that potatoes for export must not be shipped unless mature and fit for bagging. Some exports on behalf of the German authorities had contained immature or poor-quality potatoes. Brée also made it clear that there were enough chemicals to cover 6,000 vergées of spraying on three occasions, as well as enough lead arsenate mixture for the entire potato crop. All sprays were to be free of charge to farmers. Each farmer would lift his own crop, but labour would be made available if required.

The 1941 potato season envisaged the clamping of 5,000 tons, to begin at the end of July. Brée made it clear that merchants would be solely in charge of storing potatoes for export and he reiterated that the States would buy all potatoes, be responsible for clamping and would regulate the lifting of the crop. Brée quoted a letter from Field Command 515 demanding potato prices to be fixed initially and then to decrease weekly. Production costs in 1941 were carefully calculated, per vergée, at £33-15-0 for côtils and £33-6-0 for ploughable land.

On the 28th May the Potato Price Advisory Board met again. Brée read a letter from Field Command requesting 10,000 tons of potatoes. The price the German authorities would pay would be the maximum price fixed in France. In consequence of the German demands, the quantity of potatoes supplied to Guernsey for clamping was reduced from 5,000 to 3,000 tons. On the 30th May, Brée attended their next meeting. He confirmed that the Board, "...should be in no doubt that 10,000 tons of potatoes were required by the German authorities".[15]

Jersey Produce Merchants Association

The 1940 potato crop that was not clamped was delivered to the agricultural merchants for storage and shipping. On the 4th November 1940 the merchants were paid £4,246-17-4 for the above service from the "Potato Fund Occupation Account". On the 30th December the JPMA asked the DOA what terms it would consider paying their members for the 1941 potato crop. Its reply on the 10th January 1941 was that it would pay 7/6 per ton for storage. Only one merchant "...asked for additional remuneration...but no increase in the agreed rates of storage could be considered".

Jersey Potatoes Delivered to St Helier Harbour and Exported to Europe and Guernsey to the Order of the German Authorities – November 1940 to May 1941

Date of German Requisition	Date of Shipment	Amount of Export	Value of Shipment	Notes of Shipment
18th October 1940			£6,808-4-0	The DOA reduced the amount owed by £3,973-4-0. The reduction was made up as follows: Credit to the German authorities for invoice 10th August 1940: 30 tons potatoes at £7 a ton, £210. Credit to the German authorities for sacks supplied to the DOA: 70,000 bags at 9d each, £2,625. Thereby making a total credit of £2,835.
9th December 1940		53½ tons	£321	The potatoes were "taken by the German authorities, originally part of a consignment for the civil population of Guernsey". An invoice of £321 sent to the German authorities.
6th and 7th December 1940	6th and 7th December 1940		258RM 79Pfg	A payment approved by the German Harbour Commandant in respect of freight charges due to the German Harbour Commandant. This in respect of two consignments of potatoes to Guernsey.
		£26-10-8 254RM 72Pfg		Sum received for potatoes from the German authorities to be credited to the "Potato Fund Occupation Account".
27th January 1941				Brée was authorised to make a payment of 311RM 22Pfg to the German authorities in respect of freight charges on the last consignment of potatoes shipped to Guernsey.

31st January 1941	Twenty sacks of potatoes	The DOA approved the action of Brée in authorising payment to the Freight Manager, Jersey, in respect of twenty sacks shipped to the order of the German authorities at Granville. The Treasurer of the States was charged to pay this amount, debiting the "Potato Fund Occupation Account". Treasurer of the States to receive and credit £6-14-2 to the "Potato Fund Occupation Account" from the German authorities for twenty sacks supplied to the order of the German authorities at Granville. The DOA approved payment of 7RM 94Pfg in respect of the freight charges on twenty sacks of potatoes shipped to the order of the German authorities at the Hôtel Moderne at Granville. Furthermore, the DOA asked the Department of Finance to arrange for Mr Jouault of the Jersey Purchasing Committee in Granville to receive and credit to the Potato Fund Occupation Account" the sum of £6-15-8 from the Hôtel Moderne, c/o Zufahrstelle, Granville, for twenty sacks of potatoes supplied to the establishment on the orders of the German Field Command in Jersey.
17th February 1941		Potato clamps were opened at Les Platons, Trinity, under the supervision of Edwin Gibaut, "for the requirements of the civil population of Paris".

(Continued)

Date of German Requisition	Date of Shipment	Amount of Export	Value of Shipment	Notes of Shipment
		488 tons	£2,440	In view that the "Société d'Importation et de Repartition des Pommes de Terre de Semence" had provided the sacks for two consignments of potatoes shipped by the DOA to the orders of the German authorities, it was decided to credit the Société the sum of £36- 2-6, being the amount charged in respect of sacks at the rate of 15/- per ton. The secretary was charged to write to Mr J. L. Jouault, pointing out to him that the prices at which the potatoes, purchased by the German authorities, for the needs of the civil population of Paris, were invoiced at £5 a ton, including sacks.
17th March 1941				DOA approved the action of Brée in authorising the payment to the Freight Manager, Jersey, 46RM 25Pfg being the freight on a shipment of potatoes to Guernsey for the requirements of the German troops there.
7th April 1941				DOA approved the action of Brée in authorising 2,615RM 75Pfg to the Freight Manager in payment of freight on potatoes sent to Paris.
15th April 1941				A sum of 604RM 47Pfg was approved for payment chargeable to the "Potato Fund Occupation Account" in respect of potatoes shipped to Guernsey and Paris.

21st April 1941		The DOA approved the action of Brée in authorising for payment to the Freight Manager, Jersey, the sum of 121RM 88Pfg being the freight charges on potatoes shipped to Paris and Guernsey.
29th April 1941		A payment of 38RM 53Pfg was approved, being the freight charges on a consignment of potatoes sent to Granville.
5th May 1941		Brée sanctioned the payment of 455RM 38Pfg to the Freight Manager, Jersey, in respect of potatoes shipped to Carenton, Granville and Guernsey.
	6th May 1941	The DOA approved Brée's action authorising payment of 455RM 72Pfg to the Freight Manager, Jersey, for potatoes consigned to Domfront and to Guernsey.
19th May 1941		Potatoes for the Germans in Guernsey, an account of 53RM 12Pfg was due to the Freight Manager, Jersey. The Treasurer of the States was charged to debit the amount to the "Potato Fund Occupation Account". The DOA authorised Brée for the payment of 1,326RM 69Pfg in respect of freight chargeable to the "Potato Fund Occupation Account".
30th May 1941		The DOA approved the action of Brée in authorising payment of 183RM 70Pfg to the Freight Manager in respect of potatoes shipped to Domfront and Guernsey.

Field Command 515

By September 1940, Pelz, Head of Agriculture and Food Supply for Field Command 515, was happily ensconced at his charming house, Little Court, Mont Cochon, St Lawrence, where he employed a Swiss housekeeper, Miss Elsa Brunner. His first priority was "...to get to know about the circumstances of the islands". He travelled to Guernsey, Jethou, Alderney, Sark and Herm. Pelz met many of the leading civil servants and politicians in the islands, also visiting and meeting the leading farmers. The fact that Pelz toured Jersey so extensively, checking farms and crops, gave him a detailed appreciation of local agriculture. This makes it difficult to understand why he has been almost wiped out from the occupation historical record. Pelz regularly met with Brée, whom he describes as the "Minister of Agriculture". At Christmas 1940, Brée gave Pelz an alarm clock as a gift.

On the 29ᵗʰ September 1940 Pelz wrote a long letter to his friend in Austria. The letter is both interesting and informative because of its date and origin, providing a real insight into Pelz's perception of the Channel Islands at a very early stage of the occupation. As a senior officer of the German Military Government his love affair with the Island is clearly shown. (Refer to end of chapter.)

Pelz, a lover of animals, found a dog in one of the Channel Islands which he named "Herm". The transportation by the German military of dogs into the Island raised real worries concerning the importation of rabies, although whether any cases of rabies did occur is not known. However, on the 23ʳᵈ November the Commandant of Field Command 515, Colonel Schumacher, wrote to the Bailiff ordering that all dogs when outside the owner's house be leashed and muzzled. The matter was forwarded to the DOA who subsequently issued the Rabies (Jersey) Order, 1940, as a precaution against the introduction and spread of rabies on the Island.

In continuing their charm offensive with the Island's civilian population, Field Command 515's veterinary surgeon Dr Kempt offered his services free of charge to local farmers. Pelz's superiors ordered him to organise a Christmas party for 100 children aged between eight and thirteen years. Pelz, furthermore, was told to provide the children with food and be present at the party. He described many of the children invited as "mostly poor" many of whom had fathers absent from the Island because they were fighting.[30]

News of the Christmas party was published in the press under the headline: "One Hundred Poor Children Entertained by German Authorities". The article described, "One hundred poor children selected by the Town Hall authorities were the guests of the German Field Command yesterday and spent a most enjoyable time. They were given a party complete with tea, cakes and games. There was a fine Christmas tree. It took place at the Continental Hotel. KVR Pelz was in charge of the arrangements and showed himself most attentive to the wants of the youngsters".

On the 17th March 1941 a Frenchman, François Scornet, aged twenty-two, was executed in the grounds of St Ouen's Manor. Scornet had escaped from France with a group of young men in an attempt to join the French forces in England, but they were caught after landing in Guernsey. Scornet was tried by the Field Command and sentenced to execution as the ringleader.[31] "Scornet is believed to be the only civilian to have been executed on British soil during the Second World War".[32] The repercussion of Scornet's execution by a firing squad sent immediate shock waves throughout the agricultural farming community in the Island. Previously, farmers' relations with Field Command 515, and especially with Pelz, had been amicable. Many farmers believed that Scornet's execution at St Ouen's Manor was a graphic warning to the Island's civilians. The German Field Command, understanding the extent to which the execution had affected islanders and, "Not wishing that the oak should become a symbol of resistance, the Germans immediately felled the tree".[33] The tree was presumably where Scornet stood when he was executed.

The coffin of François Scornet was supplied by Douglas L. Sinnat, Funeral Directors, 40 La Motte Street, St Helier. Their invoice dated 24th September 1941 and sent to the "Field Kommandant, Victoria College House" stated, "Plain coffin supplied to St Ouen's Manor. £4-10-0". The burial costs were paid from the German quartermaster's account and reimbursement requested on the 19th December when Field Command 515 sent the account to the States of Jersey. No mention was made of Scornet by name in the correspondence.

On the 16th December Field Command 515 ordered the States to register every civilian in Jersey over fourteen years of age. On the 30th December the Identification of Persons (Jersey) Order, 1940, was announced. The registration process was to commence from the 2nd January 1941. Almost immediately a problem arose concerning the individual identification photographs required by the Field Command and stapled on the card. There was simply not enough photographic paper or developing chemicals available on the Island to photograph over 40,000 individuals. As a result, "…the photograph part of the business is to be left in abeyance owing to the insufficient stock of materials".[34]

Field Command 515 subsequently purchased the photographic paper and chemicals from France on behalf of the States. The entire process of obtaining these materials was only completed by October 1941. The responsibility for ordering the materials fell to KVR Dr Reffler, Field Command 515 and were handed to the Island representative, the Chief Aliens Officer, Clifford Orange. The total cost for these photographic materials was 22,842.40 French francs. KVR Dr Reffler sent the invoice to the Bailiff on the 24th December 1941. The Bailiff forwarded the invoice to the Lieutenant-Bailiff, Philip Ernest Brée (a relative of Touzel John Brée), who in turn sent copies to Orange and to the President of the Department of Finance and Economics, with the instruction, "Kindly attend to this matter as soon as possible". The matter of the invoice remained unresolved until the 3rd January 1942, when Orange noticed a mistake or double entry on KVR Dr Reffler's invoice. The mistake was highlighted and dealt with.[35]

Clifford Orange has, over the past two decades, received criticism from historians as an overzealous bureaucratic administrator who stepped over the demarcation line to cooperate with Field Command 515, through the implementation and control of the registration process.[36] Orange, however, would have been warned by the Bailiff, Alexander Coutanche, in an unambiguous command, to comply with Field Command 515's orders.

KVR Hans Egon Pelz. Private Letter to Sepp Bartelt, 29th September 1940[37]

I wrote this letter at that time to my friend, bank clerk and later insurance director Sepp Bartelt in Salzburg. He gave it back to me in 1964.

O.U. 29 Sept 1940
(Jersey Little Court)

Dear Sepp,
Today, on a lovely fresh Sunday morning, the horn of a cheeky steamer got me out of bed sooner that I had intended and I am looking forward to talking to you for fifteen minutes.

The slanting sun is shining on the small desk in the window recess, and when I look up through the small Dutch-type window panes, the wide bay of St. Helier lies in front of me in a delicate morning blue, covered by soft cumulus clouds that are strung together on the horizon. In the east I see the pier jutting out into the sea. A white smoke trail is rising from the "Norman", which was recently used as a freighter, then I see lots of black reefs and jagged peaks projecting from the water, because the tide is low, and finally, limiting the view to the east, there is the picturesque Elizabeth Castle about 500m from the beach, making a grand impression with its beautiful castle-like silhouette in a delicate hue.

All this I watch from this little place from which I am writing to you and I am smiling happily. But I see even more. In front of me, in grey-blue, lies St. Aubins Bay in a soft sweep towards the west, rising to a steep coastline, on which little white houses cling, and which then suddenly falls into the sea. Between this reddish brown area in the west and the castle in the east there is the glittering water of the sea.

When in the morning the tide is foaming onto the cliffs and the beautiful white waves run against the sandy parts of the bay, we hear the roaring in our chaste bedrooms. I am smiling again, dear Sepp, for you can truly believe me I have no talent as a writer and my letters are mostly pretty down-to-earth. For three weeks I have been living here above the bay on Cambrai Hill and our beautiful country seat is Little Court. I am not able to portray the beauty of this place for you. It is almost like in a fairy tale. I live together with two men of our command. Although we are all very different it works pretty well, and every day after work we only wish to go back home to Little Court.

I was very lucky when accidentally this beautiful modern house was offered to me as a domicile, which some lousy Englishman abandoned who fled to Old England. There is everything: a marvellous garden of more than one hectare, flowers, hedges, well looked-after golf lawns, a gardener with a house, garage and two carts, a tennis court and a big greenhouse which daily supplies us with mountains of green and red grapes, and two women as willing hands and, last but not least, two cute dogs names Sumi and Tanto, as well as a little grey pigeon which, sitting on a finger, makes bows and coos. So, dear Sepp, it is no wonder that I am trying to tell you all this and that I become poetical when writing this, so that I have to smile myself.

This island is an interesting piece of land. My journey from Luxembourg via St. Germain and other rundown and derelict villages, via Mont St. Michel to Granville, was not quite pleasant, and the voyage by boat was virtually warlike. After all the endless filth in France the cleanness on this island was an outstanding agreeable contrast. It is a purely English country and you do not hear a word of French, although many can still speak it. The island originated in red granite and is very fertile. Its mild, even climate is caused by the Gulf Stream which often generates a considerable swell. I was very much astonished about its richness of southern flora, about laurel and sweet chestnut trees, palm trees and mimosa. Hydrangea and fuchsia blossom on walls, hollies surround fields, fig trees and tamarisks blossom in abundance.

The little town of St. Helier has been hit by tourism from France for many years. The farmers in the interior of the island mainly grow vegetables and tomatoes, which is astonishingly productive. In the fields the gazelle-like Jersey cows are grazing, pale yellow like roe deer, which are distinguished and famous for their highest amount of fat of their milk up to 6.2%. The island is like a garden in the south, east and north. Numerous little roads go through the countryside, narrow but with tarmac and often bordered by nice oak trees on which ivy climbs up. There you find the houses of the farmers built of red stones, very tasteful and nice, not shabby at all. The north is less developed. Here gorse and heather are dominating. And finally, the west is strangely like steppe and wasteland.

On the other islands Guernsey, Alderney, Sark and the others it is similar. On Sark a woman rules. She even speaks a bit of German and is the sovereign ruler of the country and of about 500 subjects. When she promulgates laws, they are fixed in handwriting on the wall of the vegetable shop opposite her house and everybody has to take notice of them. So we are better off in Jersey. We have a parliament and a president, as well as about seven ministers and all the other chambers and corporations, just as they belong to a big country, and the little island itself claims three British lions and proudly calls itself "States of Jersey". While the people in France are unapproachable and often show hostile faces, this cannot be said about the British. In a remarkable way they keep their composure, but they are easier to win over. The males are easy-going in posture and style; the girls and women are generally dressed smartly and attractively and their makeup is not as loud as that of the French women. These people have Norman blood and are not very tall; rather they are medium big, blond and blue-eyed, although sometimes you find pure dark-skinned types.

There are no big blocks of flats; everybody lives in little country houses which are often very pretty and often they are splendid properties. As wealth tax on the island is very little, there are, or rather there were a lot of millionaires here, who built themselves nice country seats. Ours is also like that.

So, Sepp, I really have to sign off now. Now you know more about Jersey than many a university professor, and I have to say that, in spite of some difficulties, my work makes quite good progress. Of course I try to speak with the women in English every day and I hope that in some weeks I will have understood something.

Bye, old chap, let me hear from you, if the terrible raging of war has not yet got hold of you and made you end up somewhere. Give my regards to the lasses (Dirndl) and lads (Buamba) and especially your wife and son, and please receive my warm-hearted regards from across the far water.

From your old

Irreformable / uncorrigible

Pelz

References

1. Le Quesne, E. 1999. The Occupation of Jersey Day by Day, p. 2.
2. Jersey Evening Post, 3rd July 1940.
3. Jersey Evening Post, 8th July 1940.
4. Jersey Evening Post, 13th July 1940.
5. JFU Minute Book.
6. Theo Elsche was a German engineer and builder whose company employed local labour during the occupation. One of his employees, a local carpenter, stated that not only did he receive far higher wages from Elsche than from local employers, but in addition Elsche provided a daily soup kitchen where local workers were provided with free meals. When the carpenter was injured, falling off a scaffold whilst in Elsche's employment, his employer personally delivered a hamper of food and fruit to his home.
7. Le Quesne, op. cit. p. 5.
8. Jersey Evening Post, 20th July 1940.
9. Jersey Evening Post, 2nd August 1940.

10. Le Quesne, op. cit. p. 6.
11. A côtil is a steep south-facing field which had to be farmed by hand. Some côtils are extremely fertile due to their aspect.
12. 40 perch = 1 vergée = 4/9 of an acre.
13. Jersey Archive. L/D/09/A10.
14. Jersey Archive. C/B/A1/6.
15. RJA&HS. Potato Advisory Board Minutes. The title of the Board varies in the source documents. It is also called the "Potato Price Advisory Board" and the "Price Advisory Board" and either four or six members are mentioned.
16. Seaweed collected during the winter. It was subsequently put on the fields and ploughed into the soil before the potatoes were planted. It was a first-rate fertiliser.
17. Jersey Archive. C/B/A1/3 and C/B/A1/4.
18. RJA&HS. Jersey Herd Book. HBN 44067 and 47869.
19. RJA&HS. Jersey Herd Book. HBN 45781.
20. RJA&HS. Folio 112.
21. Jersey Evening Post. 5th July 1940.
22. Jersey Archive. C/A5/21.
23. Jensen, Sören. "My story in the Island of Jersey, Channel Islands". I would like to thank Carolyn Labey and her family for allowing me access to Sören Jensen's autobiography.
24. Jersey Archive. D/Z/H5/141.
25. This German officer would have been KVR Hans Egon Pelz, Head of Agriculture & Food Supplies, Field Command 515. Pelz often introduced himself as an expert in agricultural matters. He had a degree "Ingenieur" from an agricultural university in Vienna.
26. Jersey Evening Post. 13th January 1941.
27. Jersey Evening Post. 25th January 1941.
28. Archive. D/Z/H5/141/2.
29. Le Quesne, op. cit. p.35.
30. Pelz, Hans Egon. Damals Erinnerungen. 2013. p. 583.
31. Ramsey, Winston G. The War in the Channel Islands. Then and Now. 1981. pp. 216–219 gives an account of Scornet.
32. Jersey Evening Post. 24th June 2017.
33. Le Quesne, op. cit. Footnote by M. Ginns, p. 117.
34. Sinel, L. The German Occupation of Jersey. 1984. p. 34.
35. Personal correspondence.
36. For a detailed appraisal see:
Fraser, D. The Jews of the Channel Islands and the Rule of Law 1940-1945. 2000.
Sanders, P. The British Channel Islands under German Occupation 1940-1945. 2005.
37. Pelz Family Archive. My thanks to the Pelz family for allowing me to use the letter.

Chapter 6

June to December 1941

Cattle

"Live cattle from France had been imported by the German army of occupation and led along the roads to sundry destinations."

Thomas Le Quesne Blampied, States of Jersey Veterinary Surgeon

After the Field Command had demanded from the States a weekly quota of local meat, the RJA&HS had set up a Cattle Slaughter Executive Committee comprising the President of the RJA&HS, Carlyle Le Gallais, the two Vice Presidents, John Buesnel Michel and Francis Le Boutillier, and Eugene C. Perrédès, Robert Wilson Carson and George A. Romeril.[1]

On the 7th June 1941 the RJA&HS received a letter from the Field Command regarding the supply of local meat and a meeting of the Cattle Slaughter Executive Committee was held. Each parish had fulfilled its quota since the inception of the scheme. All agreed on the necessity for continual endeavours to maintain, "a weekly quota by voluntary methods"[2] In addition, it examined a list of bulls of serving age and decided, before any sires were slaughtered, to examine the progeny of these bulls. At the same time all younger bulls were to be inspected.

During the summer of 1941, live German cattle imports into Jersey were numbering over fifty a month. Thomas Blampied on the 24th October 1941 reported that: "Live cattle from France had been imported by the German army of occupation and led along the roads to sundry destinations". Brée was asked to investigate this report and, in the event of its accuracy being established, "To make strong representations to the German Field Command 515 on the danger likely to arise for the cattle of the Island if this practice is not stopped".[3]

On the 13th September 1941 new problems arose. Mr A. J. Barette failed to register three calves: June Royal Queen, Silvery Blossom and January Royal Doreen. This was a serious infringement of the Jersey Herd Book rules. A subsequent application made by the farmer was refused. The cattle remained unregistered. In addition, Clifford Le Vesconte's Jersey Herd Book certification and qualifications had been lost in a fire at his residence. These were for cattle served by his stud bull. Le Vesconte and all the respective owners of cattle served by his bull had to swear an affidavit protecting the Jersey Herd Book from misuse, if the original certificates were recovered.

The DOA wrote to Le Gallais on the 25th November asking him to lay before the authorities of the Jersey Herd Book a proposal that, "...owing to the present very serious situation in regard to the supply of milk for the requirements of the population, all calves should be slaughtered as soon after birth as possible, with the exception of a number of both heifers and bull calves to be selected by the Herd Book each month.[3]

On the 29th November 1941, Brée called an "urgent" meeting with twenty-one of the leading Island farmers who kept herds. The topic for discussion was: "The Public Milk Supply". The DOA wanted, in order to ameliorate the public milk supply, only a small percentage of calves to be registered in the Jersey Herd Book. The remaining calves had to be slaughtered, releasing a greater quantity of milk for the local population. This measure had already been enforced in Guernsey. Brée made it clear that, whilst the DOA and Superior Council could order this measure, they wished the RJA&HS to undertake the selection of calves to be retained. He furthermore made it clear to these leading farmers of, "The serious state of affairs confronting the DOA" and he earnestly appealed to all farmers "...to release as much milk as possible for the vital needs of the population".

After compiling a thorough inventory of the Island's cattle population and calf registrations, the following course of action was decided.

1. That for the months of December 1941, January and February 1942, only sixty calves a month should be registered and retained.[3]
2. That no bull calves should be registered and retained.
3. All calves, except those selected for retention, must be slaughtered within fourteen days of birth.
4. An official order would be made that the birth of any calf must be reported within 24 hours.
5. A "Selection Committee" of Carlyle Le Gallais, John Michel and Francis Le Boutillier will be set up.

The above recommendations were submitted to the DOA on the 1st December 1941. The DOA in turn recommended the report to the Superior Council and that, in the event of the Superior Council accepting these recommendations requiring the slaughter of all calves, the DOA would issue an immediate Order exempting sixty calves monthly. In addition, it would also exempt two bull calves each month.

On the 15th December the Newly-Born Calves (Jersey) Order, 1941, came into effect. A meeting of the RJA&HS on the 20th December would, "... proceed with the selection of heifer calves to be exempt from slaughter".

The meeting made it clear to the DOA that only officers of the RJA&HS would carry out the terms of the order and only deal with calves born after 15th December 1941. They, furthermore, decided to select for exemption from slaughter half the quota for December 1941, amounting to thirty heifer calves.

Le Gallais, Michel and Le Boutillier met and agreed upon the policy for the selection of calves for slaughter.

1. The preference be given to the calves of "highly commended" cows or, in the case of calves by "unqualified stock", preference be given where the dam is "highly commended. This was the highest qualification that could be awarded to a cow when assessed for entry to the pedigree section of the Jersey Herd Book, after she had calved for the first time.
2. That due consideration be given to the capabilities of the sire.

In addition, the officers of the RJA&HS discussed the Island's milk shortage and made the following suggestions.

1. In order to ascertain the whereabouts of the Island's milking stock, all auctioneers be asked to furnish a list of all purchases of cattle at auction sales held in recent months.
2. A letter be sent to every member urging them to send all the milk possible to town.
3. A circular be sent to all cattle owners reminding them of the Newly-Born Calves (Jersey) Order, 1941 and explaining the procedures to be adopted. On the 22nd December 1941, H. G. Shepard, Secretary of the RJA&HS, wrote to the DOA with a copy of the circular describing the operation of the order. The DOA approved the circular.

Pigs

In June 1941 six farmers were called in by the DOA in connection with infringements of the Pigs (Control) (Jersey) Order, 1941. Five were given a verbal warning. The last, in view of his "unsatisfactory explanations", was referred to HM Attorney General. In July, approximately thirty farmers were called in for interviews. The majority concerned allegations that no written declarations had been forwarded to the DOA. One farmer Mr E. Barette, who came in the place of his father, Mr A. J. Barette, was interviewed. He allegedly had failed to declare not only the pigs in his possession, but sought to mislead the DOA's inspector, Mr J. W. Blampied, as to the actual number of pigs so held by him.[3]

Most farmers were given a strict verbal warning by Brée. He favoured this rather than going through the judicial route. However, a small number of farmers who had not adhered "...to their future observance of the Order" were referred to the Attorney General. One such farmer, Mr R. E. Fauvel, desired to "apologise for his unhelpful attitude" when interviewed and asked the DOA to withdraw proceedings. Brée, however, deciding that a sacrificial lamb on the altar of the court would make his point crystal clear, refused to alter his department's decision.[3]

It also became apparent to Brée and the DOA that pigs were moved around geographically, in order to foil the registration process. In September 1941, Mr A. Rive and Mr André Garton of 8 Bath Street, were interviewed. Rive had been discovered having four pigs in his personal custody that belonged to Garton. These pigs had not been declared. The case was immediately forwarded to the Attorney General.[3] In addition, a Mr A. Jeanne was also interviewed concerning an allegation that he kept pigs that were unregistered. Jeanne immediately surrendered the information that these pigs were the property of a Mr Cornish, Gorey. The DOA instructed him to return the pigs to the owner. No further action was taken.

In August 1941 the Connétables met to discuss the encouragement of pig breeding. They proposed that farmers could either retain 20% of a carcass from the States abattoirs and sell it on the open market for a new price of 1/6 per pound weight; or alternatively, farmers could secure 25% of a carcass and sell it at the old price. In September the DOA replied to the Connétables saying that "No increase of pig breeding could be anticipated until adequate supplies of feeding stuffs are available". The DOA decided to defer the Connétables' proposal until pig feeding stuffs were available. However, it also decided to the first release of 15 tons of grain for pig and poultry feed. In October the Little Sisters of the Poor were allowed to slaughter pigs for the requirements of their community and hospice. The pigs were in their possession and registered.

Labour – The Agricultural Workers Bonus

In June 1941 the pay books for the Agricultural Workers Bonus were recalled and substituted by vouchers to the value of 14/- a week, to cover the period 14th June to 4th October 1941. The bonus was payable to both single and married men. The main provision for entitlement was that farmers paid their workers a wage of not less than 36/- a week. Farmers' sons were ineligible to register for the vouchers.

On the 27th June a delegation of the JFU met the DOA. The topic for discussion was: "The fixing of hours of labour for agricultural workers". A joint agreement was made:

1. Agricultural workers will work 56 hours a week. The farmer will arrange the times.
2. A notice will be published in the press drawing attention to this and pointing out that, where agricultural workers do not conform to the prescribed hours of work, the employer may refuse to sign the Agricultural Workers Bonus voucher for that week.

The DOA decided that any disputes between farmers and employees in terms of hours should be referred to the Department of Labour panel in the parish concerned. It also decided to publish a further notice drawing to the attention of farmers the "declaration" which they signed in connection with the Agricultural Workers Bonus, by which they undertook to notify the DOA in the event of any of their employees in receipt of the bonus leaving their employ. The farmers were also instructed to sign vouchers weekly and not several weeks in advance. The vouchers were redeemable at the main Post Office in Broad Street. On the 7th July 1941 the Superior Council agreed to meet the costs for the scheme.

The scheme itself brought up a number of problems. The first was the question of boys who were already in receipt of the State's Apprenticeship Grant. It was feared that some of these apprentices would forsake their occupation to enable them to draw the Agricultural Workers Bonus as agricultural labourers. Secondly, Brée and the DOA decided, on the 14th July, that the bonus would not be paid to a farmer himself, who held a Cultivation Order issued under the Cultivation of Lands (Jersey) Order, 1940. However, on the 21st July, non-payment of the bonus to farmers themselves was rescinded. This especially had caused an immense wave of bitterness amongst farmers holding a Cultivation Order and Brée decided quickly that the ill feeling was simply not worth the problems it subsequently created.

On the 16th September the DOA and Department of Labour met to discuss the Agricultural Workers Bonus scheme which was due to end on the 4th October. Both departments decided to recommend to the Superior Council that the bonus should continue until further notice. The conditions would be as follows:

1. Men over nineteen years of age would receive a bonus of 14/- weekly.
2. Men under nineteen would receive a bonus of 7/- weekly.
3. Men had to work 56 hours a week, and in accordance with the requirements of their employer.

In October, a supplementary credit of £12,500 was opened to meet the costs involved in the payment of the bonus until the end of 1941. A proposal by the Department of Labour to increase the bonus by 10% was opposed by Brée and the DOA. In November the DOA refused the extension of the bonus to women agricultural workers.

Milk Control

> "The supplies of milk now coming from the country are insufficient to meet the requirements of the urban population of the island."

Milk Control Section Report, DOA – 19th December 1941

In late May 1941, R. O. Weeks, Head of the Milk Control Section of the DOA, received a communication from Mrs J. M. Perrot, Grouville. Mrs Perrot alleged that a young boy by the name of Le Saint had been paid 7/6 a week by a licensed milk retailer called Miss M. A. Le Cornu, Longueville, to collect milk each morning and evening from Mr Alfred J. Jeanne of Radier, Grouville. This milk was subsequently sold by Miss Le Cornu. The sale of the milk was "...believed to be made to residents of Old Grouville Hill".[4]

In response, Weeks made it clear that allegedly Miss Le Cornu had rendered a false statement in connection with the Milk Control (Jersey) Order 1940. This was by not stating that Mr A. J. Jeanne was the registered producer of milk that she then sold. A further allegation was that Miss Le Cornu declared each month that the milk was from her own cows. In addition, Weeks alleged that Miss Le Cornu had evaded the milk levy. Jeanne was a producer of milk registered with Tanguy Diaries Limited and therefore only allowed to supply that dairy with milk. He was not registered to sell milk to a licensed milk retailer, i.e., Miss M. A. Le Cornu.

Weeks concluded that: "The matter is rendered more serious in view of the fact that the Committee of Island Defence went out of its way to help Miss Le Cornu on the 19th April 1940 by allowing her to extend her business and become a licensed retailer, instead of a licensed producer-retailer". Weeks' allegations were forwarded to the Attorney General who subsequently decided upon instigating an appropriate investigation.

On the 5th June 1941 the Attorney General wrote to the Connétable of Grouville, Mr P. W. C. Briard, requesting, "I shall be obliged to you if you will cause the fullest possible investigation to be made regarding the matters at issue and will inform me of the result of those investigations at your earliest convenience". The Connétable investigated both Miss Le Cornu and Mr Jeanne by ordering Centenier Harold Brée (Touzel Brée's son) to produce a report on the case, which was completed by the 9th June.[5]

The report stated clearly that Miss Le Cornu, faced with a shortage of milk owing to several of her cows becoming "dry", obtained a daily supply of milk from Tanguy's Dairy in order to maintain her customers' requirements. However, the deliveryman from Tanguy's Dairy, Mr E. Le Quelenec, could not guarantee delivery of the extra milk she required by 9 a.m. each day. Therefore, Le Quelenec was collecting milk each morning from Mr Jeanne's farm, which was in the same neighbourhood as Miss Le Cornu, she then took the amount she required, and the balance was duly collected from her farm by Le Quelenec, when completing his round later the same morning. Miss Le Cornu therefore had the extra milk she needed to serve her customers at the usual hour.

The Centenier's report concluded that, whilst pursuing his investigation further, he discovered that the statement made by Mrs J. M. Perrot was "...

not altogether true". It was evident to him that, "The boy Le Saint is not wholly employed by Miss Le Cornu, for several weeks he has been in the custom of taking back the empty can or cans, each evening, to Mr Jeanne's farm, Miss Le Cornu giving the boy the sum of one-shilling weekly for his trouble and act of kindness".[4]

On the 10th June Connétable Briard sent the report to the Attorney General, who then informed Brée on the 13th June. Both men decided "The best course will be to take no further action in this matter".

This case study of Miss Le Cornu's alleged infringements of milk control orders is interesting for three reasons. Firstly, it demonstrates that close neighbours were willing to instigate denunciations. Secondly, that a States department, the civil service and law enforcement agencies all carried out a diligent investigation and due processes were followed to verify or discredit adherence to milk control orders. Thirdly, that there was an immediate response to such allegations or infringements.

On the 9th June 1941, the registration of all the Island's milk consumers under the Milk (Registration with Retailers) (Jersey) Order, 1941 was implemented, greatly increasing the workload for the Milk Control Section of the DOA. Weeks was given authority to employ additional staff. On the 16th June the DOA approved additional orders:

1. The DOA will issue new Registration documents for the purpose of the Order.
2. The documents are the property of the DOA and cannot be assigned or unlawfully possessed by any other person.
3. Registration documents issued in respect of deceased persons and of persons leaving the Island for more than fourteen days must be surrendered to the DOA.
4. Milk retailers must furnish the DOA with all returns, and any information so required.
5. The parent or guardian of a child under sixteen years of age and the curator of a person under interdiction may act for a child or interdict.
6. False statements for the purpose of obtaining milk and fraudulent use of the registration documents will be punishable.

These new directions provided for the re-registration of all consumers of milk and required holders of registration documents to comply with all instructions. The new milk certification of registration was ready by the 20th June and implemented on the 7th July.

On the 13th June farmers were requested not to mix morning and evening milk as "This practice is liable to lead to loss of milk owing to it turning sour". This led to new collection times from the farms of 7.30 a.m. and 5.30 p.m.

In the summer of 1941, the problem of unhygienic – often referred to in documents as "dirty milk" – and adulterated milk was increasing. On the 27th June the Sanitary Inspector, Public Health Department, inspected the condition of the Vauxhall Dairy. In view of the facts of the report and in virtue of the powers of the Milk Control Order, the dairy's retailer's licence under the name of J. L. Mulholland was suspended. The following week Tanguy's Dairy Limited took over the territory of Vauxhall Dairy and the retailer's licence was reassigned to Mr H. E. Aubin. A report by the States Analyst for 1941, on samples of milk which were tested from around the Island, described a large number of samples and noted "... the unusual number of prosecutions for the sale of adulterated milk". The report, furthermore, emphasised "...a marked rise in the number of prosecutions...in view of the extreme importance of milk as a source of fat and of first-class protein". The major prosecutions were tabulated as follows.[6]

Milk Prosecutions 1941

Date of Prosecution	Extraneous Water %	Deficiency of Fat %
February 10th	14	Nil
March 24th	11	12
April 22nd	Nil	40
June 21st	39	Nil
June 21st	7	31
June 21st	41	43
June 21st	Nil	16
June 21st	21	30
June 21st	54	Nil
September 20th	16	Nil
Undated	32	Nil
Undated	32	Nil
Undated	31	Nil

Milk retailers and milk producer-retailers who adulterated, or took the fat content from milk, were normally given a formal warning if the infringement was not a large deficiency, as a percentage. Early in September the DOA interviewed Mr I. J. Le Flohic, proprietor of the United Dairies, 25 Hue Street, who had recently been presented before "justice" for the second time upon a charge of milk adulteration. He was warned that, should he be the subject of any further proceedings in connection with milk, the DOA would withdraw his retailer licence.[3]

Perhaps as a consequence of these problems in the retailing of milk, the DOA decided to enforce strict conditions and to exercise further rigour in the issuing of milk retailer licences. All retailers were warned to ensure that they only sold to their registered customers. They were to check that their milk deliveries were made in the territory allocated to them. Finally, they had to be absolutely certain that the daily quantity of milk supplied to each household did not exceed a half pint of full cream milk for each adult and 1 pint for each child under fifteen years of age. The only exceptions were for customers who were invalids or held medical certificates. The DOA also decided to incorporate a circular letter with an additional clause: "The sale of whole milk by the glass as well as the use of cream, whole milk or skim milk for the making of ice cream is strictly forbidden". The very next day, Mr G. Retrossi, Café Mignon, The Esplanade, wrote a letter to the DOA protesting against the prohibition of whole or skim milk imposed on his establishment by the order. He claimed that his entire business consisted of the manufacture of ice cream. The DOA, however, refused to alter its decision, which Weeks conveyed to Mr Retrossi.

The following week Sören Jensen wrote to the DOA explaining he could manufacture cheese from skim milk. Rather surprisingly, Jensen was informed that when skim milk was available, they would contact him. This was the end of the DOA's communication with Mr Jensen and the question arises: why was his offer rejected out of hand? The answer probably lies in the fact that 83% of the Island's skim milk went to farmers, and was used for feeding calves, heifers, and other livestock. The natural instincts of Le Gallais and Brée would certainly have been to maintain this distribution to the very people who supplied milk and produce for the Island, and who maintained prize Jersey herds.

On the 23rd June 1941 Weeks checked the milk records of the Victoria Dairy, although the reason for his doing so is not clear. However, that same week Victoria Dairy had been given permission, because of the condition of their milk, to use gas outside their permitted hours to treat the milk arriving from collections. Weeks, as Secretary of the Milk Control Section and now designated 'Manager and Secretary', had recently extended the scope of his bureaucratic powers. The additional milk legislation had greatly increased his range of responsibilities and led to a commensurate raising of his importance and salary. He wrote to the Victoria Dairy and informed them that he now wished to scrutinise their financial records. On the 10th July he received a letter from Alex Picot and Company, the auditors of the dairy, "...refusing on behalf of the dairy to allow Mr Weeks to examine the books and records of the dairy". Brée therefore decided to ask the Attorney General for advice concerning the legal position of the DOA arising from the refusal. The Attorney General replied and advised Brée that the DOA was to ask Barton Mayhew & Company to undertake the examination of the dairy's records. The subsequent audit demonstrated that there were no problems or discrepancies discovered in the dairy's books and records.

Also on the 23rd June Dr R. McKinstry, the Medical Officer for Health, requested that he receive "...particulars of the shops and offices which were receiving supplies of milk for the making of morning or afternoon tea". The DOA, two weeks later and in view of Dr McKinstry having approved all applications for additional milk to shops and offices, decided to inform the Superior Council that it proposed to withdraw these milk supplies after 30th August 1941. This would be extended to the States' textile works at Summerland, Rouge Bouillon.

The Superior Council agreed to the suspension of milk for shops and offices. It added, however, that if the Medical Board had concerns over the issue, it could ask the DOA to allow dispensations. The DOA agreed but reserved the right to accept or reject any recommendation of the Medical Board.

On the 15th August, Dr McKinstry wrote to the DOA referencing the milk supply as an important substitute for the lack of extra rations of other foods, but the DOA had decided that it must reduce all extra calls upon the Island's milk supply. Under pressure from the Medical Officer the DOA convened a meeting between the Department of Essential Supplies, the Medical Officer and itself for the following week. The DOA planned the meeting "In an endeavour to decide upon a basic policy to operate for the future in deciding upon the issue of extra rationing of milk". Le Gallais was instructed to prepare a report for this meeting and in particular the quantity of skim milk available. His report made clear the percentage of skim milk that was distributed on the Island: the public 15%; establishments 2%; and farmers 83%. On the 21st August Brée and Le Gallais, representing the DOA, met with Edwin Le Masurier and Thomas Mourant, the Department of Essential Supplies, Dr McKinstry, and A. Le Gresley, Food Controller. In addition, Weeks, with the appellation of "Secretary/Accountant of the DOA's Milk Control Section", was invited to attend.

The question of extra milk rations was thoroughly discussed with divergent and expressive opinions set forth. The decision was made to modify the previous order by deleting the permission therein granted for shops and offices to appeal to the Medical Board for a continuation of their supplies. In addition, all extra rations of milk would be reviewed by the Medical Board and no further milk would be granted without the recommendation of the Board. The three departments agreed that a new Medical Board comprising Dr McKinstry, Dr H. F. Blampied and Mr A. C. Halliwell, FRCS, be appointed to decide upon all questions relating to the extra rations of milk. The DOA recalled its order that it had the right to either accept or reject any recommendation of the Medical Board.

On the 28th July, Mr R. W. Jackson was alleged to have manufactured butter from his milk without the necessary butter licence. The matter was referred to the Attorney General who subsequently decided to prosecute. Mr E. C. Benest, whose cows yielded 28 pots of milk, failed to deliver it to the collecting dairy; he was formally warned, and the matter concluded. Mr E. W. Pallot was formally interviewed to explain the reasons why his household of two people was consuming 10 pots of milk weekly but only possessed one cow. He immediately agreed to send in all his milk to the dairy. On the 18th August milk collection times were changed to 8.00 a.m. and 5.30 p.m.

On the 1st September, the Milk Control Section wrote to all milk retailers and producer-retailers who were licensed under the Milk Control (Jersey) Order, 1940, demanding that they distribute whole milk on the following basis: 1 pint of whole milk per child and a half pint per adult. They were warned that any infringement would mean their licence would be withdrawn. It was made clear that any extra milk must be approved and granted only on the recommendations of the Medical Board and Department of Essential Commodities. The cessation of extra supplies to establishments prompted an immediate response from the Honorary Secretary of the Victoria Club requesting his members continue to receive their extra milk. The Honorary Secretary was given an immediate refusal, and in addition, the Milk Control Section stopped all supplies to the Alliance Club, the Mechanics' Institute and the YMCA.

Additional milk for vulnerable groups now became a disagreement between McKinstry and Weeks. The former wrote to the DOA on the 3rd September recommending the issue of additional milk to children under two years and to the "inmates" of Miss Newman's Home for Aged Women. Le Gallais agreed to discuss the matter with Dr McKinstry. An increasing volume of requests for additional milk had cascaded down to the Medical Board. The decision was made to authorise Le Gallais, Weeks and Dr McKinstry to liaise with the Food Controller and to find a solution to this problem. On the 8th September, the Milk Control Section decided to reduce by half the supply of milk to restaurants and cafés; in addition, making the quantity consist of 33⅓% full milk and 662/3% skim milk. On the same day Dr McKinstry wrote to the DOA and recommended that the States Textile Department at Summerland be granted a supply of skim milk to replace the full milk previously withdrawn. The DOA refused to agree to the request.

The reasons given were firstly, that granting extra skim milk to Summerland would encourage shops and offices also to ask; and secondly, the quantity of skim milk available was not sufficient to cope with the increased demand. The final premise is difficult to fully understand considering 83% of skim milk was distributed amongst farmers. Eleven days later, Brée reported that the DOA's refusal to grant skim milk to the Textile Department at Summerland had been referred to the Superior Council by the Medical Board. The Superior Council decided, despite Brée's recommendations, to allow an extra allocation. Le Gallais was extremely angry and demanded that a statement be inserted in the record of "This energetic protest against the action of the Superior Council in this matter".

Dr McKinstry, with one victory under his belt over the issue, decided to pursue the request for extra milk for children under two years of age. The Medical Board on the 3rd September recommended that an extra milk allowance be given by the Milk Control Section. Their request was successful and on the 21st September a notice was published in the Evening Post that, from 1st October, children aged not more than two years would be entitled to receive a total quantity of one and a half pints of full cream milk daily.

The Milk Control Section, under the leadership of Weeks, continued its efficient examination of milk production and consumption. On the 26th September, the DOA formally interviewed Mr P. V. Sarre, Bel Royal on the subject of his household consumption of milk. Brée charged Sarre to ensure he took steps to reduce his family's consumption and to send the appropriate amount to the dairy so that the Island's butter production could be increased. No further action was deemed necessary.[3]

On the 23rd September 1941 notice was given of new milk collection times for dairy farmers.

Month	A.M.	P.M.
October 1941	8.30	3.30
November 1941	9.00	No collection
December 1941	9.00	No collection

On the 22nd October the leading dairy farmers wrote to the DOA, through the auspices of the RJA&HS and the JFU, requesting a subsidy of 2 pence per pot, out of public funds, for the milk they produced. The reason given was to meet the increased costs of production arising from the lower yields from cows in the absence of concentrates and the additional costs of labour. The DOA decided to increase the amount paid until the 30th April 1942 when it would revert to its original price.

On the 29th October, Weeks drew attention to "The continual fall in the amount of butter manufactured by the Don Street Dairy and the unauthorised sales of milk to the German forces by producer-retailers". Weeks was charged to produce a list of producer-retailers who sold milk to the German forces so that appropriate action could be taken. In addition, Weeks wrote to all milk producers, in English and in German, to the effect that they must not supply milk to members of the German armed forces except against orders from the German Catering Services, York Street, St Helier. On the 3rd November, Weeks brought to the attention of the DOA the problem "...concerning the serious position likely to arise as a result of the increasing supplies of milk required by the German forces of occupation on the Island". The DOA, therefore, decided to ask Brée and the Bailiff to "...take up the matter directly with the German Field Command, with a view to a reduction being made in the supplies of milk required by the German forces". Both men discussed the matter with the Field Commandant. Subsequently, in view of the evidence of the German Field Command and in accordance with their instructions, Weeks was instructed to revoke all produce-retailer licences issued in virtue of Article 3(1), Milk Control (Jersey) Order, 1940, and Article 3(2) of the order. On instructions from Field Command 515, three producer-retailer licences were revoked in those cases where the DOA was dissatisfied with "...the conduct of how the holder of such licences carried on his business". These were Mr Abraham J. Baal, Miss Matilda A. Le Cornu and Mr A. L. Le Mière.

At the same time the Milk Control Section, "In view of the present very serious situation regarding the supply of milk available for the population" decided to "withdraw all licences which have been issued for the manufacture of butter". On the same day the DOA appointed a sub-committee comprising Brée and Le Gallais to again hold a meeting with Dr McKinstry with a view to securing a further reduction in the milk consumption of the various categories of people receiving extra milk.

On the 12th and 27th November, OKVR Dr Casper, on behalf of Field Command 515, wrote to the Bailiff concerning the implementation of an entire reorganisation of the Island's milk control.[7] Dr Casper ordered a completely new model based on the Guernsey example. He informed the Bailiff of the specific principals that Field Command 515 wished to implement.

1. Every farmer will be obliged to deliver up all his milk.
2. All milk is to be collected, processed, and distributed by a central depot or dairy commissioned for the purpose.
3. The Field Command will cooperate with this reorganisation.
4. The new Milk Order is to be implemented in 1942 when all milk licences will be revoked.
5. The reorganisation of milk collections is to be completed by December 1941.
6. Dr Casper instructs that a representation be sent at 11.00 a.m. on 10th December 1941, with a progress report, to Room 20, College House. [Room 20 was KVR Pelz's office.]

The reasons for Dr Casper's demands were clear: "There is no doubt that a stricter collection of milk will be made necessary by the altered circumstances and to ensure the distribution of milk and butter".[8]

The Bailiff immediately forwarded Dr Casper's demands to Brée, who responded to the Field Command that he would defer the matter until the 1st March 1942. Furthermore, he produced a detailed list of arguments as to why the Guernsey milk control model would not be achievable in Jersey.

1. The reversal of an immemorial custom of milk distribution would be a problem.
2. The changes would adversely affect one third of the Island's population. This consequently would be to the detriment of 12,740 people.
3. 390 licensed farmers would be affected as retailers.
4. The new model would produce less milk because 390 farmers would receive 9¼ pence instead of 1/- per pot of milk. The maximum benefits of milk production would go to the dairies.
5. Transport difficulties would render the scheme impracticable.
6. The scheme would be prejudicial to public health.
7. No changes would be effected until the winter of 1942.

On the 17th December, Brée reported that the German authorities had decided to postpone their requirement that all producer-retailer licences be withdrawn and Dr Casper's proposed milk control scheme was dropped. Brée, Le Gallais and Dr McKinstry met to discuss the provision of extra milk for diabetics and for stokers of the Jersey Gas Light Company Limited.

On the 17th December 1941 the Bailiff, the Attorney General, Brée, OKVR Dr Casper and KVR Pelz met to discuss the question of Milk Control. They agreed upon the following proposals:

1. The changes to Milk Control would be implemented on the 1st March 1942.
2. Compulsory milk testing would be introduced for all farmers. Every farmer would be visited at least twice a month by a Milk Tester who would be present at both the morning and evening milking.
3. All milk yields would be entered in his control book and on a control card. The control card would remain in the possession of the farmer.

Casper and Pelz made it clear that "Experienced milkers shall be appointed for the milking tests, men who are not only honest, but above all, men who are masters of the technical side of milking and who can act as models and teachers in this line. It is a well-known fact that much milk is lost on many farms through incorrect milking".

In a radical move to deal with the problem of dairy farmers not supplying their quota of milk, a new inspectorate was established. These new inspectors were called "Milk Testers". They worked under Milk Control to check and verify milk yields from all the Island's dairy farmers. Advertisements were placed in the press soon after the 23rd December inviting men to apply for the position. Commonly described as "Inspectors", these "Milk Testers" became the most disliked and despised officials sent out by the DOA during the German occupation.

The appointment of Milk Testers was a response to Field Command 515 demanding a more rigorous milk control organisation, and it was also in consequence of a report by the Milk Control Section of the DOA on the 19th December which stated that "The supplies of milk coming from the country are insufficient to meet the requirements of the urban population of the Island". The inference of this unwitting evidence is that dairy farmers were keeping supplies of milk which should have been delivered to the collecting dairies. On the 23rd December, Brée and Le Gallais met the Dairymen's Committee of the Chamber of Commerce. They discussed "The present serious shortage in the supplies of liquid milk available for the requirements of the population". The meeting consequently recommended to the Superior Council, "...that there should be a weekly milkless day for adults whilst supplies are short". The Superior Council rejected the proposal. Instead, it "...decided that a voluntary reduction of supplies of milk to adults, if necessary, be operated by the milk retailers".

The rationalisation of collecting, processing and distributing the Island's milk supply had the strong imprint of Pelz's analytical and strategic thinking. He was fully aware of milk yields because of his extensive knowledge of Island dairy practices. He had come to know on a personal level many of Jersey's cattle-breeding fraternity and dairy farmers. In addition, he understood the working of the Jersey Herd Book and the methodology of the RJA&HS in recording milk tests and yields for its members. However, this milk testing and recording was carried out only by dairy farmers who wanted it. Pelz, after implementation of the new Milk Control Order, wanted a compulsory regime of testing and recording. In addition, he instructed that such tests and milk yields be forwarded to the Herd Book. Pelz explained that this was essential and valuable for examining and judging Jersey cattle.

In late December 1941 Field Command again instructed the Bailiff that he must reorganise the Island's Milk Control. The German Military Government wanted the model to be closely based on the Guernsey Milk Control Law.[9]

Brée discussed the matter with the Superior Council on the 30th December. His report stated, "In view of the fact that the letter conveys the instructions of the Occupying Authority the DOA has no alternative but to take the necessary measures to give effect to instructions contained in the said letter.[10]

Cultivation Orders

> *"The Bailiff addressed the meeting pointing out it is essential that the Island should be, as far as possible, self-supporting and asking that the Honorary Inspectors will do their utmost to ensure that the best possible use is made of the arable land in the Island."*

Meeting of Bailiff, DOA, and Honorary Parish Agricultural Inspectors – October 1941
The 1942 Cropping Plan

The Cultivation of Lands (Jersey) Order, 1940, was the most important law the DOA enacted to control agriculture during the German occupation. It defined the DOA's powers and instructed farmers what to grow, where to sow and when to harvest. It supervised all their agricultural inputs and collected all their outputs. It was responsible for the storage and distribution of all locally grown produce. It also enforced a well-run and organised inspectorate regime which scrutinised the crops and offered advice to farmers. The inspectorate had powerful rights of entry into farm buildings and all fields.

On the 20th June 1941, Brée directed Mr J. B. Arthur to destroy 8 vergées of potatoes grown under direction of a Cultivation Order; the field was "poor and weedy". On the same day the veterinary surgeon, Edgar Messervy, was allocated a petrol allowance of 5 gallons a week – the same as Thomas Blampied – in order to carry out DOA orders. On the 23rd June, Mr J. F. Pirouet was ordered to clear up within seven days the dock weeds in a field of 4 vergées of wheat.

The increasing number of German troops arriving in the Island led to increasing sales of agricultural produce by Jersey farmers to members of the armed forces. In response, the Field Commandant wrote to the DOA, instructing them that notices be sent to every farmer and grower drawing attention "...to the requirements of the German Field Command that no agricultural produce or stock is to be supplied to members of the German forces unless they produce an order signed by the German Field Command authorising such purchases". This notice was typed and sent to all farmers in both English and German.

The increase in German military units on the Island also led to encroachments by them when carrying out field exercises. This directly led to problems with farmers. A letter from solicitors Renouf, Ereaut and Gibaut to the DOA on the 2nd July 1941, claimed financial compensation for Harold Le Brocq, in respect of a heifer found drowned in a tank on the Moie (La Moye) golf course after straying. Le Brocq alleged that the German army of occupation had destroyed his fence. John du Val, Connétable, and a member of the DOA, and Edward Rive Egré, Honorary Parish Inspector, both of St Peter, immediately inspected the site and forwarded a report on the condition of Mr Le Brocq's fence. It concluded that the fence was in a very bad state of repair and not cattle-proof. The DOA refused Le Brocq's claim. However, the following week saw eight claims made by farmers in respect of compensation for damage resulting from the occupation of their land by German military forces. The DOA awarded them a total of £154- 6-6. Brée, on the 25th July, submitted these compensation awards to the Superior Council. The Superior

Council, in an attempt to halt a cascade of further claims by farmers, refused to authorise them and directed that all such claims by farmers be filed by the Department of Finance and Economics. The claims would be considered after the termination of hostilities. However, where cases involved exceptional hardship for farmers, the Superior Council, would consider the issue on its individual merits. All eight claimants were informed of the decision.

On the 30th June the DOA interviewed Mr and Mrs E. Le Chevalier concerning a report by the Honorary Parish Inspectors that 4 vergées of wheat under Cultivation Orders was seriously neglected. The case was referred to the Attorney General, who in turn wrote to the Honorary Inspectors requiring that the field be re-inspected, and a judgement made whether Mr Le Chevalier had by his neglect and incompetent husbandry permitted the destruction of the crop. The subsequent report was extremely unfavourable. The DOA, therefore, rather than press for a prosecution, stopped the payment of any weighbridge tickets held by him. The reason for this action was that Mr Le Chevalier had drawn financial assistance under the agricultural credit scheme.

In August 1941 Field Command 515 requested to take grass turf from the racecourse at Les Quennevais for the requirements of the airport. Mr D. T. Langlois of Franc Fief Farm wrote to Field Command demanding the restoration of his requisitioned farm.[11] Field Command subsequently wrote to the DOA asking, on behalf of Langlois, for a solution to the requisitioning of his farm to which the DOA replied, making it clear that it was unable to accede to Mr Langlois' request.

By the summer of 1941 the DOA was the sole purchaser of all cereal and potato crops. It was responsible for the storage and marketing of these crops, and it also had full control of milk collection, distribution and rationing. In addition, it had a network of agricultural inspectors checking on pigs, cattle, cereals, potatoes and milk production as well as storage of agricultural outputs. In an attempt to rationalise the Department, the secretary, Colin Marie, proposed on the 1st September that he establish a separate section as a Trading Department to deal with accounting for the potato and cereal harvests. The scheme was subsequently approved by the States Auditor.

These changes meant a considerable increase of staff at the DOA in order to deal with the forthcoming harvests, and all clerks had their wages increased to £3 a week. It was also an opportune time for the leading DOA "apparatchiks" to promote themselves. On the 8th September, Philip George Cabot, Chief Clerk, was appointed as "accountant" in charge of the new Trading Section at a weekly wage of £5. Cabot immediately requested additional clerical staff and was joined in the same week by Mr A. C. Walker, followed by Mrs M. E. Gates, Mr S. G. Cartes, Mr H. G. Brideaux, Mr B. Bateman, Miss Kathleen Picot and Mr George Alfred Norman.

On the 27th August, Field Command 515 wrote to the DOA informing it that, "It must supply Guernsey with the necessary seed for growing 300 hectares of cereals and 500 hectares of potatoes for 1942". The DOA wrote to the Controlling Committee in Guernsey for particulars of their requirements. On the 15th September Brée proposed his 1942 cropping plan to representatives of Guernsey and Field Command 515. At the meeting the decision was made that only potatoes would be planted on côtils in 1942. Brée had learnt from experience that growing cereal crops on côtils presented problems as they were more "droughty" than deeper soils, yielded less, and were problematic to harvest. His original draft cropping plan for 1942 was as follows.

Crop	Area in Vergées
Barley	300
Rye	300
Wheat	11,200
Oats	3,600
Early potatoes	5,130
Seed for 1943	2,500
Late varieties	1,500
Mangolds	3,320
Hay and grazing	12,000
Area for cultivation 1942 – Total	39,850

The Superior Council met to discuss the DOA's Trading Department, particularly wanting to investigate the unsatisfactory condition of the trading accounts. A minute of the meeting makes it clear that a new system of accounting was needed:

"The [Superior] Council took into consideration the following minute of the Department of Finance and Economics, dated 10th September 1941".

"The President informed the Department that the States Auditor has reported on the unsatisfactory condition of the Trading Accounts of the Agriculture Department and that he considered it essential that a new accountancy department be organised to deal with trading accounts relative to this season's potato and cereal crops".

The Department of Finance and Economics decided to refer the matter to the Superior Council with the recommendation that the joint departments of Finance and Agriculture should, in conjunction with the States Auditor, go into the whole of the Trading Accounts for the purpose of, firstly, verifying the outstanding balances on last season's trading accounts and, secondly, reorganising the accountancy department of the Trading Section to deal with this season's crops.

As a result, the DOA nominated Brée and Le Gallais to form a sub-committee to discuss with the Department of Finance and Economics "The operation of the Trading Section of the DOA". On the 23rd September Brée and Le Gallais met with Jurat Edgar Aleck Dorey,

President of Finance and Economics, concerning the status of the Grain and Potato Control – formerly known as the Trading Section of the DOA. Dorey made it clear its directives would have to be followed exactly. On the 3rd October, P. G. Cabot was put in charge of the "Grain and Potato Section".

In the same week allegations were presented to the DOA that Mr J. Vautier, St Ouen, was not cultivating his farmland; and that Messrs J. C. Langlois, R. H. Langlois and E. G. Langlois of St Saviour had allowed their crops to fall into a poor condition.[3]

These allegations were handed to Mallet and Le Gallais to investigate. Their subsequent reports into the condition of the cereal crops on the land in St Saviour ordered the Langlois family to cut and thresh their barley field, as well as two further fields of cereals, and deliver the grain to the DOA. Mr J. Vautier was found not to have cultivated 10 vergées of farmland in 1941, although he had been instructed to do so with directions issued under the Cultivation of Lands Order, 1940. In view of this apparent refusal to comply with DOA orders, Vautier's case was forwarded to the Attorney General with a view to instituting proceedings.

On the 30th September 1941, Brée presented his proposed 1942 cropping plan to the Bailiff and the Honorary Parish Inspectors. At a meeting on the 11th October the Bailiff addressed the full DOA Committee and the Inspectors, who were:

St Brelade	J. J. Le Boutillier	H. M. Gibaut
St Clement	J. P. Le Masurier	E. J. Malzard
Grouville	S. G. Le Couilliard	E. S. Le Geyt
St Helier	P. J. Mourant	P. L. Baudains
St John	J. Gartrell	C. Le Couteur
St Lawrence	F.J. Ahier	H. W. Maillard
St Martin	P. Ahier	G. Le Masurier
St Mary	P. Le Feuvre	E. J. Le Ruez
St Ouen	G. E. Huelin	E. G. Vautier
St Peter	G. H. Le Rossignol	E. R. Egré
St Saviour	P. Gallichan	C. Quenault
Trinity	C. P. Ahier	A. R. Le Brun

A comprehensive explanation of the 1942 cropping plan was given by Brée to all attendees. The Bailiff also addressed the meeting. "He pointed out that it is essential that the Island should be as far as possible self-supporting and asked that the best possible use is made of the arable land in the Island".

1942 Draft Cropping Plan – Prepared by T. J. Brée

Copy Sent to Bailiff and Honorary Inspectors – 30th September 1941

Parish	1940 Area	Barley	Rye	Wheat	Oats	Potatoes Local Use	Seed for 1943	Late	Mangolds	Grazing & Hay	Total Vergées
St Brelade	2,500	100	150	250	400	250	150	50	300	700	2,350
St Clement	1,400	50		250	200	220	150	50	120	300	1,340
Grouville	2,900	50		650	450	300	150	100	300	800	2,800
St Helier	2,000			500	325	250	150	75	200	700	2,200
St John	3,400			1,100	400	200	150	100	300	1,100	3,350
St Lawrence	3,900			1,300	475	350	200	75	400	1,000	3,800
St Martin	4,100			1,550	400	300	150	100	300	1,200	4,000
St Mary	2,700			650	250	180	100	75	250	1,150	2,655
St Ouen	5,000	200	150	1,550	350	650	250	75	400	1,200	4,825
St Peter	3,900	100	50	1,100	300	500	200	100	300	1,100	3,750
St Saviour	3,800	100		1,600	200	250	150	75	200	1,050	3,625
Trinity	5,000			1,700	400	375	200	125	450	1,700	4,950
	40,600	600	350	12,200	4,150	3,825	2,000	1,000	3,520	12,000	39,645

In October 1941 Brée extended the financial assurances he had given to farmers the previous year. On the 31st October he announced, "In view of the lack of artificial fertilisers", that he had decided to make a ½ reduction in the total area allocated to potatoes in the 1942 cropping plan. The new reduced parish allocation, in vergées, was as follows.

St Brelade	385
St Clement	260
Grouville	472
St Helier	365
St John	385
St Lawrence	535
St Martin	472
St Mary	347
St Ouen	793
St Peter	686
St Saviour	493
Trinity	672
Total	5865

In October, Mrs Mary Jane Perreau, St Ouen, the owner of 4 vergées, failed to cultivate her farmland. The DOA decided to requisition the land, "To ensure that it is properly cultivated and kept in the useful employment for the requirements of the Island." The DOA dealt not only with the non-cultivation of farmland, but also the deliberate destruction of crops. A report on a field of barley in St Lawrence led to a prosecution. In November, four farmers were referred by the DOA to the Attorney General for deliberately neglecting their crops and not fulfilling Cultivation Orders. On the 12th November, the Honorary Parish Inspector for Grouville, Mr S. G. Le Couilliard resigned on the grounds of physical disability and three extra clerks were employed by the DOA.

In December, the DOA convened a meeting of the Honorary Parish Inspectors to discuss the 1942 ploughing season and three decisions were made.

1. The Honorary Parish Inspectors are to supply the 1942 petrol ration for their respective parishes to the ploughing contractors nominated in each parish. The method of distribution to be left to the Inspector.
2. The use of a Fordson or any large type of tractor of more than 14 horsepower is not permitted.
3. The petrol allocation must strictly be used only for the purpose of ploughing.

At a further meeting of the Honorary Parish Inspectors, it was decided that the ploughing contractors would be paid £1-10-0 per vergée and in turn each contractor would be required to pay to the DOA the sum of 13/6d per vergée ploughed by him, to cover the cost of fuel and administration supplied by the DOA. In addition, the contractor must state the horsepower and age of his tractor. The Inspectors decided that the maximum depth for ploughing wheat and oat fields should be 6 inches. Each contractor was required to keep a logbook showing the name and address of each farmer for whom he ploughed and the number of vergées so ploughed.

1 gallon of petrol was allocated per vergée, plus 2 gallons each week for transport between farms – provided that the contractor worked at least four days in that week. Subsequently the petrol allowance was increased to 1⅛ gallon per vergée in respect of oats and 1½ gallons per vergée in respect of potatoes. After numerous differences of opinion between the Inspectors, the maximum depth was withdrawn and became discretionary for each Inspector. The ploughing contractors for the 1941 season were as follows.[12]

J. E. A'Court
G. Baudains
P. J. Blandin
A. G. Cotillard
J. W. de Gruchy
J. W. du Feu
E. Dupays
H. E. Egré
J. P. Godfray
S. B. Helier
A. J. Hervé
Y. Jonny
S. Petry
E. Le Riche
L. C. Pallot
P. Pirouet
C. W. Poignard
A. E. Prouten
C. S. Rondel
P. F. Bisson
C. W. Burrel

In December 1941 four more inspectors were appointed under the Potatoes (Sales and Returns) (Amendment) (Jersey) Order, 1941, and sworn in at the Royal Court: O. Hamon, J. W. Blampied, S. Le Gresley and J. Le Maistre

On the 23rd December, the DOA requisitioned two new Ferguson tractors belonging to Dr C. Mattas. He ran a successful general practice in Jersey and was well known amongst the Island's boxing fraternity, attending matches as the resident doctor.

The month of December saw a large area of agricultural land requisitioned by the German authorities and advertisements were placed in the local press informing farmers whose land had been requisitioned to send details, in writing, by the 7th January 1942 to their Connétables.

Potatoes

"The Price Advisory Board was informed that 10,000 tons of potatoes were required by the German authorities."

The Price Advisory Board was set up by the Superior Council to establish the price paid to farmers for potatoes and on the 28th May 1941 it met to discuss a letter received by Touzel Brée. He had been informed by the German Field Command that 10,000 tons of potatoes were required by the German authorities.[13]

The DOA, on the 4th June, recommended to the Superior Council that if potatoes were exported on behalf of the German authorities, it would require farmers to be reimbursed, as the price paid for potatoes by the German authorities was different to the price paid to farmers by the Price Advisory Board. The loss or profit between the two would be borne by the States. On the same day a JPMA delegation comprising J. M. Norman, Chas Gruchy and C. Mossop met with the DOA to discuss the issue of potato exports for the German authorities. The JPMA agreed to pack, and deliver to the quay at St Helier Harbour, the 100 tons which the DOA had been instructed to ship on the 7th June for the requirements of the German authorities, at whatever price may have been sanctioned by the Superior Council. The JPMA agreed that these potato exports would not be weighed at their stores but that all loads would be over the official weighbridge prior to shipment. Each Connétable would act as an "allocation officer" for the supply of these potatoes from their respective parishes.

The Price Advisory Board comprised: Messrs V.J. Bailhache, President, F. P. Le Quesne, J. B. Michel and H. Sutherland. Meetings were held during June 1941 between the Board, the DOA, the farming unions, and the Superior Council, in order to come to an agreement on the probable yield for the 1942 season. No estimate could be agreed upon between the differing interest groups which proved problematic for Brée and the DOA because it was essential to know what quantity would be needed in 1942 for the local population. The Board did agree that, once its control was established, it should be possible to bring the estimated crop and estimated consumption into line and establish what would be the real surplus available for winter provision.[13]

On the 12th June, the Price Advisory Board met a delegation of the Superior Council – Jurats Dorey and E. P. Le Masurier – and the DOA. The meeting was convened to cover all the pricing elements of the 1942 crop. All parties agreed to the DOA's suggestion that 1,000 tons of seed potatoes be secured for 1942, and to plant the same area as was estimated to have been grown in 1941. An extremely protracted and detailed discussion took place. All the elements of the costs of production and agricultural inputs were scrutinised: digging, harvesting, wage subsidy, delivery to market, fertilisers, credits, various overheads, and depreciation. The final cost of production for the 1942 crop was calculated at £28-13-6 per vergée. The cost which the Advisory Board had calculated on 23rd May was £33-6-0. It was agreed by all parties that the price paid to farmers would be left to the DOA for adjustment. Brée made it clear that good quality potatoes used for clamping would have a premium of 9d per hundredweight.

On 20th June the DOA received a letter from "Dr Broach" of the German Field Command.[14] He wanted to know what provisions had been made for combatting Colorado Beetle should the pest manifest itself. The Colorado Beetle problem was discussed between D. Simpson and E. J. Woodcock, both of whom were scientific advisors to the DOA. They advised that the DOA should endeavour to purchase 5 tons of lead arsenate, or calcium arsenate, in powder form for the production of a wet spray. Dr Brosch was asked to purchase the chemicals on behalf of the Island.

On the same day the DOA, having examined the export figures for potatoes on behalf of the German authorities, decided to set up three new potato accounts: the German, Guernsey, and Clamping Accounts. They were to be used forthwith to pay farmers for their weighbridge tickets, and into which monies from the sale of potatoes would be paid. The Department of Finance and Economics was instructed to open the new accounts. A previous account, entitled "The Potato Account 1941", was henceforth to be used for making payments in respect of bagging, transporting, and shipping, with the amounts so paid debited "pro rata" to the German, Guernsey, and Clamping Accounts.

In late June 1941, the JPMA wrote directly to the Superior Council complaining that farmers were undercutting them in the retail trade. The Price Advisory Board was instructed to examine this question and in turn they recommended:

1. That it is not practicable to control the entire distribution of potatoes through the merchants. There has always been a custom of allowing farmers to dispose of their produce to the retailer.
2. Fixed prices are to be established – but not a maximum – which will prevent under-selling.
3. On certification from an inspector a deduction of 10% on grower/distributor prices and on distributor/retailer prices can be allowed in the case of inferior potatoes, thus creating a second grade of potato which can be sold at a lower price.
4. In the case of retail sales, for a large quantity, a concession on the fixed retail price per pound weight can be made.

On the 27th June the DOA notified all Parish Allocation Officers that, when allocating potatoes for shipment on behalf of the German authorities, special consideration should be given to enable the owners of large herds to replace those fields with root crops for their cattle. On the same day, J. M. Norman wrote to the DOA with confirmation of the packing allocations for the various merchants' stores in connection with "...the export of potatoes to the order of the German authorities" which were approved by the DOA. A week later Mr Norman wrote again with a revised packing allocation for the German exports and this was also approved. On 30th June, all farmers who supplied potatoes for export by the German authorities were paid by the DOA for the delivery of their product upon presentation of their weighbridge tickets.

On the 7th July, all farmers with Cultivation Orders to grow potatoes were instructed to keep up to 125 boxes of seed per vergée for the 1942 crop, to be planted on the same area as they had been directed by individual Cultivation Orders for 1941. On the same day the JPMA was informed that their packing and shipping charges for potato exports ordered by the German authorities would only be paid on the weight exported and not on the weight the merchants had taken from their respective stores.

At a meeting of the Price Advisory Board on the 11th July, Mr Norman suggested that, apart from the representatives of the JFU and RJA&HS, two independent farmers, T. J. Ahier and P. C. Mourant, should be allowed to represent their respective colleagues. J. B. Michel insisted that a revision be sought for the prices paid to farmers as the yield was far lighter than expected. In fact, the entire 1941 crop had "A lack of exact figures in regard to the area of potatoes grown." The Board went further with its criticism of the DOA; not only was there apparent confusion regarding the total amount grown in 1941, but the DOA was experiencing continued problems with obtaining exact figures for the amount being stored by the merchants.

On the 28th July the DOA appointed two inspectors to check all potato stocks in merchants' stores. They were Mr O. P. Gautier and Mr J. F. Blanchet and they were to share a weekly wage of £2-15-0. On the 1st August, the DOA interviewed a delegation from the JPMA comprising Chas Gruchy, John Amy, and Bernard Horsfall, concerning the provision and distribution of potatoes for the requirements of the Island. The delegation expressed the opinion that the DOA should act "...as a distributor of potatoes in the manner that was in operation last year." It furthermore confirmed that a proportion of the Island's requirements would be stored by merchants selected only by the JPMA. Four days later the DOA received a letter from the JPMA asking that the DOA "Assume responsibility for securing supplies of potatoes as from 1st September (1941) as the members of the JPMA cannot face the financial burden entailed by the purchase of potatoes for storage." The DOA immediately asked the Superior Council to authorise that it "Act as the sole channel of distribution of potatoes between farmer and merchant and to prepare such legislation as may be required to effect this."

In a further attempt to secure an increased supply for the civilian population, Brée contacted Field Command 515 to receive consent for the temporary cessation of shipments on their orders. In addition, 2,000 tons would be put into store for the Island's population. Colin Marie was instructed to inform all Parish Allocation Officers to secure this quantity for immediate storage. Brée's actions in securing extra potatoes for the Island's requirements were approved.

The JPMA, now responsible for storage of the Island's potatoes, was voicing its requirements as to exactly on what terms its members would be willing to store them for the benefit of both the civilian population and the German authorities. On the 11th August the DOA approved the terms:

1. The DOA will pay to the storing merchant 10/- per ton irrespective of the period covered by such storage.
2. The DOA will pay a further 1 penny per hundredweight to cover the cost of sorting potatoes in store on its behalf, three to four weeks after such potatoes have been taken into store. Any wastage found at the time is to be immediately reported in writing to the secretary of the DOA.
3. A further payment of 1 penny per hundredweight for bagging potatoes will be made to those merchants who must supply the DOA's potatoes to other merchants for the requirements of the local trade.

On the 18th August, reports arrived that eelworm had been discovered at James' Bichard's market garden, Sancroft, Millbrook; his potatoes were immediately purchased by the DOA. The same day a letter was received from German Field Command referring to a request, the previous week, to cease the export of 2,000 tons on behalf of the German authorities. Field Command 515 made it clear that it would not tolerate the suspension of potato shipments during the period of the cereal harvest and, furthermore, demanded that 10,000 tons of potatoes be made available. On the 19th August, the DOA charged the Treasurer of the States to credit the German Field Command in Guernsey with £1-8-9 in respect of five bags of potatoes despatched from Jersey which the Field Command alleged had never been delivered. The Treasurer debited the amount to the "Potato Fund Occupation Account".

At the end of August, a letter from Field Command 515 informed the DOA that, "It must supply Guernsey with the necessary seed for sowing 300 hectares of cereals and 500 hectares of potatoes for 1942." It was decided to enquire from the Guernsey Controlling Committee exactly what were the particulars of their requirements before proceeding.

On the 23rd August, the DOA requested W. Dennis and Sons Ltd to release 75 tons of potatoes held in storage, to fulfil an order received from Field Command 515 for the export of 100 tons. The DOA charged the German Field Command £9 per ton. The funds were posted to the credit of "Potato Storage Fund".

P. G. Cabot reported that a shipment of potatoes to the order of the German authorities, but not yet shipped, had been transferred to Dennis and Sons, for distribution to the German forces in the Island. The DOA decided that these potatoes came under the storage agreement made with the merchants and not under the "shipment agreement". Therefore, the merchant concerned was entitled to the sum of 10/- per ton storage charge, plus the sum of 1 penny per hundredweight, the cost of bagging. Cabot was subsequently charged to debit these payments to the German account. In addition, Brée was authorised, "To approve payment to W. Dennis and Sons Ltd, the sum of £1,538-10-2 in respect of potatoes purchased by W. Dennis and Sons Ltd, for providing supplies of potatoes for the German troops of occupation of the Island."

On 8th September, Brée rescinded an order of the 9th August and now permitted the lifting of all types of maincrop and other varieties of potatoes. Farmers were ordered to deliver them to the JPMA stores, with the exception of chats.[15] In addition, they were informed that, once their potatoes were in store, they would be sorted for suitable seed which would be given back to them for the 1942 season. The DOA also decided that farmers who delivered late varieties into store would be allowed to take back a quantity for their own use. On the first delivery of twenty-two barrels the farmer was permitted to take home five and, for every subsequent twenty-two barrels delivered, the farmer was allowed to keep one, to a maximum of fifteen barrels. P. G. Cabot, in charge of the new Trading Section of the DOA, oversaw the entire process and became fully responsible for all potato and cereal transactions. In his new position Cabot had noted that the above delivery process and the transfer of potatoes from certain stores to the stores of W. Dennis and Sons Ltd, had resulted in potatoes not being officially weighed at the weighbridge. This resulted in stocks shown on the DOA's books no longer being accurate. He therefore re-examined all the returns made by merchants and carried out a full stock-take of potatoes in storage.

Cabot soon discovered further problems – some potatoes delivered to the DOA stores were sub-standard. He had received a report on the 20th August from the Chief Inspector, Mr A. V. Godfrey who described a load of "Kerr's Pink" variety delivered by Mr E. F. Vibert which were green and in poor condition owing to the large amount of "chats". The DOA's employees sorted the entire load and removed the chats. He was ordered to be present at the sorting of the load, the chats were weighed, and the labour charges deducted from Vibert's potato ticket. Two days later, the Chief Inspector reported on two loads brought in by Mr J. Blake, Les Varines, St Saviour, which had been poorly sorted. His loads were re-sorted, and the chats removed. Blake was only paid for the potatoes that remained and the chats were returned to him. In the same week Mr G. Le Bailly, St Martin, also had his delivery re-weighed and the chats removed.

Early in October 1941 the DOA issued an Island-wide directive that all "Royals" were to be lifted no later than the 31st October. During the lifting, eel worm cysts were discovered at the farm of Mr E. Le Ruez, St Mary. He was ordered to treat the field with three parts "slag" and one part potato salts. After the treatment the fields were sown with oats for 1942.

Jersey Produce Merchants Association

On the 1st October 1941, the JPMA wrote to the DOA with a request for "Additional payments for the performance of services with the storage of potatoes". This demand for increased remuneration for the storage of the Island's agricultural produce was, for the JPMA, a new and excellent source of revenue and the merchants became very skilful at increasing their revenue when it came to the storage of produce on behalf of the population.

The JPMA demanded payment from the States of Jersey for the storage, care, packing, transportation and shipping of all Island produce. Brée refused to increase payments; however, in his typical conciliatory manner, he replied to the JPMA outlining a list of revised figures for 1942.

1. The DOA will pay for the sorting and grading of main crop, seed and ware at 3 pence per hundredweight. (The JPMA wanted 6 pence per hundredweight.)
2. The sorting of Royal potatoes will be at the same rate as in 1941 – 1 penny per hundredweight, not 3 pence as sought by the JPMA.
3. Storage barrels are to be obtained at a merchant's own expense.

The JPMA initially refused the DOA's offer as set out on the 1st October, but on the 17th October agreed to the terms.

On the 21st October the DOA suggested to the JPMA that a number of their stores be appointed to handle the potatoes on the DOA's behalf. These would become distribution points for the disposal of fixed weekly quantities of potatoes during the winter of 1941. Each distribution store would have a licence. In effect, the merchants would be acting as wholesale distributors for the DOA. The price was fixed at 7/2 per cwt.

The following week, licences allowing the selling of specified quantities of DOA potatoes were granted to seven merchants:

John Terry Ltd	26 tons
W. Dennis and Sons Ltd	15 tons
Marks and Riches Ltd	20 tons
Job and Son	12 tons
A. E. Laurens	10 tons
Chas Gruchy & Co Ltd	5 tons
R. P. Amy	5 tons

On the 14th October, an order for seed potatoes was received from the German authorities. To comply with the order a notice was put in the press asking for seed of the Royal variety. Farmers were paid 9/- per cwt. On the same day the DOA approved arrangements by Cabot to pay the merchant C. S. Bailhache the full amount due to him for storage of potatoes which had been removed as a result of his store being requisitioned by the Germans. The potatoes had been collected from Bailhache's store by W. Dennis and Sons on behalf of the German authorities. As a result, the DOA ordered Dennis and Sons to replace 14 tons, 7 cwt and 2 quarters of potatoes drawn out of the DOA's stores of C. S. Bailhache, or to pay for the above quantity at a rate of £9 per ton. On the 13th October a further report by Cabot, concerning potatoes supplied to the Germans by W. Dennis and Sons, suggested that in the case of 8 tons 8 cwt 1 quarter and 26 lbs, which they had sold to the

German forces and from whom they had received payment, no handling charge should be paid to the company as "The firm had already taken the profit arising from the disposal of these potatoes." The company wrote back on the 6th November requesting that the handling charge be paid but the DOA refused to modify its decision.

On the 10th November, a report from the Grain and Potato Control Section stated that the question of storage of potatoes sold to German troops by W. Dennis and Sons had been resolved. The company had agreed to the deductions and therefore, being without prejudice, to any claim that it might submit in respect of the storage of potatoes for the German troops. Another quantity of potatoes weighing 4 tons and 4 cwt sold by Dennis and Sons had no handling fee payable by the DOA. The DOA also refused to pay the sum of £3-0-10 in respect of bagging a quantity of potatoes released to them by Messrs Martland's store, as these potatoes were released to W. Dennis and Sons in bulk at £9 a ton.

On the 24th October, the DOA authorised the Treasurer of the States to delete two invoices from its audit sheet Number 14, dated 21st July 1941, as payment had been made, "...direct to the office of the DOA by the German authorities." The first invoice dated 5th July 1941 was to supply 8.879 tons at 107.50 RM, the total being 954.49 RM. The second invoice dated 12th July 1941 was to supply 19.835 tons of potatoes at 102.5 RM, the total being 2,033.08 RM.

On the 25th October, Brée convened an important meeting of the Honorary Parish Inspectors with the DOA. He addressed the meeting, sketching the general position regarding food supplies, and then attempted to make clear the situation concerning potato supplies for the civilian population. He directly appealed to them "To provide from their parishes potatoes for the consumption of the civil population at the rate of 80 tons per parish as a minimum requirement and to send to the DOA a detailed return showing the quantity of potatoes held by each farmer for the requirements of the DOA." He stated that potatoes held by farmers for the DOA would be paid at 9/5 per cwt, with all transport costs covered.

On the 6th November the Superior Council made it clear that the DOA would be the sole buyer and distributor of the 1942 potato crop. It also decided to prepare legislation making it an offence to sell potatoes grown in 1942 to anyone except the DOA and also to purchase from anyone other than the DOA. At the same time the Superior Council informed the DOA that it was concerned about existing supplies and wanted detailed information to ascertain the exact quantity held by farmers. This request led to a new law, the Potatoes (Returns) (Jersey) Order, 1941, requiring all farmers to state the quantity of potatoes they held in store at midnight on the 15th November 1941. On the same day the DOA authorised communal kitchens, restaurants and the States Textile Department, Summerland, Rouge Bouillon to receive an extra weekly allocation of 22 tons out of its stock.

An Island-wide inspection of potato fields was carried out in October 1941. In St John the Honorary Inspector reported that J. E. Richards and D.

Gallichan had not dug their Royals and a report was sent to the Attorney General. In the same week the DOA interviewed four farmers – H. C. Le Maistre, A. J. Le Maistre, W. Le Seelleur and G. F. Paisnel – who, it was alleged by St Helier Deputy John H. Amy, had sold, or ordered for sale, potatoes at an excess of that specified by the New Potatoes (Maximum Prices) (Jersey) Order, 1941. An investigation was carried out and, in addition, two farmers from Trinity were questioned, Mr Jack Le Brun and Mrs Joy Cabot

On the 15th November, the DOA convened a meeting with the Connétables and the Honorary Parish Inspectors to discuss "The present shortage of potatoes". Le Gallais proposed a motion accepted by the meeting that the Connétables, together with the Inspectors, "Should endeavour to obtain from farmers the potatoes required for feeding the civil population during the coming week at a price of 9/5 per cwt at the farms. The transport of these potatoes is to be carried out by the DOA." The subsequent Island-wide visits to every farm by the Connétables and Inspectors was a radical and unprecedented measure. The Inspectors were in effect representatives of the civilian government, and the Connétables the heads of the parishes. The combination of the two suggests three issues. Firstly, it was a response to the serious shortage of potatoes; secondly the notion, be it true or not, that farmers were not fully acknowledging their stocks of potatoes; and finally, that there had to be a ratcheting up of a response by the government to these farmers.

On the 5th December a report described "A serious shortage in the quantity of potatoes of the Royal variety at the store of Marks and Riches Ltd." The Attorney General advised that the licence for the firm to act as a potato distributor be immediately withdrawn. Further problems arose with merchants regarding the storage of potatoes on behalf of the DOA.

On the 8th December the DOA asked the Superior Council to requisition 10% of all seed held by farmers. The requisitioned potatoes would be weighed, and the farmers issued receipts which would be paid by the Grain and Potato Control Section. In these dealings the Inspectors, checking the potato stocks, had begun to receive a degree of condemnation from some farmers. The Superior Council therefore ordered the Connétables to accompany the Inspectors in the course of their duty and they, in turn, were accompanied by their Honorary Police to ensure the checks were adequately carried out.

The Superior Council, on the 9th December, charged the DOA to requisition "All stocks of potatoes in excess of one ton." This was to be done by checking returns made by farmers under the Potatoes (Sales and Returns) Order. Brée was deeply disturbed by the Superior Council's order and replied that the DOA was "...gravely concerned as to the unfair discrimination which would inevitably result from the stocks of potatoes without regard to the consideration for the particular circumstances of the persons holding such stocks; and decided that it must decline to accept responsibility for making such an order." In simple terms the DOA refused to implement the Superior Council's directive. Brée replied to the request with a detailed and focused response, making it clear that the DOA was "…of the opinion that the problem would be met more equitably and with better results if the following recommendations were adopted".

1. From the returns under the Potatoes (Sales and Returns) Order there should be extracted the names of all persons holding stock exceeding 1 ton.
2. The number of members of the household of each such persons should be accounted for.
3. From the quantity of potatoes declared there should be deducted an amount equal to 2 pounds weight per member of the household per day up to 15th May 1942.
4. The amount remaining should be purchased by the DOA and, if need be, requisitioned.
5. The DOA would furnish the Attorney General with a list of farmers who were given directions to grow potatoes in 1941. Those farmers failing to make a return under the Potatoes (Sales and Returns) Order, or making a false return, would be fully checked and appropriate action taken over any stock exceeding 1 ton.
6. Without prejudice to the right of the Attorney General to prosecute any such person, if it were found that he had a stock of potatoes exceeding one ton, the DOA would requisition or purchase that stock.
7. The above procedure would be applied to persons who, as a result of inspection, were deemed to have undeclared or falsely declared stocks.
8. Finally, the DOA maintained that it should be empowered to requisition 10% of all seed potatoes held by farmers who had in their possession 100 boxes or more of such potatoes.

On the 12th December, the DOA was instructed to transmit to the Attorney General a list of farmers who had not declared the quantity of potatoes in their possession as required by the Potatoes (Sales and Returns) (Jersey) Order, 1941, the Attorney General being determined to take appropriate action. In view of the continuing shortages of supplies for the civilian population, the DOA modified its previous order of the 10th December 1941 and allowed every farmer to retain ninety-five boxes of seed potatoes for every vergée allocated to the 1942 crop as directed by the Cultivation Order. It also recommended that farmers having in their possession and personal custody 1 ton or over, would be allowed to retain 1 hundredweight for each member of the household to cover their personal needs. This would last up to 15th May 1942. On the 17th December Le Gallais completed details of his scheme for the collection of potatoes for "the requirements of the island". On the 30th December 1941 new inspectors were appointed under the Potatoes (Sales and Returns) (Amendment) Jersey Order, 1941 at a weekly wage of £3. Also, on the 30th December, W. Dennis and Sons Ltd wrote to the DOA concerning potato export orders fulfilled by them to the directives of the German authorities. The firm claimed that they were entitled to payment for

"The bagging of the potatoes released to them to enable them to complete a shipping order from the German authorities". The DOA refused any further payments.

Cereals

"Brée's efforts to collect and store the harvested crops were great feats of organisation, and the true figures of the Island reserves – which he kept in his pocket – would read very differently from the official weekly or monthly figures he supplied."

The obituary of T. J. Brée

On the 11th March 1941, the Field Commandant wrote to the Bailiff asking for the precise area and condition of the Island's cereal crop. Brée supplied the information to the Bailiff who replied to the Field Commandant on the 14th March. "The total area to be sown in wheat is 12,600 vergées, and the wheat is in a fair condition. The sowing of the spring barley has just started. Some 400 vergées have been allocated to rye, and, of this area, 300 vergées have been sown, the crop being in a fair condition. No rape is grown in the Island.[16] Pelz, who had scrutinised the Cereal Cultivation Orders, subsequently discussed the cereal crops with Brée.

Pelz was extremely efficient and thorough and checked, surveyed and made an independent visit to the areas allocated to cereals. The historical record of the German occupation of the Island has been extremely successful in whitewashing Hans Egon Pelz from its pages. Pelz was described by his contemporaries as capable and highly regarded in the performance of his duties as Head of Agriculture. The evidence from an array of primary historical sources, when cross-referenced, attest to his ability. As head of Agriculture and Food Supplies for the German Military Government, Field Command 515, Pelz was very proactive and certainly not just a desk-sitting bureaucrat. He travelled extensively around the Island checking and verifying the sowing, husbandry and harvesting of crops. He travelled to all the Channel Islands, including Alderney, and had an excellent knowledge of farming issues.

In addition, Pelz was a cattle expert with a knowledge of breeding, selection, detailed referencing and herd books. It was no stroke of luck that Pelz arrived in Jersey in August 1940. He was specifically chosen, as he himself noted, "...for a special mission." He also worked closely with the civilian management of the Island's abattoirs. The Bailiff described "...Brée as having to work with a rather tiresome but able little German, called Doctor Pelz."[17] In Sark he was described as "a German agricultural expert named Dr Pelz who sometimes helped."[18] Major Heider, Chief of Staff, Field Command 515, and later to become Platzkommandant I of the

Island, described Pelz as highly competent with an excellent command of all aspects of Jersey's agricultural economy. Dr Casper also spoke of Pelz as highly capable.[19] Karl Greier (1906-1985), a fellow Austrian and a good friend of Pelz, whom he often visited in the post-war period in Austria and who worked with Pelz as an interpreter, spoke of him as, "extremely good at his job and respected by his fellow comrades."[20] Pelz achieved the degree of "ING" in Agricultural Sciences from the University of Natural Resources and Life Sciences, Vienna. He achieved some highly commendable academic and practical examination results. In post-war Austria he became a major figure in the cattle industry.

In the occupation period Pelz played a huge role in the Island's agricultural industry. Pelz's biography demonstrates that he spent a great deal of time examining cereal crops and harvests and evidence is also found in the many documents of an official nature, in private letters, photographs and descriptions of his work. There have been, since the post-war period, alternative interpretations of Pelz's abilities and his relationship with the President of the DOA, Touzel John Brée, which in essence contradict the available evidence. Why should Brée's relationship with Pelz be of any consequence to the occupation records? The answer is straightforward enough. Brée was described by a fellow States of Jersey colleague as, "The central figure involved...in a hundred incidents of the Occupation period." Yet very little has been written on Brée and, like Pelz, he seems to have been white-washed from the record. This apparent disappearance of individuals' historical roles in the German occupation extends to other Island figures, such as Carlyle Le Gallais.

Pelz and Brée had a close structural relationship because of the very nature of their roles. The historical interpretation that has been published describes the German Military Government, and in particular Pelz, as having been continually and deliberately misled, deceived, manipulated and bamboozled by Touzel Brée. Brée, we are led to believe, was adept at setting up administrative and statistical traps to confine the German Military Government and Pelz. This is nonsense and therefore the question arises as to how and why this interpretation was published?

The answer to these questions can be traced back to 1951, the year that Brée died suddenly on a motoring holiday in southern France. Two obituaries were subsequently published in the Evening Post: one by a States Member and one by Duret Aubin, Attorney General, who during the German occupation was the Bailiff's right-hand man. It was Duret Aubin in whom Brée confided when agricultural directives were broken by Island farmers.[21] In the obituary, he gives a detailed description of Brée's responsibilities during the occupation and commented:

"In all his activities he had to be constantly on the alert against German interference, and many were the subterfuges in order that the civilian population was as reasonably supplied with milk and products of the soil as was possible in the face of continually increasing German demands.

Brée, himself a practical farmer of great experience and with vision and ability, at once realised the drastic changes and implications which the occupation imposed upon insular agriculture, and not without opposition and criticism from friend as well as from enemy, carried them through with highly successful results. In him the occupying authority met, in all matters relating to agriculture, its master, not less in guile than ability. Week after week he produced and certified, for that authority, statistics of stocks in hand and of estimated requirements which, to the very few friends who knew the real facts, caused wonder and admiration. And sometimes indeed, alarm, for he often risked grave and perhaps the greatest punishment. In his almost daily arguments with the enemy side, sometimes by obstinacy, sometimes by finesse, he gave away nothing and gained much."[21]

The other obituary from "A Member of the States Council" described Brée's relationship with Pelz.[22] "I remember on one occasion when a young, and possibly over enthusiastic officer had been given very definite orders as to the agricultural policy which must be followed and to which Touzel Brée disagreed.[23] The latter listening very carefully for some time, raised an admonishing finger and replied, "now look here my boy, etc.," in that quiet, deep voice we knew so well. His efforts to collect and store the harvested crops were great feats of organisation, and often the true figures of the Island reserves – which he kept in his pocket – would read very differently from the official weekly or monthly figures he supplied."

In 1955, an occupation publication describing Brée paraphrased his 1951 obituary.[24] It also commented, "Touzel Brée made a point, however, of keeping on friendly terms with the Germans, and aroused hostility among some Jerseymen by giving them presents of fruit and vegetables." Brée gave a package of fruit to Pelz and made no secret of it.[25] Certainly, from an early stage after Pelz's arrival in Jersey on the 9th August 1940, Brée worked closely with him, striking up and forming a close "structural relationship." In December 1940, he gave Pelz an alarm clock.

Brée's relationship with Pelz, based upon all the documentation available, is that he saw his fundamental role as maintaining disciplined relations with both Pelz and the German Military Government and administration. This provided, as Brée perceived, the basis for an equitable arrangement for the Island's civilian population. Brée, from all accounts of the RJA&HS, the JFU and the Joint Emergency Committee meetings, was highly respected by the Island's leading farming community. Indeed, Pelz regarded Brée as his equivalent, in no way inferior or a collaborator, and an individual who professionally he could work with and who fully understood the nature of the Island's agriculture and the farmers. In one meeting held between Brée and Field Command 515 at College House, Pelz, who normally has a smiling demeanour, asked Brée in a serious tone, why, after receiving Guernsey's crop returns, that island appeared to have fared better than Jersey. When Brée replied that he did not know the answer to the question, Pelz, suggested that, in light of these figures, it would be a good idea to bring the Guernsey Controller of Agriculture over to Jersey to run matters. Heider, who was present at the meeting, looked away through the office window, understanding that Pelz was not serious. Brée, however, was mortified and visibly shaken. Heider, who described Brée as "The Little Breton" and witnessed the event, further described that Pelz went on to explain to Brée that he was carrying out a joke and was not serious![26]

In 1998 a biography of Brée, which for all intents and purposes was a copy of the 1951 obituary, cemented Brée's role in occupation history.[27] He had manipulated the German Military Government, and in particular Pelz. The question arises as to the reason why Duret Aubin and others over-emphasised and in effect exaggerated Brée's role in the 1951 obituary. This is a far more complicated question and deserves an answer. Firstly, the fundamental aim of the obituary was to praise and shed light on Brée's dynamic role, as President of the DOA, as the saviour of the Island's population. Secondly, it was a description that was intentionally biased towards Brée and against Pelz. This is not to lessen Brée's huge capacity for work exemplified by the hundreds of meetings he had with the German Military administration, the Superior Council, the civilian administration, farming unions as well as the production of dairy and agricultural statistics. All this work positively allowed for a far more benign occupation by the German administration and for the Island's public institutions to essentially remain independent, as long as Brée and the DOA satisfied German demands for its agricultural and dairy requirements.

The Superior Council could remain, during the occupation and for all intents and purposes, relatively in charge, and the German Military administration and the States of Jersey had good reasons to maintain cordial relationships. The Superior Council, through Brée and the DOA, provided dairy and agricultural foodstuffs for the civilian and military population and, as a bonus, provided food for export on behalf of the military authority. If mistakes were made or shortages appeared, it was a simple matter for the German Military Government to blame the Superior Council and the DOA.

This symbiotic relationship was hurriedly forgotten immediately after liberation, and quickly put into the shredder of the historical record. This was a comparatively simple exercise. The people who ran the Island before the occupation – Coutanche, Duret Aubin, Brée, Le Gallais et al – had run the government and Civil Service during the occupation; and finally ran the Island after the occupation. It was a comparatively simple process in Jersey, unlike in other occupied territories, to understate or alter the notion of any meaningful relationship between the Island's civil servants or politicians with Field Command 515. Jersey was not the only occupied territory where this occurred. The Danish government's relationship, with its dairy and agricultural agreements with the German occupying authorities, was similar to that of Jersey's.[28]

The clearest example when viewing the relationship between Brée and Pelz and in making a judgement is from a private letter written by Pelz. In the letter he recalls, "Jurat Brée, my civilian counterpart, consulted me each time when important food products which were only available for ration coupons had to be purchased. On the subject of slaughtering Jersey cattle for meat, Jurat Brée explained to me, "you cannot eat Jerseys, they are only to provide milk". Only with great effort and serious admonition did I make Brée supply Jersey cattle for consumption, in the context of rationing".[29]

In Pelz's summary of Jersey agriculture during the occupation years he wrote:

"In the first years of occupation, the maintenance of such a large area for growing potatoes in Jersey was not possible. Thus, I limited it to 25,000 tons of all sorts of potatoes at the most; so early potatoes and later sorts could be grown. A long-keeping winter potato was completely unknown and seed potatoes had to be brought in from Germany. In this way cultivatable land was made free and used for the cultivation of grain. This was the most difficult matter. It is known that the islands had always imported grain from Canada. This absolutely went along with English trade principles, as Canadian wheat had the lowest price on the world market. The supply of cereals for the production of bread flour was enough until circa the summer of 1941. Then we had to bring all the supplies from France. The result was that, due to the high prices for grain in France, a substantial rise of bread prices would have to have taken place on the islands. We [Field Command 515] did not allow this to happen, so the Island government had to spend considerable amounts of money to subsidise bread prices until the end of the occupation. As far as I remember the money to subsidise the price almost amounted to twenty per cent of the Island budget."

On the 30th May, 30 cwt of locally grown wheat was discovered by Inspector J. G. Malzard on the premises of Mrs Moulin, Le Peupliers, St Ouen. The wheat was immediately requisitioned, and no payment made to Mrs Moulin. As the result of a report by an inspector, Mr and Mrs E. Le Chevalier were interviewed on the matter of 4 vergées of wheat they had been ordered to sow under a Cultivation Order and which had allegedly been left in a "seriously neglected condition". The matter was referred to the Attorney General.

Also on 30th May, seventy balls of twine held by J. G. Renouf and Company, shipbrokers, were requisitioned. In June the DOA requested "as soon as possible" the delivery of the reaper binders purchased from France for the requirements of the 1941 cereal harvest, along with 300 spades and 150 scythes. In addition, the DOA notified the Superior Council that additional threshing machines were urgently required and recommended to the Superior Council that Mr T. R. Binet should be sent to France to purchase two machines because he personally knew the supplier in Granville.

On the 30th June the DOA wrote to each of the Island's threshing contractors asking for details of the exact number and condition of threshing machines in their possession. The four main contractors were: C. G. Le Cappelain, J. Richard, H. Godel and O. Farrell. With the cereal harvest approaching, the DOA became increasingly worried that the threshing machines, reaper-binders and binder twine it had ordered "will not arrive in time for the harvest". It additionally asked the Department of Essential Supplies whether electric power or coal would be available for driving the machines for the coming harvest. In July the DOA requested the Superior Council to authorise a member of the Price Advisory Board to proceed immediately to France and urgently purchase additional articles:

2,500 sickles
100 metres of 3-inch belting
100 metres of 2.5-inch belting
100 metres of 2-inch belting
Horseshoe nails

The DOA also decided that the threshing machines of J. Richard and J C. Cabot should be put into working order as soon as possible.

On the 2nd July the Superior Council requested the Price Advisory Board to recommend cereal prices for 1941. The Board set up a Committee to give advice on the costs of growing cereals. It comprised: Brée, two farmers each nominated by the JFU and RJA&HS, D. Simpson, Director of the Experimental Station, and T. G. Le Cappelain representing the threshing contractors. In addition, all cereal inspectors were summoned. On the 7th July the Committee met and as a result, the Price Advisory Board wrote to the Superior Council with "An imperative need to know as early as possible what the acreage would be like". Brée replied that he considered the cereal crop prospects for 1941 to be "good" and that the probable yield per vergée would be:

Wheat	10 cwt
Oats	12 cwt
Barley	9 cwt
Rye	5 cwt

Brée considered the possibility that these figures would be about 5% below the average harvest that he knew could be produced in Jersey. He also added that the quality of the grain could only be assessed once it had been threshed and, furthermore, confirmed that the States would purchase the entire 1941 cereal crop. Farmers, however, would be allowed to buy seed for sowing in 1942. The straw would be returned to the farmer at no cost. The Price Advisory Board stated that it wanted the crop stored entirely under cover pending threshing. It was to be threshed at each farmer's discretion – either at the farm or at the threshing depot – and the grain was then to be carted directly to named stores or granaries and subsequently milled on the Island. The Board now wrote to the Superior Council asking for "...precise returns of areas sown in cereal crops: wheat, oats, barley and rye. In order to obtain the information, the Honorary Parish Inspectors are to individually report from their parishes the actual areas sown in these cereals". The DOA agreed to pay the expenses of one additional man to assist the Honorary Inspectors in obtaining the information.

On the 11th July T. G. Le Cappelain was interviewed. He informed the Board of the number of threshing outfits in the Island which was nine to ten large and six small businesses that could operate for the 1941 season. He furthermore gave details of their motive power and whether they used steam, tractor, or electric devices. Le Cappelain was informed that two threshing machines had been ordered from France and that these were equipped with wire binders. He, however, made it clear there was very little binder twine available on the Island which would be a serious problem when baling straw. Le Cappelain also provided the costs for threshing, the labour required, and the amount of fuel needed. On the 15th July, the Board met with the threshing contactors who submitted tentative costs and alternatives to the lack of twine were discussed.

On the 17th July, the Price Advisory Board held a meeting with the DOA, JFU and RJA&HS when the areas for growing cereals were discussed. The farming unions gave their opinion as to "the state of the crop" which they considered was below the average yield. However, all parties had calculated yields that did not differ greatly, agreeing that cereals would fall into two grades and that "...neglect in cultivation should be penalised".

On the 21st July the Board met with the independent farmers, represented by Mr E. J. Ahier and Mr P. C. Mourant, concerning the 1941 harvest. Mr Ahier emphasised that the loss of weight from the time of reaping to drying could be taken as 20%. Both farmers strongly recommended a treatment of sulphate of copper for the wheat crop in cases of "smut" to ensure the seed for 1942 was suitable.[30] Mr Ahier gave a detailed estimate of wheat production at 9 cwt per vergée and 10 cwt per vergée for oats "...based on experiments per vergée carried out by him some years ago". Both farmers advocated that the fairest way of threshing cereals would be at depots in each threshing district. In addition, as experienced cereal farmers, they discussed the improvement of soils used continually for cereal growing. It was agreed that the question of re-using soils for 1942 should be given a top priority when devising the next cropping plan. On the same day Brée urgently asked the Superior Council to fix cereal prices without delay. He also asked Pelz whether Jardin d'Olivet, Trinity, could be made available as a threshing depot for the 1941 harvest and he requested coal for the threshing machines.

On the 22nd July the Board met with D. Simpson. In his opinion, "the crop was about normal" and he advised that the harvest per vergée would be:

Wheat	10 cwt
Oats	10 cwt
Barley	8–9 cwt
Rye	5–6 cwt

Simpson also advised on the problem of smut and recommended the use of formaldehyde as this did not affect germination of wheat seed. He made it clear that fields used for wheat in 1941 must not be planted with the same in 1942; and advised that manure or ammonia be applied on fields to be planted with oats or potatoes. Ploughed-in seaweed was also recommended as an extra fertiliser. Finally, Simpson advised that experienced farmers should be called in to give advice on the stacking of grain.

The following day the Board met with the Honorary Parish Inspectors who were instructed to look for the best wheat seed throughout the Island for the 1942 crop. The Board also ordered the Inspectors to inform the proprietor of Franc Fief Farm, St Brelade, to make immediate arrangements to reap, sheave, stack and thresh the produce of 17 vergées of barley. On the same day the Board finally agreed upon the average yields per vergée for cereals based on the evidence given by the Inspectors:

Wheat	9 cwt
Oats	11 cwt
Barley	6 cwt
Rye	4 cwt

On 23rd July, on instruction from German Field Command, the DOA approved the Harvesting of Grain Crops (Fire Precautions) (Jersey) Order, 1941. The order made it law to take special care in the harvesting and storing of the cereal crop to ensure that no incendiary material was included in the harvest and that all precautions had been taken to prevent the destruction of stooks and stacks, as a result of the dropping of incendiary material from aeroplanes.

On the 1st August Mrs C. G. Olliver delivered a compensation letter to the DOA for 4 vergées of barley that had been eaten by rabbits; this was summarily refused. The next day the Price Advisory Board sent its report on the 1941 cereal crop. It advised on the estimated yield for all cereals and unanimously recommended that the States purchase the entire crop. On the same day a delegation of the DOA comprising Brée, Le Gallais and W. Le Seelleur (the mechanical fireman at St Helier Harbour) inspected the Island's threshing machines. Any machine not in order was requisitioned. On the 5th August, Brée recommended to the Superior Council that any machines which contractors had not put into proper working order should be serviced at the public charge and thereafter operated from public funds. The proprietors of these machines would not be given any form of compensation. However, at the termination of hostilities, the DOA would consider any claims. In order to inspect all the Island's machines, Brée secured control of the Department of Transport and Communications' workshops at La Collette. The DOA was also given two further threshing machines which needed full mechanical attention: one owned by J. W. Fiott, La Partie, St Brelade and the other by J. Priaulx, St Cyr, St John.

By August 1941 Brée was working hard completing the steps needed to expedite harvesting the cereal crop, meeting with the Price Advisory Board to discuss their report on yields. He modified several aspects where he felt the Board was wrong and altered their estimates. As a matter of courtesy, he announced that the DOA did not accept as practicable the Board's estimates on yields. Brée also ordered that cereals should not all be threshed at the same time; that oats, barley and rye should be threshed first, after which wheat would follow alone; and that a premium of 20/- per ton would be paid for wheat selected for seed. He concluded that after threshing, all grain would be carted to DOA stores.

On the 11th August the issue of petrol to the threshing contractors was authorised and the DOA published a report "The Cereal Crop 1941" which became the template for the rest of the occupation. It covered all aspects of harvesting, threshing and the allocation of grain, straw, and seed.[3]

Harvesting

Farmers would arrange for harvesting and where threshing of their crop would take place. The Harvesting of Grain Crops (Fire Precautions) (Jersey) Order, 1941, would stay in force because the order had been imposed by the German Field Command. Despite the strongest representations made by Brée to Pelz, the German authorities would not alter their position.

Threshing

All threshing would be authorised and carried out by the States. Wheat would be threshed and stacked separately. Oats, barley and rye had to be threshed first, in order to affect the separate stacking of wheat. Labour employed by the threshing contractors were eligible for the Agricultural Wages Harvest Bonus.

Allocation of Grain Crop

This would be dealt with by the wholesalers, acting as agents for the DOA. Seed requirements for the 1942 crop were: wheat 500 tons, oats 225 tons, barley 30 tons, rye 30 tons. 600 tons of oats and 60 tons of barley were reserved as "breakfast food" and growers of cereals who also owned horses were entitled to a "privileged ration" of oats consisting of 28 pounds weight per week per horse for fifty-two weeks. These growers had to declare the number of horses they owned. A permit would be issued for the purposes of this concession.

Straw

A price of £4 per ton was approved. The estimated yield was agreed as:

Wheat	15 cwt per vergée
Oats	16 cwt per vergée
Barley	10 cwt per vergée
Rye	10 cwt per vergée

Seed. An extra 20/- per ton would be paid for wheat seed provided that the grain had been stooked and threshed separately from other grain. All seed was treated for smut by the DOA.

Cost of Growing the Cereal Crop

The transport of grain from the threshing machines to the DOA's stores would be carried out by the States and a deduction of 2/6 per vergée made from the cost of cultivation to cover this service and the use of bags. The threshing would be carried out by the farming community making their own arrangements. The DOA now added the sum of £1-10-0 per vergée to cover the cost of threshing. The final figures per vergée were as follows:

Cereals: Cost of Production Per Vergée

Wheat	£13-5-3
Oats	£13-1-3
Barley	£9-14-6
Rye	£9-14-6

Cereals: Price Paid by the DOA to the Farmer Per Hundredweight

Wheat	28/-
Oats	22/-
Barley	32/6
Rye	39/-

These prices would be paid for grain of "good average quality". A "Pricing Sub-Committee" was appointed to recommend the price for grain which was not of good average quality.

Price Adjustments

The price for wheat would be a basic price and would remain in force.

Milling

This was regarded as being outside the scope of the DOA.

Supplementary Observations

The States Experimental Station would test to ascertain the degree of evaporation and how long it would take for the cereals to dry. The fertility of the soil would be checked by these experts who worked alongside the farmers and Honorary Parish Inspectors. The DOA refused to compensate any farmers for losses due to the risks of fire caused by hostilities or otherwise. It also refused to compensate for the depredations of vermin.

On the 12th August, the day after publication of the report, the Superior Council approved it for immediate implementation. The DOA decided to meet with the threshing contractors who had been appointed when the topics discussed were all matters in connection with the coming harvest.

Four threshing contractors were interviewed: T. G. Le Cappelain, J. Richard, W. Farrell and S. C. Cabot. H. Godel was absent; subsequently he was informed of the results by letter. The following points were agreed:

1. Farmers will be charged 27/- per vergée. This does not include binding charges.
2. Each contractor will supply six men for each machine comprising: one driver, one feeder, one man cutting, one man at the husks and two men on the loose straw. The farmer will provide a man to pass the sheaves.
3. No threshing is to commence without the direct permission of the DOA.

On the 14th August the DOA passed an Order on the storage of cereals and the next day met a delegation from the JPMA and the Corn Traders' Association (CTA) to decide the storage criteria. Firstly, if grain was stored in barrels, they had to be staggered with no more than two barrels in height; secondly, grain stored in bulk was not to exceed 2 feet in height; and thirdly all grain had to be turned weekly during the first month of storage and subsequently at least once each month. Also, on the 14th, the Cereal Grain (Threshing and Purchase of Crops) (Jersey) Order, 1941 was submitted.

On the same day the DOA appointed its "Threshing Inspectors", one being employed on each individual machine at a weekly wage of £3. John George Malzard was appointed as the Chief Cereals Inspector from 25th August 1941, at a weekly wage of £3-10-0. The following week, this was increased to £4-10-0.

On 18th August the DOA informed the JPMA and the CTA that the storage of locally grown grain by their members would be paid on the following basis:

1. 12/- per ton for storing and delivering grain.
2. 1/6 per ton per month for turning grain in the stores.

However, the next day the JPMA requested 30/- per ton for storage and delivery, and this was agreed by the DOA on the 22nd.

The DOA also modified its provision of labour at the threshing machines and decided to supply an extra man to assist the Inspectors; farmers had made it clear that they were not prepared to supply the labour because, "The grain is being taken over by the DOA".

The harvesting, threshing and inspection of the 1941 cereal crop was supervised by Le Gallais who was ordered to make arrangements with Malzard to plan a schedule. A £1,000 credit for preliminary expenses for the crop was made to the DOA in connection with the purchase of the cereals. The DOA also passed the final version of the Cereal Grain (Threshing and Purchase of Crops) (Jersey) Order, 1941 which gave "general directions" to farmers under the Cultivation of Lands (Jersey) Order, 1940, regarding the stacking and threshing of wheat. The above legislation was handed to the

Superior Council and to "the Field Command for approval" before it was published.

On the 22nd August it was decided that more clerical staff were needed, and Mr Philip Hubert was employed as a clerk for a weekly wage of £3. On the same day John A. Perrée was asked to put together a sub-committee to work in an advisory capacity and to propose a fixed price to be paid by the DOA for inferior grain. A joint letter from the JFU and the RJA&HS asked the DOA to agree to two points. Firstly, that grain was weighed at the threshing machines before it left the farmer's possession; and secondly, a States scheme be set up for insurance against the danger of fire, to be paid for on a contributory basis. The first request was deemed "not practicable"; the second was referred to the Department of Finance and Economics.

By the end of August, the Superior Council had placed the La Collette workshops in the hands of the DOA. Mr Cyril William Rice, the States Engineer, was charged with completing all repairs to the threshing machines and instructed to liaise with contactors to ensure their machines were serviced and ready for the start of the 1941 harvest.

C. Baudains and R. P. Amy of the JPMA, and B. Horsfall and A. P. Falle of the CTA, met with the DOA to finalise all storage payments for grain. On the 25th August, £1,000 was made available for the purchase of new threshing machines from France. In addition, Monsieur François Griegnard was credited with £10 to defray the costs of a voyage from France to Jersey in connection with the purchase of the machines. The DOA now informed all cereal farmers that selected seed would be purchased at £1 per ton in excess of the basic prices specified in the Cereal Grain (Threshing and Purchasing of Crops) (Jersey) Order, 1941.

On the 1st September, Malzard requested authority from the Attorney General to call upon the services of the Honorary Police when checking threshing sites. This was in the event of him requiring the "clearing and removal of people" not authorised to be on the sites. In a meeting comprising Brée, Le Gallais and Malzard, the DOA approved new instructions to Threshing Machine Inspectors of their powers, as they were now appointed under the Cultivation of Lands (Jersey) Order, 1940. This included written authority to the Chief Threshing Inspector and all Sub-Inspectors to enter any premises where threshing was taking place. The Inspectors were to have full control. The following week Malzard was authorised to pay Inspectors an overtime rate of 1/- per hour in connection with the 1941 cereal crop for time worked after 6.00 p.m. on weekdays and after 1.00 p.m. on Saturdays. Malzard was also allowed to employ three assistants at each threshing machine, in addition to the Sub-Inspectors. The administration for the cashing in of cereal weighbridge tickets was carried out by the Department of Finance and Economics.

On the 11th September the DOA met to discuss the use of the threshing machines purchased from France. It was decided to ask J. E. Colback Junior, and L. C. Pallot to submit tenders for the hire of the French machines for the 1941 season. The chosen contractor would then be on the same terms and conditions as other contractors. However, in addition he would have to provide the necessary motive power, fuel, lubricants, and any other requirements for operating the machines and also keep them fully serviced whilst in his charge. Colback and Pallot submitted their offers by the following day, both at the rate of 16/- per hour. Colback began work with the first machine on the 16th September, at Le Hocq Marsh, whilst Pallot was allocated the second machine upon its arrival into Jersey. On the same day the DOA released its stock of binder wire to contractors and informed them that any grain held in their possession after cleaning out their machines would belong to the DOA.

On the 23rd September the first wheat seed reserved by the Honorary Parish Inspectors for the 1942 crop was submitted for tests for its germination qualities. It was also decided that wheat seed would be stored separately under three headings: Jersey grain, French grain and 'doubtful' grain.

Mr Perrée named his Grain Sub-Committee for the pricing of inferior grain as: T. G. Marinel, J. B. Michel, S. G. Le Couilliard and J. M. Norman; the secretary was H. G. Shepard. On the 12th September Shepard wrote to the DOA drawing their attention to a number of facts. Firstly, the grain brought in from the harvest was better quality than expected. Secondly, in most cases, grain delivered by the threshing machines was badly winnowed. Thirdly, several deliveries of grain marked as 'Second Grade', were of equal, if not better, quality than others marked as 'First Grade'. The Chief Threshing Inspector was immediately informed.

On the 19th September, Le Gallais reported to the DOA that he had discovered that "The following parcels of grain in certain stores", were missing. The grain had apparently been stored by J. Martland Limited on various dates:

10 tons rye
15 sacks buckwheat
470 bags of wheat
160 bags of wheat
and by J. E. Baudains, 20 tons spring wheat.

The decision was made for two members of the DOA, John du Val and Edwin Gibaut, to carry out investigations concerning these grain stores.

On the 19th September 1941 the DOA fixed its prices for all cereals sold to the Department of Essential Commodities.

Wheat	£1-12-0 per cwt
Oats	£1-6-0 per cwt
Barley	£1-16-0 per cwt
Rye	£2-3-0 per cwt

On the 23rd September, a number of contractors reported that they had experienced problems raising a proper head of steam with the coke supplied. The Fuel Controller, Mr Stuart Philip Pepin, was asked by the DOA to supply the contractors with an alternative fuel. Mr Pepin immediately went to inspect the machines whilst they were operating as he regarded the coke he had supplied as a perfectly suitable fuel for raising steam in the boilers of the driving units. On the same day the DOA advised all contractors to finish, as soon as possible, the threshing of oats at their respective depots and to begin threshing wheat.

On the 28th September the second new machine arrived from France, having been purchased by the States for £363-19-5. At the same time Malzard informed contractors that, as from the 6th October, all machines would be operated by steam power only, as petrol supplies would cease. Each machine was provided with 2 cwt of coal per week to light up the coke. The DOA also hired an additional steam engine from T. G. Le Cappelain to operate as a delivery unit for the French machine hired to Colback Junior. On the 7th October, L. C. Pallot began work with the second machine, the motive power being produced by a tractor with a diesel engine. The Engineer and Manager of the Jersey Electricity Company, Mr F. M. Burrell, supplied Mr Pallot with 40 gallons (456 lbs) of oil per fortnight at the price of £22-15-0 per ton. The total amount used was 160 gallons.

Between the 3rd and 7th October the Honorary Parish Inspectors visited a barley field at Franc Fief Farm, St Brelade. They discovered dockweed in the field and ordered the crop to be cut down and burnt, to stop the propagation of the weeds into neighbouring fields. In addition, Mr V. Stuart and Mr J. M. Gouyette of St Saviour had retained 5 vergées of barley and oats and were ordered to thresh them.

On the 3rd October, Edwin Gibaut inspected the farm of L. H. Blight, Maufant. Deputy Gibaut, as a member of the DOA Committee, had full jurisdiction to enter farms and premises. After checking and inspecting the farm he immediately reported back to the DOA that Blight had made, "...no attempt to harvest a crop of oats", under the direction of the Cultivation of Lands (Jersey) Order, 1940. Gibaut discussed the state of the cereal crop with Blight who subsequently cut and threshed it within the week. Deputy Gibaut's report confirmed to the DOA that the farm was, 'In a seriously neglected condition", whilst Blight had already broken orders concerning the registration of pigs. Two months later, on Christmas Eve, KVR Pelz visited Cowley Farm, to give Blight's daughter Maud "a little present of a handkerchief".[31]

On the 15th October the DOA convened a meeting of the Honorary Parish Inspectors. The decision was made to increase the amount of barley for 1942 to 800 vergées; 50 vergées additionally in each parish and the balance of 200 vergées being drawn from the allocation of oats. The cropping plan was revised on the 24th October and copies sent to the Inspectors informing them of their new allocations.

On the 28th October Dennis Grosse informed the DOA that he held them financially responsible for damage to a stack of wheat by rats. The Honorary Parish Inspectors checked the stack, but the DOA refused any liability and instructed the claimant to thresh the wheat without delay. On the 31st October the DOA interviewed Mr W. Farrell, a threshing contractor. Malzard discussed with him an allegation that his threshing machine stopped working at 6 o'clock although one or two loads were still awaiting threshing. However, after an investigation it was decided that Farrell had misinterpreted Malzard's instructions. Another Threshing Inspector also alleged that contractor Jean Richard had employed only two men on his machine, and not the six which contractors had agreed to supply. Malzard informed Richard that unless he provided an adequate number of men for his machine, the DOA would stop him from working. On the 4th November, cereal seed for the 1942 crop was issued to farmers.

On the 8th December a report by the DOA's Chief Inspector, A. V. Godfray, together with a verbal report by Malzard, described the poor condition of wheat stored on the premises of the Jersey Farmers (Trading) Union Ltd. The firm was immediately ordered to turn the wheat and reduce the height of the heaps where it was stored. The cost of the work was charged to the firm and a report sent to the Bailiff and the Attorney General for consideration.

Watermills and Milling

"The flour is regarded as being an excellent foodstuff"

Report from the Medical Officer of Health on the quality of locally grown wheat milled into flour

On the 28th July 1941 the Price Advisory Board met to discuss cereal prices for 1942. It summoned Mr E. Gilley, the Island's most experienced miller, to offer advice on the threshing and milling of cereals for the current year and for 1942. Mr Gilley advised on the optimum weather desired and that it took three months for the grain to completely dry. After milling, he recommended that the flour be used immediately. He also advised on methods of stacking and threshing and on the capacity of the mills that were operating assuming that "A maximum of 75 tons of flour per week could be produced, providing water and power was available". Mills could produce, under normal conditions as Mr Gilley stated, 22 pounds of flour from a "cabot of wheat" [32] with a loss of grain weight at 5% for the first three months.

On the 20th August the lease for Grand Val Mill, which had been agreed in March between Mr Baxter and the DOA, was prepared. On the 3rd September the States Engineer informed the DOA that Mr Roderick Dobson, the owner of Ponterrin Mill, had permitted the DOA to remove the milling machinery which was to be used for the re-commissioning of Quetivel Mill. On the advice of the States Auditor, the DOA agreed to pay all the costs of milling Jersey wheat and now sold the flour to the Department of Essential Supplies. The Supervisor of the Mills, P. P. Day, under the control of the DOA, and Cabot the accountant in charge of the Potato and Grain section, were instructed to prepare details of the costs of flour production. On the 30th September the DOA decided that all wheat already in store should be made available for the manufacture of flour. French flour was being imported but when these imports ceased, flour from local mills was to be used.

At the end of October 1941, prices were set for locally produced flour and charged by the DOA to the Department of Essential Supplies at the following rates:

Wheat flour	41/- per cwt
Barley flour	64/- per cwt
Rye flour	75/- per cwt
Oat flour	92/- per cwt

On the 4th November the DOA decided that "In view of the cessation of supplies from France all DOA mills should work overtime". Overtime rates, determined for those who worked in excess of 44 hours a week, were: millers 1/9 per hour and the rest 1/3 per hour. H. F. Benest was granted an additional payment of 3/6 for the use of his tools when engaged in mill carpentry work. Eric Horton, a seventeen- year-old teenager employed at Grand Val Mill, had his wages increased from 10/- to 25/- a week. The extra milling led to the engagement of two more milling staff – William Johani and Richard Le Marchand – at a weekly wage of £2-10-0. From the 17th November, all DOA-operated mills were henceforth managed by the Grain and Potato Control Section. A "Mills trading account" was opened to cover the costs of operation and into which credits were paid.

In November the States Engineer ordered that the steamrollers employed at Grand Val and Malassis Mills be taken over by the DOA and an additional driver employed to cover the considerable overtime needed to work these mills. On the 18th November, the DOA inspected the mills at Malassis, Grand Val, Tesson and Gargate and found the first three to be perfectly satisfactory whilst Gargate was found to have a deficient water supply. In response an electric motor was installed at Gargate as an auxiliary driving unit, instead of the existing paraffin engine, as paraffin fuel was now running out. The inspection committee also decided to install a similar motor at Quetivel.

The following week it was decided to transport cereals directly from the threshing machines to the mills, cutting out the need to transport threshed grain to the stores. Subsequently all stored grain was removed from the Ann Street Brewery and sent to Malassis and Tesson Mills. It was also decided that private milling firms would be paid to produce flour. Firms milling local grain were the Jersey Farmer's (Trading) Union, Le Marquand Brothers and John Terry Limited. In further attempts to increase the milling of local grain, Mr Burrell secured a 25-horsepower electric motor as a second auxiliary drive for Gargate and an electric motor was also installed at Quetivel. These motors were to supplement the 'exiguous' (inadequate) water supply.

On the 22nd and 24th November the Public Health Department and the States Analyst submitted reports to the DOA. Both departments, having tested the flour from wheat grown and milled locally, stated that it contained neither alum nor foreign bodies, nor were there any abnormal minerals found. "The flour is regarded as being an excellent foodstuff".

On the 19th December the lease agreement prepared in August for Grand Val was finally signed with Mr Baxter. The mill was leased to the States for a period of three years at £52 a year, paid to him out of the Mills Trading Account. Mr Baxter, furthermore, was paid by the States Treasurer a weekly wage of £2 for the period of the lease. In the event of his death the Treasury agreed to pay his daughter, Miss Sylvia Nellie Baxter, a weekly sum of £1 until the end of the tenancy. In addition, it agreed to pay all rentes and parish rates.

Potato Flour

In June 1941 Percy Wakeham, trading as Busford's Limited, gave permission for the DOA to use his greenhouses for drying potato flour manufactured by Ann Street Brewery. Between June and September, the DOA spent £728-6-3 on experiments for methods of producing potato flour. On the 18th August, the Department of Essential Supplies, acting on a request from the DOA, fixed a maximum price for potato flour at 1/- per lb, sufficiently low to discourage commercial manufacture of the commodity. The DOA was determined to control the excessive use of potatoes for the manufacture of flour.

The increasing importance and use of potato flour during the occupation led the Food Controller to issue several permits for its production. Brée was instructed by the DOA "to protest" to the Superior Council about the issuing of these permits without consultation with the Department and he was asked, "...to insist upon all such permits being immediately withdrawn".

Fertilisers

The DOA, in order to conserve stocks of chemical ingredients for the manufacture of artificial fertilisers, and to ensure an equitable distribution of fertilisers to all farmers, made an order on the 20th June 1941 prohibiting the sale of the following materials:

Nitrate of soda
Sulphate of ammonia
Castor meal
Superphosphate
Dissolved bone
Bone meal
Phosphate
Boracic slag
Muriate of potash
Sulphate of potash
Nitrate of potash
Carbonate of lime

Rodney E. Andrews, the States Imports Officer, informed the DOA on the same day that "500 tons of superphosphates were being made available for the requirements of the Island, this as a matter of urgency". Also, on 20th June, the States Experimental Station's chemist, E. J. Woodcock, wrote a report on the need for artificial fertilisers for the 1942 season, identifying an immediate shortage of ammonia. Brée telephoned Thomas Blampied, who was in Granville, and asked him to endeavour to obtain 150 tons of sulphate of ammonia from the "Maison Dior at Granville" or failing that, 150 tons of nitrate of soda.

In December the DOA informed all merchants that fertilisers had to be sold on a cash basis and that farmers must produce a permit issued under the Fertilisers (Jersey) Order, 1941. On the 23rd December, Woodcock produced the figures required for the 1942 potato season. This made it apparent that there was a need for immediate imports of artificial fertilisers.

Sugar Beet

On the 28th October 1941 the DOA discussed the requisitioning of the Island's supplies of sugar beet. Brée ascertained the capacity of the canning factory at Grève d'Azette to extract the syrup from the crop and to can it.

Tobacco

> *During the period of the German Occupation the growing of tobacco*
> *was successfully undertaken. The principal difficulty in tobacco*
> *production was the curing and blending, for there were few who had*
> *any experience of the correct methods. Besides providing an additional*
> *alternative to existing crops, "Jersey tobacco would be a dollar silver".*[33]

> *"There were two families who made their fortune growing tobacco*
> *during the Occupation. Oh, I shouldn't have mentioned their names!"*

> Occupation resident

The growing of tobacco in Jersey goes back to the early seventeenth century. It may have been brought into Jersey as a crop by Sir Walter Raleigh who was appointed Governor of Jersey in 1600. Raleigh is said to have smoked his pipe during the sittings of the States of Jersey. Subsequently, it was grown on the Island in large quantities. In 1624 the Royal Court made an order banning the sale of the weed. In 1628 the English Attorney General became very disturbed to discover, "...large quantities of tobacco planted in Jersey and Guernsey, to the detriment of wheat crops, and against other proclamations".[34] He recommended to the Privy Council the destruction of the Jersey and Guernsey tobacco crops. The reasons for the destruction were: firstly, the financial claims made by the proprietors of American tobacco plantations; secondly, the loss by the British government of duties; and thirdly, the loss of wheat revenues from taxes which Island farmers had to pay to the Crown. In 1631 it was decreed that all Island tobacco plants be destroyed, and all further planting of the crop must cease. Tobacco was proclaimed as "injurious to the morals of the people" and in addition, the cultivation of it "took away bread from the inhabitants if the grounds for corn are thus employed".

In 1632 the Privy Council wrote to the Lieutenant-Governor of Jersey ordering an immediate destruction of tobacco plants and a total ban on any further planting. At the end of the seventeenth century the British government commented on the destruction of Jersey tobacco on account of, "a dishonest and clandestine trade". This was the growing of Island tobacco which was smuggled into France.[35]

The growing and curing of tobacco as a cash crop was immediately revived, on a far larger scale than has previously been thought, on the arrival of the German military forces on the 1st July 1940 and it became a highly valuable cash crop. It mitigated the loss of the lucrative early potato and tomato markets in the United Kingdom. It became an excellent source of cash flow and barter and almost a currency in itself.

A number of Jersey farmers and individual growers, very soon after military occupation took place, had the foresight to see that growing and curing tobacco was an excellent source of income, by and large relatively unregulated until the latter part of the German occupation. In fact, many farmers depended upon growing and processing tobacco to eke out their existence. Reg Langlois' grandfather grew 5 perches of potatoes and 25 perches of tobacco. The family realised the importance of growing tobacco: "He had his priorities right."[36] In addition to cultivating tobacco, Reg Langlois "bundled the green leaves together and hung them up in the rafters around the farm building to dry. He then placed them in a handmade press which was about eighteen inches long and five inches wide. It had a lump of wood on the top of it to squeeze the juice out of the leaves. I can just see grandpa now, tightening the screw bolts every day with loving care".

By the end of 1941 tobacco was being grown not only as a cash crop and used as barter, but farmers soon learnt that they could add value to the crop by drying and processing the leaves themselves. Some farmers discovered methods of producing flavoured tobacco, by adding new ingredients. This had the added benefit of also masking some of the unpleasant tastes that young tobacco produced.

The notion that tobacco could be easily grown can be seen by an article published in the local press several weeks after the military occupation. The article "Can We Grow Tobacco" pointed out that tobacco crops were common around St Malo, Brittany.[37] In addition, it mentioned that the 1940 English seed catalogues offered four varieties of tobacco seed. Therefore, it was surmised, with greenhouse growers working together with the local tobacco factories it would be "plain sailing" to produce tobacco plants.[38] It is certain that an amount of tobacco was being grown in Jersey in 1940, as it still is today; although, the cultivators of modern-day tobacco certainly do not appear to advertise the fact. The next day the local press published another article entitled "Tobacco Grown in Jersey" which described tobacco seed brought back from Kenya by a tea salesman Mr W. E. Gunner, Fauvic, and grown and cured on the property of Dr F. E. Doering, St Saviour. The seed was put out for inspection and was available at the office of the Jersey Evening Post.[39]

By the 1st December 1940 tobacco supplies were running low. The Tobacco (Rationing) (Jersey) Order, 1940 was implemented and tobacco coupons introduced. On the 31st January 1941 German military forces were issued with permits to allow them to purchase tobacco. However, even by late 1941 the DOA had no policy concerning the growing of tobacco and it was never mentioned in any cropping plan or Cultivation Order. This is somewhat difficult to understand. Evidence from the detailed ledgers of J. G. Germain and Sons Ltd clearly demonstrate that, as early as September to December 1940, substantial amounts of locally grown tobacco had been dried, cured, and taken to the firm to be cut and processed.[40]

J. F. Germain and Sons' ledgers show that, between September and December 1941, a total of fifty-five customers brought in locally grown tobacco to be processed, one of whom stands out. On two occasions – 24th November and 8th December – he brought in 29.9 lbs of locally grown tobacco leaf to be cut and processed. Therefore, accounting for the growing and drying period needed for tobacco leaf, it must have been sown in May or June 1940. The second customer who brought in large amounts was Mr L. Klein, the owner of a tobacco shop at 39 Hill Street.

The issue of locally grown tobacco did not officially confront the civil authorities until the DOA received a letter dated 11th November 1941 from Mr H. Minck, St Brelade. Mr Minck sought official approval for a scheme he wished to implement to grow sufficient tobacco for islanders, which he claimed would provide one ounce of pipe tobacco and ten cigarettes to each holder of a tobacco ration card. The amount to be grown would cover everyone's requirements for the forthcoming year, i.e., 1942. The DOA "... after mature deliberation decided, with regret, that it could not approve of the scheme outlined by Mr Minck as the extensive areas of arable land being devoted to military uses by the army of occupation necessitates the use of all cultivatable land in the production of foodstuffs for human and animal sustenance". In other words, Brée wished cultivated land to be used only for the production of food, however he did not foresee the exponential growth that would occur in 1942 in the amount of tobacco grown locally. In 1941 nearly 170 lbs were processed by one tobacco factory; in 1942 the figure became approximately 22,000 lbs!

A case study of tobacco grown in 1940 is interesting as it allows us to see what that cultivation entailed. In 1940 Alfred Vibert, at sixteen years of age and after his father's death, ran the family farm at Franc Fief, St Brelade. He immediately grew tobacco "legally and illegally" at the farm.[41] Mr Vibert purchased tobacco plants from "Pallots" in Broad Street, who had grown the plants from seed. The seeds were sown in spring in a sheltered situation. The crucial factor was to ensure that the young plants were kept out of the wind and with a southern aspect. Two types of tobacco were grown, the first a "Virginian" and the second a "French/Turkish" variety, smaller in leaf size, but preferred because of its distinctive flavour. Initially, the young tobacco plants were supported by bamboo sticks. Mr Vibert clearly remembered "The plants thrived and needed very little labour – they tended to look after themselves". When the tobacco leaves were just beginning to go golden brown, they were harvested and strung through lengths of wire. The leaves were left for several months in the loft and then taken to Chings, Providence Street, St Helier, to be processed. The cut and diced leaf was returned in the form of tobacco. The tobacco factory took 10% of the finished tobacco as payment. In addition, Chings could be paid to add molasses into the process at the factory. This gave the finished tobacco a wonderful aroma especially sought by pipe smokers. In the case of cigarettes, Chings used a brown cigarette paper imported from France.

References

1. G. A. Romeril was unanimously expelled by the JFU Council on 25th May 1945, "for having associated with the enemy during the occupation". JFU Minute Book.
2. Jersey Archive. L/D/09/A10.
3. Jersey Archive. C/B/A1/6.
4. Jersey Archive. D/Z/H5/141.
5. A senior honorary police officer of a parish.
6. Jersey Archive. C/A5/21.
7. Jersey Archive. D/Z/H5/141.
8. Jersey Archive. B/A/W31/2/34.
9. Jersey Archive. D/Z/H5/141/2.
10. Jersey Archive. C/B/A1/7.
11. Jersey Archive. C/B/A1/5.
12. Jersey Archive. C/B/A1/7.
13. RJA&HS. Price Advisory Board Minutes. Also known as the Potato Price Advisory Board.
14. His name was misspelt and should have been written as Dr Brosch.
15. Chats are the smallest potatoes. Larger sizes are mids, wares and toppers.
16. Jersey Archive. B/A/W41/9.
17. Pocock, H. R. S. The memoirs of Lord Coutanche. 1975. p. 22. Pelz was neither German nor a Doctor.
18. Marshall, M., Hitler Invaded Sark. 1967. p. 42.

19. Interviews between Alan Allix and Dennis Holmes with Dr Casper and Heider.
20. Karl Grier interviews with Alan Allix. For an account of Karl Grier, see Channel Islands Occupation Review. "Karl Grier – Reluctant Soldier". M. J. Ginns, 1981. pp. 46–66. Also, Jersey Archives. D/S/B5/18.
21. Jersey Evening Post, 27th July 1941; and JEP July 28th, 1951. The Death of Jurat T. J. Brée: A lifetime of service to the Island.
22. Probably refers to the Superior Council.
23. Hans Egon Pelz.
24. Wood, Alan and Seaton Wood, Mary. Islands in Danger. 1989, 12th ed. p. 99.
25. Interviews by Alan Allix with Maurice Thebault.
26. Alan Allix. Interview with Heider. Heider was Chief of Staff, Field Command 515. In June 1944 he became Platzkommandant I.
27. Corbet, Francis, L.M. 1998. A Biographical Dictionary of Jersey Volume 2. pp. 56–58.
28. Lund, J. (2013) The Wages of Collaboration: the German food crisis 1939–1945 and the supplies from Demark. Scandinavian Journal of History, 38:4, pp. 480–501.
29. Private letter dated 12th February 1957. The letter is from Pelz to Dr Kratzer, President of the Bavarian Administrative Court, Munich 22, Ludwig Str. 22, Germany. Dr Kratzer served as a Staff Officer in Field Command 515 during the German occupation. My thanks to the Pelz family for allowing me permission to use the letter.
30. This is a seedborne disease caused by a fungus. Smut can lie dormant within the embryo of an infected wheat seed.
31. The name Maud was misspelt by the Pelz family and written as "Maid".
32. 1 cabot = 32 pounds weight.
33. Hooke, W. D. 1961. The Channel Islands. p. 162.
34. Podger, A. Jersey 'That Nest of Vypers'. 2007. Société Jersiaise. p. 124. The original primary sources can be found in "The Acts of Privy Council" 1628–1629: Section 15-9-1628. The author advised these sources can only be found in the Reference Section, Jersey Public Library.
35. Falle, Philip. CAESAREA; An Account of Jersey 1935. Fourth Edition. p. 122.
36. Langlois, Reg. WW2 People's War. BBC History. "My Life in Jersey during the Occupation". 2004. Article IDA3403946.
37. Jersey Evening Post. 7th August 1940.
38. There were two tobacco factories. The first was Chings, known as the Jersey Tobacco Company Limited. The second is J. F. Germain and Sons Ltd, which is still trading.
39. Jersey Evening Post. 8th August 1940.
40. My thanks to Robert Germain and his company, J. F. Germain and Sons Ltd, for allowing me access to their ledgers for the years 1940–1945.
41. Interview with Mr Alfred Vibert, 2nd February 2015.

Chapter 7

January – February – March 1942

Milk Control

"Milk Control drew attention to the unsatisfactory working of the system of cattle recording prescribed by the Milk Control (Jersey) Order, 1940, and the impossibility of reconciling such records with the statements made to the various Milk Testers by farmers."

DOA Report

On the 2nd January 1942 a sub-committee was appointed to facilitate the means to effect the instructions of the German Field Command to reorganise Milk Control. It comprised Touzel Brée, John du Val and Carlyle Le Gallais. They worked closely with F. de L. Bois, the States Law Draftsman, R. O. Weeks, and H. G. Shepard. It was immediately decided that the cost of putting into effect the instructions of the German Field Command would be met by the imposition of a tax on every cow.

On the 6th January the DOA submitted the following Orders to the Superior Council.

1. The Milk Control (Amendment No 2) (Jersey) Order, 1942.
2. The Milk Control (Prices and Contribution) (No 2) (Amendment No 5) Jersey Order, 1941.
3. The Milk (Registration with Retailers) (Jersey) Order, 1942.[1]

An important demand of Field Command was the establishment of a centralised system of checks on milk production for all dairy farmers, to be carried out by "Milk Inspectors". The DOA immediately advertised for applicants for the post of "Milk Testers". It was planned that the Milk Testers would verify milk production for every individual cow as well as for the herd, being provided with a spring balance for weighing the yield. An advertisement was placed in the local press asking for spring balances but by February no satisfactory balances could be found. The DOA therefore decided to calibrate a number of milk cans in order that milk tests could be carried out by measure instead of by weight.

The fundamental changes in the new Milk Control (Amendment No 2) (Jersey) Order, 1942, were: firstly, the producer, whether registered or not, would have to sell all his milk to the DOA; and secondly, a producer could only sell milk to a licensed retailer with whom he was registered, and to no one else. All milk sold by the licensed retailer would be on behalf of the DOA. Any milk supplied which was unfit for human consumption would be investigated by the Public Health Department. All persons owning cattle had to furnish the DOA with details of births or changes in custody of animals within eight days of the event. All deaths had to be notified within 24 hours, the carcass checked by a vet and disposed of by the DOA or the Department of Essential Commodities. Milk Testers had the authority to carry out inspections and to test samples. Each producer had to pay the DOA 1/- in respect of each cow in his personal custody.

On the 12th January Weeks explained that he was unable to carry out the requirements of the German Field Command in relation to the keeping of "Control Cards" which were ordered to be on the premises where cattle were kept and to be available at any time for inspection because "No card is available in the island". Instead, it was decided that the Milk Testers would be given a copy of a report written by the owner of the cows.

Brée met with the representatives of the dairies who agreed to collect, on behalf of the DOA, the milk test fees from all dairy farmers. In turn, the dairies would keep a commission of 5% of all monies collected.

On the 17th January the DOA, along with Weeks and Shepard, interviewed applicants for the post of Milk Tester in accordance with the Milk Control (Amendment No 2) (Jersey) Order, 1942. Their wages were set at £2 a week. The first men to be appointed were as follows.

H. J. Alexander
A. C. Baudains
D. Buesnel
J. H. Carrel
P. A. Cotillard
P. E. de Gruchy
J. P. Gaudin
E. Gautier
C. D. Godeaux
E. L. Gruchy
W. Hansford
G. J. Hind
G. Huelin
S. E. Léonard
J. P. Le Feuvre

S. G. Le Gros
A. E. Le Leré
G. P. Le Sueur
H. J. Manning
J. F. Poignard
C. Talbot
R. M. Yates
L. Danican (from Guernsey)

Evidently, these twenty-three men proved insufficient in number and on the 3rd February further appointments were made:

F. P. Le Cocq
G. Cary
C. de la Cour
F. B. Jones
J. G. Malzard – appointed "Temporary Foreman Tester" at £3 a week

Also on 17th January, a meeting took place between the DOA and the collecting dairies. The dairies had requested an increase of 1 farthing (a quarter of 1 penny) per pot with regard to the cartage bonus paid to them in respect of the milk collected. The request had been made by Cyril P. Tanguy, Chairman of the Chamber of Commerce Dairies Section, on behalf of the dairies.

On the 30th January an investigation of the balance sheet of Don Street Dairy was made. It demonstrated a loss of £2,113-5-1½ for the nine months prior to 31st December 1941 and a further examination of the books showed an additional loss of £398-9-7.

It was also decided in January that the Milk Control Section would issue new guidelines concerning milk that could be retained by producers. All producers were sent a detailed explanation in a letter addressed personally to them which stated that producers could retain one pint of milk daily per head for themselves and their families, irrespective of the ages of the individual members of the family. The producers who took this milk allowance need not notify the Milk Control Section as the secretary/accountant would take these allowances into account when completing his monthly computations. In addition, the servants of producers, assisting in tending cattle, together with the families of such servants, were permitted to acquire per head an allowance of milk equal to the amount allowed to the producer. The producer was also permitted to retain, by virtue of the Newly-Born Calves (Jersey) Order, 1941 for the purpose of feeding calves, 2 pots of milk daily for three months from the birth of the calf. On the 17th February 1942, the period was increased to six months from the birth of the calf.

Problems, however, remained concerning the retention of milk by producers. "In view of certain doubts which have arisen to which milk producers are entitled to retain milk for their own families, the DOA modified its order by substituting the word household for the word families".

At the same time a sub-committee appointed by the DOA discussed matters of milk control with the Chief Medical Officer of Health. It was agreed that all diabetics who lived in their own homes would be allowed an extra half pint of milk and it would sanction, as before, an extra pint of milk daily to each of the stokers employed at the Gas Works on the days these men were employed.

It was announced in February that the cartage subsidy granted to L. J. Tanguy Limited, Victoria Dairy Limited, Jersey Dairies Limited and Fairview Dairy would cease on the 31st March 1942.

The States Vet reported to the DOA that Mr M. F. Ecobichon, St Peter, had reported the death of a heifer. Ecobichon, however, was unable to show the vet a carcass, as required by the Milk Control (Amendment No 2) (Jersey) Order. The matter was immediately sent to the Crown Officers with a view to institute judicial proceedings.[2]

On the 5th February the DOA received a letter from Robert Wilson Carson. He was a leading figure in the RJA&HS and certainly in the top rank of the Island's farmers. He was seconded to the Calf Section Committee and the Cattle Slaughter Executive. Carson's letter concerned Mr C. Talbot, a Milk Tester who worked in the district of Rozel Manor Farm. Carson alleged that Talbot was a discharged employee of his farm and wanted him moved to a new district, the reason as far as Carson was concerned being personal. Brée discussed the matter with his DOA colleagues and the decision was taken to refuse Carson's request to move Talbot to a new district. Carson, however, refused to accept Brée's decision and he took up the matter with the Superior Council which reversed Brée's decision. A new Milk Tester was sent instead to Rozel Manor Farm to examine the cattle. He was J. G. Malzard, the Chief Milk Tester. This episode is interesting and informative. Firstly, it demonstrates the influence and power that this class of farmers could call upon, and secondly, the manner in which Brée's decision was contradicted, although he was President of the DOA. Brée came from a relatively modest background; he had worked hard from the age of sixteen (upon the death of his father) to build up his farm and had climbed the political system to become a Jurat. He simply could not compete with Carson and the elite class of farmers to which he belonged. Carson refused to accept Brée's decision concerning an agricultural matter, but this was not the only time it occurred. This refusal by gentleman farmers was a recurring theme throughout the German occupation and it must have caused Brée great annoyance.

A report from the Milk Tester J. P. Gaudin, in February 1941, described the refusal of a farmer to cooperate with him. The farmer, Mr A. L. Jeanne, St Martin, had refused to inform him of the time at which he milked his cows. The Milk Tester was fully entitled to have this information furnished to him by virtue of Article 6B(i) Milk Control Order, 1940. The timings for milking cows were an essential part of the Milk Tester's data collection as this influenced the expected yield and thus could "mask" if milk was being withheld. It was decided that Jeanne be interviewed the following week by both the Chief Milk Tester and Mr Gaudin. When interviewed, and in view of Jeanne's "highly unsatisfactory nature," it was decided to refer the matter to the Crown Officers.

On the 10th February KVR Dr Reffler wrote to the Bailiff enquiring how the provisions of the order concerning milk control and the collection of milk had advanced. On the 19th February and 4th March Dr Casper also wrote to the DOA, requesting a report concerning the execution of the order. Brée replied on the 9th March that the milk collecting depot "desired by the German authorities would be in operation by the 16th March".

In early March two more Milk Testers were appointed, Mr C. W. Henry and Mr C. R. Mauger. At the same time, Weeks compiled a dossier concerning the problem of unsatisfactory milk test reports. This led to the decision to appoint an additional "Foreman Tester" and Mr C. R. Mauger was appointed at a weekly wage of £3.

Pelz wanted milk control to be made efficient and accountable. He also pushed the DOA into improving the method of recording exact numbers of cattle. His influence was behind a report of the 14th March 1942 by the Milk Control Section which drew attention to "The unsatisfactory working of the system of cattle recording prescribed by the Milk Control (Jersey) Order, 1940 and the impossibility of reconciling such records with the statements made to the various milk testers by farmers". In simple terms, if the Milk Control Section did not know the exact number of milk-producing cattle on a farm, it could not produce reliable data as to the amount of milk produced. Pelz was obviously aware of this and demanded an improvement in the recording of milk yield per cow.

In response to this the DOA formed a sub-committee comprising Brée and Le Gallais. Its remit was to investigate Milk Control and its recording of milk yields and to expedite "The appropriate steps to be taken to effect a remedy". This sub-committee issued an instruction to the Milk Testers to "...make it their business on each farm to see the owner of the cattle and verify the number of cattle on the farm and obtain full details of how many animals have been disposed of." The Milk Control Section was also ordered to ensure that the owners of cattle made an immediate transfer declaration in writing at the time of the interview, in respect of any animals which had left their land. Brée and Le Gallais, both extremely astute men, examined the issue of cattle transfers and after an examination of case studies instructed the Milk Testers to substitute the word "owning" with the expression "person in whose custody are". A new Milk Test Form was reviewed and printed, incorporating all the changes decided upon by Le Gallais and Brée.

In March 1942 the DOA, in accordance with the requirements of Field Command 515, drafted new amendments to the Milk Control (Jersey)

Order, 1940. The amendment would empower the DOA "...to revoke or suspend any and every licence issued". It was evident that the German Military Government demanded that the system of licensed retail milk sales to the local civilian population be put on a more controlled and centralised basis which they could monitor and scrutinise. The above amendment had all the hallmarks of Pelz's system which allowed for immediate inspection.

The only licensed milk retailers henceforth allowed were the following.

Name	Address
Adolphus John Allix	Yarboro Dairy, 68/70 Stopford Road, St Helier
Albert John Allo Edward Peter Allo Alfred Alec Allo	Devonshire Dairy, 59 Great Union Road, St Helier
Harold Edward Aubin	54 St Saviour's Road, St Helier
Thomas Henry Chevalier	Victoria Park Dairy, 10 Victoria Road, St Saviour
William John Davis	Mont Les Vaux, St Aubin, St Brelade and Bellozanne Dairy, First Tower, St Helier
Fairview Dairy	St Saviour
Francis Joseph Le Flohic	United Dairies, 25 Hue Street, St Helier
Louis Klein	34 Queen Street, St Helier
William Reginald Matson	Almorah Dairy, St Helier
Jeffrey James Le Marquand	Plaisance Dairy, St Ouen
Gerald Wilfred Le Masurier	Val Plaisant, St Helier
Gerald Ernest Michel	Beaumont Dairy, St Peter
Miss Winifred Pepin	Wayside Stores, First Tower, St Helier
Philip Charles Quenault	Faldouet and Gorey Dairies, Gorey
Alfred Edward Surcouf John Edward Surcouf Arthur Clifford Surcouf Clarence Frederick Surcouf	Western Dairy, Edward Place, St Helier
Edward George Syvret	Martello Stores, First Tower, St Helier
L. J. Tanguy Limited	5 Francis Street, St Helier
The Victoria Dairy Limited	5 Cheapside and Victoria Street, St Helier

The Milk (Revocation of Licences) (Jersey) Order, 1942, empowered the Milk Control Section to revoke all other milk retail licences as from the 1st April 1942. Each licence holder received notification from the DOA as to the day his licence ceased to be effective. On the same day, Milk Control amended the Milk Control (Prices and Contribution) (No 2)

(Jersey) Order, 1940 reducing the contribution payable under Article 7, Milk Control (Jersey) Order, from 1 penny to 3 farthings (¾ of a penny) per pot. It was also amended to provide that, for any sale of milk by the four collecting dairies (L. J. Tanguy, Victoria Dairy, Jersey Dairies and Fairview Diary) to another retailer, the sale price was fixed at 1/1¼ d per pot.

On the 9th March 1942, three milk lorries were taken from the Jersey Co-operative Dairy and given to Jersey Dairies Limited and Victoria Dairy Limited. The DOA wanted to facilitate a far more efficient system of milk collection. Each dairy had to pay a hire charge of £1 a week and fully maintain the vehicle.

Further rationalisation took place on the 23rd March when all Don Street Dairy's depots were taken over by Jersey Dairies Limited and several milk collection depots operated by Jersey Dairies were taken over by the Victoria Dairy Limited.

March 1942 saw the Milk Control Section continue its surveillance and reporting on any farmers deemed not to have fulfilled their orders under the Milk Control Law. Legal proceedings were initiated by the Attorney General against Adèle Martret, St Ouen, who neglected to furnish the DOA with a list of cattle and refused to sell her milk. Martret was given time to produce a record and description of her cattle and was also repeatedly requested to sell her milk to the DOA, being in breach of the Milk Control (Jersey) Order, 1940 on both counts. The DOA's patience ran out and proceedings were started.

A report of the 20th March investigated the transfer of a heifer by Mr J. M. Le Brocq, St Ouen to a "Doctor E. Dennisburg".[3] Le Brocq was interviewed the following week regarding the allegation that he had sold a heifer calf to a member of the German forces. The DOA decided that the animal had left the possession of Le Brocq and therefore no action would be taken. The issue, however, took another dimension when it was discovered that a bull calf was also involved. The bull calf was still in the possession of Le Brocq. The DOA immediately ordered him to deliver the bull calf to the abattoir for slaughter in accordance with the requirements of the Newly-Born Calves (Jersey) Order, 1941.

A further problem arose between the DOA and the German military. Milk Tester Mr Cotillard had visited a civilian farm adjacent to the Airport, St Peter. The German Military Authority refused him permission to test the yield of the cows unless he was in possession of a permit from the Airport Commandant. Brée decided to report the matter to Pelz in order to obtain the necessary permit.

On the 26th March a report by the DOA drew attention to "The fact that milk in a very bad condition owing to the filthy cans is being brought in by Jersey Dairies from Dr Charles Chichester, St Peter.[2] The DOA immediately wrote to Dr Chichester. "Owing to the filthy condition of the milk which is being received, all such milk, until further notice, will have to be cleaned by the DOA, the cost of such cleaning being charged to the Dr Chichester". In addition, the Department of Public Health was requested to send an Inspector to report on the condition of the cattle stables on his farm. A report was written by Mr L. Hammond, Sanitary Inspector, Public Health Department. The stables were not closed down. However, the Milk Control Section was directed, "...to exercise particular vigilance in relation to milk brought in from Dr Chichester". The problem of "dirty milk" was an ongoing concern to the DOA.[4] It, therefore, decided that in future any "...dirty milk" sent to the dairy would result in no credit given to the farmer. In addition, the dairy would write to the farmer to notify him.

Between January and March 1942, there was a significant decrease in the amount of milk collected. The DOA managed to provide supplies of full cream milk to the civilian population without reduction, however the same could not be said of skimmed milk, the supply of which was reduced. The DOA decided that the quantity of skimmed milk already issued to farmers for feeding their stock, should continue. Any subsequent decline would have to be borne by the civilian population. In accordance with this principle, the DOA decided that the distribution of skimmed milk to the public by the Don Street Dairy would cease. This practice had been carried out since October 1941 from the St Paul's Mission building.

In September 1940, Pelz had instructed the DOA that milk distributed in the countryside would have to be sold from depots. On the 31st March 1942, Brée requested Field Command 515 that the hours of sale be modified to permit the opening of these depots before 10.00 a.m. It may possibly have been an attempt for fresh milk to make its way to the civilian population before it turned sour.

Agricultural Labour

"John Buesnel Michel favoured some form of compulsion for workers to do agricultural work. German firms offered such high wages as to attract men from work".

RJA&HS and JFU Joint Emergency Committee

On the 2nd January 1942 the DOA recommended to the Superior Council that the Agricultural Wages Bonus should continue for a further six months from the 5th April 1942 and on the same terms as before. The aim of the bonus was to keep as many young men as possible employed in the agricultural industry and attempt to stop them working for German construction firms. Some German firms paid up to five times the going rate for tradesmen and in some cases provided hot meals for their workers. New vouchers for employers were printed with instructions on the cover for farmers employing men who were on the agricultural workers bonus scheme. These men were paid a bonus on condition that they worked 56 hours in one week. Between the period January to March 1942, a total of £6,255-2-0 was paid to agricultural workers who were subsidised by the bonus.

On the 10th February the DOA met with the Department of Labour. The discussion centred around the payment of the bonus to "casual agricultural labour". The DOA decided to request the Superior Council to approve the scheme and provide the necessary credit. It also decided to take charge of the scheme from the Department of Labour and to pay the bonus. Payments to casual labour could not exceed the amount of the bonus already paid to permanent labour. It was devised as a separate scheme and a credit of £1,500 was made available.

On the 24th February the payment of an agricultural bonus for casual labour was approved. In order to control the money paid out under this scheme receipted time sheets had to be presented for payment at the States Treasury within ten days. No farmers would be entitled to receive the bonus in respect of these time sheets if presented after the prescribed period of ten days. The DOA decided that any agricultural casual labourer who worked for the same farmer for longer than five days would be deemed a permanent worker and eligible to draw the Agricultural Workers Bonus.

On the 31st March a delegation of the RJA&HS and JFU met the DOA to discuss the ever-worsening shortage of agricultural labour on the Island. The joint farmers' delegation comprised: J. P. Le Masurier, J. B. Michel, P. Renouf, C. P. Journeaux and H. G. Shepard.

A week prior to this meeting the two farming associations met to discuss their strategy concerning agricultural labour and its commensurate problems. The Presidents and Vice Presidents of the JFU and the RJA&HS met, along with thirty-seven of the Island's most important farmers. The meeting was held under the aegis of the DOA and Brée. Michel expressed the view that some form of compulsion be introduced for labourers to do agricultural work. This could only be carried out by order of the Superior Council and the States. The labour scheme had been utilised throughout 1941. Several points were raised:

1. The Germans deliberately offered higher wages than farmers to positively attract men from farm work.
2. An increase in agricultural wages by means of a subsidy might be necessary but would lead to difficulties after the war. In other words, when the subsidy ended, farmers would have to pay the differential out of their own pockets. This was total anathema to the assembled thirty-seven leading farmers.
3. There should be more collaboration with the Department of Labour. This would ensure that the right men were sent to work on farms.
4. The problem of farmers' sons who left their family farms and worked elsewhere, in order to draw the agricultural bonus.

The general opinion of the meeting was that farm wages had to increase to compete with the favourable working conditions offered under the Department of Labour schemes. Several schemes were quoted where there was a lack of supervision by the Department of Labour, and general slackness.[5]

The thirty-seven farmers made a number of proposals to the Superior Council. These were as follows.

1. All farmers would pay a wage of £2 a week to their farm hands.
2. The minimum wage entitling a farm worker to the agricultural wages bonus to be increased from 14/- to 16/- weekly. The minimum wage for workers under nineteen to be increased from 7/- to 8/- weekly.
3. In addition to the Agricultural Workers Bonus, an additional or supplementary bonus of 5/- a week would be paid to "bona fide" herdsmen in charge of horned cattle numbering ten and over. In the case of herds exceeding 20 head in number, two herdsmen would be entitled to draw the additional bonus. In a similar manner, larger herds would be entitled to claim the bonus in respect of additional herdsmen, in the same proportion.

On the same day, the DOA decided to investigate and compile the exact number of agricultural workers in Jersey. It wrote to the Social Assurance Department and asked for a list of men employed in the agricultural sector, together with their present addresses, as shown by the Local Assurance records for September 1940.

Watermills and Milling

By the 2nd January 1942 the DOA had decided to look at the possibility of purchasing Malassis Mill. Prior to the occupation it had been closed for more than twenty years and its pond and wheel were in disrepair. Brée, Le Gallais and du Val discussed the matter with the representative of Mr and Mrs J. T. Britton, the owners of the mill. A response was sent to the DOA on the 21st January offering to sell the mill for £3,000; however this was regarded as "excessive". The DOA recommended to the Superior Council that in view of the price, the purchase of the mill should be delayed for the present time, to which the Superior Council agreed. On the 2nd February the DOA wrote to Mr Britton asking what rental would be acceptable.

Brée regarded the matter to be of the highest priority. He understood the importance to the Island's survival of taking over another disused mill. On the 13th February, Mr Britton replied that a rental of £52 per annum would be acceptable. The immediate reply was that in view of the previous rent that had been charged, this figure was too high.

Somewhat predictably, it was made clear that in view of the Brittons' attitude towards the DOA it would have no alternative, unless a satisfactory agreement was reached, but to requisition the mill. Furthermore, the DOA stated that there would then be no question of rental payments until the termination of hostilities. Mr Britton responded to the DOA within ten days. He enquired as to exactly what the DOA deemed to be a fair and equitable rental. The DOA replied that it would offer £14 a year, which was accepted. On the same day the position of night watchman for the Malassis Mill was made available.

In February a full audit and report was compiled on wastage of grain at all the DOA mills. Gargate was found to have the highest wastage rate of 4.4%, on top of normal wastage. In the same month, Harold Gilley, now the Senior Miller at Quetivel, received an increase in salary from £3 to £3-5-0 weekly.

An article appeared in the local press entitled "Jersey's Flour Mills".[6] It gave a detailed description of the renovation work carried out by the "energetic leadership of Jurat T. J. Brée in conjunction with the Department of Labour". All the mills which had been renovated were described: Tesson, Gargate, Quetivel, Grand Val and Malassis. The article is both interesting and informative, detailing recent history concerning the operation of the mills.

The first load of Jersey wheat had been received and milled at Malassis on the 17th November 1941. This would have been grain from the 1941 wheat harvest. On the 20th November 1941 this Jersey flour was sent to the bakers. The miller was William Henry Hawkins. All men employed in mills worked a 12-hour shift, 8.00 a.m. to 8.00 p.m., six days a week. The flour produced from Island wheat baked into a heavy and damp loaf, the reason being that grain needed storing for at least nine months. This, however, was impossible "…in the circumstances that presently the Island found itself".

Some 25% of the wheat in Jersey loaves came from French flour while the Island's total production of wholemeal flour was 60 tons a week. This necessitated additional steam power, as well as water power at Malassis and Grand Val. There were two mills in St Peter's valley, Tesson and Gargate, where the millers, brothers Edwin and Ernest Charles Gilley, had previously worked for many years. They understood the complexities of their craft and were highly regarded professionals. Both mills were equipped with dynamos.

The task of dressing the Island's millstones had been carried out by Harold Gilley (son of Edwin), and with all the mill's running at full capacity new staff were employed and changes implemented. Claude Le Geyt Lucas became Assistant Miller at Quetivel Mill, and Claude Vincent, Assistant Miller at Tesson, both at £2-10-0 a week. Samuel Gilley (son of Edwin) was appointed at Quetivel Mill and Francis Morin was employed to patrol the millstream at St Peter's Valley at a weekly wage of £2-10-0.

Cultivation Orders

On the 2nd January 1942, the DOA approached Mr Arthur Winter Falle and asked him to replace Mr Raymond Labey as Honorary Parish Inspector for

Grouville. On the 9th January, Horace L. Copp and Stanley John Godfray were appointed as Inspectors under the Potatoes (Sales and Returns) (Jersey) Order, 1941. These men worked for the Potato Collection Board at a weekly wage of £3 and were also given an extra ration of bread. On the 13th January the DOA purchased a further threshing machine at a cost of £201. On the same day Mr L. H. Blight, who had recently been tried at the Royal Court for not fulfilling cereal Cultivation Orders, and in view of remarks made in and by the Royal Court on the 3rd February, was interviewed by the DOA. Blight was told to plough his fields and sow with wheat and oats in accordance with the principles of good husbandry. He was ordered to complete the task by the 31st January. The Honorary Parish Inspector Charles Quenault was instructed to make a series of inspections and to report on his cultivation. His reports were positive, and no further action was taken against Blight.

On the 16th January the German Field Command informed the DOA that Mr William John Poingdestre, Grouville, had allegedly been discovered retaining a quantity of wheat, oats and barley of which he was the grower. These tip-offs from the Field Command to the DOA were by no means unusual; Pelz regularly toured the Island and inspected farms and barns. In addition, Pelz made himself aware of the Cultivation Orders sent out by the DOA and he became personally involved in their distribution to farmers. The German authority made it clear to the DOA that they required Poingdestre to be presented before a judicial court. In response the DOA charged Colin Marie to write to the Attorney General informing him of the circumstances and requesting proceedings to be instigated. On the 18th February the DOA requisitioned his entire load of grain. Poingdestre informed the DOA that he wanted to be paid for the grain and, in addition, wanted to retain a portion of it. His contention was simple enough, the grain that had been obtained from him was "…a result of gleaning". The DOA refused to surrender any of the requisitioned grain and decided to defer the question of any payment to a later date.

In January the DOA increased the petrol allowance for the States Vet to 4 gallons a week and all Honorary Parish Inspectors were given an allowance of £1 for telephone calls when carrying out their duties.

On the 20th January the DOA received a letter from Vivian J. Bailhache, solicitor for George Dorey, Trinity. Mr Dorey's farm had fallen into "poor condition" and Bailhache had been appointed as his representative. Mr Bailhache informed the DOA that Mr George Dorey Junior would run the farm henceforth and consequently he requested no further interference. The DOA agreed, adding two conditions. Firstly, the farm was to be run on the principles of good husbandry and secondly, his father was forbidden to interfere in the working of the farm.

In February, J. G. Malzard, the Chief Threshing Inspector, forwarded a report regarding grain which it was alleged was in the custody of Mrs A. Fauvel, St Martin. She was told to appear before the DOA where she stated that Malzard had given her permission to thresh wheat by hand. The DOA expressed its disappointment at the action of the Chief Threshing Inspector in giving such permission without first obtaining the sanction of the DOA. He was charged to arrange for the grain in Mrs Fauvel's possession to be brought into a DOA store. The cost of transport was debited against Mrs Fauvel. The following week the DOA also alleged that she had kept back a quantity of grain contrary to the requirements of the Cereal Grain (Threshing and Purchase of Crops) (Jersey) Order, 1941. Mrs Fauvel, in a second interview with the DOA, offered "certain explanations". She was warned that in the event of any repetition of the alleged offences the DOA would have no alternative but to submit the case to the Law Officers of the Crown with a view to instituting legal proceedings.

On the 20th February the DOA met with Edwin Woodcock of the States Experimental Station. The issue under discussion was an amendment to the Cultivation of Lands (Jersey) Order, 1940 and, in particular, to satisfactorily manage a number of farmers who, for any reason, had not received directions concerning what and how much to cultivate and the method of disposal of their crops. All farmers should have been notified by the 1st March 1942. Those individual farmers who had not received Cultivation Orders were asked to notify the DOA by the 8th March.

Brée was adamant that, where agricultural land had not been satisfactorily worked, the DOA would cultivate this land and recover the costs from the occupier. He ordered an Amendment to the Cultivation of Lands (Jersey) Order, 1940 but at the last minute he decided to withdraw gardens from the amended order. Such an application of the law would have necessitated more inspections and the employment of more bureaucrats.

On the 14th February the German Field Command informed the Bailiff that the Guernsey States Dairy was prepared to sell an Alfa Laval electrically driven milk separator for £260, with free delivery from St Peter Port Harbour. The DOA recommended to the Superior Council that the machine be purchased. On the same day the DOA received an offer from a French agricultural agent of one hundred tons of wheat seed for sale, which was also accepted. Also, in late February, Mr G. Le Breuilly wrote to the DOA for permission to import three harvesting and reaping machines from France. No objections were made, and permission was granted.

On the 24th February the DOA met with the Department of Finance and Economics to discuss the steps to be taken to secure repayment of agricultural credits advanced against the security of 1941 crops and which some farmers had failed to repay. The Department was represented by Jurats Edgar Dory and Ernest Labey. Also present was the Treasurer of the States, Herbert Frank Ereaut. It was decided to write to these farmers requiring them to make payment within seven days. Failure to repay the loans would lead to "...pain of legal proceedings being instituted against all defaulters". On the 10th March the DOA decided that no further claims for crop failure in 1941, from causes alleged to be outside the control of the farmer, would be entertained. The DOA Secretary was charged to stop any further claims being submitted. All Honorary Parish Inspectors were informed of the decision.

On the 24th March Ereaut reported to the DOA the amounts unpaid by farmers who had been advanced credits against their 1941 crops. It was decided to secure these non-payments against the 1942 crop. Furthermore, it was decided that these farmers, who were indebted to the DOA, would be told to execute a "Bond or Agreement" empowering the Treasury to debit proceeds of the 1942 crop with the amount due in respect of the 1941 crop.

On the same day the Jersey Allotment Council (JAC) wrote to the DOA asking for the provision of petrol to scarify and plough 10 vergées of land which had been lent to the JAC by the FB Playing Fields Trust. It also asked for 300 boxes of seed potatoes and the necessary fertilisers. The DOA allowed the JAC 20 gallons of petrol and the seed potatoes. The matter of fertilisers was deferred.

On the 14th March, Mr P. J. Blandin met with the DOA regarding the breaking of an axle of the tractor he was using in his capacity as a ploughing contractor. He asked for financial assistance with the cost of repair as otherwise he would not be able to carry on his work. It was decided to assist Mr Blandin and the Honorary Parish Inspectors for St Clement were instructed to allow him 2 gallons of petrol per vergée whilst ploughing with his Fordson tractor.

In March the Price Advisory Board recommended to the Superior Council that the prices and methods of handling potato and cereal harvests should be the same as in 1941 and advised that sanctions should remain the same as previously.

A letter dated 6th March was received from Mr P. Pirouet, a ploughing contractor appointed by the DOA. He stated that, during the course of his contract, he had used more than the regulation quantity of petrol allowed for the amount of work he had done. He therefore requested he should not be required to pay the full amount due to the DOA under the terms of the agreement. The DOA refused his request.

On the same day, the DOA wrote to John Amy, a St Helier Deputy, and Miss Frazier, who were in charge of the Communal Kitchen, Philip Street, St Helier. They were thanked for their efforts in carrying out experiments in "The use of green potatoes for providing human food". Miss Frazier was requested to insert a paragraph in the Evening Post informing the public of her method of using green potatoes.

Towards the end of March, the Honorary Parish Inspectors were ordered to check the progress of farmers who had been given cultivation directions to sow wheat for the forthcoming season. The Inspectors were ordered that, if they found any farmer who had failed to sow his wheat seed, it should be returned immediately and substituted with oat seed.

A report from Mr J. W. Blampied, an Inspector appointed for the purposes of the Pigs (Control) (Jersey) Order, 1941, described a visit to a property at 16 Ann Street, St Helier. He witnessed three pigs in the possession of Mr P. G. Poingdestre. These pigs were not registered; Poingdestre admitted he had two pigs in his custody. The DOA proceeded to institute a case through the Attorney General.

On the 31st March the DOA was requested to provide "A codification of the various orders relating to agriculture". The need to review agricultural legislation meant a commensurate "redrafting" of the Cultivation of Lands (Jersey) Order, 1940, in order to cover all the requirements of existing legislation in relation to the cultivation of land.

On the same day, the DOA learnt that one of the two Ford Ferguson tractors that had been requisitioned from Dr Constantinos Mattas in December 1941 had already been sold by him. The second tractor was sold to Mr L. C. Pallot, Sion Works, Trinity. However, it seems clear that the tractor which the DOA had been unable to requisition had in fact been left in storage by Dr Mattas at St Helier Garages, Bath Street, St Helier. On the 14th November 1941 St Helier Garages had written to Dr Mattas:

"Dear Sir,
We have been informed by the German Authorities that they require more of our garage space and have instructed us to remove cars etc. garaged here.

We, therefore, have to ask you to kindly arrange to remove your Ford Ferguson Tractor and implements before next Thursday the 20th inst.

We regret the inconvenience caused, but you will understand that we have no alternative in the matter.

Your early attention will oblige.

H. Brée
Managing Director".[7]

The mystery remains as to why a Greek General Practitioner from Sofia, Bulgaria, who had arrived in Jersey in 1922, should own two brand new Ford Ferguson tractors almost certainly worth £300 each.

Dr Mattas appears to have been in Germany between the 7th August 1935 and 8th June 1936. In addition, he was in Berlin on the 13th April 1935 and on that date he had sent a postcard to his address at 92 Bath Street, St Helier. He wrote that Berlin was not as beautiful as London or Paris. In addition, he stated that the German people adored Herr Hitler very much. During the occupation, Dr Mattas officiated as the medical officer at local boxing tournaments. His alien's card demonstrates that he often left Jersey at regular intervals before the Second World War. All these aspects of his life are intriguing.[8]

The DOA decided at the end of March 1942 that, if any of its employees fell sick, they would be paid a reduced salary for an initial period of two weeks. After two weeks of incapacitation, they would be paid two-thirds of their normal salary. In the event of continued absence, the matter would be referred to the DOA for a decision.

Potatoes

"The DOA received a letter dated the 27th January 1942 from the German Field Command 515 asking for 33,500 kilogrammes of seed potatoes for planting at the airport and undertaking to replace these potatoes in March with German late potatoes. The island is not in a position to supply the seed potatoes asked for".

DOA note

On the 16th January 1942, the secretary of the Potato Collection Board, H. G. Shepard, informed the DOA that he had to chase up farmers who had not made the required declaration specified in the Potatoes (Sales and Returns) (Jersey) Order, 1941.

In the same month the German Field Command asked for 33,500 kilogrammes of seed potatoes for planting on their farm near the airport. There was also a second German farm nearby, Don Bridge Farm. It undertook to replace these in March with German late potatoes. It was made clear to the German authorities "That the island is not in a position to supply the seed potatoes asked for".

Several weeks later a report from the Grain and Potato Control Section sought advice as to the disposal of a quantity of green potatoes being held by merchants on behalf of the DOA. It was decided to supply ten tons of these potatoes to the German authorities at the airport, towards fulfilling their request for seed.

In February the DOA decided to reduce the quantity of eating potatoes which could be retained by each farmer. The Order of December 1941 allowed for 2 stone per fortnight per member of the household, but in future this would be reduced to half a stone (7 lbs). The reduction came into force on the 2nd March 1942.

A report from the Potato and Grain Section described that Mr A. G. Binet, Trinity, had refused to surrender his potatoes as required by an Order of the 10th February 1942. A requisition was ordered and he was allowed to keep potatoes in excess of the 309 boxes required. However, the requisition order was recalled and instead, the Grain and Potato Section was authorised to cash Binet's weighbridge tickets. Four days later, Mr Binet complained to the DOA. Therefore, the matter was given to the Chief Inspector, Mr Godfray, to review. His subsequent report did not support Mr Binet. Brée, who was annoyed, demanded that Binet be charged the transport costs to which the DOA had been subjected as "...a result of Mr Binet's unsatisfactory conduct".

On the 3rd March, Mr H. du Feu, Mr E. W. Touzel and Mr J. Morin were interviewed concerning an allegation that seed potatoes had been sold without a permit, in breach of the Potatoes (Sales and Returns) (Jersey) Order, 1941. Mr du Feu expressed his regret, and no further action was taken against him. The unsatisfactory nature of Touzel's and Morin's answers led to a possible referral to the Law Officers of the Crown. Brée, however, in typical manner, decided against legal proceedings. He gave both men a severe verbal rebuke, thereby concluding the matter.

In March the issue of the price of glasshouse potatoes for 1942 was discussed. The DOA decided to recommend to the Superior Council that Mr Vivian J. Bailhache's Price Advisory Board be appointed to recommend the price. The DOA also decided that glasshouse potatoes should only be lifted and disposed of under the terms of a licence, issued by itself. The Superior Council approved the PAB to fix the prices. In response Brée recommended to the Superior Council that the glasshouse grower should be paid 6½ pence per lb; and the price paid by the public to be 7 pence per lb.

On the 26th March Brée met with members of the PAB and delegates of the Glasshouse Growers Association. He stated in a sombre manner that the Island's crop of old potatoes would last only until the 10th May 1942. He therefore wanted glasshouse potatoes grown "...to bridge the gap until the first outdoor-grown potatoes were fit to dig". Brée estimated a potential area of glasshouse potatoes as 75 vergées, producing 2 tons per vergée. These potatoes were to be grown and lifted only under licence.

Brée, himself a grower of glasshouse potatoes, presented a schedule of costs which amounted to £123-13-0 per vergée. The members of the GGA submitted their production costs as £139-50 per vergée. A growers' remuneration of 15% of the selling price was accepted by all parties.[9]

On the 31st March the DOA issued its policy for the 1942 Potato Crop.

1. The lifting and sale of all potatoes grown in 1942 will conform with directions issued under the Cultivation of Lands (Jersey) Order, 1940. All cultivation and selling of potatoes must be with a DOA permit. These permits are issued by the Parochial Allocation Officers.
2. The purchase of the potato crop by the DOA will be effected as follows:
   a. Farmers will be allowed to sell by retail in their own neighbourhood as many potatoes as the Potato Allocation Officers allow to be lifted for this purpose.
   b. The whole of the rest of the crop (except for potatoes retained by growers for eating or for seed), will be purchased by the DOA.

3. The DOA, in collaboration with the Department of Essential Commodities, will release these potatoes, through wholesale merchants and retail distributors, to the general public.
4. All potato prices are fixed:
   a. Growers to the DOA.
   b. DOA to Wholesalers.
   c. Wholesalers to Retailers.
   d. Retailers to the Public.
5. When the crop is fully matured and the DOA has acquired all the potatoes which are estimated to be required to supply the civilian population until the 1943 crop becomes available, the prohibition upon lifting potatoes without a permit will be revoked and the general public encouraged to purchase and store potatoes for their own needs during the winter of 1942–1943.
6. The DOA estimates it will need to purchase 10,000 tons of potatoes in order to satisfy the needs of the civil population until the maturity of the crop. It anticipates that the purchase of potatoes for the civilian population will start at about Whitsuntide.[10] The DOA will purchase, and set aside by storing and clamping, the full amount needed for the civilian population as soon as the crop has reached full maturity.
7. The DOA does not, however, have information as to the quantity of potatoes which will be required by the German occupying forces both for export and for consumption locally. Figures are available only for the Island's civilian population.

Fertilisers

"Brée contacted the German Military Field Command 515 in order for the German Military Government to regain the quantity of phosphates and sulphate of ammonia, improperly retained by the Guernsey authorities."

DOA meeting

On the 20th January 1942 the DOA ordered superphosphates and sulphate of ammonia from France. Ten days later it met with Mr Woodcock to discuss the type and quantity of fertilisers needed for the 1942 season.

It was agreed that the mixing of fertilisers would not henceforth be carried out in places where both foodstuffs and crops were stored. Fertilisers obtained from France were to be invoiced to merchants at £8 per ton. This price involved a financial loss which would be borne by public funds. The apparent reason for incurring this loss was because of the long delays in receiving invoices for goods purchased from "the mainland".[11]

The retail prices for fertilisers for 1942 were set at the following rates.

Fertiliser	Per Ton
Nitrate of soda	£16-10-0
Nitrate of potash	£29-10-0
Potassic nitrate of soda	£15-10-0
Hoof and horn meal	£25-10-0
Castor meal	£10-10-0
Superphosphate	£8-0-0
Bone meal	£15-2-6
Bone flour	£11-10-0
Dissolved bones	£14-0-0
Phosphorite	£8-5-0
Phosphatic chalk	£7-2-6
Sulphate of potash	£17-0-0
Muriate of potash	£14-15-0
Potash salts	£9-10-0
Kainite	£7-10-0
Dried blood	£32-0-0

The DOA informed the JPMA of these prices and it was also agreed that a retail price of £18- 15-0 per ton would be the charge for ICI fertilisers already held in storage. The price for imported tomato manures was fixed at £17 per ton. All retail sales had to be paid in cash.

Brée informed the Superior Council of the above prices, however it was unwilling to provide any further subsidies for fertilisers. It instructed the DOA to invoice phosphates from France at a price to cover the total outlay by the DOA including purchase, transport and all ancillary costs. This was to ensure that no loss fell upon public funds as a result of purchasing fertilisers.

On the 17th February, fertiliser for potatoes was mixed and prepared, ready to be issued to famers upon presentation of their 1942 agricultural directions. The rate issued was 2 cwt per vergée. In the case of ICI fertilisers, the rate of issue was 1½ ton per vergée.

On the 13th March a shipment of artificial fertilisers comprising phosphates and sulphate of ammonia, consigned to Jersey, had been taken to Guernsey and mistakenly unloaded. The DOA contacted the Guernsey authority to "...forthwith return this to the island". The Guernsey authority, however, claimed that the chemicals had already been mixed into compound fertiliser. Brée immediately requested the Bailiff to ask Guernsey to return the fertilisers, either in their original condition or mixed. "This material is essential to the production of crops in the island". It appears that there was no response from the Guernsey civilian authorities. In consequence, Brée contacted Field Command 515 and asked for it to regain the phosphates and sulphate of ammonia, "...improperly retained by the Guernsey authorities". On the

25th March, Field Command 515 replied that it was not possible to arrange for the return of these fertilisers.

In the same week, Mr Woodcock recommended the use of the remaining stocks of fertilisers for making a "top dressing" with a theoretical composition of 10.2% of nitrogen and 14.3% of potash, the total quantity available being 80 tons.

Sulphate of ammonia	35 tons
Nitrate of soda	5 tons
Sulphate of potash	25 tons
Nitrate of potash	15 tons

An additional quantity of 15 tons of nitrate of potash was available to be applied alone. Merchants were also authorised to issue liquid manure as a top dressing upon receipt of farmers' cultivation directions.

Cereals

On the 20th January 1942, Normans Limited offered to store the larger of the DOA's threshing machines, together with 14 tons of binder wire, at their store in Le Breton Lane for £2 per quarter. The offer was accepted. The DOA ordered Mr Fred Le Seelleur, Assistant Foreman at the La Collette workshop, to inspect the machine. However, when the machine arrived at the Le Breton Lane store it was found to be too large, and it was subsequently stored with John Terry Limited.

In the same month the DOA wrote to Mr J. W. Fiott, La Moie, St Brelade, and thanked him for the loan of his threshing machine. They also offered to pay him any out-of-pocket expenses that he had incurred.

On the 27th January L. C. Pallot, wrote to the DOA asking for compensation for 20 gallons of petrol that had been stolen from him.[12] The DOA refused his request.

In March T. G. Le Cappelain wrote to the DOA on behalf of the Island's threshing contractors, asking that balers required for the forthcoming season be purchased in France. The Superior Council decided to purchase six baling machines, to be hired out to the various contractors.

Cattle

The Newly-Born Calves (Jersey) Order 1941 took effect on the 15th December 1941. The DOA transferred authority to the RJA&HS to select all calves to be exempted from slaughter. The Selection Committee had its first meeting on the 27th December and subsequently met once a week. It decided that calves of show prize winners, recorded dams, and Gold Medal Certificate winners which were recorded as "pure and tested ancestry" would be exempt from slaughter.

Between January and March 1942 between sixty and eighty heifer calves were exempted, along with three bull calves.[13]

Jersey Produce Merchants Association

"W. Dennis and Sons Limited wrote to the DOA asking for a financial reimbursement to them in relation to the cost to which they had been put in collecting from the German authorities of occupation, at the insistence of the DOA, certain monies in respect of potatoes sold to the German authorities".

DOA meeting

In January 1942, the DOA revoked the Potato Distribution Licence granted to Marks and Riches. This was because of a shortage of DOA potatoes held in its store. The DOA carried out, and reported on, a detailed analysis of potatoes that were unaccounted for. The report was studied, and the decision taken to "Sanction the unauthorised transfer of five tons and twelve hundredweight of potatoes from the stocks of the DOA to those of Marks and Riches".

The DOA made a claim of £80-15-8 from Marks and Riches, allowing for a 6% loss in the weight of potatoes due to shrinkage whilst in storage. The President of the JPMA wrote to Brée appealing against the revocation of the licence whereupon Brée held a meeting to discuss the claim against Marks and Riches. It reassessed its claim to £96-15-8.

In response the Director of Marks and Riches, Mr A. R. Riches, met the DOA. He repeated his appeal against the revocation of his company's potato distribution licence. Brée, after receiving from Mr Riches the necessary assurances as to the measures adopted to eliminate the possibility of any further mistakes being made in stock stored on behalf of the DOA and, having cautioned Mr Riches as to the consequences to be apprehended in the event of any further shortages being discovered, it was decided to restore the licence to the firm.

In February a report concluded that the wastage of potatoes by Le Rossignol and Company was 12.8% of the total stored. The DOA decided to allow a wastage of 7%, before debiting the value of any shortage in excess of 7%. Further shortages of potatoes stored on behalf of the DOA became apparent. Sidney Horman Limited had a shortage of 13 cwt. They were told to refund the DOA the value of the loss, allowing for a wastage of 7%, and were also told that they would no longer be allowed to store potatoes on the DOA's behalf. In February, Mr J. E. Baudains refused to remove from his depot all the stored DOA potatoes. The store was to be requisitioned by the German authorities. He was given a warning that unless he moved all the potatoes the work would be carried out at his expense and, in addition, his lorry would be taken away.

In the same month a report concerning a stock of wheat stored on the premises of the Jersey Farmers (Trading) Union Limited and George Blampied Limited described the unsatisfactory conditions in which the grain was stored. The stores were "...musty and there was a presence of rat excretion in considerable quantities". The DOA immediately ordered that the wheat be sent to the mills to be cleaned.

In March the DOA carried out a further survey of the quantity of potatoes stored in JPMA premises on its behalf. It discovered that three merchants demonstrated a shortage in excess of 7%. The President and Vice President of the JPMA were interviewed. Brée made it clear to J. M. Norman and Charles Gruchy, respectively, that any of their members demonstrating a shortage would be required to reimburse the DOA for the loss sustained as a result of such a shortage. Brée agreed to transmit "...confidentially to the President the list of merchants showing the percentages of loss of potatoes in the respective stores". Brée, in his usual "modus operandi", was attempting to deal with the issue of missing potatoes without resorting to judicial proceedings. He effectively gave the problem back to the JPMA to resolve themselves.

As a result, the President of the JPMA wrote to Brée on the 12th March. He stated that the merchants concerned had declined to pay for the shrinkage and suggested that the DOA meet the merchants involved. Brée now decided enough was enough. He contacted the Attorney General for advice on the position of the DOA. On the 30th March the Attorney General produced a report in view of which Brée met representatives of the JPMA on the 10th April and stated that he would not tolerate the disappearance of his department's potatoes, which were held on behalf of the Island's civilian population.

It was decided that the JPMA would arrange a meeting with the merchants concerned to reach a mutually satisfactory settlement. P. G. Cabot, the accountant in charge of the Grain and Potato Section, was authorised to attend. The DOA decided that, if an agreement proved impossible, it would set up an "Arbitration Board" to adjudicate over any proposed settlement with the merchants. The DOA, however, would have the final decision over the ratification of any settlement.

On the 15th April, Brée reported that the President of the JPMA, Mr J. M. Norman, had called upon him with an offer to accept the principle of arbitration. Mr Philip Gallichan, St Saviour, was appointed by the DOA to act on its behalf while the JPMA appointed its own representative. An independent Chairman was agreed upon, Mr Vivian J. Bailhache. On the 2nd June the Arbitration Board concluded its report on the outstanding claims made against a number of merchants in relation to the storage of potatoes on behalf of the DOA. The report appears to have been accepted by both parties.

Whilst this dispute was ongoing, another merchant, W. Dennis and Sons Limited, wrote asking for financial reimbursement in relation to the costs to which it had been put in collecting, at the insistence of the DOA, certain monies from the German authorities in respect of potatoes which it had sold to them. The DOA decided to make Dennis and Sons a payment of £16 to reimburse these costs.

References

1. Jersey Archive. B/A/W31/2/31; BA/W31/2/42 and B/A/W31/2/39.
2. Jersey Archive. C/B/A1/7.
3. The German officer in question was Hauptmann (later Major) Dr Dannenberg. He arrived in Jersey in September 1940 to replace Hauptmann Gussek as Inselkommandant until the arrival of Oberst Graf von Schmettow. Dr Dannenberg then became Kommandant of the 1st Kp. MG Battalion 16, for a period between 1940 and 1941.
4. Whilst interviewing farmers who kept dairy herds during the occupation, the subject of "dirty milk" often arose. This was the exact expression often cited by them when discussing the problems of hygiene and milk collection.
5. RJA&HS and JFU Joint Emergency Committee Minutes.
6. Jersey Evening Post, 20th February 1942.
7. Letter kindly made available by Mr Alan Allix.
8. Jersey Archive. D/S/B1/1991.
9. RJA&HS Price Advisory Board Minutes (also called the Potato Price Advisory Board).
10. Seventh Sunday after Easter. Depending on when Easter falls it is usually between the last week in May and first week in June.
11. France or Continental Europe.
12. Approximately 91 litres.
13. Jersey Archive. L/D/09/A10.

Chapter 8
April – May – June 1942

Milk Control

In April 1942 the morning milk collection times remained at 8.00 a.m. The evening collection was changed from 5.00 p.m. to 5.30 p.m. On the 4th April, a Milk Control Section report highlighted unsatisfactory aspects of milking taking place in the Island. The DOA had appointed C. R. Mauger as a Foreman Milk Tester, who was now made responsible for the six eastern parishes. J. G. Malzard became the Foreman Milk Tester for the six western parishes.

In the same week, four of the collecting dairies which did not provide skimmed milk to the civilian population on a Sunday were ordered to make it available.

A report of the 16th April drew attention to an "...alleged breach of the Milk Control Order on the part of J. B. Michel, St Peter".[1] Mr Michel was told to attend an interview with the DOA on the 21st April concerning the allegation. The fundamental problem for Brée was that Michel was Vice President of the RJA&HS and served on a number of important agricultural committees. In addition, Michel was a close associate of Carlyle Le Gallais, adjoint member of the DOA and in charge of all policies on milk control.

Michel appeared before the DOA on the allegation that he had committed a breach of Article 5(2) of the Milk Control (Jersey) Order, 1940, as amended by Article 2 of the Milk Control (Amendment No 2) (Jersey) Order, 1942. He was alleged to have "Sold four of his cows to his former customers for milk and while retaining these said animals in his personal custody had allowed the said former customers to draw free supplies of milk whereas he would sell all the milk produced by the cows in his personal custody to the licensed retailer in whose register his name is entered, furthermore, the said Mr Michel has, in writing, stated that he has transferred these said animals whereas they have not, in fact, left his custody".[1]

The DOA sent the matter to the Attorney General along with the Milk Control report. On the 28th April the Attorney General wrote to the Connétable of St Peter, John du Val, setting out the information he had received from the DOA. John du Val was also a member of the DOA but on the day of Michel's interview with the DOA he had been absent.

This letter detailed the changes in ownership of Michel's herd from the 21st January to 10th April 1942. The Declaration of Transfers for Mr Michel's cattle to Captain H. Ballantine, G. O. Fairlie, Arthur Clare Halliwell and Chas E. Read were all completed. However, on the 10th April a milk yield test by Mr G. Cory demonstrated that, despite the four previous transfers of cattle, Mr Michel's herd constituted the same number as at midnight on 21st January.

The precise allegation which the DOA made against him was that "The animals transferred by Mr Michel to the four persons in question never left his personal custody but that he nevertheless supplied free milk to the households of those persons whereas, as a registered producer, within the meaning of the Order, he should, in accordance with the provisions of Article 5(2) of the Milk Control (Jersey) Order, 1940, as amended, have sold all the milk produced by the cows in his personal custody, with the exception of that which he was permitted by the department to retain for consumption by himself, the members of his household and his servants, to the licensed retailer with whom he is registered in pursuance of the Order, that is to say, Jersey Dairies Limited".[2]

The Attorney General requested the Connétable to further investigate the matter. He wanted information on two points. Firstly, the number of cattle in the personal custody of Mr Michel, Captain Ballantine, Mr Fairlie, Mr Halliwell and Mr Read. Secondly, the names of those constituting their respective households and servants.

The Connétable replied to the Attorney General on the 30th April clarifying the above points and the Attorney General responded to the Connétable on the 4th May. Michel now claimed to have "…let some grazing to each of the four gentlemen concerned". The Connétable was then instructed to investigate the nature and extent of that grazing. The handwritten reply from John du Val was, "These cows graze with J. B. Michel anywhere on the farm where there is grazing. They are all together".[3]

The DOA discussed Michel's case on the 29th May 1942. Their problem was that Michel was an influential and important individual in the agricultural governance of the Island. He was on the Price Advisory Board set up by the Superior Council and the Calf Selection Committee empowered by the DOA.

Michel was not only a leading figure in cattle breeding and a major exporter of pedigree cattle, but also a prominent spokesman for the leading band of Island farmers who held considerable political, economic and social power. In addition, he was a crucial member of Le Gallais' inner circle. However, Michel was convicted by the judicial authority. The amount of milk lost to the civilian population was enormous, amounting to 948 pots.[4]

This figure was based upon a document written in 1942 by C. F. Journeaux for the RJA&HS.[5]

Brée was determined that Michel should step down from the agricultural committees of which he was a member. A DOA meeting concluded, "In view of the conviction of John Buesnel Michel, one of the Vice Presidents of the RJA&HS, under the Milk Control (Jersey) Order 1940, the DOA is of the opinion that it would be highly improper for the said Mr Michel to sit as one of the officers of the Agricultural Department of the said society appointed in virtue of an Act of the Department dated 2nd December 1941, to select the calves which shall be exempted from the provision of Article 2(i) Newly-Born Calves (Jersey) Order, 1941 and it was decided to notify the President of the RJA&HS".

By the 2nd June, Le Gallais had made it clear that he refused to comply with the DOA's wish. He wanted Michel on the Calf Selection Committee. In response Brée asked Le Gallais to postpone a meeting of the forthcoming Calf Selection Committee because Michel had not been withdrawn from that body. When again Le Gallais refused, Brée decided to take the matter to the Superior Council. Brée, in a somewhat surprisingly uncompromising mood, made it clear that the DOA "...is strongly of the opinion that the said Mr Michel, is, by the fact of his conviction, unfitted to form part of a body carrying out functions delegated to it by the department".[1]

On the 3rd June Colin Marie wrote a formal letter to the RJA&HS. The letter was read out at an RJA&HS meeting at which twenty-seven of the Island's leading dairy farmers were present. The letter said "I am directed by the DOA to inform you that it is of the opinion that it would be highly improper for Mr J. B. Michel, in view of his recent conviction under the Milk Control (Jersey) Order, 1940, to continue to act as one of the officers of the Agricultural Department of the RJA&HS incorporated in connection with administration of the Newly-Born Calves (Jersey) Order, 1941. C Marie".[6]

Le Gallais at once addressed the meeting. He explained that he and Jurat Brée had unsuccessfully tried to persuade Mr Michel to tender his resignation and went on to explain why Brée demanded Michel's resignation. Brée was of the opinion that Michel, having disobeyed an order emanating from the DOA, should not officiate on the administration of further orders.

Michel now addressed the meeting. He stated his position and the events leading up to the prosecution. He, furthermore, maintained that having been elected by the RJA&HS to sit on the Calf Selection Committee, he would only resign at their wish.

Le Gallais and Michel left the room. The Chair was taken by Francis Le Boutillier. Whilst they were out of the room, Mr E. C. Perrédès and Mr C. Le Couteur proposed that "As it is understood from the President's statement that in any circumstances the Selection Committee appointed under the Newly-Born Calves Order will be called upon to resign shortly, there is no necessity for Mr J. B. Michel to resign from the Committee". In simple terms, Le Gallais had announced that if Michel was to resign the entire RJA&HS Calf Selection Committee would stand down. This was an extremely quick-witted decision demonstrating Le Gallais' alert mind. The RJA&HS was the one and only organisation with the knowledge and expertise that could effect and execute Jersey calf selection for slaughter on behalf of the DOA.

Le Gallais and Michel returned to the room. Le Gallais then found it necessary to answer a question regarding the supply of fresh milk to the German Commander of Field Command 515 without a permit. The milk was supplied by Le Gallais from his farm, Roselands, St Saviour.[7]

On the 15th June, the RJA&HS wrote to the DOA making its position very clear, as had been agreed by its 3rd June meeting. In response, Brée and the DOA decided to revoke its Order to the RJA&HS to carry out the duties of the Calf Selection Committee. Brée immediately replaced it with a new committee: Mr George de la P. Hacquoil, Mr P. C. Mourant and Mr Philip Ahier, Deputy of St Martin. A letter was sent to each of them asking them to be good enough to act as the new Selection Committee. By the 23rd June all three had declined to serve. In consequence, Brée decided to approach John A. Perrée personally with a request that he chair a new Calf Selection Committee with the authority to name two other persons to assist him. Brée suggested to Perrée the following men: G. de la P. Hacquoil, P. C. Mourant, P. Ahier, G. Messervy and P. Le Feuvre. Brée, furthermore, in the event of Perrée being unwilling to act as Chairman, decided that he would supervise the Committee with the assistance of Edwin Gibaut and Wesley Mallett.

On the 30th June, the Superior Council instructed Brée that he was to immediately retract his demand for the dismissal of Michel and replacement of the Calf Selection Committee. The reasons for this are not stated in any of the sources. It is, however, feasible to surmise two possible reasons. Firstly, it had become evident to the Superior Council that the RJA&HS was the only organisation with the detailed knowledge and expertise to supervise the selection and therefore the continuation of the very best pedigree stock. The continuation of the Jersey pedigree breed took precedence over Brée's individual preferences as to who should supervise the Calf Selection Committee. In late 1941, when Dr E. Lauprecht spent several months in Jersey carrying out scientific research on the fat content of milk from local high- yielding cattle, he received the assistance of Le Gallais, Le Boutillier and Michel and was allowed access to RJA&HS records.[8] Lauprecht returned in early 1942 to Germany. He conducted the Jersey-German crossbreeding programme under Jonas Schmidt at the Kaiser Wilhelm Institute near Rostock. The use of RJA&HS records by Lauprecht, as far as post-war documents demonstrate, has never been recorded. H. G. Shepard's December 1945 account of the occupation years appears to make no mention of the episode.[9]

Secondly, although Brée was very well respected as a hardworking President of the DOA and an intelligent and able farmer in his own right, who had improved himself from a relatively humble background, had, by his decision to dismiss Michel, acted somewhat above his station. Michel had broken the law and Brée wanted to demonstrate that no one was beyond and above the law. He, however, could not compete with opposition from the farming establishment who still held considerable political and social power during this period.

The Milk Control Section had increasingly become the most important and largest section of the DOA. Weeks and his army of bureaucrats and Milk Testers were continually checking the milking process and milk records of farmers. From April 1942 onwards the Milk Control Section discovered increasing infractions of the milk laws.

On the 16th April 1942, it reported alleged infractions of milk orders by Harold Shakespeare Carter and Philip Vaudin Sarre. The two were charged to appear before the DOA, the allegation being that they had broken the Milk Control (Jersey) Order, 1940 in that as producers they did not sell the whole quantity of the milk produced by their cows, or any of it, to the DOA. Mr Carter had signed a statement that he held in his personal custody one cow, when in effect the cow in question was in the personal custody of Mr Sarre. Therefore, Carter had been drawing free supplies of milk although he was not a member of Sarre's household. Both men were accused of signing "…transfer declarations which appear fictitious".[1] The case was forwarded to the Attorney General.

Sarre wrote to the DOA appealing against possible legal proceedings. The letter was forwarded to the Attorney General. Also included in this correspondence is information concerning a discussion between Sarre and the DOA. This was a request for Sarre to cut down his household's milk consumption and to send the surplus arising from the reductions to the collecting dairies.

On the 19th April, Brée reported that the Crown Officers were of the opinion that proceedings against Sarre should not be continued on the grounds that the DOA had failed to inform him where his milk was to be taken in order that the DOA might purchase the milk. Brée did not agree and instructed the Law Officers to continue proceedings. He argued that it was a fact that all milk producers had to themselves ascertain the depots from which their milk was collected as, at the time of the Milk Control (Jersey) Order, 1940, coming into operation no notifications of collecting depots had been sent to producers who did, in fact, apply at the Milk Control Office for information as to the location of the collecting depots. Brée decided to draw to the attention of the Crown Officers the interview between the DOA and Mr Sarre on the 26th September 1941 as, in the view of the DOA, Mr Sarre had "No intention of sending his surplus milk to a collecting diary for the benefit of the island population".

Another report, of the 15th April, detailed an apparent shortage in the quantity of milk sold to the DOA by Mr P. Perchard. He was called in for an interview to explain why, being a registered producer, he was not selling all milk produced by the cows in his personal custody to licensed retailers with whom he was registered. Mr Perchard made "certain explanations" and was warned of his future conduct in relation to carrying out the provisions of the Milk Control (Jersey) Order, 1940.

On the 20th April Advocate P. N. Richardson sent a letter to the Milk Control Section concerning his client, Mr J. B. Larose, defending an allegation that Larose was being "...constrained to supply a German officer in the neighbourhood with one pot of milk a day". The DOA decided to bring up the allegation with the German Field Command. German military personnel were only allowed to purchase agricultural produce directly from a farmer by acquiring an individual permit authorised by Pelz. A letter was sent to the Field Command with a request that immediate steps be taken to terminate the practice. In addition, Brée made Pelz aware of the infraction.

In late April the DOA ordered detailed examinations to be carried out on milk production. Two herds were found to produce smaller quantities than the average. On the 2nd May the DOA sent a letter to every dairy farmer who had been found, as a result of checking the records, to have retained in their possession milk, produced by their cows, over and above the quantity to which they were entitled. All farmers were given information as to the amount of milk which each individual could retain as free supplies. This included the amount that could be kept for each calf. Finally, they were reminded of the steps to be taken to become a Registered Producer under the Milk Control (Jersey) Order, 1940.

On the 7th May Weeks formally requested an increase in his salary. He was in charge of an extensive bureaucratic empire: milk inspection and recording, cattle registration and transfers, registration of milk retailers and consumers, milk collecting depots and dairies. Also, as head of a large number of staff – administrators, clerks, typists, short-hand secretaries – Weeks obviously felt his salary was not commensurate with his workload and responsibilities. On the 15th May, Brée recommended to the Superior Council that a "bonus" of £25 be paid to Weeks annually during the continuance of the present hostilities and he justified it to the Superior Council in light of Weeks' increased workload in the control of cattle and milk consumer registrations.

Brée, acting upon instructions from the Superior Council in May 1942, directed that the maximum quantity of milk supplied by a licensed retailer to his adult registered customers would be increased by a quarter pint but only to persons who were not drawing extra milk in virtue of a medical certificate. It was announced that, as prescribed by Articles 2 and 3 under the Milk Control (Jersey) Order 1940, registered customers born before 30th June 1925 would receive ¾ of a pint of fresh full milk a day. Customers born after 1st July 1925 would receive 1 pint of milk per day.

At the same time Field Command 515 requested that two further Milk Testers be employed to carry out their instructions of December 1941 for more rigorous controls. The DOA immediately employed Mr George R. Huelin and Mr G. M. Davey, commencing on the 1st June 1942, at a wage of £2 a week.

On the 26th May the DOA reviewed the Island-wide distribution of skimmed milk. It was decided that despite the reduction in the quantity of skimmed milk available, there would be no reduction made in skimmed milk issued to farmers for feeding to stock. The reduction would have to fall upon the civilian population. The above decision suggests just how powerful were these dairy farmers. In addition, it demonstrates that the DOA continued to protect its highly valued pedigree herds by ensuring that calves that were not slaughtered would keep their allowance of skimmed milk. Since only the best calves were now kept it was imperative for the future of the Jersey breed that these calves received skimmed milk.

In June the Milk Control Section made further detailed examinations of milk yield records. They discovered apparent shortages from five farmers. Four of them gave satisfactory explanations for the shortages, which were accepted. They were given warnings that, should there be any further "Attempt to retain for the use of his household, a quantity in excess of that authorised by the DOA", judicial proceedings would be initiated against them. A further three farmers were summoned and questioned. All three had plausible explanations which were fully accepted by Milk Control and no warnings were issued.

On the 30th May, the DOA was informed by Mr L. F. Le Flohic of the United Dairies, 25 Hue Street, St Helier that he had sold his business to Mr L. J. Tanguy of Tanguy's Dairy Limited. On the same day the DOA, in view of "...certain doubts which have arisen to the extent to which milk producers are entitled to retain milk for their own families", modified its Act of the 30th January 1942 by substituting the world "households" for the word "families".

On the 16th June, Weeks dismissed a Milk Tester, Mr Adolphus George Le Feuvre; the reason given was insubordination. Le Feuvre was given a hearing and a week's wages. The same week another Milk Tester, Mr F. H. Carrell gave his notice. He was immediately replaced by Mr Maxwell Brée at a weekly wage of £2.

On the 26th June, the DOA decided that every six months the Milk Control Section would carry out an audit of the registration of milk consumers and their licensed retailers. The reason appears to be that a check was required to ascertain if there was any alteration of status for a juvenile consumer who had become an adult. The whole audit seems to have been a huge amount of extra work for a simple re-examination of the existing milk registration records. A possible explanation may have been that Field Command 515 and Pelz wanted to check what every milk consumer was allowed and was obtaining from Milk Control.

In the same week the Milk Control Section set about checking the amount of milk allowed to be retained by producers. A new form was devised, printed, and left with the milk test certificate that was given to all dairy farmers by the Milk Testers. This new form read:

"Under the provisions of Article 5 of the Directions dated 15th January 1942, under the Milk Control (Jersey) Order, 1940, the DOA gives authority to a producer under the said order to retain milk as follows:

Free Supplies: For the producer, the servants of the producer and the households of such servants at the rate of one pint per day for each person irrespective of the age of such persons.

Calves: For those calves exempted from the provisions of Article 2(i) of the Newly-Born Calves (Jersey) Order, 1941 in virtue of directions issued under the said Order at the rate of two pots per day up to the age of six months and for calves not so exempted at the rate of two pots per day for fourteen days from the birth of the calf."

Cultivation Orders

In April 1942 the States Vet wrote to the DOA that he was unable to obtain hay for the Island's horses. Brée approached Field Command 515 with a view to securing a cargo of hay from Sweden. In the same week all the previous agricultural laws – eleven in number – were enacted for a further year.

During April the DOA notified all threshing contractors that they would not be allowed to thresh except under the issue of a licence. Each contractor was required to state the number of threshing machines available for the 1942 cereal crop. All machines were inspected on the 1st June by Mr Le Seelleur, Assistant Foreman at the La Collette workshop. Two contractors, J. E. Colback Junior and L. C. Pallot, were requested to quote prices for working the 1942 season, using the machines and equipment belonging to the DOA. These were the threshing machines which had been imported from France. Colback quoted 8/- an hour and Pallot 7/6 an hour. In addition, Mr Pallot was authorised to make spare parts which were needed by the DOA for any machine which broke down. On the 26th May both tenders were accepted.

On the 24th April, Field Command 515 wrote to the DOA requiring that a full census of cattle, horses, pigs, sheep and poultry be carried out. The nature of the request had all the hallmarks of Pelz's modus operandi. The DOA in response sent a letter to farmers explaining the animal census and requested the RJA&HS to assist in completion of the census.

On the 28th April Mr E. Le Maistre, who had allegedly neglected 3 vergées of wheat, was dealt with by the DOA. He was told that he had only one week to rectify the problems listed. An Honorary Parish Inspector was sent to check, and the problems were rectified. On the same day the DOA appointed Le Gallais and Mallet to run a sub-committee which was to meet the threshing contractors and discuss the issue of changing from string binding to wire binding, because it had become impossible to obtain further binder twine from France. After the meeting it was decided to charge Le Gallais to arrange for a man to proceed to France to purchase the necessary parts to convert string trusses to wire.

In April, Mrs J. M. de Carteret, Les Roches, St Peter, whose farm residence at La Chesnée, Coin Tourgis Sud, St Lawrence, had been taken over by the German Army, requested assistance from the DOA. She asked for financial assistance to meet the cost of securing alternative accommodation and the replacement of root crops destroyed by the German army. The DOA recommended to the Superior Council that, in view of the hardships arising in this particular case, sufficient money be advanced to Mrs de Carteret against the possible amount of compensation payable, to enable her to pay the rent account which totalled £83-16-8.

On the same day the Honorary Parish Inspectors of St Peter, Mr E. R. Egré and Mr G. N. Le Rossignol, sent a report regarding the alleged failure of Dr Charles R. Chichester, St Peter to carry out the cultivation directions issued to him for the 1942 growing season. After Brée had interviewed the two Inspectors, legal proceedings were instituted against Dr Chichester.

On the 1st May the DOA recommended to the Superior Council that the Honorary Parish Inspectors carrying out their duties in enforcing the Cultivation of Lands (Jersey) Order, 1940, should be furnished with a "Letter of Authority" in English and German for production, when necessary, to the "Forces of Occupation of the Island". This document set forth the fact that the Inspectors had been sworn in before the Royal Court for the purpose of supervising the carrying out of Cultivation Orders. These Honorary Parish Inspectors had actually been set up at the insistence of the German Field Command, a fact that appears to have been kept somewhat in the shadows by the DOA to the Inspectors themselves.

On the 2nd May the Foreman of the States Experimental Station, Mr P. E. Mourant, handed in his notice. Mr Yves Marie Le Liard was appointed as his replacement on the 3rd August. This would explain the reason why the photograph taken by Pelz in July 1942 at the Howard Davis Farm, shows a group of Jersey and Guernsey agricultural experts, including Brée, with Jules Pierre Gréard. He has been identified as the former "Foreman" of the States Experimental Station by Dr Frank Le Maistre. Gréard had been the foreman before Mourant and had worked at the Howard Davis Farm for many years. He, therefore, appears to have been taken out of retirement and seconded to fill the gap between Mourant resigning and the subsequent appointment of Le Liard.

On the 6th May, Mr G. Baudains, a DOA-appointed ploughing contractor, alleged that a farmer, Mr H. Peyet, had refused to pay him £5-5-0 for ploughing 3½ vergées. The Honorary Parish Inspectors were charged with interviewing the farmer and securing payment to the contractor.

On the 19th May Brée met Field Command 515 and, in discussions with Pelz, it was decided that the DOA would issue three pints of petrol per vergée to each farmer in respect of half the area which he had been directed under his Cultivation Order to devote to hay and grazing for the 1942 season. The reason was to allow farmers to mow some of their own hay as it was impracticable for all mowing to be carried out by contractors. Pelz gave permission to issue 2,300 gallons of petrol at the rate of 3 pints per vergée. This demonstrates that the structural relationship built up between Pelz and Brée could quickly deal with issues and achieve a solution.

On the same day, it was decided to send Mr Harry Denton Mourant (a machine fitter) to France with the aim of purchasing spare parts for threshing machines. Brée asked the Superior Council that Mr Jouault, who represented the States office in Granville, should accompany Mr Mourant on his journeys in France to assist him. It appears that Mr Mourant had "...but an indifferent knowledge of the French language in his efforts to secure the various machinery supplies for which he will be visiting France". Mr Mourant was given £2,000 in cash for making payments for machinery and spare parts. In addition, he was given £25 to cover his personal expenses while in France.

On the 29th May the DOA made a recommendation to the Department of Public Instruction that boys of fourteen years of age and upwards be released from school for harvest work on various farms. These boys began agricultural work on the 15th June.

In early June, Field Command 515 decided that its soldiers' home at St Brelade's Bay Hotel would cultivate additional food crops and instructed the Bailiff to surrender to it 80 litres of agricultural petrol.[10] In addition, Field Command employed Irish nationals to look after the pigs which were kept behind the hotel. In the same week the DOA asked the German Field Command for a further forty lorries to be licensed, to complete the 1942 harvest on time.

On the same day, Mr J. B. Arthur was interviewed by the DOA. He allegedly had failed to grow 5 vergées of wheat specified by his Cultivation Order. In view of the fact that potatoes planted in 1941 in the same field by Mr Arthur had been a complete failure, he was ordered to hand over the 5 vergées to another farmer to grow mangolds or swedes. As Mr Arthur had drawn the first instalment of agricultural credits on 19 vergées, it was decided to bring to attention "...the whole circumstances before the Law Officers of the Crown".

Also, a report was forwarded concerning the farm of Leonard H. Blight, Maufant, St Saviour. His wheatfield was found to be "...in a deplorable condition". He was immediately ordered to remove the dock weeds in the adjoining fields within seven days. In addition, he was ordered to plough the wheat field and sow turnips. Finally, he was given a warning concerning the menace of not keeping his land weed free.

On the 28th June all DOA clerks were given a pay rise of between 5/- and 7/6 week. Miss Luxon, a shorthand typist from the Milk Control Section, left and was replaced by Miss Marion Journeaux at a weekly wage of £1-10-0.

Pigs

"Mr Daghorn admitted he hadn't buried the animal. He in fact slaughtered and salted the meat for the consumption of his family and himself".

The States Vet

On the 10th April 1942, Miss Eva Querée, Grouville, was interviewed by the DOA concerning a report by Mr J. W. Blampied, the Pig Inspector appointed under the Pigs (Control) (Jersey) Order, 1941. It was alleged she had purchased a pig from Mr E. G. Langlois and had not made a declaration of the transaction. Miss Querée, furthermore, admitted that in breach of the Livestock (Restriction on Slaughtering) (Jersey) Order, 1940 the pig had been slaughtered and half had been consumed by the household and the other half had been disposed of to Mr A. M. Labbé, 2 Market Street, St Helier. The case was referred to the Attorney General and Mr Labbé prosecuted for the purchase of a pig, in breach of the Rationing (Jersey) Order, 1940.

Two weeks later, Mrs Le Neveu, St Brelade, was reported as allegedly purchasing a pig from her brother-in-law, Mr J. Le Neveu, and not making a declaration to the DOA. This was an infraction of the Pigs (Control) (Jersey) Order, 1941. The pig subsequently died, and its death was not notified to the DOA as required. Mrs Le Neveu was questioned by the Inspector Mr Blampied, and she denied being in possession of any pigs. Mr Blampied, however, refused to accept her account. He questioned her a second time and finally Mrs Le Neveu admitted having two pigs in her possession purchased from her brother-in-law, but the purchases had not been declared. The DOA decided that in view of her unsatisfactory explanation the case should be submitted to the Attorney General.

Problems continued for the Le Neveu family. Several weeks later, Mr Le Neveu was again investigated by the DOA. This time the allegation was made that he had not sent all the milk he should have to the collecting dairy. He appeared before the DOA and asked to explain, "The very considerable shortage which had been established in this case". Le Neveu was warned that any further "...attempt to retain for the use of his household a quantity in excess of that authorised by the DOA, judicial proceedings would be initiated against him".

The DOA increasingly dealt with a spate of pig infringements. Mr J. Le Lievre, St Peter, allegedly did not declare a pig and Mr J. G. Rondel, St Lawrence, the purchase of a sow. Mr Le Lievre also failed to declare the death of his sow. He made a full admission and was not prosecuted under the Livestock (Restriction on Slaughtering) (Jersey) Order, 1940.

Mr C. Benest, St Peter, a blacksmith, fared less well. He purchased two pigs without making the required declarations. Furthermore, when one of the pigs died, he failed to make the appropriate declaration. During his interview,

Mr Benest admitted that the second pig had been slaughtered. The matter was subsequently sent to the Attorney General.

Another report on Mr E. Daghorn, St Brelade, alleged that he had purchased a sow from Mr P. M. Huchet, and it had not been declared. When the animal died, again there was no official declaration. Mr Daghorn stated that he buried the carcass, however the States Vet found no evidence of a buried carcass. Mr Daghorn finally admitted he had not buried the animal - in fact he had slaughtered it and salted the meat for consumption by himself and his family. The reports were forwarded to the Attorney General.

Brée now decided that pig declarations were simply not working. He emphasised the "Slackness which exists with the making of the required declarations" under the Pigs (Control) (Jersey) Order, 1941. The DOA decided to obtain advice from the Attorney General to amend the law requiring pig declarations to a more rigorous and prescribed form. The Attorney General replied, advising on measures to prevent, in particular, the giving of "Fictitious names and addresses by the purchasers of pigs". In consequence, the DOA prepared a new order for submission to the Superior Council which provided that no sale of pigs or cattle could be affected, except under a licence issued by the DOA.

On the 14th May Mr H. W. Jean, St Lawrence was reported by an Inspector. He had allegedly failed to declare the death of two pigs and had slaughtered the animals. He admitted the facts and the matter was placed in the hands of the Law Officers.

Jersey Produce Merchants Association

On the 10th April 1942, the DOA instructed the "Cereals Storage Sub-Committee" comprising John du Val and Wesley Mallet, to examine the condition of all locally grown cereals stored on behalf of the DOA by the merchants. The examination officers were accompanied by the Presidents of both the DOA and the JPMA.

Immediately, two of the most important merchants, W. Dennis and Sons Limited and John Terry Limited, complained directly to Brée that the sum of 1/- per cwt paid to them under the Home-Grown Potatoes (1942 Crop) (Maximum Prices) (Jersey) Order, 1942, for handling potatoes on behalf of the DOA, was insufficient. The two firms argued that to cover expenses an allowance of 1/6 per cwt should be paid to them. Brée looked into the matter. Several weeks later he paid an additional 6d per cwt for delivery of potatoes on behalf of the DOA.

On the 12th June, the DOA rented the premises of 31 Commercial Street, St Helier from Mr Frank Tregear. The building was leased for the "period of the hostilities" for £100 a year. Brée and du Val inspected the premises and immediately terminated the tenancy of the storage sheds at Broadfields, St Lawrence.

In the same week a report by the Grain and Potato Control Section produced details of shortages which had been established in the stocks of main crop potatoes stored on behalf of the DOA for a period between 1941 and 1942. Brée asked for a meeting with the President, J. M. Norman, together with Mr Charles Gruchy, Vice President, and Mr Edward Becquet. The meeting took place on the 23rd June. The DOA decided that any JPMA merchant who demonstrated shortages in excess of 15% in main crop potato stocks held on behalf of the DOA would be dealt with individually. The merchants with shortages of the 1941 main crop were F. Giddens, T. Mayo and Company Limited, Chas Gruchy & Company Limited, W. A. Nicolls and Sons and Normans Limited, and all were invoiced for their individual shortfalls.

In June the DOA and JPMA agreed on the price the DOA would pay for storage of the 1942 crop. The following rates were agreed:

Storage of potatoes	15/-	a ton
Sorting of potatoes	5/-	a ton
Bagging of potatoes	2/6	a ton

In addition, a joint committee was established with the power to make recommendations to the DOA in relation to the storage of the 1942 crop. The DOA's representative was George Messervy; Charles Gruchy was the JPMA representative. This joint committee made its first recommendation in July 1942. All claims were paid except for John Terry Limited who claimed for 60 tons of sorting but was authorised for 42 tons.

Watermills and Milling

On the 10th April 1942, Mr J. Brandy sent a letter to the DOA asking for compensation in respect of 54 cwt of grain destroyed by the DOA when it reconditioned the Malassis Mill. It was decided to pay Mr Brandy a grant of £25-4-0.

On the same day, it was decided to employ extra labour at the stores to winnow locally grown grain before it was sent to the mills for grinding. Milling of locally grown grain was also carried out by private companies. In April one of these, Le Marquand Brothers, West Park, asked for a price increase to cover the impending increase in the price of electricity. This was agreed by the DOA.

In May the DOA recommended to the Superior Council that Mr Samuel Edwin Gilley, in charge of Quetivel Mill, be given a wage increase from £2-10-0 to £3-5-0 weekly. (He had probably taken over as senior miller from his brother Harold Ernest.) A claim was made for compensation by a farmer, Mr A. Chevalier, St Peter, who demanded damages in respect of drainage to his meadows near the mill. The alleged damage was caused by a reconditioned water course. Initially, the DOA refused to accept his claim.

However, after a States Engineer investigated the matter the farmer was given £5 in full discharge of any further claim.

On the 30th June, the DOA allowed mill staff to draw a weekly allowance of 4 lbs of wholemeal flour, free of charge, under the supervision of the miller. The night watchmen, transport staff and outside mill workers were allowed 2 lbs and the following week four extra individuals were allowed an allocation: the two roller drivers and two steam attendants were allocated 4 lbs per week, and P.P. Day, the Mills Supervisor and J. H. Lewis, Clerk of the Mills, 2 lbs per week.

Agricultural Labour

Between the 4th April and the 13th June 1942, the sum of £4,659-4-6 was paid out to cover the Agricultural Workers Bonus Subsidy. On the 17th April the DOA requested a supplementary credit of £20,000 to cover payments for the Workers Bonus up to the 3rd October 1942. Field Command 515, however, refused to allow the subsidy to continue up to October. The reason was simple. The fortification building programme was underway, and the Germans were desperate for labour, including agricultural labour. On the 21st April the DOA stated that "In view of certain requirements of the authorities of occupation" it recalled its requirement for £20,000 credit and amended it to £5,000 in order to meet payments for a six-week period, from the week ending 11th April. On the 29th May the DOA made the request for the £5,000 credit from the Department of Finance and Economics.

On the 28th April, George Wakeham and Bashford's Limited made an application for their men employed in glasshouses to be allowed the Agricultural Workers Bonus. These applications were refused.

Three weeks later the DOA approved a scheme for providing casual agricultural labour for the months of June, July and August 1942. A notice was distributed to farmers.

Fertilisers

On the 7th April 1942, M. C. Le Vesconte, St John, applied to the DOA for extra artificial fertiliser to enable him to secure a good crop of hay. His previous crop had been destroyed by fire. In view of the circumstances the DOA allowed him to draw an additional 18 lbs per vergée on the area he was directed to grow in his Cultivation of Lands (Jersey) Order for 1942. In the same week authorisation was given to a request from merchants for a discount of 7½% on phosphates and sulphate of ammonia supplied to them.

On the 24th April, the DOA discussed the issue of artificial fertilisers for the 1942 cereal crop. It approved an issue of a top-dressing allocation at a rate of 16 lbs per vergée for cereals grown in accordance with directions issued to farmers under the Cultivation of Lands (Jersey) Order, 1940. This fertiliser was made available to farmers from the following merchants: W. Dennis and Sons Limited, W. Nicolls and Sons, F. Le Sueur and Son Limited and C. S. Bailhache. The price was fixed at 19/- per cwt. Payment had to be in cash and for quantities greater than 1 cwt. If a farmer wanted less than a hundredweight, he was told to bring his own bags.

On the 18th June, John Terry Limited offered to store 1,525 bags of nitrate of potash on behalf of the DOA for the year 1942 at a cost of £25, to which the DOA agreed. In the same week W. Nicholls and Son Limited was paid for storing and handling 24½ tons of sulphate of ammonia at the rate of 5/- a ton. The members of the JPMA had become very adept at finding new avenues of income stream during the German occupation.

Potatoes

In April 1942 the price of glasshouse potatoes was set at 6½ pence per pound to the grower and 7 pence for the price paid by the public. On the 1st May, Mr J. D. McCann, St Saviour was allegedly in violation of the Glasshouse Potatoes (Jersey) Order, 1942, having lifted and sold glasshouse potatoes without first obtaining a licence from the DOA.

Also in April, a letter was received from the Controlling Committee of the States of Guernsey addressed to the Bailiff of Jersey. The Guernsey Committee requested Jersey to supply 1,000 tons of potatoes. The DOA decided that "The situation regarding the supply of potatoes is too critical to allow any reply being made to the request of the committee at present. The matter will be further considered by the DOA in due course".

On the 1st May the Price Advisory Board recommended the price of potatoes for the year 1942. The DOA disagreed with their recommendation. On the 8th May Brée discussed the matter with the Superior Council. It was agreed to keep potato prices the same from 19th May until 27th June, when the issue would be reviewed. The prices were as follows.

Period 18th May to 27th June	The DOA will pay to the Grower	The Retailer will pay to the Wholesaler per	The Public will pay to the Retailer
	per cwt: 23/6	cwt: 24/6	per lb: 3 pence
	per 100 kg: 22RM 16Pfg	Per 100 kg: 23RM 10Pfg	per kg: 17.6Pfg

On the 12th May the DOA approved the provisions of the Home-Grown Potatoes (Maximum Prices) (Jersey) Order, 1942. It allowed farmers to retain, for the 1943 season, 130 boxes of seed potatoes in respect of each vergée which they had been directed to plant in 1942.

At the same time the DOA requested the Connétables to act as Allocation Officers in connection with the disposal of the 1942 crop. If unable to carry out this request they were told to appoint a deputy. The Parish Allocation Officers appointed were as follows:

St Brelade	H. M. Gibaut and J. J. Le Boutillier
St Clement	J. P. Le Masurier
Grouville	Centenier Le Huquet
St Helier	P. J. Mourant and A. Tarr
St John	J. Le Masurier, Connétable
St Lawrence	J. W. Baudains, Connétable
St Martin	C. P. Billot, Connétable
St Mary	C. Bisson
St Ouen	F. Le Boutillier, Connétable
St Peter	J. du Val, Connétable
St Savour	G. J. Mourant, Chef de Police
Trinity	J. E. Cabot

On the 19th May, some forty of the most important potato farmers met to discuss prices. Brée was invited to this meeting and asked to act as Chairman.[11.] He began by referring to the prices set for new potatoes: 23/6 per cwt for May and 14/- per cwt for June. He, furthermore, made it clear that farmers would receive no subsidies, in any form, for growing potatoes. J. B. Michel in turn told the meeting that, as a member of the Price Advisory Board, he had not been informed of the drastic alterations made to potato prices by the Superior Council. Brée was asked questions by the farmers concerning how the allocation of digging would be carried out, what supply the German authorities would take and when digging for seed would be allowed. He was also asked to fix potato prices for July as soon as possible and, at the very latest, by the 8th June.

The meeting ended in a satisfactory manner for Brée. He had expected it would be difficult and confrontational however the meeting in fact passed a "Hearty vote of thanks for Jurat Brée for presiding". Brée concluded by replying that he was always ready and willing to hear complaints and explain or advise on any agricultural matter. He appealed for cooperation amongst all farmers whilst they were all experiencing such difficult times.

In the same week, a report sent to the DOA alleged the illegal digging of potatoes by Mr J. Le Bailly, St Brelade. The report alleged he had dug up potatoes and either sold or consumed a quantity without having first obtained the necessary licences from the DOA, issued under the Potatoes (Sales and Returns) (Jersey) Order, 1941. Mr Le Bailly appeared before the DOA and was warned of the consequences of his actions. Brée, however, decided to defer the matter and consider it at a later date. He probably realised that he had made his point concerning the consequences of the farmer's infringements and Brée preferred, if there was an alternative, not to send Jersey farmers for judicial proceedings.

On the 1st June, weekly potato allocations for each parish were set until the 29th June 1942.

Parish	Week ending 01/06/42	Week ending 08/06/42	Week ending 15/06/42	Week ending 29/06/42
St Brelade	10	13	11	10
St Clement	8	11	9	9
Grouville	12	15	15	12
St Helier	8	11	9	9
St John	8	10	9	9
St Lawrence	15	18	16	15
St Martin	10	15	12	6
St Mary	8	12	9	9
St Ouen	28	30	22	30
St Peter	20	22	22	18
St Saviour	12	18	15	12
Trinity	20	25	23	20
Total tons	159	200	172	159

*Weight in tons

In the month of June, the DOA and Superior Council disagreed on the price to be paid to farmers. The DOA insisted it should be 12/- per cwt. Brée appears to have refused to accept the price wanted by the Superior Council. He informed the Council that 12/- per cwt was "…the lowest price which can be paid to farmers without involving them in a financial loss". Brée stood his ground in support of farmers and his recommendations were finally accepted. In consequence the Home-Grown Potatoes (1942 Crop) (Maximum Prices) (No 2) (Jersey) Order, 1942, was approved with prices to farmers fixed until after June 1942.

On the 24th June two reports were received by the DOA. The first detailed the disposal of French seed potatoes throughout the Island and the second the quantity of Royal seed potatoes supplied to the German authorities and the quantities of French seed supplied in return by the German authorities.

Cattle

On the 29th November 1941, Brée had held an urgent meeting with the RJA&HS. He had opened the meeting with an extremely important problem concerning the "…public milk supply".[6] He stated that to ameliorate the problem of a shortage of milk only a small percentage of calves must be registered in the Jersey Herd Book; the rest would be slaughtered which would in turn release a greater quantity of milk for the civilian population.

This seemingly drastic action of slaughtering a majority of the Island's pedigree calves had already taken place in Guernsey.

Brée spoke in a determined manner. This was "A serious state of affairs" and the alternatives facing the DOA were even worse than his proposal. He appealed to all dairy farmers "...to release as much milk as possible for the vital needs of the population".

Since 1st July 1940, all exports of calves and heifers had ceased. In 1938 and 1939 exports of up to 60 heifers in one shipment were certainly commonplace. The increasing number of heifers in the Island was noticed. Denis Vibert, in notes made before his escape to England in September 1941, commented: "The stock of cattle is on the increase as there is no normal export trade. The Germans have bought for export a few prize cattle only".[12] In fact, so many poor-quality Jersey cattle were being exported just before the German occupation that it had threatened to undermine the export market to the United Kingdom.

The RJA&HS meeting in November 1941 had decided upon an extremely radical plan to deal with the increasingly urgent milk shortage. It had calculated the cattle population, documented calf registrations, and decided upon four measures.

1. Sixty calves a month would be registered as pedigree stock.
2. No bull calves would be allowed registration between December 1941 and February 1942 (this was later amended). The president and two Vice Presidents of the RJA&HS would act as a "Selection Committee".
3. All calves, except for those selected, would be slaughtered within fourteen days of birth.
4. An official order would be made that the birth of any calf must be reported within 24 hours.

The above points laid the basis for the Newly-Born Calves (Jersey) Order,1941. It took effect from the 15th December 1941.

Between December 1941 and March 1942, the calf-selection process had worked efficiently. The Calf Selection Committee made a series of prompt decisions in which heifer and bull calves were selected for slaughter. A small number were kept, the very best of the Jersey breed.

The first problem concerning the Calf Selection Committee appeared on the 10th April 1942. Mrs E. N. Stapleton, St Brelade, wrote to the RJA&HS complaining that her bull calf "Kabul Prince" had not been exempted. The letter was forwarded to the DOA who, in turn, decided it would not interfere with the decision to slaughter Kabul Prince and Mrs Stapleton's letter was returned to the RJA&HS by Brée. His message was unequivocal: "I am to inform you that my department is not prepared to interfere with the decision of the officers of your society in this matter acting, as they are, as a body constituted in virtue of directions issued under the Newly-Born Calves

(Jersey) Order, 1941". A letter was also sent to Mrs Stapleton of the DOA's decision.

Brée decided that the issue was so important that he took Mrs Stapleton's letter to the Superior Council on the 17th April. The Superior Council fully backed Brée and the RJA&HS. It commented that the order of the selection committee had to be immediately carried out and the bull calf slaughtered. Mrs Stapleton met the selection committee on the 25th April when they explained their decision and the bull was taken for slaughter.

A week later Mr J. F. Luce, St Lawrence, was reported to have breached the Newly-Born Calves (Jersey) Order, 1941, and was instructed to appear before the DOA. It was alleged that he had not slaughtered a heifer calf within 14 days of birth, as required by the order. The calf had been refused exemption from the provisions of Article 2(i) of the order. Mr Luce informed the DOA that he had "no intention" of carrying out the provisions of the order in relation to the calf. In response to Luce's negative reply Brée decided to lay the facts before the Attorney General with a view to proceedings being expedited. The Attorney General wrote back to the DOA asking for clarification as to why the calf had to be slaughtered.

Brée replied firstly, it was essential in the public interest that the calf in question be slaughtered as otherwise the Newly-Born Calves (Jersey) Order, 1941, will be held in contempt. Secondly, milk was fed to calves for a period of six months and the view of the DOA was that to cut off milk supplies to a calf at the age of less than six months was an act of cruelty. The calf was sent to the slaughterhouse and there was no legal action against Mr Luce. In the same week, Mrs A. Tourveur, St Ouen was summoned to the DOA for refusing to allow a calf to be slaughtered. The matter ended with a verbal warning.

In late April the German Field Command ordered the DOA to carry out an Island-wide census of cattle. Pelz wanted to know exactly the number of cattle and where they were kept on the Island. The letter was sent to the RJA&HS to order dairy farmers to cooperate and work together with the DOA to complete the request.

The RJA&HS met every week to discuss the calf-selection process. They kept extremely detailed notes for each calf exempted and each selected for slaughter. Dairy farmers who applied for a reconsideration of calves chosen for slaughter were offered a full explanation as to the reasons why a decision had been made. The scheme was basically well run and transparent.

Early in May a further report alleged that Mr E. Le Brun, St Lawrence, had neglected to slaughter a bull calf as instructed by the Calf Selection Committee. Brée interviewed Mr Le Brun whose replies to questions as to why the bull calf was not sent for slaughter drew no sympathy and Brée forwarded the matter to the Attorney General.

Pelz now turned his attention to meat prices and the civilian population. In late April, Pelz had written a letter to the Bailiff entitled "Meat Prices" in which he requested the Bailiff to enact an order to bring the price of meat sold to the consumer into line with the actual cost of production and "... obviate the necessity for a States subsidy". No reply had been forthcoming and, on the 13th and 26th May, Pelz again wrote to the Bailiff with the same request. After receiving three letters from Pelz to deal with civilian meat prices the Bailiff replied on the 30th May, some five weeks after the initial letter.[13.]

The time lapse between Pelz's first letter and the Bailiff's response is interesting. Hitherto, requests or orders from Field Command to the Bailiff were almost invariably dealt with within 48 hours and certainly not five weeks. It appears the Bailiff's response to Pelz was due to his increasing irritation by Pelz's constant stream of requests. This point is drawn to the attention of the reader of Coutanche's biography.[14] The Bailiff's response seemingly was one of prevarication to Pelz. However, on the 1st June 1942, the Meat (Maximum Retail Prices) (Amendment No 5) (Jersey) Order, 1942 was made law, in which Pelz's issues were addressed.

The Department of Essential Supplies on the 8th May 1942 wrote to the DOA. The matter concerned "...the heavy loss being incurred under the present system of paying for cattle brought in to the abattoirs at live weight, ascertained over the public weighbridge on the day on which such animals are brought in, owing to the practice of a certain number of farmers filling the animals with food and drink immediately prior to such weighing". In consequence, the DOA recommended to the Superior Council that all cattle brought into the abattoirs for slaughter should be weighed over the public weighbridge on the day following that upon which the animal had been brought in. Payments were then made to the owner of these animals upon the live weight ascertained at that time.

On the 16th May the RJA&HS slightly altered the criteria for the Calf Selection Committee in order to embrace three categories for grading calves. These were: the show or tested ancestry; the size of the herd; and previous exemptions made to individual dairy farmers. On the 19th May the DOA extended the provisions of the Newly-Born Calves (Jersey) Order, 1941, until July 1942.

A meeting of the RJA&HS was held on the 13th June to deal with an objection concerning the Newly-Born Calves Order, made by Mr C. Le Couteur. His complaint was that the order was not being administered according to the rules. Le Couteur's complaint went back to the RJA&HS meeting on the 29th November 1941, when it had been decided that no bulls would be exempted between the months of December 1941 and February 1942. However, the DOA had allowed two bull calves to be exempted in January and February. Perrédès questioned the entire order and proposed: "Seeing that there is at present a surplus of milk, the operation of the Newly-Born Calves Order be suspended as from Saturday, 6th June [1942] and this until such time as the supply of milk becomes less". The proposition was accepted by the RJA&HS and was sent to the DOA suggesting that the Act be suspended as there was a surplus of milk for the civilian population.

The response from Brée and the DOA was immediate and clear. The DOA would not accept the suggestion passed by the RJA&HS resolution. Brée made the definitive statement to all dairy farmers, that there was not a surplus of milk for the civilian population. In addition, he made it clear that the suspension of the order would increase greatly the number of calves consuming milk during the period when the available surplus of milk would be continually decreasing.

Brée, however, was in a difficult position. The DOA needed the services of the RJA&HS to expedite the Newly-Born Calves Order. The Society's Selection Committee was the only body which could make the order a real success. The DOA, with a number of other problems that needed dealing with - the 1942 potato and cereal crops, the organisation of the threshing contractors and new contracts with the agricultural merchants to be agreed - put the issue of calf selection and slaughter onto the back burner.

References

1. Jersey Archive. C/B/A1/7.
2. Jersey Archive. L/F/54/C/D/1. Document, 28th April 1942.
3. Jersey Archive. L/F/54/C/D/1. Document, 4th May 1942.
4. Approximately 2,154 litres or 3,792 pints.
5. RJA&HS. 1942. C. F. Journeaux. "Basics upon which the cost of milk production has been calculated".
6. Jersey Archive. L/D/09/A10.
7. Carlyle Le Gallais supplied the majority of the Staff Officers of Field Command 515 with fresh milk. The DOA gave him a backdated licence, thus allowing the sale of the milk to become legal. This was the only example of a backdated milk licence being sanctioned by the DOA during the German occupation.
8. Lauprecht, Dr E., 1942. Vol 17, pp. 369–386. Züchtungskunde. Herausgegeben von der Deutsche Gesellschaft für Züchtungskunde Unter Mitwirkung der Tierzuchtinstitut an Deutschen Hochschulen. Die Rinderzucht auf der Insel Jersey.
9. RJA&HS. Report of the Committee for the years 1940–1945, 8th December 1945.
10. Jersey Archive. B/A/W40/14/1.
11. RJA&HS and JFU Joint Emergency Committee Minutes.
12. Vibert, Denis. Personal account of the German occupation. This was a written account given by Denis Vibert to the late Joyce Le Ruez. My thanks to Pam Laurens and the executors of Joyce Le Ruez's estate for allowing me access to her private papers.
13. Jersey Archive. B/A/W31/1/72.
14. Pocock, H. R. S., 1975. The Memoirs of Lord Coutanche, p. 22.

Chapter 9

July – August – September 1942

Potatoes

On the 3rd of July 1942, Field Command 515 informed Brée that they required 7,000 tons of potatoes for the use of the German forces. This was to be delivered by August. The DOA, in view of the quantity required, increased the allocations required from each parish.

Parish Allocations Sent to the DOA for the Months of July, August and September 1942

	July	August	September
St Brelade	60	90	30
St Clement	60	90	30
Grouville	90	120	40
St Helier	55	90	30
St John	55	90	30
St Lawrence	90	140	30
St Martin	70	110	40
St Mary	60	75	25
St Ouen	160	240	80
St Peter	120	180	50
St Saviour	80	120	40
Trinity	120	180	60
Total	1,020 tons	1,525 tons	485 tons

On the 1st July W. Dennis and Sons Limited sent a letter to the DOA. The firm requested the DOA to release to them 22 tons of potatoes in order to reimburse the German authorities a similar quantity, which the company had borrowed from them. The DOA authorised the 22 tons of potatoes from its stocks at a price of £12-5-0 a ton. Dennis and Sons wrote back to the DOA "Taking exception to the price charged by the DOA for potatoes to the firm for the return to the German authorities."

On the 7th July all farmers were instructed that seed potatoes could only be sold between farmers by the issue of a permit from the DOA.

On the 14th July Brée requested the Attorney General to carry out a police investigation into the allegation that potatoes had been sold to the Organisation Todt (OT) by a farmer. The allegation was made that Mr A. G. Dallain, St Mary, had sold potatoes to members of the OT without first obtaining the necessary licence from the DOA.[1] This was the first mention of the Organisation Todt by the DOA in an official meeting. The issue was brought up because of an infringement of the appropriate Order. No mention is made of the conditions of forced or slave workers.

The question of the treatment of the forced or slave workers is not covered by this study. However, a memorandum dated 27th November 1942 and sent to the German Chief of the General Staff is both interesting and informative.[2] The memorandum was a report of an inspection of Guernsey and Jersey fortifications carried out between the 22nd to 25th November 1942. The German Officers inspecting these fortifications travelled to the Islands, having originated from Le Mans, France. On the 23rd November they flew from Dinard to Guernsey on an OT aeroplane. The next day the inspection team was met by the newly promoted Lieutenant General Müller and the Island's fortifications were inspected. On the same day they flew to Jersey and were met by Major General von Schmettow (who was promoted in September 1942 from the rank of Colonel). An inspection of Jersey's fortifications and defences was carried out. On the 25th November the inspecting staff were flown back to Le Mans. The final paragraph of the memorandum was:

"Questions discussed by the Division Commander and the Island Commander.

The Division Commander and Island Commander, Jersey, see a danger for the troops due to the state of the foreign OT workers: dirt, lice and the danger of epidemics. Measures should urgently be taken. This shortcoming has been reported to the O. Qu. West [this was Field Marshall Gerd von Rundstedt]. Its decision remains to be expected."

The extract demonstrates that, since the arrival of OT workers into Jersey in late 1941, the German Military Command saw the OT workers as a serious and potential threat to the state of health of their troops in Jersey. No mention is made of the dangers to the Island civilian population or any area of concern for the OT workers.

On the 17th July the Attorney General wrote a letter to the Connétables. He described cases where, firstly, farmers were selling potatoes to private individuals. He made it clear that this was a breach of the order sent out by the DOA, whereby farmers could only sell their potatoes to the DOA. Secondly, that the manufacture of potato flour to sell was in breach of the Potato Flour (Manufacture for Sale) (Jersey) Order, 1941. The Attorney General made it clear that the Honorary Police should take stringent measures to report the above infractions. The Attorney General gave his reasons to the Connétables for the importance of the letter: "If there is not to be a serious, and perhaps calamitous, potato shortage next Winter and Spring, there should be no illicit trafficking in, or wastage of potatoes".[3]

The clamping of the 1942 potato crop began on the 27th July. Wheat straw was purchased for the potato clamps. The sites chosen were: 2 vergées owned by Mr C Hotton, St Mary, the amount paid being £7 for such period as the field was required for clamping potatoes; and the second field, 1½ vergées, situated near the States Experimental station, Trinity. The total clamping costs for the 1942 season were £3,993-18-5.

By the 31st July deliveries of German potato seed had been completed. There was however a shortfall of 9% in the total quantity expected.

On the 28th August an Inspector, Mr O. P. Gautier, described a load of potatoes delivered to the DOA as "unfit". The potatoes were brought into the store by Mr J. J. Le Marquand, Junior, St Peter. The Inspector alleged that after a discussion with Mr Le Marquand on the state of his potatoes, and contrary to DOA instructions, he took the potatoes back to the country. In view of the "...truculent and offensive attitude" of Mr Le Marquand he was called in for an interview with the DOA the following week.[4] As a result of his interview, it was decided to requisition all the potatoes on his premises.

Mr Le Marquand wrote to the DOA asking for a second interview. In view of his previous attitude towards the DOA, the Committee refused to see him. On the 24th September Mr Le Marquand's advocates, Ogier and Le Cornu, wrote on his behalf, asking for a payment of £20-8-0 in respect of the potatoes which had been requisitioned. The DOA decided that, in view of its requisition order, the question of payment would be left for consideration until the conclusion of hostilities. His advocates were informed. In addition, Mr Le Marquand was instructed to hand back to the DOA the weighbridge tickets in respect of the requisitioned potatoes.

On the 1st September a report was received that various stores holding DOA potatoes were in "...a congested state owing to the failure of the German authorities to export to Guernsey the quantities of potatoes to be exported." In view of this, the DOA decided to postpone the allocation of potatoes from the parishes, to be brought in for sale to the DOA, until the situation improved.

Watermills and Milling

On the 3rd July 1942, the DOA recommended to the Superior Council that the wages of the Assistant Millers should be increased as follows.

Name	Mill	Increase Weekly
Eric Gilley	Tesson	50/- to 52/6
M. Le Mottée	Gargate	50/- to 55/-
W. H. Lucas	Gargate	50/- to 52/6
P. A. Hervieu	Malassis	50/- to 55/-
H. F. Bennett	Malassis	50/- to 60/-
R. Le Marchand	Malassis	50/- to 52/6
W. Jotham	Malassis	50/- to 60/-
E. F. Josse	Grand Val	50/- to 60/-
F. J. Horton	Grand Val	50/- to 55/-
C. P. Le Sueur	Grand Val	50/- to 52/6

The DOA also decided that all men employed in DOA mills would be entitled, after one year's service, to one week's paid holiday each year. Brée somewhat surprisingly disagreed with the implementation of the holiday entitlement, however he was overruled by the DOA full committee.

In July, a report highlighted a serious shortage arising from the milling of wheat by the Jersey Farmers (Trading) Union. The shortages were described as "very high". The DOA decided that action would be taken. The firm was ordered to immediately cease milling cereals belonging to the DOA.

In the same month, the DOA received a report from the States Engineer, Mr C. W. Rice. The report stressed that urgent repairs to the culverts under the roadway, carrying the millstream to Grand Val and Malassis Mills, should take place immediately. He was given permission to carry out all urgent repairs.

Again, in July, shortages of grain at Gargate appeared to be increasing. The DOA carried out an investigation at the mill. It decided that the door giving access to the mill premises from the attached dwelling house should be permanently closed thereby not giving access to the mill premises. It was also decided that Ernest Charles Gilley would cease to be a miller at Gargate and be reappointed the stone-dresser for the DOA. He was put on a wage of £1 a week plus 1/6 per hour for the work on dressing stone. Mr Maurice Le Mottée was appointed as miller at Gargate and his wage increased again, from 55/- to 60/- a week.

The following week Mr Gilley made requests to the DOA to reconsider its decision. Although the DOA replied, it would not reconsider. It appears that he continued to be employed at Gargate Mill in the capacity of "an assistant miller" until 26th June 1943. Mr Gilley then found it difficult to perform his duties, almost certainly due to ill health. The DOA, in a rather unique decision, "...decided that as the DOA is in the occupation of the mill from which, prior to such occupation, Mr Gilley drew his livelihood, it would be recommended to the Superior Council that Mr Gilley should be paid £1-15-0 weekly for such period as the mill remains in the DOA".[5]

On the 27th July, a report examined the loss of grain at all the mills. After a study of the figures Brée wrote to the millers and stated he was "very dissatisfied" with the losses. He warned the DOA millers that, unless a considerable reduction in their losses occurred, the DOA would be obliged to take "serious measures". He added that he would investigate the "... considerable shortage which had been established in Quetivel Mill."

On the 4th September, as a result of German fortifications being constructed, and the possibility of cessation of milling at Gargate, the DOA asked Normans Limited, Commercial Buildings, for permission to install on their premises the auxiliary milling plant that was at Gargate Mill. Brée arranged with Mr J. M. Norman that no charge would be made in respect of the milling apparatus being moved to the premises until such time, and only, for the period as the apparatus was actually in use.

Jersey Produce Merchants Association

In July 1942, the DOA approved its list of merchants for storage of DOA potatoes for the period 1942 to 1943. The following were selected.

R. P. Amy
C. S. Bailhache
J. E. Baudains
E. Becquet
W. Bird and Son Limited
George Blampied
The Country Gentlemen's Association Limited
W. Dennis and Sons Limited
T. Dorey and Company Limited
R. A. Deffain
T. du Feu
A. P. Falle and Sons Limited
Giddens, Barette and Company
Guiton and Lucas
Sidney Horman Limited – nothing for present
The Jersey Co-operative Wholesale Society
Jersey Farmers (Trading) Union Ltd
Job and Sons
A. E. Laurens
Le Marquand Brothers
O. J. Le Mottée Limited
S. E. Le Brocq
Marks and Riches Limited
J. Martland Limited

T. Mayo and Company Limited
C. Mossop
Normans Limited
E. N. Pirouet
Randall's Brewery
J. Spearman
C. Syvret
John Terry Limited
G. Touzel
W. Gaudin – nothing for present
P. J. de Gruchy – no grain is to be stored
A. C. Sarre – oats subject to further consideration

All merchants were ordered to ensure that any remaining wheat in store was moved to separate premises before potatoes were brought in for storage. Two representatives, one from the JPMA and one from the DOA, were confirmed to act as a consultative committee in connection with any problems with the storage of DOA potatoes for the period 1942 to 1943. The DOA representative was George Messervy and the JPMA representative Charles Gruchy.

On the 10th of July the DOA met a JPMA delegation in connection with the shortage of space for the storage of 1942 and 1943 potatoes. It was decided that the JPMA would arrange the allocation of storage on behalf of the DOA, including the quantity of potatoes allocated to each of their members. In addition, merchants who had "suitable floors" could store potatoes in bulk, provided they were stored in piles not exceeding five feet in height. A space of 12 to 18 inches would be left between each pile. On the 18th August, the consultative committee recommended the appointment of Mr S. C. Le Blancq as an arbitrator between individual merchants and the DOA in the event of a disagreement. The DOA agreed to this proposal.

On the 14th August, the DOA met the JPMA to discuss the terms upon which merchants would undertake to store the 1942 cereal harvest on behalf of the DOA. An agreement was reached for the JPMA to store the crop for 30/- a ton.

On the 25th August, the JPMA and the Jersey Corn Merchants Association (JCMA) met to discuss the 1942 storage of cereals. The meeting comprised: J. M. Norman, President of the JPMA, E. N. Pirouet, President of the JCMA, and B. Horsfall. The central issue was the proposed storage charge for the privileged issue of oats.[6] The delegates wanted to charge 30/- per ton; the meeting finally agreed upon a figure of £1 a ton storage charge. However, the DOA agreed to pay the merchants 30/- per ton for grain other than privileged oats stored on behalf of the DOA. Grain was to be stored in conformity with regulations issued by the DOA.

The DOA also set up a sub-committee of Le Gallais and Gibaut to supervise the threshing of the 1942 cereal harvest. They were instructed to investigate, and secure, additional storage space for grain and to report back. The sub-committee immediately inspected the stores of George D Laurens,

Lower Bath Street, Orviss Limited and De Veulle and Company, Hill Street. All the above agreed to undertake the storage of grain.

On the 2nd December the JCMA wrote to the DOA, requesting an increase in respect of wheat seed stored; this to cover the additional floor space and labour necessitated by the preparation of this seed. The DOA recommended to the Superior Council an additional payment of 3/- per ton in respect of the storage of wheat seed. The JCMA replied, accepting the additional payment of 3/- per ton, but asking for a future remuneration to be set at 3/9d per ton for the storage of seed wheat.[7] The DOA, however, "...was not in the mood to reconsider a change or increase." The JCMA seems to have accepted the above message and withdrew the request.

In September, W. Dennis and Sons Limited sent a letter to the Petrol Controller, which was forwarded to the DOA. It requested that the company be paid extra in respect of the hire of their lorries when required to work overtime transporting grain from the threshing machines to the DOA stores. The DOA refused to pay any overtime rates.

At the same time the DOA, having considered the difficulties in transporting and storing grain that had been threshed, investigated the transport of grain from the threshing machines to town stores that took place in the evening, when it became a problem to receive and check the loads before the end of the day. The DOA asked the sub-committee of Gibaut and Le Gallais to take all necessary steps to secure accommodation in the country, where loaded grain lorries could be kept safely under lock and key. The keys were to be retained by the DOA's Threshing Inspectors during the period of storage. The sub-committee recommended that, in the event of a lorry containing a part-load of grain and threshing gear belonging to the DOA remaining in a countryside store overnight, the lorry would be allowed to proceed in the morning to the farm at which threshing was to take place in order to deliver the gear, and the part-load of grain then had to be immediately taken to town to offload at a DOA store. It was also decided that in every case where loaded grain lorries were stored overnight, the DOA's officers would have to count the bags of grain on each lorry before locking up and recounting when opening the store the following morning.

However, the storage of grain overnight in the country did lead to pilfering of grain. In November, Mr Oliver Pierre Gautier, an employee of the DOA, was interviewed concerning alleged shortages discovered in loads of grain stored overnight in the custody of the DOA.[4]

Fifty-two sacks of oats in the store of the T. F. Pirouet and Sons were found missing one morning. This was followed by another delivery to the store of sixty-six sacks of oats, when four bags went missing. Mr Gautier was reprimanded for his admitted failure to carry out the instructions of the DOA; namely, that the loads on the lorries must be counted when coming into overnight storage and again when leaving the following morning. The farmers who lost oats were compensated by the DOA.

On the 25th September, the DOA wrote to five merchants asking for an explanation as to why there was a large shrinkage of the barley held in their stores on behalf of the DOA. The five stores were: The Country Gentlemen's Association Limited, W. J. Gaudin, Giddens Barette and Company, Marks and Riches Limited and W. Nicholls and Sons Limited. The DOA decided no further grain would be sent and the five companies were questioned concerning their "...heavy shortages". Three gave satisfactory explanations. "Nicholls & Sons, however, furnished no explanations whatever." Nicholls and Sons was duly informed that, unless they made a satisfactory explanation within seven days, they would be debited with the value of the shortage of barley in question. After various discussions, the DOA deferred consideration of their explanations until definitive figures were available as to any shortages which might be found in stocks of wheat held by them on behalf of the DOA. The losses in barley at Marks and Riches was less than 4% and the DOA took no further action.

Cereals

On the 28th July the Honorary Parish Inspectors were instructed to select fields of wheat which they considered would be suitable for seed for the 1943 crop.

A few days earlier, a meeting had been held between the JFU and the RJA&HS, comprising some forty of the important cereal growers. Brée was in the chair and began by stating the importance of the approaching threshing season for both farmers and the owners of threshing machines. Threshing contractors had agreed to their remuneration and the conditions under which threshing would be carried out. All the threshing machines were licensed and had been mechanically checked and serviced.

At this meeting, the farmers made it clear that the threshing charges paid by them in the 1941 season had been too high. Seven farmers were appointed as a sub-committee to discuss this with the threshing contractors: C. P. Journeaux, P. Le Feuvre, J. Le Boutillier, C. G. Pallot, J. B. Michel and E. C. Perrédès.[8]

The following week, the DOA decided that all payments for grain would be made upon the production of a weighbridge ticket issued by a public weighbridge.

On the 7th August, a report was produced advising changes to be implemented for handling the 1942 harvest.

1. The supervision and control of the harvest will be dealt with by the Grain and Potato Section of the DOA.
2. The Chief Inspector will be responsible for supervision of the classification, weighing and storage of all grain.
3. An "Assistant" will be appointed for each Sub-Inspector at the threshing machines and will determine the percentage of grain which each farmer is allowed to keep.
4. For the purposes of the control of the harvest, the Island is divided into two sections, namely, "East and West". An inspector will be appointed to take charge of each section. He will supervise the

working and general operation of the threshing machines and the transport of grain from the machines to the public weighbridge. The inspectors will have control of the Sub-Inspectors and their Assistants at the threshing machines. They will determine the dates upon which these Sub-Inspectors and Assistants will begin and end their duties. The Inspectors are responsible for notifying the Grain and Potato Control Section of all appointments of Sub-Inspectors and Assistants. They are also responsible for terminating their contracts.

a. A Sub-Inspector will be appointed at each threshing machine ensuring that the work is properly carried out. In this he will be aided by the Assistant Inspector. All "Sub-Inspectors" will operate under the directions of the District Inspector to whom he will refer in cases of difficulty.

b. The Sub-Inspectors will check that the grain is properly sacked, and each sack labelled with the name of the farmer who has brought the grain to the machine. Such labelling is to be carried out in accordance with the directions issued by the District Inspector.

c. Sub-Inspectors will be provided with a triplicate receipt book indicating the name of the owner of the grain brought to the threshing machine, the nature of the grain so brought, and the number of sacks filled for transport to the DOA stores. The original ticket will be handed to the farmer, a duplicate handed to the carter who will transport the grain, which he will then hand to the DOA official on the public weighbridge. The triplicate will remain in the book. All receipt books on completion are to be handed to the District Inspector who will arrange for the books to be delivered to the Grain and Potato Section.

d. The Sub-Inspectors will assume full responsibility for the DOA sacks at the machines and are required to check that grain is put into clean sacks. Special sacks are reserved only for wheat seed.

5. All grain is to be classified at the public weighbridge. Any grain of inferior quality will be submitted to a sub-committee for valuation. The grower of inferior grain will be immediately informed in writing of its classification. Where wheat seed is selected by the Honorary Parish Inspector, the Sub-Inspectors must mark the receipt in respect of such grain accordingly.

6. A Sub-committee is appointed to value all grain classified as inferior quality by the DOA officers. The grower of inferior grain is entitled to be present when the grain is examined by the Sub-Committee.

7. Arrangements will be made with the Department of Transport and Communications for the cartage of grain from the threshing machines to the DOA stores. The District Inspector is responsible for arranging the time, date and places when and where such cartage facilities are required.

8. The DOA weighers at the public weighbridge will keep a separate record of all grain tickets in alphabetical order. This will enable the proprietors

of grain brought into DOA cereal stores to obtain their tickets without difficulty. The DOA weighers require a signature from the drawers of each ticket issued by them and the farmer is required to sign for the ticket.

9. Payment for the grain will be made by the Grain and Potato Section upon presentation of the weighbridge ticket not less than seven days after delivery of the grain to the DOA store.

10. Wheat reserved for seed will be stored in special stores. The Honorary Parish Inspectors will provide the District Inspectors and Sub-Inspectors with a list of wheat selected for seed.

11. All DOA inspectors have the power to postpone the threshing of any load considered unfit.

12. The owners of private threshing machines are allowed, under the direction of the District Inspectors, to provide arrangements and dates for threshing, in order for a Sub-Inspector to attend at the time.

13. All threshed grain will be brought into town each evening and stored in DOA premises. After overnight storage, only a DOA employee is allowed to open the store in the morning.

14. Sacks will be issued for each threshing machine from the DOA's depot at 31 Commercial Street.

15. Each Sub-Inspector is responsible for the store of sacks issued at the machine to which he is attached.

    a. A privilege issue of oats will be made to growers of cereals who are the owners of horses.

    b. An allowance of 7½% of all grain delivered to the DOA's stores will be returned to the farmer, on condition that he collects the grain from the DOA store. The percentage will be calculated on the weight of grain delivered over the public weighbridge into the store on behalf of the farmer.

16. All wheat must be stacked separately. In cases where this is not possible, and in order to avoid mixing, the wheat is to be stacked on top of other varieties of cereals.

Within a week the allowance of 7½% of grain to the farmer was changed to one bag in thirteen and was to be made direct to the farmer at the threshing machine. On the 11th August, a notice was put in the local press inviting applications for Inspectors for the 1942 cereal harvest. The wage was £3 a week. The working day was from 8.00 a.m. to 6.00 p.m., with one hour for lunch. Any additional hours worked was overtime.

On the 14th August, the provisions of the Cereal Grain (Threshing and Purchase of Crops) (Jersey) Order, 1941 was modified for the 1942 cereal harvest.

On 18th August, all threshing contractors were instructed to have their machines ready for inspection by Carlyle Le Gallais and A. W. J. Le Seelleur. On the 21st August the contractors were informed that work would begin within several days.

The same day, John Perrée was asked to be Chairman of the Pricing Committee for inferior grain. He declined, whereupon George Messervy accepted the position and appointed two assistants: Charles Gruchy and N. Pirouet. H.G. Shepard was co-opted to act as secretary.

On the 28th August, the DOA decided that the privileged issue of oats would be given directly to farmers from the threshing machines and not from the store at 31 Commercial Street. On the same day, the salary of Assistant Threshing Inspectors was fixed at £2-10-0 a week.

The previous week saw the interviewing and selection of Threshing Inspectors for the 1942 Cereal Harvest. The two District Inspectors were Mr Frank Le Maistre, Laboratory Assistant at the States Experimental Station, responsible for the Western District, and Mr O. P. Hamon, La Rocque, Grouville responsible for the Eastern District. Their salary was £4 a week and they were not allowed to claim overtime.

The Sub-Inspectors appointed at the threshing machines, at a weekly wage of £3, were:

J. F. Blanchet
S. G. Buesnel
R. Ching
T. de La Haye
P. G. Dubois
J. A. Huelin Junior
H. F. Huelin
W. A. Pallot
J. C. Steel
H. Vautier
C. Wills

A Threshing Sub-Committee was set up on the 2nd October comprising Edwin Gibaut and Carlyle Le Gallais. They were to work in concert with the Grain and Potato Control Section. and to govern the conduct of the District and Sub-Inspectors. Both men were subsequently appointed in the same capacity for the 1943 Cereal Harvest.

On the 28th August the 1942 Cereal Threshing Contractors were appointed by the DOA.

Name	Address	Number of Machines
T. R. Binet	Les Côtils, Trinity	1
S.J.C. Cabot	Les Cateaux	1
W. T. Farrell	Sandown, Parade Road, St Helier	1
T. G. Le Cappelain	St Peters' Works, St Peter	4
L. C. Pallot	Central Motor Works, Sion, Trinity	1
J. Priaulx	St Cyr, St John	2
J. Richard	La Grande Maison, St John	2

Total number of threshing machines for 1942 season = 12

On the same day, the operating rules for contractors were set out in detail.

1. **Maximum Charges:** for threshing on the farm, the rate is £2-10-0 per hour. The minimum charge for threshing on a farm is £15 plus the cost of moving the machine. For threshing at depots by load, the rate is 16/6 per load. For threshing barley, an additional charge of 1/- per load is allowed. For moving the threshing machine from one farm to another and setting up, £2, irrespective of the distance travelled.
2. **Control of Threshing:** all threshing contractors are to work under the direction of DOA Inspectors who have the power and authority to postpone any threshing.
3. **Hours of Work:** Threshing contractors are to work from 8.00 a.m. to 6.00 p.m. One hour is allowed for lunch. In suitable weather, the inspector can sanction a longer working day, however, no contractor is to work beyond 8.00 p.m. A contractor can start before 8.00 a.m. but must make prior arrangements with the Inspector. An Inspector must be in attendance if the contractor starts before 8.00 a.m.
4. **Rotation:** All loads of cereals are to be threshed in strict rotation of booking. At depots, oats, barley and rye are to be threshed before wheat.
5. **Staff:** Each threshing contractor must employ at all times a minimum of five men while threshing.
6. **Start of work:** contractors must notify the District Inspector at least two days before they wish to start work.

On recommendation of the Threshing Sub-Committee, a lock-up hut for storing DOA grain sacks was made. This was set up at the threshing depot of W. T. Farrell at St Ouen. The "sweepings" of all machines at depots were to be threshed and handed over to Inspectors to be delivered to the DOA stores.

It was also decided to allow extra bread rations for heavy work, such as that of the Sub-Inspectors and their assistants. The Threshing Sub-Committee of Le Gallais and Gibaut was allowed the power to dismiss Sub-Inspectors if their conduct was unsatisfactory. They could also recommend the appointment of new men and were given authority to allow District Inspectors an entitlement to overtime payment, in the same manner as Sub-Inspectors and their assistants. Men employed by the contractors were not eligible to draw the Agricultural Wages Bonus. The Threshing Sub-Committee also appointed Mr H. D. Mourant of Raffray Engineering Company to supervise the issue of binder twine. Baling was ordered to be done with one tie in cases where the string or wire used was supplied by the DOA.

On the 1st September it was decided that the number of threshing machines, totalling twelve, necessitated two extra Sub-Inspectors and Mr C. A. de la Haye and Mr P. S. Gibaut were appointed.

On the 8th September, Field Command 515 and Pelz made it clear that all necessary arrangements should be made for threshing to take place at the depots on the 13th September. All farmers were informed and Pelz, during the threshing season, busied himself inspecting cereal fields and depots and checking on the progress of the contractors.

In the same week as the above order was made, the Threshing Sub-Committee, after examining the transport of threshed grain, ordered that large capacity lorries be sent to threshing machines during the afternoons, in order that larger loads of grain could be cleared. The smaller lorries were therefore utilised to clear grain from the threshing machines each evening. This had the effect of rendering the overnight storage of grain easier. At the same time, the Honorary Parish Inspectors were telephoned "Requiring them to see that all cereal is brought under the cover of barns or are stacked not later than tomorrow night, 12th September 1942, as required by the German authorities in occupation of the Island." On the 21st September, the time for terminating evening threshing was changed from 8.00 p.m. to 7.00 p.m.

On the 25th September, a meeting of the DOA and the Threshing Sub-Committee took place. The following decisions were made.

1. The Fuel Controller will be asked to arrange with Theo G. Le Cappelain to "...measure the five fire boxes of the engines operating the threshing machines, with a view to estimating the fuel consumption of each of the engines, so that the issue of coke made to Le Cappelain for the driving of his engines may be accurately computed".

2. The Connétable of St Lawrence is to be informed that fifty-three DOA sacks were stolen between the 31st August and 18th September 1942 from the threshing depot set up in Mr T. A. Pallot's field at Bel Royal. He is instructed to institute an investigation into the alleged theft.

3. The Western District Inspector, Le Maistre, is empowered to purchase twelve bundles of sisal (a plant fibre, like jute) from W. T. Farrell, Grantez, St Ouen, at a price not exceeding 12/6 a bundle.

4. In the event of a farmer requiring the use of a threshing machine that is not working in his district, the farmer will have to wait until all growers in the district in which the machine was actually operating have completed their threshing.

Pigs

On the 24th July 1942, the Livestock (Jersey) Order, 1942 was made law. An article was inserted requiring a detailed declaration to be made when any person delivered or took custody of any cattle or pigs.

By the 14th August, the DOA had interviewed Mrs R. A. M. Gruchy in connection with an allegation that she slaughtered a pig without obtaining the necessary licence. Furthermore, that she was in breach of the Livestock (Restriction on Slaughtering) (Jersey) Order 1940, and the Pigs (Control) (Jersey) Order, 1941. She had not declared the pig to be in her custody. Brée took the view that this was a relatively minor misdemeanour over one pig, he severely reprimanded her, and warned of the consequences of any future breaches. No judicial proceedings were instigated.

Cultivation Orders

On the 7th July 1942 the Department of Essential Commodities published a notice drawing attention to the provisions of the Potato Flour (Manufacture for Sale) (Jersey) Order, 1941. It was made clear that no permits to manufacture potato flour would be granted without prior consultation with the DOA. In the same week Miss Marian Journeaux joined the Milk Control Section as a shorthand typist at a weekly salary of £1-10-0.

On the 18th July the Harbour Master gave notice to the DOA to vacate its offices at the weighbridge by the following week, these offices being taken up by the German authorities. Consequently, the DOA took up the offer of John F. Renouf to lease offices situated at Mulcaster Street for an annual rental of £26.

The Glasshouse Potatoes (Jersey) Order, 1942 made it mandatory that all glasshouse potatoes were sold only to the DOA.[9] In July, the DOA met with the Glasshouse Growers' Association (GGA). The GGA Committee comprised: J. H. Syvret, E. J. Le Feuvre, J. S. McCann, D. Wakeman, R. Dobson and E. C. Oldman. The cropping plan for glasshouse potatoes for 1943 was discussed. All farmers having a glasshouse of over 227 square feet were required to cultivate it under the directions of the DOA. They were also directed to plant potatoes in at least 75% of the area. On the 7th August 1942, the DOA sent out a notification that any person who had 10 perches or more under glass had to notify the department.

On the 21st August, the acute shortage of hay was discussed. The DOA accepted the States Vet's proposal that hay should be imported from France.

On the same day, after a large number of compensation claims had been received from farmers in respect of the failure of crops and subsequent hardship, the DOA decided to recommend to the Superior Council that no compensation be paid. One such claim had been sent directly to the DOA by Mr C. E. Vibert, St Peter, claiming for a vergée of failed wheat. His claim was refused.

As a result of these claims for crop failures, the Honorary Parish Inspectors were informed that no compensation would be paid in respect of failed crops in their respective parishes. The secretary, Colin Marie, was instructed to deal with such claims himself without bringing them to the attention of the DOA. Marie was ordered to write back to the farmers and inform them that no form of compensation was available. Marie, however, was also instructed that where alleged crop failures were "exceptionally severe" he was to refer the matter to the DOA Committee.

Claims for crop failures continued to be made by farmers. In consequence the DOA decided to recommend to the Superior Council that a "Compensation Advisory Committee" be reappointed to investigate claims for financial compensation where financial hardship was severe and evident. Such a body had been originally set up on the 10th December 1941 but had been subsequently disbanded.

In September, J. Gartrell, Deputy of St John and Honorary Parish Inspector submitted claims for the failure of cereal crops on behalf of two farmers: John B. Syvret and E. L. Henry. Both claimants were refused any compensation. A further claim was sent in by J. B. Méhrust, St Lawrence, for crop failure which he had sent in to the DOA the previous year, however the DOA could not find his original claim. The Honorary Parish Inspector Mr T. A. Pallot was instructed to send details of the claim in question, with an accompanying report as to the circumstances under which the claim was submitted. The report was sent to E. A. Dorey, Chairman of the Compensation Advisory Committee.

By the summer of 1942 many farmers had found their cultivated fields ringed by barbed wire entanglements. The DOA received a stream of complaints. Some claimed they could not enter a cultivated field which urgently required attention. Brée took up the matter directly with Pelz. On the 29th August the Field Commandant wrote to the DOA in answer to Brée's protests made to Pelz. He clarified that "The troops are prepared in almost every case to allow the farmers to the enclosed field. I therefore expect the DOA to notify farmers to the effect that each occupier concerned shall on his initiative get in touch with the competent commander of the troops with regard to cultivating the land within the wire. Every farmer must consider it his duty, even under the more difficult conditions of war to make his land productive. I shall penalise any owner of land not complying.[10]

In late August 1942, Mr Godfray, the DOA's Chief Inspector, became ill. He was replaced whilst on sick leave by the newly appointed Deputy Chief Inspector, Mr P. Hubert.

In September the DOA paid two compensation claims for damage by the German forces of occupation. John Vigot, Grouville, was awarded £40 and F. G. Le Rossignol, St Brelade, was awarded £10. This was followed by a further claim made by Mr L. Cole, St Martin, who claimed that a German unit had damaged a crop of potatoes. He was compensated by an award of £15. Two further claims were made: Mr Y. Hidrio, St Peter, was awarded £25 and Mr P. Renouf, St Peter, £30 for the loss of 2 vergées of oats destroyed by German forces. Before any claims were settled a full report was made by the respective Honorary Parish Inspectors.

In August all male clerical DOA staff were awarded a salary increase of 5/- a week. Female clerical staff appear not have been given any form of commensurate salary increase.

On the 2nd September the Honorary Parish Inspector, St Brelade, H. W. Gibaut wrote to the DOA. His letter stated that his work in the capacity of an Inspector was seriously interfered with by "…the lack of clips and tubes". Brée made a recommendation to the appropriate authority that Mr Gibaut's application for his bicycle receive preferential treatment and consideration "In view of the importance to the Island of the work carried out by the Honorary Inspectors."

On the 15th September the DOA considered a letter from the German Field Command 515 concerning the purchase of agricultural machinery for 1943. It drew up a list of requirements detailing the reasons for the need of machinery.

It is interesting as this demonstrates the very proactive and increasing reliance that the DOA had in its relationship with Field Command 515 and the head of the Agricultural Section, Hans Egon Pelz. Almost all agricultural inputs were now being sourced by Pelz and Field Command, using an extensive network of Field Commands throughout France. The German administration in the Channel Islands was very amenable to accessing and transporting these agricultural inputs to the islands on an ever-increasing scale.

On the 29th September 1942, the Cultivation Plan for the 1943 season was discussed and agreed upon by the DOA and Honorary Parish Inspectors. At a further meeting on the 10th October, in the Board Room of the RJA&HS, the following were present:

DOA
Touzel John Brée
Edwin Denize Gibaut
Carlyle Le Gallais
Wesley John Mallet
Colin Cecil Marie

Honorary Parish Inspectors

St Brelade	H. M. Gibaut
St Clement	J. P. Le Masurier
Grouville	S. G. Le Couilliard
St Helier	P. J. Mourant
St John	J. Gartrell, C. Le Couteur
St Martin	P. Ahier, G. Le Masurier
St Mary	E. J. Le Ruez
St Ouen	G. E. Huelin, E.G. Vautier
St Peter	G. H. Le Rossignol
St Saviour	P. Gallichan, C. Quenault
Trinity	C. P Ahier, A. R. Le Brun

Cropping Plan for 1943

Barley	400	Vergées
Rye	260	Vergées
Wheat	10,000	Vergées
Oats	3,000	Vergées
Potatoes (early)	4,475	Vergées
Potatoes (1944 seed)	1,700	Vergées
Potatoes (late)	1,000	Vergées
Mangolds	3,000	Vergées
Hay and grazing	12,000	Vergées
Vegetables	600	Vergées
TOTAL	36,435	Vergeés

The meeting was opened by Brée. He stated that owing to "...the land requisitioned by the German authorities in occupation of the Island, it is impossible at present to ascertain the actual area available for cultivation." He asked the Honorary Parish Inspectors to send in their allocations for each farmer in order for the DOA to be in a position to know the areas which it was proposed to devote to the various crops. Brée ended the meeting by stating he had received a letter from the German Field Commandant, dated the 6th October 1942. The letter requested the ploughing up of all stubble, for which petrol would be made available, and the clearing of bracken.

Agricultural Labour

Between the 27th June and 19th September 1942, a total of £9,691-4-0 was paid out for the Agricultural Workers Bonus. Agricultural labourers took a signed voucher from their respective employer to the main Post Office in Broad Street, St Helier, where the voucher was exchanged for cash at the counter.

On the 7th August, the DOA decided to continue the scheme, after the end date of the 10th October 1942, for another twelve months. On the 1st September, a further credit of £5,000 was requested from the Department of Finance and Economics. After various applications were received by men employed by the threshing contractors, the DOA re-stated that these men were not eligible to draw the bonus.

In August the DOA received a letter from the German Field Command, ordering that the Agricultural Workers Bonus should be discontinued after the 3rd October 1942. On the 11th August, the DOA met with the Presidents of the Departments of Finance and Economics and Labour, Jurat Dorey and Deputy Le Quesne respectively. It was decided that Brée and du Val be appointed as members of a sub-committee to meet the German authority to discuss and secure the continuance of the bonus. Jurat Dorey and Deputy Le Quesne would also attend the meeting.

The sub-committee discussed the German order that the present voucher scheme would expire on the 3rd October. Brée was of the opinion that the German Field Command would accept an alternative scheme. The proposals for the new scheme were as follows.

1. That single men shall not be eligible to draw the Bonus.
2. That the Bonus shall be:
   a. 5/- to a married man in respect of his wife living with and maintained by him.
   b. 5/- in respect of each child of which such man is the father up to a maximum payment of 10/- in respect of such children provided that such children are maintained by him.
3. That the minimum wage payable by farmers who wish to have the benefit of the scheme shall be 40/- weekly.

These proposals were made to Field Command on the 29th September. On the 2nd October, they were rejected by the German authorities who had devised a new scheme which they wanted to be implemented. To comply with the orders of the Field Command, the DOA decided to ask the Superior Council to charge the Department of Labour to require that all workers applying to register with them should produce a certificate as to the nature of the work performed, to the "...end that no agricultural or horticultural workers may be registered for employment by the Department of Labour."

The DOA also decided to look at the method of computing the minimum wage paid to agricultural workers, when granting financial assistance in respect of payments made in kind. It decided on the following.

1. Where an employer provides free living accommodation for an agricultural worker employed by him, the value of such accommodation shall be assessed at 5/- weekly.
2. Where an employer provides his agricultural workers with free meals, the value of such meals shall be assessed at 2/- per day; namely 1/- for dinner and 6 pence each for breakfast and tea.

The sources are not exactly clear as to whether all the above proposals were implemented, but the majority seem to have been accepted by all interested groups.

Horses

"The stock of horses in Jersey cannot be renewed and rejuvenated because of a lack of local breeding facilities. The predominating principle must therefore be as to cover as many mares as possible in order to raise young horses."

KVR Hans Egon Pelz

From the beginning of the German occupation, the DOA had spent considerable sums of money and resources purchasing and importing horses from France. As farmers faced increasing difficulties obtaining fuel for tractors, they became more dependent on horses to work their fields. By 1941, there was a chronic shortage of agricultural working horses. Pelz decided that a possible answer to this shortage was to breed local horses. The DOA was informed of the plan and on the 23rd May 1941 it announced that Mr Leonard H. Blight, St Saviour had agreed for his stallion to be utilised by farmers, free of charge, for breeding purposes.[11] However, it appears that Blight's stallion, over the period 1941 to 1942, had not been sufficiently up to the task of increasing the Island's population of horses.

Exactly one year later Pelz, on the 28th May 1942, decided he would implement a new plan to solve the problem of an Island-wide shortage of agricultural working horses. Pelz produced a report entitled "The breeding of horses" which was forwarded to the Bailiff. Pelz stated that he had personally inspected Leonard Blight's stallion and was of the opinion that, "The stock of horses in Jersey cannot be renewed and rejuvenated because of a lack of local breeding facilities. The farmers are, therefore, always dependent on importing expensive horses from France. The predominating principle must therefore be as to cover as many mares as possible in order to raise young horses. Farmer Blight's stallion should, therefore, be permitted to cover the mares as soon as the horse owners show any interest. It is true he is 16 years old and no longer very capable."

Pelz's proposal was for Field Command 515 to begin negotiations in St Lô to purchase a stallion. There was a horse stud farm at St Lô. After the purchase of a suitable stallion, a person would be entrusted to set up a Jersey "Covering Station" where as many mares as possible could be covered. Pelz was sure this would rejuvenate the local horse stock. He would find a suitable person to send to France to expedite the purchase of the stallion. The Bailiff forwarded the report to the DOA.[12]

In August 1942 the Field Commandant, Knackfuss, wrote to the Bailiff. The letter was referenced "Muster of Horses". Knackfuss ordered every horse, irrespective of its use, to be seen by the German authority between the 5th and 7th August. All owners of horses were notified by their respective Connétable. There appears to have been no written response to Knackfuss, however the Bailiff made a written note on the bottom of his letter which read, "This matter had been discussed with Attorney General. There is no question of requisitioning".[13] The DOA met to discuss the matter. The only reference to the muster of horses was a note: "The German authorities instructed all Island horses were to be submitted to them for examination." A clerk from the DOA, Cyril Vallois, was instructed to work three evenings and to carry out German orders.[1]

In September, Miss Smith, Mont à L'Abbe, St Helier sold her horse to a German officer, George Zimmermann. The States Vet had visited the premises to requisition the horse and had been informed of the sale. Brée took up the matter with Field Command 515 and Pelz.

Milk Control

*"Le Gallais was asked about supplying milk to the German
Commandant without a licence"*

RJA&HS Committee Meeting

The supply of butter had been a problem since early in the occupation. In November 1940, Pelz had held a series of meetings with Carlyle Le Gallais concerning the rationing of milk. The fundamental reason was to ensure the control of the Island's butter supply. Pelz made it clear to the civilian authorities that he wanted enough local butter produced in order that:

1. There was a weekly allowance of 4 ounces of fat per person in the civilian population.
2. An Island reserve of butter was built up.

On the 28ᵗʰ November 1940, Field Command 515 had received 30,000 kilograms of butter, shipped from Granville and delivered to Jersey. On the 10ᵗʰ December 1940, Pelz and Brée jointly agreed on a two-week trial of voluntary butter rationing. All dairies and producer-retailers were instructed as to the exact amount of butter they could sell to their customers.

On the 18ᵗʰ August 1941 OKVR Dr von Stein had written to the Bailiff a letter entitled "Reserve of Butter for the Winter". Dr von Stein ordered that at least two months' supply of butter be put aside as a reserve for the winter. It was to be at least 40 tons "...in order that all possible difficulties may be met." He demanded that the request was complied with as soon as possible. The letter concluded with the charge that "...if sufficient butter cannot be saved from the present production, the sources of supply of fresh milk must be supplemented or cream collection depots at the farms arranged. The cream from these depots must then be sent to the dairy to be turned into butter. I request that you give the matter your immediate attention".[14]

Butter production did not improve sufficiently fast for the Field Command. By 27ᵗʰ August 1941 OKVR Dr von Stein was again writing to the Bailiff. "I have several times pointed out that the control of milk in Jersey is insufficient and insecure. You are aware that in Guernsey all milk is skimmed, and only skimmed milk is supplied to the consumer." Dr von Stein underlined his plan to the Bailiff. "The DOA will give its special attention to the question of the control of milk. In this connection, as is the case in Guernsey, the collection of milk, the skimming of the same and the manufacture of the cream into butter is to be the aim. In Guernsey I have two large milk separators with a capacity of 3,000 litres per hour, which may be purchased by Jersey. I expect, therefore, you will submit your new more extensive plan for the collection of the milk to me. KVR Pelz is ready at any time to discuss the matter".[14]

By September 1941, the issue of "Milk Control and Butter Production" had been taken up by Dr von Stein's replacement, OKVR Dr Casper, who wanted to know why butter production had dropped by 20% in August that year. On the 8ᵗʰ October 1941 Field Command 515, in a letter entitled "Butter production" had written to the Bailiff demanding a full monthly report forthwith on the production and distribution of butter. The first butter production report was sent two days later after the Field Commandant had telephoned demanding an immediate answer to his initial request.

On the 10ᵗʰ February 1942 KVR Dr Reffler, Field Command 515, wrote to the Bailiff requesting information on the collection of milk through the implementation of the amended Milk Control Order. Dr Reffler conveyed the information that in his last conversation with a representative of the "District Chief of the German Military Government in St Germain" he had been given orders that milk consumption in the Channel Islands must be on the same basis as in France. This was "Dar Militärbefehlshaber in Frankreich". The headquarters was the Hotel Majestic, Avenue Kléber 19, Paris. The telephone number was Kléber 6800/09. Jersey and the rest of the Channel Islands were part of the German Military Government in France and in theory had to follow all regulations made for the German-occupied districts of France. Dr Reffler stated to the Bailiff that only skimmed milk was supplied to persons over six years of age in France. Therefore, regulations in Jersey would have to be amended and milk supply fall into line with France. The letter finally pointed out that this form of milk rationing had been in force in Guernsey for a year.[15]

In the same week of February 1942 Dr Reffler had written a second letter to the Bailiff reiterating that the Guernsey Dairy was prepared to sell an "Alfa Laval electrically driven milk separator with a capacity of 3,000 litres." The price was £260. He finished the letter with the advice "I request you avail yourselves of this opportunity so as to have sufficient machines for skimming the milk."

On the 29th June 1942, OKVR Dr Casper took up the matter and wrote further to the Bailiff. His letter was referenced "Skimming the drinking milk to produce butter." Dr Casper made it clear that butter production had to be increased and that importation of butter to Jersey would soon be cut. He therefore ordered, "That as a sequel to my order made hitherto all consumers of milk over 14 years of age shall, as from the 1st August 1942, receive only skimmed milk." Nursing mothers and the sick would receive the present ration of full milk upon the presentation of a doctor's certificate. Casper ended the letter by making it clear that the month of July allowed sufficient time to make all the necessary orders and put in place the technical measures to organise the practical measures required.

The order from the German Military Government in Paris and the forceful manner it was being implemented by Field Command 515, that the Island civilian population was to cease being supplied with full-fat milk, incensed Brée. He refused to accept that the order was a 'fait accompli' and it spurred him into immediate action. On the 7th July Brée laid before the Superior Council the following practical considerations concerning Field Command 515's order.

1. The practicalities of skimming all the Island's milk will make it unfit.
2. The Island's Medical Officer of Health had made it clear 2 ounces of butter and an issue of full-fat milk is more valuable than increased milk rations.
3. There is insufficient machinery in the Island to deal with the separation of the total milk supply.
4. The offer of a separator from Guernsey is of no value since no pasteurised milk can be obtained.
5. If the whole of the milk supply is separated, it would not provide a ration of one-half pint of milk daily during the winter months.

After consideration of Brée's report, the Superior Council sent a detailed response to Field Command 515 and Dr Casper, which reflected Brée's analytical thinking.

1. If the skimming of milk comes into operation, there is a danger the milk will turn sour before distribution. If the skimmed milk is not sour before distribution, it would become so within 12 hours. The reasons are: the warm weather conditions in August and September, the lack of refrigeration space, and the inadequacy and slowness of the milk transport.

2. If the skimming of milk is postponed until Autumn, thereby removing the danger of milk turning sour by warm weather, there are still major problems existing. These are: firstly, the total volume of milk decreases in Autumn and Winter until it reaches its lowest ebb in February. Secondly, owing to the very large number of children under 14 years of age in Jersey, approximately one quarter of the total volume of milk will not be available for skimming, as it is estimated that one quarter of the population (children, nursing mothers and the sick) will be on full milk. From the three quarters of the total volume available for skimming, would be taken away by the removal of the cream, one quarter in volume. Therefore, the amount of skimmed milk left would not be sufficient to give a daily ration, in the Autumn, of more than one half pint per head of population and in the Winter, more than one quarter pint per head. The volume of milk would in terms of food value be unsatisfactory.

3. In the circumstances that exist in Jersey, in particular "The unduly heavy proportion of children in the total population, the skimming of milk is neither practical or desirousness".[16]

On the 31st July 1942, a conference was held between the Commandant Field Command 515 Colonel Knackfuss, the Attorney General Duret Aubin, Brée, and Jurat Le Masurier, Department of Essential Supplies. This conference was held soon after a delegation from the Superior Council had discussed the matter with Dr Casper. The outcome of the conference is interesting and informative. It demonstrates the structural relationships that had developed and matured between the German Military Government and individuals in the Island's civilian authorities. Brée, Coutanche, Duret Aubin and Le Masurier had all combined and for all purposes been successful in halting the demands of the German Military Government in Paris. This had been achieved by the persuasion of Knackfuss, Dr Reffler, Dr Casper and Pelz of the error of the order for the cessation of the supply of full-fat milk to the civilian population of Jersey. On the 1st August Knackfuss informed the Bailiff of his concluding decision.

"In appreciation of the reasons put forward, I am prepared to agree that no alteration in the system for the distribution of milk and fat need to take place before the end of September 1942. During this period, you undertake to examine the means by which the Island of Jersey will be able to be self-supporting with regard to fat and dairy products. The object to be kept in view with regard to the fat ration for the civil population is that this may be retained at its present level without imports from France. In this regard the point must not be lost sight of that a three month's reserve of fat must be continually on hand in cold storage. You will also have the faulty machinery at the dairy replaced and have in stock a reserve for the setting up of milk depots or collection depots".[15]

In July 1942, reports were received by the DOA concerning a shortage of milk sent to the dairies by farmers. Six farmers were written to asking for explanations as to the low yields they were experiencing. Every one of them gave their reasons and all were accepted. In the same week, Dr C. R. Chichester, St Peter, wrote to the DOA alleging that during May 1942 he had sent to the Jersey Dairies Limited 223½ pots of milk, but was only credited with 100 pots. The dairy had also refused to inform him of the daily quantity of milk received from him. The DOA, acting on legal advice, wrote to the dairy and asked for details of milk suppled from Dr Chichester's farm.

At a DOA meeting in July, Le Gallais submitted a letter dated the 25th June 1942 received from KVR Pelz. The letter stated:

"In the supply of milk to the German Field Command, you have so far punctually carried out my verbal instructions regarding delivery of milk to the quarters of the Field Command. [These being Linden Court, White Lodge, Braeside, Newlands, and Langford House] I request that accounts for the milk so far delivered to these houses be drawn up and sent to the Field Command. Hereafter, from the 1st July [1942] onwards the milk is to be paid by the occupants of the above houses.

Signed

Pelz KVR."[1]

The fact that Le Gallais had been providing fresh milk to the Staff Officers of Field Command 515 had already been an issue brought up at an RJA&HS Committee meeting on the 13thJune 1942. At this meeting, Le Gallais was asked about supplying milk to the German Commandant without first obtaining the appropriate Milk Control Licence.[17]

This correspondence from Pelz to Le Gallais unsettled Brée and placed him in a difficult position. Le Gallais was an "adjoint" member of the DOA but had in simple terms broken the Milk Control Order. Above all, he was in charge of establishing the Island Milk Control and, in addition, he was not only the President of the RJA&HS but also a member of several important agricultural committees. Brée, therefore, decided that the DOA in order, "...to regularise the position of the said Mr Le Gallais in relation to the said Order" issued him a producer-retailer licence, under the Milk Control (Jersey) Order, 1940, backdated to the 21st December 1941 and confined to the homes of Staff Officers of Field Command 515. It is perhaps Interesting to note that Carlyle Le Gallais' backdated Milk Control Licence was the only example allowed during the entire German occupation of the Island. It was never repeated by the DOA.

Subsequently, on the 23rd March 1943, Le Gallais was authorised a renewal of his licence for a further twelve months, by virtue of the Milk Control (Jersey) Order, 1940. It specifically states that the Producer-Retailer Licence for Carlyle Le Gallais, Roselands, St Saviour, is on the same terms as the July 1942 licence.[4] Therefore, Carlyle Le Gallais and his Roselands herd, regarded as one of the top dairy herds on the Island, had supplied the Staff Officers of Field Command 515 with fresh mill for the period 21st December 1941 until the 23rd March 1944.

On the 25th June, the DOA interviewed Mr J. Le Gresley, St Brelade. He was a registered milk producer, but it was alleged he had not sold all the milk produced by cows in his custody to the retailer with whom he was registered. Brée warned Le Gresley of the "...serious consequences which would result of any further failures."

The DOA, in view of the butter requirements of Field Command 515 and to facilitate the provision of a stock of butter for the winter of 1942, decided that from the 16th August, the additional quarter pint of milk authorised on the 22nd May 1942 would be withdrawn.

On the 21st August, Mr A. A. Pitcher was interviewed by the DOA. It was alleged in a report that he had not sold all the milk produced by his cows to a licensed retailer. Brée gave him a severe reprimand and a warning of the consequences in failing to carry out the requirements of the Milk Control Order.

In the same week, a report was sent to the DOA containing allegations against Adolphus John Allix, Yarboro Dairy, 68–70 Stopford Road, St Helier, on a charge of milk adulteration. Allix was a registered milk retailer. The DOA revoked his licence and allocated his customers to another retailer. The following week Advocate Valpy met the DOA to discuss the decision to revoke his licence, after which the advocate applied for a retailer's licence to be granted to Adolphus Charles Allix, the father of Adolphus John. The licence was granted.

On the 4th September, Brée instructed the Milk Control Section that the Don Street Dairy might be called upon to handle the whole of the Island's milk production "...as is contemplated by the German authorities of occupation!" Brée forwarded a report to the Superior Council concerning the requirements of the dairy if the change was implemented.

On the 15th September, a clerk in the Milk Control Section, Mr Eric F. Dowdall, was called up for deportation to Germany. Miss Pauline Gulliford was appointed in his place at a salary of £1-5-0 a week. The Milk Control Section lost two further employees as a result of German deportations to Germany, Mr F. Minchington and Mr J. Firmin. Mr Louis Le Dantec was employed in their place.

As from the 20th September 1942, the milk collection times were adjusted to 8.30 a.m. and 5.30 p.m.

In 1942, 483 samples of milk were tested. In 1941 the figure had been 290. The Public Health Department in its summary of milk quality reported that "Despite the general assumption on the part of the lay mind, there has been no falling off in the quality of Jersey milk due to war-time feeding conditions. The quality of the milk is only affected in the most extreme cases of under-nourishment of cows: it is only the quantity which is affected by ordinary changes in food." Milk prosecutions in 1942 due to adulteration were as follows. [18]

Date	Added Water %	Fat Deficiency %	Police Court	Royal Court
January 30	11	29	Adjourned	
May 05	7	26		£40 fine
May 05	7	9		
July 13	8	Nil		Abandoned
July 13	20	Nil		Abandoned
July 13	5	Nil		Abandoned
October 13	23	Nil	£10 fine	
October 28	18	Nil	£3-5-0 fine	
November 23	16	60	£10 fine	
November 30	Nil	66		£20 Fine
December 22	17	Nil		
December 22	27	Nil	£5 fine	

Cattle

Having initially accepted the question of calf selection for slaughter, by the summer of 1942 it had become an issue which led to increasing levels of acrimony between the DOA, dairy farmers, and the Calf Selection Committee of the RJA&HS. In late June, the DOA wrote to the Committee empowering them to allow a calf to be retained "Beyond the statutory period of 14 days if such retention facilitated the work of the committee in selecting calves to be exempt from slaughter."

On the 4th July the Calf Selection Committee re-submitted a scale of points for use as a basis for selection of calves exempted from slaughter. The new system was unanimously adopted and put into operation for all calves born on or after the 1ˢᵗ July. The new Scale of Points was far more detailed and comprehensive than the original of 1941. Its fundamental rationale was to ensure that the best pedigree cattle were retained.

Scale & Counts	Points
On number of cows in herd: 1 or 2 cows	No points
3 and 4 cows	2 points
5 to 8 cows	4 points
9 to 11 cows	6 points
12 to 14 cows	8 points
15 to 20 cows	9 points
Over 20 cows	10 points
a) Dam of calf Highly Commended	4 points
Commended	1 point
b) *Prizes won by Dam*:	
At an Island show as a cow	3 points
At an Island show as a heifer-in-calf	2 points
At an Island show as a yearling	1 point
At a parish show as a cow	2 points
At a parish show as a heifer-in-calf	1 point
Island championships	2 points
Sweepstake or championship parish show	1 point
c) *Production Record of Dam*:	4 points
Medal certificate or 500 lbs fat	2 points
Certificate of Merit standard	2 points
Awards or records of near relative of dam	1 point
Sire of dam 'star' bull or Island winner	1 point
Sire of calf 'star' bull or Island winner	2 points
General reputation of herd (in case of a tie)	1 point
On each previous refusal of exemption	1 point
Deduction from total for each exemption granted	

The calves decided on by the Committee at any meeting to be exempted from slaughter to be those scoring the highest total number of points. In cases of equality, points to be allotted (as above) on the reputation of the herd.
a) If the dam of the calf is an unqualified heifer-in-milk, those points are
   credited on her dam
b) Prizes:
   1ˢᵗ, 2ⁿᵈ, 3ʳᵈ or 4ᵗʰ at an Island show
   1ˢᵗ, 2ⁿᵈ, or 3ʳᵈ at a parish show

This new Points System, although transparent, certainly had a bias towards herds that were, firstly, larger in number and, secondly, contained animals that had been successful in cattle shows. Owners of calves were allowed to make applications for reconsideration. If vacancies arose by the death of an exempted heifer calf, these could be filled at the discretion of the Selection Committee.

On the 8th August, the Calf Selection Committee received a suggestion that the Points System should be amended, especially with regard to points credited for milk production. The Committee refused to change the system based on milk production figures, giving the following reasons. Firstly, any change in the scale of points would cause delays in its decisions owing to the necessary calculations; and secondly, any change would affect only a small number of calves. This decision annoyed a number of already irate dairy farmers who were extremely vociferous in demanding a change in the Points System. After repeated arguments a revised scale was put into operation in August. The new system was as follows.

Scale & Counts	Points
Points for cows in herd:	
1 or 2 cows	No points
3 or 4 cows	1 point
5 to 7 cows	2 points
8 to 10 cows	3 points
11 to 14 cows	4 points
15 to 20 cows	5 points
Over 20 cows	6 points
Calf of Highly Commended dam or bull	1 point
Calf of Commended dam or bull	No points

On the 19th September it was decided that, where in any one week a cattle breeder applied for the exemption of two calves, one of which was granted and the other refused, the breeder was given the option of deciding which calf he wanted to retain.

On the 11th August, the DOA and the Department of Essential Commodities modified the Livestock (Jersey) Order, 1942, and amendments were also made to the following laws:

a) The Livestock (Restriction on Slaughtering) (Jersey) Order, 1940
b) The Livestock (Sales) (Jersey) Order, 1940
c) An Order of the DOA, dated July 8th 1940, prohibiting the slaughter of horses
d) The Pigs (Control) (Jersey) Order, 1941
e) The Newly-Born Calves (Jersey) Order, 1941
f) Article 6A of the Milk Control (Jersey) Order, 1940, as amended (covering transfer of cattle to be notified to the DOA)

The modified Livestock (Jersey) Order, 1942, had the following provisions:

1. No person can transfer custody of cattle or pigs unless and until a licence has been issued by the DOA. Within eight days of the completion of the transfer, a written notice is to be given by the DOA to the person to whom the licence has been granted.
2. There is a complete prohibition of the slaughter of cattle, horses, pigs and sheep except under licence from the DOA.
3. Within 48 hours of calves or pigs being born, notice is to be given to the DOA with particulars relating to the birth.
4. All calves are to be slaughtered within fourteen days of birth except those selected. No compensation is payable for slaughtered calves. If a calf is not slaughtered as required, the DOA will slaughter the animal and dispose of the carcase as it sees fit.
5. Within 24 hours of the death of any cattle, horse, pig or sheep, the owner of the animal is required to give written notice to the DOA.
6. The DOA can make directions requiring any information concerning cattle, horses, pigs and sheep.
7. Any DOA official is authorised to enter premises, where there are grounds for supposing cattle, horses, pigs, or sheep are to be found.
8. The Order comes into force on the 1st September 1942.[19]

Field Command and the Proposed Forced Evacuation of Twenty-three Farms

On the 31st August 1942, Field Command 515 wrote to the Bailiff. The letter, entitled "Evacuation of Farms", was direct and made the Bailiff fully aware that "It is possible that on military grounds a large number of farms in St Peter, St Mary and St Lawrence will have to be evacuated." The next day, one more farm was added to the list, making the total number twenty-three. The possibility of losing this number of working farms to the German military forces was viewed as an impending disaster by the Superior Council and the DOA. Brée without doubt would have contacted Pelz concerning the proposed requisition of farms.

In addition, Knackfuss charged the Bailiff to expedite the following:

1. Each individual occupier is to be given instructions as to where he shall go when the order to evacuate is given. The order to evacuate will be given by the Befehlshaber Jersey [Island Military Commandant].[20] It will be best if neighbouring farms are chosen and exact instructions as where to process worked out for each family.
2. The farmers who are leaving their houses shall take food, the necessary household utensils and their animals with them. In the places to where they are going, accommodation must be reserved.

3. Their farms which it is intended to evacuate must be left in proper condition.

4. The occupiers of the farms are to be informed that the construction of shelter trenches will be commenced in the next few days.

5. I request that by the 10th September 1942, a list with a sketch be submitted showing the new accommodation for the farms listed above.

The Field Commandant KNACKFUSS, Col.[21]

The farms listed for evacuation were as follows:

I	Oak Farm and Cottage	St Peter
II	Penarth House and Farm	St Peter
III	St Anastase House	St Peter
IV	Glenrose Farm	St Peter
V	Maison de Haut	St Peter
VI	Petit Alva Farm and Cottage	St Peter
VII	Les Aix Farm	St Peter
VIII	Victoria Farm	St Peter
IX	Parklands Farm	St Peter
X	Middlewood Farm	St Peter
XI	Cardiff House and Farm	St Peter
XII	Oaklands Farm	St Peter
XIII	White House	St Peter
XIV	Highfield Farm	St Peter
XV	L' Aleval – both sides of road	St Peter
XVI	Perquages Farm	St Peter
XVII	Les Chasses Farm	St Mary
XVIII	St Matthew's Church, Presbytery and Clubhouse	St Mary
XIX	Les Bessières Farm	St Peter
XX	Maison Le Bas Farm	St Lawrence
XXI	High View Farm	St Lawrence
XXII	Le Lourn Farm	St Lawrence
XXIII	Gargate House Mill	St Peter

"The order to farmers in the Coin Varin Vingtaine of St Peter to evacuate their farms was issued on the 2nd September 1942. The effect of such an order can hardly be imagined," observed Sinel.[22]

The order for famers to evacuate their properties was for military purposes for the construction of fortifications. The order, however, had to be approved by the German Military Government and its administration. In effect the German Military Authority in Jersey could not requisition these farms without due authorisation from Field Command 515, who in turn would inform their superiors in Paris. Copies of the requisition were typed and sent to Paris. The entire process was checked by the lawyers at Field Command 515, such as Dr Casper and Dr Kratzner, who ensured that due process was followed under the Hague Convention. It should be noted that, from the start of the occupation, the Field Command 515 lawyers were assiduous in demonstrating to all parties that requisition of land and buildings was carried out with due legal process and under the auspices of the Hague Convention. This perhaps was to demonstrate to the authorities in Britain what could be expected in the event of German conquest. Pelz informs us that Field Command 515 was to be the first administrative unit to be deployed in the event of an invasion of Britain.

The order to evacuate this number of farms was extremely troubling and distressing for Brée. The loss of so many farms was detrimental to the Island's agricultural production. In addition to losing their farms and livelihoods, somewhere had to be found to house farmers and their families. Pelz made it clear to the German military that prime agricultural land should not be lost, unless absolutely necessary, when constructing fortifications. Whenever a military unit requested farmland, it had to complete a pro forma for Pelz, giving reasons for its military importance.

Certificate

Unit asking for the requisition of farming land _____

Is the land suitable for cultivation? _____

Is it worthwhile cultivating this property? _____

Is it wasteland or virgin land? _____

Was the land cultivated by the farmer? _____

Does the farmer need this land for his business? _____

Is the farmer willing to rent this field to the troops? _____

Can the requisition be granted? _____

Signature Squadron Leader – Ambacher Captain _____

The twenty-three farmers and their families never left their farms or their land. Within several months a small set of military bunkers including the "Headquarter Kernswerk" were constructed. This was the Festung Headquarters, ready for use in the case of an Allied attack on the Island.

The reasons why Knackfuss' order to the Bailiff was never implemented remains a mystery. There appears to be no documentation as to why the twenty-three farms were never evacuated. The decision to construct such a large area of fortifications would certainly have had to be authorised by the German Military Government in 1942. There are two possible explanations. Firstly, Pelz may have objected to the construction of such a large group of bunkers and fortifications over an area of prime agricultural land. Secondly, construction over an area which covered several hectares would have easily been spotted and offered a major strategic target for the Allies. Therefore, the decision was possibly reversed by von Schmettow, the Island Military Commandant.

Agricultural Matters of Common Interest Between Jersey and Guernsey 6–11 July 1942

Between the 6th and 11th July, a deputation of Dr A. N. Symons, Mr Michael Wynne Sayer and Mr Louis A. Guillemette visited Jersey to discuss agricultural and various other shortages between the two Islands.[23] Mr Guillemette was Secretary to the President of the Guernsey Controlling Committee and Assistant Secretary to the Bailiff of Guernsey. He kept a record of these events in a diary, which he kept secret.[24] Dr Symons was a medical practitioner and an important figure in the Guernsey hospital. Mr Sayer was an agricultural expert who had moved to Guernsey just before the German occupation. He was deported to Germany in late 1942, unlike Robert Wilson Carson, an eminent expert on Jersey pedigree cattle, who was regarded by Pelz as too important to be deported and who remained in Jersey.

The three Guernsey delegates met with the Bailiff of Jersey, Alexander Coutanche, the Field Commandant Colonel Knackfuss, Dr Casper, Pelz, H. F. Ereaut, and Jurats Dorey, Le Masurier and Brée.[25]

A wide range of issues were discussed. These included a shortage of coal and fuel supplies in Guernsey, a shortage of insulin in Jersey whilst Guernsey had an apparent surplus, and the offer of cereals and seed potatoes by Jersey. Other topics included radios, currency and the effect of Reichsmarks on the economy, and possible interventions by the Red Cross.[26]

During a conversation between the delegates of Field Command 515 and Guernsey, Coutanche suggested the possibility of requesting medicines from the Red Cross. This brought about an immediate reprimand from OKVR Dr Casper who insisted that medicines would be forthcoming from Germany and supplied by Field Command 515. The problem of the continued shortage of potatoes in Guernsey was also discussed at length and various ways to solve the question of the severe shortage of potatoes.[27]

In one confidential meeting without any German staff present, the Bailiff informed the delegates that, in several months, there would be a British landing near Cherbourg. This was to form a bridgehead against German forces. He, therefore, expected the Channel Islands to be cut off from France for many months. This being the case, both Jersey and Guernsey would have to assist each other with supplies. The Bailiff also discussed the progress of the war and impending practical problems when de-militarisation occurred.[26]

On the 14th July, Guillemette informed the Controlling Committee of the States of Guernsey of "The cordiality of the reception extended to the members of the deputation while in Jersey and the opinion held on both sides that better relations between the Islands were likely to accrue from more frequent personal contacts between representatives of both communities".[23]

During this visit, KVR Hans Egon Pelz met with the Guernsey delegates and two photographs were taken on his personal camera, one by Elsa Brunner, his housemaid, and the other by Pelz himself. The first was outside "Little Court", Mont Cambrai, St Lawrence, and the second was at the States Experimental Station, Trinity.

The photograph outside Little Court shows the following individuals. From the left, Michael Wynne Sayer, Louis Guillemette (1910–1977), and Jurat Touzel John Brée (1881–1951). Next to Brée (and identified by the late Dr Frank Le Maistre) was Ernest George Ing, Dip.Hort.Sci. (1906–1984) an expert on plant diseases. The final individual is Pelz himself (1902–1986).

Ernest Ing was appointed to the States Experimental Station in December 1933. Frank Le Maistre was already employed there as an assistant. He, therefore, worked closely with Ing for over six years and was able to positively identify him.

The identification of Ing by Dr Le Maistre poses a dilemma. The fundamental problem is that there are no extant documents demonstrating that Ing was on the Island during the German occupation. The last written reference recording that Ing was in Jersey is dated the 7th June 1940. The reference cites a joint report, published by Dr Small and Ing of the States Experimental Station, on the eelworm outbreak.[28] No references have been found confirming Ing's residency and he appears not to have had any identification card, nor are there any official Jersey or German references extant.

The next reference to Ing is to be found in a document entitled "Colorado Beetle Staff" which was dated several days after the liberation of Jersey. It states that the DOA, in view of another infestation of Colorado Beetle, recommended to the States of Jersey the following: "Dr Thomas Small, the States' Mycologist, and Mr Ernest G. Ing who both…left their post at the evacuation [this last quote is a later addition to the document] in June, 1940, to be recalled in order that their expert services may be available for dealing with any serious infestations of the Colorado Beetle which may be found on the Island." A sum of £650 was made available to provide the salaries of Small and Ing.[29]

The Jersey authorities wrote to both Small and Ing asking them to return to Jersey. Only the correspondence relating to Small is extant with no correspondence pertaining to Ing available. Brée went directly to the Bailiff and asked for the re-instatement of Small who was working at Manchester University as a researcher for the Ministry of Agriculture and Fisheries.

On the 12th June 1945, the Bailiff requested the SCAO (Senior Civil Affairs Officer) to arrange Small's return to Jersey.[30] On the same day, the DOA met to discuss the Colorado Beetle outbreak. A letter was read from Ing that he "Regretfully declined the offer of the re-instatement on the staff of the States Experimental Station."

The last individual on the Little Court photograph is Pelz. It is unique for several reasons. Firstly, it is probably the only photograph of a high-ranking Staff Officer from Field Command 515 who is not dressed in military uniform whilst on duty. Standing orders from Field Command stated that Staff Officers when outside with civilians had to be dressed in uniform. In effect Pelz was not allowed to wear civilian clothes. Secondly, it allows us an important and rare glimpse of Brée himself. Brée appears to have been extremely camera-shy and very few photographs of him during the German occupation have been discovered. Thirdly, there is not a single document pertaining to this meeting (as yet discovered) in either Jersey or Guernsey.

The second of Pelz's photographs shows the group at the States Experimental Station, Howard Davis Farm, Trinity. On the far left is Sayer, followed by Ing, Guillemette, Brée and Pierre Gréard. This photograph was snapped by Pelz himself. Pierre Gréard was appointed Foreman of the States Experimental Station in 1911. He had been in charge of the farm as Foreman, along with his wife and three staff. He retired in December 1933.[31]

The fact that Pierre Gréard is photographed alongside Brée in July 1942 can be explained by the resignation of Foreman Mourant in June and the appointment in August of the next full-time foreman, Le Liard. Therefore, Gréard was a temporary replacement.

References

1. Jersey Archive. C/B/A1/7.
2. Private correspondence.
3. Jersey Archive. L/F/54/C/D/8.
4. Jersey Archive. C/B/A1/8.
5. Jersey Archive. C/B/A1/9.
6. The privileged issue of oats was sold at a low cost to farmers who kept horses that were used in agricultural work. The horses had to be used in the fulfilment of DOA cultivation directions.
7. Also known as the Jersey Corn Traders' Association. The JCTA and JCMA appear to be the same body.
8. RJA&HS. JFU and RJA&HS Joint Committee Minutes.
9. Jersey Archive. B/A/W3/2/43.
10. Jersey Archive. L/F/54/C/D/2.
11. Jersey Archive. C/B/A1/6.
12. Jersey Archive. B/A/W31/2/51.
13. Jersey Archive. B/A/W31/2/57.

14. Jersey Archive. B/A/W31/8-9.
15. Jersey Archive. B/A/W31/2/34.
16. Jersey Archive. D/Z/H5/141/2.
17. Jersey Archive. L/D/09/A10.
18. Jersey Archive. C/A5/21.
19. Jersey Archive. B/A/W31/2/59.
20. Head of the German military forces, General von Schmettow.
21. Private correspondence.
22. Sinel, L., The German Occupation of Jersey. The complete diary of events from June 1940 to June 1945. 1984 edition. p. 99.
23. Guernsey Archive. A5/076-09.
24. Guernsey Press, 4th May 2005 "The Secret Diaries".
25. Guernsey Archive. BA/EC/64-6.
26. My thanks to Ms Josie Day, daughter of Louis Guillemette for allowing me to reference his diary.
27. Jersey Archive. B/A/W45/37.
28. Jersey Archive. C/B/A1/4.
29. Jersey Archive. C/B/A1/11.
30. Jersey Archive. B/A/L35/6.
31. The States Experimental Station, Howard Davis Farm, Trinity, 1936 report, p. 11.

Chapter 10

October – November – December 1942

Pigs

"I have recently ascertained that farmers have been selling four-week-old pigs at a price exceeding RM80. I am resolved that in the event of a repetition of such cases to prosecute."

Field Commandant to the Bailiff

In September 1942 the Field Command instructed the Department of Labour to go around the Island and collect acorns for feeding to pigs and in early October, Pelz sent out a notification for all residents whose land had oak trees to also collect acorns.

On the 2nd October a report concerning the death of a pig registered to Mr A. J. R. Nicolle, St Martin was received. The report contained a letter from Advocate P. N. Richardson with information about the pig. Nicolle was at this time in the public prison serving a sentence for the theft of a cow. It was decided that no action could be taken until he was released in several months' time.[1]

On the 23rd October the Field Commandant wrote to the Bailiff. The letter was entitled "Fixing the price of pigs for fattening". The letter demanded that the DOA should fix the maximum price of suckling pigs. Colonel Knackfuss was unhappy with the current situation. He wrote, "I have recently ascertained that farmers have been selling four-week-old pigs at prices exceeding RM80. I am resolved that in the event of a repetition in such cases to prosecute".[2]

The matter was deemed sufficiently serious for Brée to chair a meeting of the joint JFU and RJA&HS Committee on the 29th October, attended by C. Le Gallais, F. Le Boutillier, P. Le Feuvre and T. G. Le Marinel. Brée began the meeting by stating that the German authorities had demanded a pricing fix on suckling pigs. The German Field Command had asserted that as much as £8 had been charged for four-week-old pigs.

After discussion, Brée was advised to fix the price of suckling pigs at £3 a head. He was also strongly advised that an increase in the price of pork of 3 pence should be implemented so that a farmer received 1/7 per lb. Brée promised that he would look into the price of suckling pigs.[3]

The next day the DOA brought in the Suckling-Pig (Maximum Price) Jersey Order, 1942. The Order fixed the maximum price for the sale of suckling pigs at £3 each. On the same day that the Order was passed, the DOA recommended to the Department of Essential Commodities that the Fat Stock (Provisional Prices) (No 7) (Jersey) Order, 1941, should be amended with an increase in the price of pork paid to farmers for pigs and sows (excluding boars) to 1/7 per lb.

The following week, Brée informed the DOA that the price of pork paid to farmers had been increased. He stated the decisions that had been made. Firstly, to cut off the pig's head and hand it over to the farmer; secondly, that 10% of the carcass minus the head be given to the farmer; and finally, that 1/7 per lb would be paid for the remaining nine-tenths of the pig without the head.

On the 30th October, Mr A. Le Gros, St Peter, was alleged to have been discovered in the possession of an unregistered pig. His explanation was accepted but he was warned to follow all DOA requirements in future. The following week a declaration was received from Mr E. Le Brun, Junior, St Lawrence. He stated that he had sold three pigs to Mr R. P. Le Cornu, St Mary. The latter, when requested by Inspector Mr J. W. Blampied, allegedly declined to make any suitable declaration that he had acquired these three pigs. The DOA sent two subsequent letters to Mr Le Cornu asking for a response to these declarations and decided that, in view of his failure to comply with the provisions of the Pigs (Control) (Jersey) Order, 1941, to refer the matter to the Attorney General for the institution of proceedings against him.[1]

Watermills and Milling

The deportations to Germany of British-born Channel Island residents, ordered by Hitler, also involved milling staff. The First Assistant Miller at Malassis Mill, Mr H. E. Bennett, would have reported to KVR Pelz at College House. Pelz obviously did not have the necessary reasons to allow Mr Bennett to remain on the Island as an essential worker in the agricultural economy and he was deported. His position was taken by promoting Mr R. Le Marchand with a salary increase from £12-12-6 to £3 a week. His appointment began on the 5th October 1942.

On the 2nd October Brée recalled the Act of November 1941 and now paid overtime rates at all DOA-owned mills. All overtime work except on Sundays, in excess of 44 hours a week, was paid at time and a quarter, irrespective of the grade of the mill employee. On the same day Mr W. Poingdestre was appointed to the milling staff at Grand Val as an assistant to the Head Carpenter. His salary was £2-10-0 a week, plus an additional sum of 6/6 per week for the use of his tools.

On the 6th October a report showed that the upkeep of the mills and streams amounted to £3,500. In the same week Colin Marie's salary was increased, from £300 to £350 a year.

On the 16th October, Brée decided to appoint Ernest Charles Gilley as one of the millers at Gargate, at a salary of £2-10-0 a week. However, the following week, since Mr Gilley had been incapacitated owing either to illness or to an accident, it was decided to suspend his appointment. On the 12th January 1943 Mr Gilley, having recovered, resumed his duties as a miller at Gargate.

In October 1942, the first report was produced concerning the percentage of loss of grain from all DOA-controlled mills. Brée was asked to investigate the high percentage of loss at Quetivel Mill. He determined that "...this appears to be due to the action of men engaged upon the repair of the mill in question. The current shortages are reasonable". The report also examined milling carried out by John Terry Limited on behalf of the DOA. It showed a loss of grain of 2.9% which was viewed as acceptable.

In November men who had been in the employment of the DOA at the mills for twelve months had their wages increased by 2/6 a week. The increase now meant that mill employees went from being paid £2-12-6 to £2-15-0 a week. The men who received the increase were: C. R. Le Sueur, W. Jotham, W. H. Lucas and Eric Gilley. It was decided not to increase the salary of the 'boy', E. J. Horton, "...in view of the fact that he is adequately paid at the moment". On the 1st December all millers were notified that grain had to be "...passed through the screen before being milled".

Milk Control

> *"The keeping of cows by persons without farms...is to cease...the purpose is to control the holding of cattle by persons who are not farmers and previously kept no cattle and who now keep a cow for the purpose of receiving a greater quantity of milk".*

KVR von Aufsess, Field Command 515

On the 9th October, Mr G. W. Le Masurier of 63½ Val Plaisant, St Helier, the holder of a milk retailers' licence, was instructed to appear before the DOA with legal representation. The following week he appeared for an interview accompanied by his solicitor, Mr S. G. Crill. The Sanitary Inspectors had alleged that he refused to obey instructions from Milk Control concerning the "...holdings of certain milk cans".[1] After discussions, the DOA decided to take a lenient view of Mr Le Masurier's infringements of the Milk Control (Jersey) Order, 1940. He admitted fault and promised to comply with instructions from future DOA officers.

A report of the 9th October detailed the situation in respect of persons who had been deported to Germany. It was decided to publish a notice confirming it was an offence against the Milk (Registration with Retailers) (Jersey) Order, 1940, to accept milk delivered in virtue of registration documents issued to persons who had been deported from Jersey. It, furthermore, was decided that the names of all persons who had been deported must be removed by the producers from their lists of persons entitled to free supplies of milk, and that no milk was to be retained in respect of such persons. The cessation of milk supplies to persons who had been deported was by and large a success; however, in early December the DOA engaged the services of a man on a short contractual basis. He was to call at the dwellings of forty-two of the persons who had been deported in order to ascertain which retailers were supplying the persons deported with milk prior to their departure.

On the 20ᵗʰ October a report was received concerning Mr A. Baal, St Saviour. It covered the supply of milk in relation to persons who should not have been in receipt of such supplies and who were not part of his household nor his servants. The DOA implemented an investigation which allegedly identified seven individuals who were not entitled to draw supplies from Mr Baal. They were ordered to immediately register with a licensed retailer for their supplies of milk. The seven allegedly drawing the milk were: George Davey, Elvina Davey, Mark Davey, Kenneth Davey, Mrs Mary Jane Baal, Miss Anna Baal and Mrs M. Bisson.[1] A further report compiled on the 13ᵗʰ November investigated if any of the above individuals had been employed by Mr Baal in tending his cattle. The main problem now was that, despite Colin Marie communicating the previous decision of the DOA, Mr Baal had declined to conform to its decisions. The following week the matter was referred to the Attorney General with a request that proceedings be taken against Mr Baal in respect of his refusal to discontinue such supplies.

At the same time as the above alleged misdemeanours were being investigated, a licensed retailer was being dealt with for supplying milk to unauthorised individuals. The Allo brothers were allegedly seen supplying milk to Mrs Ellen Truscott and her family at Langley Park, St Saviour. The Milk Control Section investigated and found no registration documents licencing the Allo brothers to supply milk to the family. The brothers were written to and warned that any repetition of this offence would lead to legal proceedings.

On the 20ᵗʰ October a Milk Tester, Mr Maxwell Brée, was put on two-thirds salary due to an impending operation. Two weeks later he was put on half-pay for a further two weeks. On the 26ᵗʰ October the caretaker at Don Street Dairy was allowed his living accommodation at the premises free of charge and his rental payments were stopped. In return he was made responsible for cleaning the DOA offices at Don Street Dairy.

In view of the apparent increase in farmers not conforming to Milk Control orders, the Foreman Milk Tester, J. G. Malzard, was ordered to increase his supervision of the surveillance of milk producers and the amount of milk sent to the various dairies. In consequence, Mr Malzard, during the course of his increased surveillance, noticed milk shortages from the herd of Dr Charles

Chichester. Malzard's subsequent report alleged "...certain shortages which have been discovered in the quantities delivered by Dr Chichester to the licensed retailer on whose register his name appears."[1] Marie wrote to Dr Chichester with a warning. He, however, seemed somewhat oblivious to these communications. The DOA, after repeated attempts to converse with Dr Chichester, decided that "In view of Dr Chichester's deliberate unwillingness or inability to provide any satisfactory explanations of the shortages in question, the DOA charged its Secretary, subject to the advice of the Attorney General, to write to Dr Chichester warning him that should the shortages in question continue, the DOA will find itself compelled to take the necessary steps to requisition the cattle in the custody of Dr Chichester".

On the 1st November, the evening collection of milk from farms was discontinued. In the same week, L. J. Tanguy Limited took over the milk retailer licence of Mrs L. Klein, 31 Queen Street, St Helier.

The question of islanders who had never been farmers keeping cows became very much an issue. On the 3rd November, Field Command 515 sent a letter to the Bailiff titled "Keeping of cows by persons without farms". With the letter KVR von Aufsess sent the Bailiff a copy of an Order by the Guernsey administration forbidding the keeping of cattle by persons who were not farmers and who previously had kept no cattle. The reason for this was clear: it was to stop anyone receiving a greater quantity of milk than they were entitled to. The Field Command wanted the same Order issued in Jersey.[4]

The Bailiff replied on the 10th November. He explained that the Guernsey Order was of no value in Jersey. The reasons he gave were: firstly, that the transfer of cows was already controlled by the Livestock (Jersey) Order, 1942, and secondly that milk was controlled by the Milk Control (Jersey) Order, 1940, as amended.

In 1942 an average Jersey cow provided approximately 40 litres of milk a week.[5] Therefore, the DOA was fully aware that the keeping of a cow by a private individual who was unregistered was a serious threat to the milk control regime and could not be allowed to continue unregulated. Six days after von Aufsess' letter, the Milk Control Section informed Brée that the quantity of milk being retained by producers was increasing. Brée decided to collate all the milk production data before holding a full discussion on the issue.

On the 20th November Mr W. V. Farnham, Val Plaisant, St Helier purchased a cow. He wrote to the DOA asking that he be allowed to retain the milk from this cow for himself and his family. The cow was to be kept at Bagot Manor, St Saviour, where it would be grazed alongside another farmer's herd. The DOA decided that the cow was not in the custody of Mr Farnham and refused him permission to retain any of the milk.

On the 27th November the Connétable of St Helier complained to the DOA about queues of people waiting to draw supplies of skim milk at the premises of licensed retailers and suggested that skim milk should be distributed between certain specified hours. The DOA informed him that his suggestion would not stop the practice of queues forming. The quantity of skim milk available was insufficient to provide a supply to all applicants and, consequently, people needing skim milk would continue to form a queue before the specified hours at which the distribution began.

In December, in view of the quantities of milk being retained by producers, Mr R. Godel was engaged on a temporary basis by the Milk Control Section and Mr N. A. Syvret was hired as a temporary Milk Tester whilst Mr C. Godeaux was indisposed due to illness.

At the same time the Jersey Mental Hospital applied to the Milk Control Section for authority to retain the milk produced by its own cows. The decision was made that this milk was to be retained only for the "inmates" of the hospital, together with members of the institution staff who lived on the premises. In addition, the households of the Medical Superintendent and the employees of the institution who carried out work on the farm attached to the institution were allowed to retain milk. Other members of staff who lived in houses at the estate of the institution or elsewhere were not eligible to draw milk from the produce of these cows.

A further application was received from Mr C. P. Billot Junior, St Martin, asking for authority to retain milk from the produce of his cows in order to supply his father and mother. Since his parents did not form part of his household as a milk producer, nor were they his servants, the request was refused.

In the same week, Mr P. H. Baudains and Mr P. Ahier, neither of whom were custodians of cattle, nor formed part of the households or were servants of custodians, wished to be allowed to draw supplies of milk directly from a milk producer. Their requests were refused.

On the 15th December, Snowden Blampied, St Lawrence, was summoned by the DOA to answer an allegation that, being a milk producer, he had not delivered the whole of his milk produced by his cows. The allegation was thought so serious that after discussions were held he was warned, "...that unless there was a decided improvement both in the quantities of milk sold to the DOA and the cultivation of his farm, the DOA will find itself compelled to consider depriving him of his farm".[1] The Honorary Parish Inspector was instructed to keep Blampied's farm under observation and to report back. On the same day, a licensed retailer, Mr J. J. Le Marquand, Plaisance Dairy, St Ouen, appeared before the DOA in respect of a complaint by the Milk Control Section that he was allegedly "...not exercising sufficient control over the distribution of milk in his area". He was given a final warning. Any repetition would lead to his licence being revoked.

On the 18th December the Dairymen's Committee decided it would only issue skim milk to the public on Mondays and Wednesdays.

On the 22nd December it was decided that the quantity of skim milk available to farmers with calves was insufficient to permit every farmer to receive a distribution. Preferences to allocate skim milk henceforth was given to farmers who had in their custody calves aged two to six months which were exempted from the provisions of Article 5(i) of the Livestock (Jersey) Order, 1942. They were allowed to purchase skim milk at the rate of 1 pot a day per head for these calves.

The reasons for the reduction in skim milk supplies had been a topic for discussion during the previous month. A meeting was held between the RJA&HS, JFU and DOA on the 14th November, chaired by Brée. Present were the Presidents and Vice Presidents of the RJA&HS and the JFU, John du Val and Colin Marie of the DOA, and leading dairy farmers. Brée opened the meeting stating that the Island's milk supply was causing immense anxiety. The reason was simple: the milk supply was not sufficient to provide milk for the population and the situation was exacerbated by the need to maintain a butter supply as in future no butter would be imported from France. Brée considered the only method of increasing milk supplies to the people was to reduce the allowance to calves.[6]

Cattle

On the 16th October the DOA interviewed Mr C. C. R. Le Brun, Rozel. He had allegedly failed to register a bull calf and delayed its slaughter beyond fourteen days. Le Brun was "…administered a reprimand" and warned that any future breaches would lead to proceedings of a legal nature. A week later the DOA interviewed Mr Charles H. Jarnet, St Martin, who allegedly was in breach of the Newly-Born Calves (Jersey) Order, 1941. He failed to declare the birth of a bull and a heifer. After listening to Mr Jarnet's explanations, Brée's patience had reached its limit. He referred the matter to the Attorney General.

On the 17th November the DOA, after a protracted period where milk production was continually decreasing due to farmers "steadily increasing" the amount of milk they retained for their calves, the DOA changed the quantity of milk which producers could retain for their families. The DOA enacted an order that, from 1st December 1942, milk producers were allowed to retain one pint of milk for themselves and for each of the members of their respective household who lived with them under the same roof. Furthermore, servants of producers who had three or more cows in their personal custody, the servants being employed wholly in tending the cattle, were authorised to acquire for themselves and for each member of their families who lived with them under the same roof, 1 pint of milk daily. This milk being acquired from the produce of the cows in the custody of the producers.

The order also enacted that milk producers were allowed to retain 2 pots of milk daily for each calf exempted from the provisions of Article 5(i) of the Livestock (Jersey) Order, 1942, for a period not exceeding one month from the birth of the calf and 1 pot per day thereafter until the calf attained the age of six months. In addition, calves which had not been exempted could be fed 2 pots daily for up to fourteen days.

On the 21st November the DOA informed the RJA&HS that the Livestock (Jersey) Order, 1942 would be modified. These changes were made so that in December 1942 and January and February 1943, the number of calves exempted would be no more than sixty in one month and in December no bull calves would be exempted. In January and February, the number of bull calves exempted would be three per month. Brée met the Calf Selection Committee to discuss the exemption of bull calves. He made it clear that the Committee did not have to necessarily exempt any bull calves for these months and in addition, he emphasised that he fully endorsed the discretion of the Selection Committee as to the exemption of bull calves.

Early in December Mr F. Moisan, St Brelade was alleged to have transferred a cow and heifer to E. C. Perrédès, St Saviour, without first obtaining a licence. After hearing Moisan's explanations the DOA decided to defer the matter until it had interviewed Perrédès. Both men were warned to observe all provisions concerning livestock orders in future.

On the 19th December, sixteen of the Island's leading cattle breeders met "informally" to discuss the current situation regarding the stability of the Island's pedigree herds. It was reaffirmed that, under the existing wartime conditions, the officers of the RJA&HS would continue to act as an Emergency Committee in order to conduct affairs with the DOA. Perrédès began by discussing the system by which calves were selected for exemption from slaughter. He was highly critical and proposed a new sub-committee to examine the matter and to make improvements. In consequence a new sub-committee was formed: John Perrée, P. G. Cabot, P. C. Mourant, B. G. Perrée, P. O. Brée and E. C. Perrédès.

A discussion was held on the "...decidedly unsatisfactory" system whereby cattle sent to the abattoir were weighed and slaughtered on the day after their arrival. Furthermore, it was agreed that there was a necessity for an increase in livestock prices, owing to increased costs in labour and feedstuffs due to the German occupation.

Three recommendations were made.

1. The DOA to review the scale or prices paid for livestock. The price for cows and bulls over eighteen months old to be 8 pence per pound weight; maiden heifers and bulls under eighteen months, 10 pence per pound weight and calves 1/- per pound weight.
2. All cattle for slaughter to be weighed not more than six hours after arrival.
3. Farmers to be given the opportunity to be present when their cattle were weighed.

Potatoes

"An order was made to requisition from Mr Blampied the whole of his potatoes with the exception of six hundredweight which he retained for the feeding of his household consisting of seven persons

and 100 boxes of royal seed for the planting of one vergée which he is permitted to grow. The DOA, furthermore, decided to make a recommendation to the Superior Council that four vergées of land in the occupation of Mr Blampied should be requisitioned".

DOA report

On the 14th October 1942 the DOA interviewed Mr Alfred Bechelet, St Peter, on the shortage of potatoes that he had allegedly delivered. He had been directed to supply 8¾ tons, but he delivered less than 2 tons. Mr Bechelet claimed he had no more potatoes available. The DOA "carefully investigated the circumstances" and decided there was no evidence that the farm had not been satisfactorily cultivated by Bechelet.[1] He was ordered to deliver 292 boxes of seed potatoes which he had retained for his own use and, in addition, he was ordered to deliver ¾ of a ton of potatoes which he had retained for his household. Brée decided that this was insufficient retribution. He ordered the Honorary Parish Inspectors to inform Bechelet that in 1943 he would only be allowed to grow 1 vergée of potatoes. The remainder of his fields would be compulsorily set aside for the cultivation of oats, rye and root crops for his cattle.

Two weeks later, Mr R. S. Langlois, St Helier, was summoned to appear before the DOA concerning an allegation of a shortage of potatoes that should have been delivered. The DOA ordered him to deliver 4 tons by the 4th November. He was also informed that, in the event of a failure to deliver these potatoes and without further notice, a requisition order would be implemented. In addition, the Parish Honorary Inspectors were notified that in 1943 Mr Langlois' potato allocation must not exceed 2 vergées. Langlois subsequently delivered the full weight of potatoes stated on his Cultivation Order. No more penalties were implemented.

Further cases of alleged non-delivery of potatoes as designated by the DOA Cultivation Orders were dealt with. On the 3rd November Mr P. de la Haye, St Helier, had to offer an explanation as to his failure to deliver any potatoes as required by the directions of the Cultivation of Lands (Jersey) Order, 1940. These Cultivation Orders were given directly by the DOA to individual farmers. They were detailed and specified: the crops to be grown, the area for each crop, the inputs to be used and where to obtain them, and finally the number of outputs and dates to deliver to DOA stores. Pelz himself was well aware of Cultivation Orders and apparently was involved in their distribution.

In view of Mr de la Haye's failure to offer a satisfactory explanation, the DOA ordered him within seven days to deliver "The whole of the potatoes which he had reserved for seed with the exception of 95 boxes of seed potatoes". The Chief Inspector was instructed to make a full examination of the farm. The subsequent report recommended that de la Haye be allowed to grow 1 vergée of potatoes in 1943. The rest of his fields were to be devoted to the cultivation of oats, rye, mangolds and grazing.

The following week, the DOA wrote to Mr F. Bechelet Junior, St Ouen. He had been ordered to deliver 14 tons of potatoes however had delivered none, the explanation being that his farm was "...unsuitable for the cultivation of potatoes under present circumstances". Bechelet was ordered to appear before the DOA and the following week he arrived with his advocate, H. W. Giffard. The advocate gave an explanation as to why the 14 tons of potatoes had not been delivered.

The DOA, not convinced of the veracity of Advocate Giffard's reasons "...expressed its profound dissatisfaction with the manner in which the cultivation of the farm had been carried out in the past". An immediate order was made for Bechelet to cultivate, in 1943, 1 vergée of potatoes, 1½ vergées of mangolds and 10 vergées for the production of hay and grazing. Bechelet, furthermore, was told "...forthwith to deliver to the DOA the whole of the seed potatoes in his possession with the exception of 100 boxes".[1]

A report of the 18th November highlighted the alleged failure of two farmers, Mr Walter Benest and Mr Hugh Alexander Flinn, both of St Brelade, to supply potatoes to the DOA. They were given three days to offer an adequate explanation as to why they had failed to comply with DOA directions. Walter Benest responded within the week. The DOA was not satisfied with his explanation and summoned him to appear before the Committee. After hearing the explanations put forward by Benest the DOA deferred its decision until it had ascertained the quantity of potatoes which he had retained for consumption by his household of seven persons.

A subsequent inspection of Benest's fields revealed that he had not planted the correct quantity of potatoes. It was also discovered that Benest had retained for consumption by his household approximately one ton of potatoes. The DOA decided that Benest must deliver half a ton of the potatoes he had retained.

On the 24th November a complaint was made by the Grain and Potato Section against Mr J. Le Neveu, St Brelade, in connection with a delivery by him of 8¾ tons of potatoes which it considered to be of an allegedly "unsatisfactory quality". Mr Le Neveu appeared before the DOA on the 1st December. In view of his explanations the Honorary Parish Inspectors were instructed to produce a report as to the suitability of his farm for growing potatoes. The subsequent report was sent to the DOA on the 8th December. In view of this report the DOA wrote to Mr Le Neveu informing him that the DOA was not satisfied with the results of his 1942 cultivation. He was given a warning that, in the event of further causes of complaint, the DOA would take serious measures.

On the 27th November four more farmers were investigated by the Honorary Parish Inspectors as a result of their alleged failure to comply with directions to deliver specified quantities of potatoes to the DOA. They were A. S. Raworth, St John, A. J. Henry, St Brelade, L. M. Green and H. F. Allain of St Martin.

On the same day Brée informed the DOA that Field Command had offered French seed potatoes for planting in the Island. Brée entered negotiations for the purchase of 500 tons of these potatoes. The following March, 1943, Brée informed his Committee that a quantity of seed potatoes of the "Royal Kidney" variety had been received from France and further supplies were forthcoming. Pelz was instrumental in the sourcing of these French seed potatoes. When the potatoes arrived, they were issued to farmers who already had Cultivation Orders and the Honorary Parish Inspectors were told to provide a list of farmers to whom they would recommend these seed potatoes should be issued, for growing as a first or second crop, and also to indicate the area which each farmer should be allowed to cultivate. It was decided that the seed potatoes would be issued to farmers at a rate of 15 cwt per vergée with the price set at £1 per 50 kilogramme bag.

Within a week, the DOA decided that in view "...of certain information furnished by the President" the area devoted to these French potatoes would increase. However, several farmers allocated by the Honorary Parish Inspectors to grow the French seed were financially not in a position to pay for them. They had been directed to grow these potatoes in 1943 under the Cultivation of Lands (Jersey) Order, 1942. Brée decided that these farmers should sign a bond to allow the DOA to deduct the value of the potatoes supplied from the value of the crop subsequently sold by the farmer to the DOA. This arrangement was submitted to and approved by the Superior Council.

On the 27th November the DOA wrote to the Connétables asking whether they wished to buy potatoes for distribution to the poor at Christmas, and to inform the DOA of the numbers of poor to whom such a distribution would be made.

A report sent to the DOA from the Honorary Parish Inspectors for St Peter on Mr C. E. Le Cornu, stated that he had allegedly failed to comply with directions to deliver 23 tons. In addition, the Inspectors were "not satisfied" with the potatoes previously delivered by him, amounting to 15½ tons. Le Cornu was summoned to appear before the DOA; he ignored the summons but eventually offered an explanation. The DOA ordered him to deliver within seven days a half ton of mids and a further half ton from the quantity (estimated at 25 cwt) that he had retained for the consumption of 6 persons. On the 22nd December Le Cornu delivered 15 cwt of potatoes. Brée decided to accept this as fulfilling the requirements of the DOA.

On the 1st December the DOA was informed by the States Treasury that Field Command 515 had paid RM80 10Pfg for a consignment of potatoes, however there was no supporting documentation concerning the sale from the Grain and Potato Section. After investigation, it was discovered this was a payment in respect of freight charges for the export of potatoes on behalf of the German authority. Subsequently the sum was credited to the "Freight Account". It was also ascertained that the sum formed part of a payment due by Field Command 515 to W. Dennis and Sons Limited in respect of a private sale of potatoes made to Field Command by the firm. The DOA subsequently authorised the Treasurer of the States to pay this sum to W. Dennis and Sons Limited.

On the 4th December the DOA interviewed Mr A. F. Henry, St Brelade, who was alleged to have failed to deliver 7 tons of potatoes. Mr Henry claimed that his failure was "...due to the considerable thefts of produce which had been perpetrated by the German forces of occupation or the foreign workmen employed by such forces". The matter was discussed with the Honorary Parish Inspectors. This discussion led to a letter being sent to Mr Henry warning him "...that the DOA is very dissatisfied with the results of his cultivations in 1942 and that it will find itself compelled to take drastic measures". The Honorary Parish Inspectors were ordered to observe all his cultivation and send in periodic reports of the state of his fields and crops.

On the same day, the Honorary Parish Inspector, St Lawrence, made a verbal report on the alleged non-delivery of 3½ tons of potatoes by Mr Le Cornu who was told to appear before the DOA. He was interviewed on the 11th December and given a warning that, in the event of any fault being found in his cultivation in 1942, the DOA would requisition his farm.

On the 15th December, Mr A. C. Fiott, St Brelade, and Mr P. Jarnet, St Martin, were called to an interview by the DOA for allegedly not delivering specified quantities of potatoes. After interviewing both men, the Honorary Parish Inspectors were instructed to visit the farms and ascertain the exact quantity of potatoes in their custody. On completion of the reports Mr Fiott, who had not brought in 4½ tons of potatoes, was given a warning that serious steps would be taken against him if such a failure happened again. The report on Mr Jarnet's 1942 potato cultivation was considered unsatisfactory and he was warned "...unless there is a considerable improvement in 1943 the DOA will be obliged to have recourse to severe measures".

On the 18th December Mr D. Gallichan, St John, appeared before the DOA concerning his alleged failure to deliver 6 tons of potatoes. After hearing his explanation, the DOA decided to order him to deliver of thirteen barrels from the quantity which he had retained for consumption by his household, together with all the small potatoes which he kept in sacks. He was warned as to his future cultivation and informed "Unless there is a marked improvement therein, the DOA will find itself compelled to resort to severe measures".

On the same day, Mr E. R. de Gruchy, St Mary, was interviewed when he offered explanations for his alleged failure to deliver 12 tons of potatoes. In addition, the Honorary Parish Inspector conducted a report into de Gruchy's potato cultivation. After receiving the report, the DOA decided to examine all the chats still in his possession; if they were suitable de Gruchy would be ordered to deliver them to the DOA. The following week de Gruchy delivered twelve barrels of chats. Wesley Mallet valued them at 6/- per cwt.

On the 22nd December a list was sent to the DOA of individual farmers who had allegedly failed to comply with the directions issued to them under the Cultivation of Lands (Jersey) Order, 1940, requiring them to deliver specified quantities of potatoes to the DOA. They were N. R. Cope, St Martin, P. Pirouet, St Peter and J. Le Bailly, St Brelade.

Cope was ordered to replace his 1943 assigned area for potatoes with cereals, except for 20 perches for the consumption of his household.[7] Pirouet gave no satisfactory explanations. The Chief Inspector was despatched to his farm to report on the quantities of potatoes, wheat and oats found there. After the inspection, Pirouet was told that the DOA was "…profusely dissatisfied with the results of his cultivation in 1942". He was warned of the consequences to his 1943 cultivation if no marked improvement was evident.

An inspection was also carried out at Le Bailly's farm and an investigation into potatoes in his possession. Afterwards he was ordered to deliver to the DOA all the potatoes which he had retained for his household, except for 5 cwt, and any seed potatoes in excess of the quantity required to fulfil the directions issued in relation to the cultivation of his land in 1943.

On the 21st December, a report described the alleged non-delivery of 17 tons of potatoes. In this case, the farmer, Mr J. Ware, St Clement, was immediately referred to the Attorney General.

In January 1943 a second report on Snowden Blampied, St Lawrence, alleged that he had failed to deliver any potatoes to the DOA.[1] On the 27th January the DOA's Chief Inspector visited the farm, and a comprehensive inspection was made in order to ascertain the quantity of potatoes in Mr Blampied's possession. Colin Marie was ordered to take steps to requisition from Blampied's farm "The whole of the potatoes in his possession with the exception of 6 cwt which may be retained for the feeding of his household consisting of seven persons, and 10 boxes of royal seed for the planting of one vergée which he is permitted to grow". The DOA, furthermore, decided to make a recommendation to the Superior Council that 4 vergées of his land should be requisitioned. In February the DOA received a letter from Le Masurier, Giffard and Poch, acting on behalf of Mr Blampied. They stated that the DOA had requisitioned 250 boxes of royal seed and their client required payment for these at the price of 2/6 per box. The DOA agreed to the proposal.

Cereals

On the 2nd October 1942, Edwin Gibaut was made Chairman of the 1942 sub-committee to oversee threshing of the cereal harvest. The DOA met several days later to discuss the season. The first issue was threshing at Don Bridge Farm, which was in German occupation. It was decided to arrange for T. G. Le Cappelain to thresh the harvest; however, he was told not to interfere in any manner whilst carrying out the work. Frank Le Maistre, who had been seconded from the State's Experimental Farm to work as a District Threshing Inspector, reported that Mr P. J. Norman, St Peter, had brought in three-quarters of a load of wheat to thresh, whereas in his opinion the stock should have yielded two full loads. The DOA authorised him to investigate the matter.

On the 16th October there was a robbery at a DOA store. The theft was one bag of oats belonging to Mr F. Pinglaux, St Brelade. The Honorary Police were instructed to investigate the matter. The Connétable, in a subsequent report, stated that the theft occurred whilst it was in transit from the depot at Corbière to the DOA store in St Helier. The DOA decided to pay the owner for the stolen bag of oats.

In October the issue of seed for sowing the 1943 cereal crop was discussed. The following quantities and prices were allocated in virtue of the Cultivation of Lands (Jersey) Order, 1942:

Top quality graded wheat, 90 lbs per vergée	26/- per vergée
Wheat, 90 lbs per vergée	23/6 per vergée
Barley, 90 lbs per vergée	25/6 per vergée
Rye, 90 lbs per vergée	31/6 per vergée
Oats, 90 lbs per vergée	20/3 per vergée

On the 23rd October, Brée reported that Mr S. England, Grouville had allegedly "…been found to be threshing wheat and oats with a private threshing outfit, the property, it is alleged, of Mr C. Buesnel, St Saviour, the said machine not having been approved by the DOA". The matter was forwarded to the Attorney General. On the 13th April 1943, the DOA made a payment to Mr England for the wheat sequestrated by the Royal Court, on the value of 152 lbs. The DOA had the wheat delivered to their cereal store at 31 Commercial Street.

This was not the only case of illegal threshing. A report by Mr O. P. Hamon, Eastern District Threshing Inspector, informing the DOA that Mr C. C. R. Le Brun, St Martin allegedly "…had been discovered illicitly threshing grain", was forwarded to the Attorney General for investigation. Subsequently, the DOA appointed Wesley Mallet to value "…the product of this illicit threshing" after the case went to the Royal Court. The grain was taken into custody by the DOA and put into store in Commercial Street, valued at 20/- per hundredweight.

On the 27th October, the DOA and the Threshing Sub-Committee met to discuss the progress of the 1942 season. The meeting was handed a report by the Honorary Parish Inspectors concerning Mr E. P. Laisney, Trinity who, having been directed to grow 2½ vergées of barley, had on threshing allegedly delivered only 21 lbs of grain. In view of the report Laisney was ordered to appear before the DOA and was "…reprimanded for his imperfect husbandry and warned as to the consequences of any further complaint in relation to the cultivation of his land".

At the same time, the Honorary Parish Inspectors of St Saviour submitted a report on the alleged condition of the cereal crop of Mr J. W. Starck, further comments being made by Mr Hamon. The St Saviour Inspectors also submitted a report on Mr Frank Ozouf, who had been directed to sow barley as a second crop. The results were deemed unfit for delivery to the DOA.

Both Starck and Ozouf were summoned to appear before the DOA to discuss the reports. Mr Ozouf's explanation as to the condition of his barley crop was accepted by the DOA. Starck, however, was warned that "drastic action" against him would be taken. The DOA decided that, in 1943, he should plant 4 vergées of potatoes in a field heavily infested with couch grass. He was ordered to clear the area, manure it and plant potatoes.

The meeting also agreed that threshing contractors would have permission to thresh gleanings unless the owner of gleanings was able to procure a permit to thresh these himself. In cases where such permits were issued, the DOA waived the obligation that the resultant grain had to be offered for sale to the DOA. Colin Marie notified the threshing contractors of the decision.

In November, Mr C. F. Jean, St Peter informed the DOA that 12 vergées of rye had not been successfully cultivated and had failed completely. He asked for £10 compensation and was given £7-10-0, the amount he had paid the ploughing contractor. Another farmer, Mr E. Rault, St Lawrence, claimed compensation for the failure of 6 vergées of oats. He claimed that the crop failure had caused him severe hardship and he could no longer meet his expenses. The Honorary Parish Inspectors were instructed to report on his farm and investigate the standard of cultivation of his crop and to find out if it had been looked after in a satisfactory manner. The DOA, after viewing the report, decided that "…in view of the poor cultivation of the crop" it refused to consider the claim.

In November 1942, a report was filed from the weighbridge concerning Mr Emile Thébault, St Helier. Mr Thébault had brought a load of oats to the weighbridge and an official ticket issued had been marked as "wheat"; he had been paid for his oats at the price prescribed for wheat. He was subsequently interviewed and told to refund the overpayment in respect of the weighbridge ticket.

At the end of November, in an effort to complete the threshing season, W. T. Farrell was given permission to move his threshing machine from the depot at Grantez, St Ouen, in order to thresh at St Peter, St Mary and St Lawrence. Farrell was allowed 60 gallons of petrol a week to complete the season. At the same time, final valuations were made for the pricing of inferior grain. Several sacks of grain which had reached the DOA cereal stores were described as "dirty". The reason for this "dirty grain" was either because of defective threshing or negligence by the farmer.

On the 4th December, the DOA examined the failure of Mr E. P. Allo, St John, to complete the threshing of his wheat crop. It ordered the District Threshing Inspector to notify Mr Allo that, unless he completed his threshing by noon, 7th December, the DOA would resort to severe measures to ensure compliance with its requirements.

On the 11th December, Mr C. C. R. Le Brun and Mr E. Le Marquand were ordered by the DOA to thresh no later than the 16th December the whole of the grain in their possession. On the same day, the two District Threshing Inspectors were given full authority to enter any premises in which they had reason to suppose that there was any grain which had not been brought to the approved machines for threshing.

On the 21st December, Frank Le Maistre returned to his duties at the States Experimental Station. On the 25th December, Mr Hamon had his contract terminated as the threshing season was now ended. In the same week, Mr F. P. Le Bailly, St Ouen reported 1 vergée of wheat seed had been stolen. He was instructed to swear an affidavit in relation to this loss and was required to purchase replacement seed.

The DOA received a letter on the 24th December from Advocate P. N. Richardson written on behalf of his client, Mr A. A. Laurens, Trinity, requesting that his client's threshing machine be restored. The threshing machine had been placed in the custody of the DOA after the Royal Court had prosecuted Mr Laurens for illegal threshing and the machine confiscated. The DOA decided to retain the machine and Advocate Richardson was informed.

Two final claims were made by farmers for compensation for cereal crops in 1942. The first claim was from Mr E. F. Egré, St Peter who had been unable to cultivate 5 vergées of wheat. His claim was refused. The second was from Mr A. G. de Gruchy, St Ouen who claimed 2¾ vergées of his barley crop had failed and that, consequently, he had suffered severe financial hardship. The Honorary Parish Inspector, Mr E. G. Vautier, investigated the cultivation of the barley crop and refused to endorse any compensation.

Horses

On the 16th October 1942, a horse was requisitioned from Dr H. G. Oliver who had just been deported to Germany. The DOA informed the States Vet, Thomas Blampied, to arrange for the horse to be put in "useful employment". In November, the horse, a chestnut mare with a white nose, was valued by Blampied and Edgar Messervy at £25 and a report forwarded to the Administrator of Dr Oliver's property, Mr A. C. Halliwell FRCS. In May 1943, Mr Halliwell wrote to the DOA asking for the requisition order to be released from the 30th May, the release being conditional upon Dr Florence E. Sexton, to whom the horse had been hired by the DOA, paying to the DOA the hire charge up to the 29th May.

More horses were requisitioned. A mare belonging to Major Gerald Allen, Trinity, was requisitioned with orders that the animal be put into useful work. Brée instructed that she be put into harness but in October Major Allen requested for the mare to be returned, as she was in brood and he wanted her back in his custody. In March 1943, Major Allen wrote to the DOA requesting that his mare be served. The DOA decided that it would allow him to breed from the mare, but in view of the fact that the only stallion available in the Island was working quietly in harness, the DOA replied that it could not accede to his request.

A severe shortage of working horses had become apparent during the threshing season in 1942. In October, the DOA recommended to the Superior Council that it purchase twenty-five horses from France, to be made available to farmers. It appears that the recommendation was not accepted. The DOA, however, persisted with its proposal that additional horses must be imported. Brée consulted with farmers and was convinced of the urgency of the problem.

On the 4th November, Mr René Le Mans, a horse breeder from Hocqigny, Normandy, wrote to the DOA indicating "…the current prices of horses in France". The DOA decided to refer the matter to the RJA&HS Council. Brée's notion was for the Society to consider the possibility of applying to the Imports and Exports Advisory Committee to purchase a number of horses from mainland France for subsequent sale to farmers.

On the 20th November, Le Gallais reported to the DOA that the RJA&HS had invited farmers who required horses to notify the Society so that arrangements could be made to purchase their requirements in France. The DOA instructed Brée to support these applications when the issue came before the Superior Council.

In late November, the Connétable of St Helier made a request to the DOA for assistance in obtaining hay for feeding horses used by St Helier Parish. The DOA decided it could not assist the Connétable, however Brée, using his relationship with Pelz and contacts with the Field Command, decided "…to press the German Field Command 515 to deliver to the Island the quantity of hay which the Field Command had promised to supply from France." After a discussion with Pelz, Brée informed the Connétable that, on delivery of the hay in question, it might be possible to sell him a quantity.

On the 29th December, the DOA recommended to the Superior Council that horses purchased in France should be shipped from Granville and that shipments should not be deferred until the full number allocated to Jersey had been received at Granville.

Fertilisers

In early November, Pelz and Brée discussed the collection of vraic. Pelz was well aware of the significance of vraic; he was a university-trained scientific agriculturalist and had a real understanding of the importance of this natural fertiliser when applied in the correct manner to the land. On the 3rd November, Field Command 515 gave permission for farmers to collect seaweed at La Pulente and at the slipway near Pointe Etacquerel.[8]

On the 11th November, Mr Woodcock recommended the following retail prices for fertilisers, which were agreed by the DOA and the JPMA was informed.

Nitrate of soda	£18-10-0	Per ton
Nitrate of potash	£32-0-0	Per ton
Potassic nitrate of soda	£29-0-0	Per ton
Sulphate of ammonia	£17-0-0	Per ton
Hoof and horn meal	£28-10-0	Per ton
Bone meal	£17-10-0	Per ton
Bone flour	£13-15-0	Per ton
Dissolved bones	£17-10-0	Per ton
Sulphate of potash	£19-0-0	Per ton
Nitrate of potash	£16-10-0	Per ton
Potash salts	£11-0-0	Per ton
Kainite	£8-7-6	Per ton
Dried blood	£35-0-0	Per ton
Cereal mixture	£21-0-0	Per ton
Tomato manure	£20-0-0	Per ton

The DOA fixed prices for artificial ingredients which were imported from France, and which were sold to the "Mixing Merchants" at the following rates – ex-store and exclusive of the bags.

Ammonia	£14-10-0	Per ton
Phosphates	£12-2-6	Per ton

The DOA approved these prices for the proposed sale of artificial fertiliser by the JPMA.

The Jersey Produce Merchants Association and the Jersey Corn Merchants Association

On the 17th October 1942, a report on T. Mayo and Company Limited demonstrated "...the considerable shortage which has been discovered in the stock of wheat of the 1941 crop, held on behalf of the DOA". The firm was notified that it would be required to refund the value of the grain. In the same week, grain which had been inadequately tended was released from the custody of the merchants who stored it and was redistributed.

At the beginning of November, the JPMA wrote to the DOA, asking that men working in the stores of their members should be entitled to receive, against payment "...a monthly allowance of wheat." The DOA decided that the quantity of wheat available for the requirements of the Island was insufficient to permit such an allowance.

On the 20th November, the DOA appointed Randalls Limited, Jersey's main brewer, as an additional company to store grain, on the same terms as it had given to the JPMA.

On the 2nd December, the Jersey Corn Merchants Association (JCMA) wrote to the DOA asking for "An increase in the payment it had agreed." In September 1942, it had accepted payment for storing wheat seed at 7/6 a ton. The JCMA argued that the proposed increase was in consideration "…of the additional labour and floor space necessitated by the preparation of such grain for sowing." The DOA considered the matter and decided to recommend to the Superior Council that an additional payment of 3/- a ton should be made for wheat seed, to cover the additional handling and floor space, insisting however that the JCMA would have to signify a willingness to accept this increase in the event of it being sanctioned by the Superior Council. On the 12th December, the JCMA made a further request that the DOA increase the extra remuneration from 3/- a ton to 3/9 a ton. The DOA refused and on the 22nd December the JCMA withdrew its request for the extra 9 pence for handling wheat seed.

In late December the Grain and Potato Section submitted a report setting forth the percentage loss of grain from the 1941 cereal harvest held in store on behalf of the DOA, with the proposal that a shrinkage of up to 3% was acceptable. Any firm demonstrating a larger percentage loss would be obliged to refund the DOA the value of the excess loss. The President of the JPMA, J. M. Norman, wrote back to the DOA with counter proposals. A meeting was held between the JPMA and the JCMA to discuss the issue. Brée, in the meantime, met with the Crown Officers to discuss the losses ascertained in the quantity of wheat and oats held by the JPMA and the JCMA from the 1941 harvest.

In February 1943, the DOA met with the Department of Finance and Economics and the Crown Officers. After considerable discussion, it was decided that merchants who had shown a percentage loss exceeding 3% would be dealt with individually by the DOA and negotiations would be entered upon to resolve the question of reimbursing the loss. A sub-committee of Brée and Gibaut was formed to interview merchants in an attempt to arrive at a settlement.

Cultivation Orders

From 6th October to 13th November 1942, £1,607-18-6 was handed out through the Agricultural Workers Bonus Scheme. No further payments were made after the 13th November for the year 1942.

In October, Brée announced that the Superior Council had decided that compensation to farmers for damage to their crops by German forces would be considered, after the termination of the present hostilities. However, in cases of financial hardship, there would be special circumstances to allow for grants on compassionate grounds. These would be investigated on a case-by-case basis.

A further recommendation was made to the Superior Council that, where a crop had been grown in pursuance of a directive under the Cultivation of

Lands (Jersey) Order, 1942, compensation would be paid out at the time of the harvest.

Five claims were made to the DOA in respect of damage to crops by the German forces. One of these, made by George Michel, Val de la Mare, St Peter was accepted. The damage on his farm was to crops destroyed by the construction of a German railway.

In October 1942, Mr T. P. Mourant, Deputy of St Saviour and Chairman of the Jersey Allotment Council (JAC), met the DOA to discuss the allotment scheme which had been in operation in 1942. He requested that a rectory field of 13 vergées in St Saviour be used for allotments. The Honorary Parish Inspectors, however, were not in favour of the proposal and "declined the permit".

In November, the DOA began discussing the logistics of the 1943 ploughing season. The problem was the acute shortage of petrol. It was decided to appoint ploughing contractors as in 1942. A notice was published in the local press inviting contractors to apply. On the 27th November, the DOA met those who had applied, to discuss conditions. The DOA issued the following terms.

1. The price to be charged to farmers is set at £1-10-0 per vergée.
2. The amount to be refunded to the DOA in respect of each vergée is 11/6.
3. The refund is to be made at the office of the DOA and, at the same time, the Logbook required by clause 7 below is to be produced for verification.
4. In the event of there being any increase in the price of petrol, the amount refunded to the DOA will be reduced by an amount equivalent to the increase in the price of petrol.
5. The allowance for fuel for ploughing is 1¾ gallons per vergée. In addition, contractors will be allowed 2 gallons per week for transport from farm to farm. This allowance is conditional upon the contractors having worked no less than four days.
6. Each contractor is required to keep a Logbook showing the name and address of each farmer for whom ploughing has been carried out, together with the number of vergées ploughed for each farmer. Each entry to be signed by the farmer to whom such entry refers.

In November, the German Field Command agreed to 200 lorries being used for agriculture in 1943 and issued licences for the use of these lorries.

The same month saw further claims for compensation. As a result of an agreement between the Superior Council, the RJA&HS and the JFU, a memorandum of understanding was written in order to somehow regularise claims for war damage. The terms were as follows.

1. All farmers cultivating land under the Cultivation of Lands Order are advised that in the event of any loss of crops, as a result of compulsory evacuation or military occupation, they should immediately advise the Department of Finance and Economics giving full particulars.

KVR Pelz at College House, Headquarters of Field Command 515. *(By kind permission Alan Allix)*

Hans Egon Pelz, self-portrait. *(By kind permission Alan Allix)*

Corporal Soeldner at College House. *(By kind permission Alan Allix)*

St Brelade's Bay Hotel. Pelz (top left), Dr Lauprecht (top, fourth from left), Colonel Knackfuss (bottom, third from left), Schwester Elizabeth Bergmann (Red Cross Sister), November 1941. The hotel became Soldatenheim II. *(By kind permission Alan Allix)*

Little Court, Mont Cambrai, July 1942. Left to right: Michael Wynne Sayer (Guernsey agricultural representative), Louis Guillemette (Secretary to Bailiff of Guernsey), Touzel John Brée (President of Jersey Department of Agriculture), Ernest Ing (Jersey Horticultural Advisor), Hans Egon Pelz (Head of Agriculture and Food Supply, Channel Islands Field Command 515). *(By kind permission Alan Allix)*

Glasshouse at Howard Davis Experimental Farm, Trinity, Jersey. Left to right: M. W. Sayer, E. Ing, L. Guillemette, T. Brée, Pierre Gréard (farm foreman). July 1942. *(By kind permission Alan Allix)*

Above: Football match in front of College House, St Helier, Headquarters of FC515, between Jersey XI and German Luftwaffe XI, August 1940. *(By kind permission Alan Allix)*

Right: Minck's "tobacco plantation". Pelz holding tobacco leaf, on his left Major Pokorni, Head of Utilities Field Command 515. *(By kind permission Alan Allix)*

Fern Valley, where six-weekly target practice was held. Left to right: Pokorni, unknown, Pelz, W. Heider (Chief of Staff), Volken (Interpreter). The car is a requisitioned local vehicle, J1005. *(By kind permission Alan Allix)*

Pelz inspecting crop of oats with a Sonderfurher. The latter has the distinctive arrow collar patch. *(By kind permission Alan Allix)*

Pelz in a field of barley with a Feldpolitze. This is the only photograph extant of a German policeman. *(By kind permission Alan Allix)*

Fields at the back of Samarès Manor, St Clement. Left to right: Heider, unknown, Pelz on his horse Bellini, Knackfuss, Dr Casper (OKVR), Baron Aufsess (KVR), unknown. *(By kind permission Alan Allix)*

Pelz with a Sonderfuhrer, possibly at Plémont. *(By kind permission Alan Allix)*

Knackfuss, with Staff Officers of FC515, talking to OT workers. *(By kind permission Alan Allix)*

St Brelade's Church. Colonel Schumacher, first Kommandant of Field Command 515 (far left with binoculars), General Otto Stulpnagel, Governor of Paris (front row on left). *(By kind permission Alan Allix)*

Pelz in the grounds of Samarès Manor. *(By kind permission Alan Allix)*

Victoria Pier, St Helier Harbour. Irish paid workers from Ronez Quarries in front of temporary slaughterhouse. *(By kind permission Alan Allix)*

Staff Officers FC515 on St Aubin's Beach. In the middle is Elsa Brunner, Pelz's housekeeper. *(By kind permission Alan Allix)*

Top left: St Brelade's Bay Hotel. Left to right: Heider, Pokorni, unknown. *(By kind permission Alan Allix)*

Top right: Fern Valley. Left to right: Volken, Pelz, Pokorni. *(By kind permission Alan Allix)*

Above: Pelz inspecting a Jersey cow for export to the Kaiser Wilhelm breeding station near Rostock. *(By kind permission Alan Allix)*

Right: Touzel John Brée in his Jurat's robes, 1938. *(By kind permission Mrs Leslie Averty)*

The first cattle show
after the occupation,
at John Perrée's
farm, Oaklands,
St Saviour. *(By kind
permission Jersey
Evening Post)*

Left: A cattle show
at Springfield,
St Helier.

Below: Broadfields,
St Lawrence. Touzel
Brée inspecting
potato clamps, 1940.
*(By kind permission
Société Jersiaise)*

2. In receipt of the claim, it shall be filed with the DOA. The Inspectors will inspect and assess the value of the claim and damage.
3. In receipt of the Inspector's Report, the Department of Finance and Economics shall notify the claimants of the amount of the assessment.
4. In cases where the farmer asks for immediate financial aid, the Department of Finance and Economics is authorised to advance the amount of the assessed damage against assignment by the farmer to the States of Jersey of all compensation which may become due to him at a later date, relative to the claim in question.
5. For the guidance of the Inspectors to ensure uniformity, a scale of expenses in connection with the cultivation of land shall be drawn up by the DOA, such scale to include labour and materials only, no consideration being given to the question of rent or damage to land or buildings or loss of profits.
6. In the event of the farmer being dissatisfied with the Inspector's assessment of the damage to loss of crops, he will be given the right to appeal to a special tribunal.
7. Claims where loss and damage cannot be accurately computed will be filed for consideration at the end of the hostilities.

All previous claims were re-submitted to the Honorary Parish Inspectors, along with a scale of values for agricultural damage which Brée had sent to the Superior Council for approval.

Also in November, a letter was received by the DOA from Mr Philip Hamon, L'Etacq, St Ouen informing the DOA that the German Forces of Occupation had almost enclosed his farm with barbed wire entanglements. In addition, "Nobody was allowed to penetrate the farm without a permit issued by the German Forces."

The issue of barbed wire entanglements around fields and cultivated areas had recently been dealt with. On the 28th August 1942, KVR von Aufsess had written to the Bailiff a letter entitled "Cultivation of land within wire entanglements." Von Aufsess informed the Bailiff that any farmer concerned "…shall on his own initiative get in touch with the competent commander of the troops with regard to cultivating the land within the wire. Every farmer must consider it his duty even under the most difficult conditions of war, to make his land productive. I shall penalise any owner of land not complying".[9] On the 5th September, OKVR Dr Casper ordered a notice to be published concerning von Aufsess' request.

On the 2nd December, Mr F. E. Jandron, St Peter, sent in a compensation claim of £50 for 4 vergées of wheat and mangolds, both of which had failed. The DOA forwarded his claim to the Compensation Advisory Committee. This had been re-constituted after being terminated in late 1941. Mr Jandron claimed he was experiencing severe financial hardship because of the crop failures. The DOA recommended to the Compensation Advisory Committee that Mr Jandron should not receive more than £20 for the loss of his crops.

Further claims for the failure of crops which had been grown under Cultivation Orders were investigated. Mr E. F. Egré, St Peter, claimed for compensation for the failure of 5 vergées of wheat. The DOA would not entertain any compensation or recommend that the matter was investigated further. The claim, however, did not end at this point. In a rare difference of opinion with Brée, Mr G. H. Le Rossignol, one of the Honorary Parish Inspectors for St Peter, had expressed dissatisfaction directly to the Bailiff with the above decision to reject the compensation claim. Mr Le Rossignol was of the opinion that, as the crop was left in the ground on the directions of an Honorary Parish Inspector, the DOA should have recommended the payment of compensation. After due consideration of the matter, however, the DOA refused to change its initial decision.

Another claim for compensation was made by Mr A. G. de Gruchy, St Ouen. This was for the loss of 2¾ vergées of barley. The Honorary Parish Inspector reported that de Gruchy had not suffered financial hardship and the claim was dismissed.

The final claim for compensation was made in December 1942. It was submitted by Mr G. A. Vautier, Egypt Farm, Trinity. His claim related to 3 vergées of turnips, which he was required to grow for the German authorities, and which they had declined to purchase when ready and in consequence was a total loss. In view of the circumstances, the DOA sent a claim to the Compensation Advisory Committee.

On the 25th November, Field Command wrote to the DOA concerning the growing of vegetables for the year 1943. The letter made it clear that the Field Command wanted an increase in vegetable cultivation. The order was given that "All professional market gardeners and farmers should form an Association, in order to prepare a plan in regard to such production." The order had come directly from St Germain, Paris. In other words, from the top of the German Military Government.[10]

The DOA decided to call a meeting of the principal vegetable growers, and to communicate to them "The requirements of the German authorities and to invite them to set up the committee proposed in the letter to control the growing, collection and distribution of the vegetables grown."

On the 4th December, the DOA met with the RJA&HS and the JFU. Brée was in the chair with E. Gibaut, W. Mallet and C. Marie representing the DOA; C. Le Gallais, J. B. Michel and F. Le Boutillier represented the RJA&HS; and P. Le Feuvre, C. P. Journeaux, T. G. Le Marinel, E. N. Pallot, P. H. Renouf, G. A. Romeril and A. G. Houguez, the JFU. At the request of Brée, Marie read the letter received by the DOA from the German Field Command regarding the cultivation of vegetables in 1943. It ordered that 625 vergées of vegetables be cultivated in 1943 to produce 5,014 tons (an average of 400 tons per month). The Field Command also ordered the formation of an "Association of Market Gardeners and Farmers" to control the cultivation of vegetables, advise growers and arrange the distribution of agricultural inputs. The issue of a lack of fertilisers was a problem. When addressed to Field Command 515, Pelz and von Aufsess made it clear that "Although the artificial fertiliser allotment has not been satisfactorily solved, nevertheless, the plan must be carried out."

Brée pointed out that the DOA had already allocated 600 vergées for the cultivation of vegetables and no shortage had occurred in 1942. The meeting discussed what, exactly, the German Field Command had requested and visualised the difficulties that would arise in executing their plan.

Brée suggested that the RJA&HS and JFU were best placed to implement the preliminary steps in executing the German order. He, furthermore, suggested that the two farming associations form a committee to oversee the cultivation of vegetables. Philip Le Feuvre, seconded by John Michel, proposed forming a vegetable committee to investigate the cultivation of vegetables, to consult growers and produce a report for submission to the DOA. The meeting went on to discuss what were regarded as insuperable difficulties in carrying out the German Orders and that the cultivation of vegetables was already at its maximum.[6]

A Vegetable Cultivation Committee was subsequently appointed to oversee the growing of vegetables in 1943, in accordance with the cropping plan of the 3rd November 1942 issued by the German Field Command. The Committee comprised: Le Feuvre, Le Marinel, Journeaux, Michel, Le Boutillier and Pallot. Chaired by Le Feuvre, it met for the first time on the 16th December to prepare a reply to the German Field Command on the cultivation of vegetables in 1943.

Le Feuvre distributed to members a schedule of crops issued by the Field Command. A draft report was compiled, setting out the reasons why the scheme was impractical. There was a lack of seeds, fertilisers, and insecticides and additional problems were "The danger of oversupply and cultural difficulties". It was decided that the Committee would consult with seven of the most important vegetable growers and a meeting was organised for the 2nd January 1943 between the Committee, the growers, and Brée representing the DOA.

The vegetable growers attending on the 2nd January were S. G. Le Brouilliard, G. J. Godel, J. H. Syvret, J. R. Le Quesne, T. G. Le Feuvre, G. C. Le Cornu and J. J. Le Marquand. Brée was in the chair and as before he read aloud the letter from Field Command 515, setting forth the scheme of vegetable growing which was ordered to be put into operation. This included the crops to be grown and the tonnage to be produced. Le Feuvre added to the report that soils in Jersey varied greatly from one farm to another and from one field to another. Also, some areas were simply not suitable for vegetable cultivation. It was made clear to the German authority that there had been no scarcity of vegetables in 1942 and, in fact, the military authorities had often refused to accept produce as being surplus to requirements.

Mr Syvret criticised the actions of "...certain persons who ordered farmers to grow and supply vegetables despite the fact that they had received crop allocations from the DOA." In simple terms, what Syvret was implying was that farmers had received "conflicting orders" to grow vegetables on behalf of the Germans. Farmers were well aware of Pelz's role as Head of Agriculture, Field Command 515, and of his influence on agricultural policy. Brée, in reply to the above comments, advised growers of the course to pursue, if such demands were made. The report was unanimously endorsed and subsequently forwarded to the DOA.

The members of the Vegetable Cultivation Committee, along with Brée, were interviewed by the German Field Command on the 11th January 1943 in Room 20, College House, when the report was submitted. The difficulties inherent in the German cropping plan for the cultivation of vegetables in 1943 were explained. The German Field Command and Pelz were advised and "Received instructions to submit a revised plan for cultivating such vegetables, without interfering with the existing conditions of market gardening and insufficiency for the requirements of the troops".[6]

The Committee met again on the 13th January and made amendments to its report. It advised that, in addition to the area already allocated to vegetable cultivation, a second crop should be grown. This second crop would comprise:

Second Crop	Area (Vergées)	Yield per Vergée (Tons)	Total Yield (Tons)
Cabbages	30	5	150
Carrots	100	4	400
Broccoli	50	5	250

The Committee agreed that "...these quantities estimated as the production of 180 vergées should guarantee a satisfactory [crop] for the troops in 1943." The second crop was allocated by the Honorary Parish Inspectors under Land Cultivation Directives. All those farmers ordered to grow vegetables under a Cultivation Order were given a guarantee that any quantity surplus to requirements would be bought at a fixed price. Le Feuvre, Pallot and Journeaux were to accompany Brée on the 19th January 1943, to Room 20, College House, to inform Pelz and the Field Command.

A further meeting was held by the Committee and Brée, who accepted all their recommendations. He, furthermore, made the following suggestions. Firstly, when a grower had been ordered to grow cabbages, carrots or broccoli, under the revised scheme, he should receive the current wholesale price less 20% for any marketable produce not absorbed, i.e., surplus to the requirements of the German authorities. Secondly, it was probable that the DOA would purchase surplus quantities at the prices stated for distribution through the usual channels.[11] Thirdly, growers with greenhouses under Cultivation Orders would grow potatoes as a first crop; a second crop of tomatoes would be allowed on 75% of the area and the remaining 25% would be at the discretion of the farmer for vegetable cultivation only. All tobacco cultivation in greenhouses was forbidden.

On the 22nd January 1943, the DOA adopted the report in full. It was referred to the Superior Council in order to empower the DOA to purchase any surplus vegetables arising out of the cropping plan. In February the DOA issued formal directions to all greenhouse growers, ordering a second crop of greenhouse tomatoes.

The German order for an increase in vegetable cultivation to supply their troops in 1943 is both interesting and informative. Firstly, the original order emanated from the headquarters of the German Military Government, St Germain, Paris. Secondly, although vegetable cultivation in Jersey in 1942 had been sufficient to cover the needs of the German troops stationed on the Island, Field Command 515 had to implement the Paris Order even though it was not necessary. Thirdly, it clearly demonstrates the structural relationships that had been built up since 1940 between Field Command 515 and the agricultural associations and individuals. Pelz skilfully used these relationships to help fulfil agricultural orders from his superiors. The increase in vegetable cultivation, ordered by Paris, was initially given to the Bailiff. The DOA and Brée, in consequence, made use of the Island's leading farmers, both from the RJA&HS and the JFU, to organise a Vegetable Cultivation Committee to produce a detailed report, as requested by the German authority. Fourthly, the Committee co-opted the leading market garden and greenhouse growers to finalise their 1943 cultivation plans. Finally, the report and plans were discussed and revised between the Committee, Brée and the DOA and, representing Field Command 515, KVR Pelz. This culminated in a successful conclusion. The original Vegetable Cultivation Order from Paris was successfully implemented after its approval by the Superior Council.

The implementation of the order from Paris was completed. If, however, the vegetable Cultivation Order had not been carried through, it might have led to the possibility of direct intervention from the German Military Government in France. This was the last alternative that Field Command 515 wanted. It therefore suited both the Island civilian and German authorities to work together. These structural relationships had been carefully built up and nurtured since August 1940 and were now bearing fruit.

On the 11th December 1942, a report sent to the DOA concerned a farm owned by Mr George Dorey Junior, Trinity and covered the manner of cultivation of his land. Dorey was summoned to appear before the DOA. The Honorary Parish Inspectors were told to produce a detailed observation "…in relation to the manner the above had carried out the cultivation of his farm." The subsequent report was far worse than Brée had expected. He appointed a sub-committee of Gibaut and Le Gallais to make a further inspection and to report back the following week. The sub-committee's report alleged that the farm was: "In a very neglected condition."

Brée, realising that the cultivation of the farm was poor and that radical action would be needed, called in the solicitor V. J. Bailhache in order that he could take advice as to appropriate legal action in relation to the farm. Mr Bailhache was interviewed concerning the alleged failure of George Dorey

Junior to cultivate the farm, within the principles of good husbandry as required by the DOA. After a discussion, the DOA decided that the 50 vergée farm was too large to be worked unaided by Dorey. Bailhache undertook to arrange for the letting of 25 vergées and to report back to the DOA.

A month later Mr Bailhache requested the sub-committee to visit the farm and report on the best course to be pursued in relation to the cultivation of the remaining fields. The sub-committee's subsequent report decided that Mr Dorey "...must give up his occupation of the following land and for the fields to be rented". Mr Dorey was permitted to continue the cultivation of part of the farm for a further twelve months. He would not be allowed to grow any wheat and was ordered to return to the DOA store the wheat seed which he had drawn for sowing 17 vergées.

The wheat seed was returned and the DOA subsequently modified its previous decision, allowing him to keep an extra 3 vergées and permitting 4 vergées of wheat cultivation.[1]

In December, a further five farmers were warned by the DOA that it was not satisfied with the results of their 1942 cultivation. They were warned that if they continued into 1943 in the same manner, the Department "...would be obliged to take severe action". One farmer was given a clear warning that his farm would be requisitioned.

In late December the DOA requisitioned a poorly cultivated farm from Mary Jane Perron, L'Etacq, St Ouen. It was put out for tender and was taken by Mr R. G. Amy, St Ouen.

References

1. Jersey Archive. C/B/A1/8.
2. Jersey Archive. B/A/W31/2/62-63.
3. RJA&HS and JFU Joint Emergency Committee Minutes.
4. Jersey Archive. B/A/W31/2/64.
5. This figure is based on RJA&HS milk production graphs.
6. RJA&HS and JFU Joint Emergency Committee Minutes.
7. 1 perch = 484 square feet.
8. Jersey Archive. L/F/54/C/D/3.
9. Jersey Archive. B/A/W31/2/58.
10. Jersey Archive. B/A/W31/2/60.
11. The original word on the document was "intended". This was replaced by the word "probable".

Chapter 11

January – February – March 1943

Cattle

"It is recommended that a file be kept of the farmers in which the dates of the animal census be entered. In this way the control of slaughtering for the black market, especially with regard to pigs, will be facilitated. According to reports, the slaughtering of pigs under the eyes of the inspectors for the black market has reached such a pitch that deliveries to the slaughterhouse have sunk to a minimum".

Field Commandant to Bailiff

On the 8th April 1942 OKVR Dr Casper wrote to the Bailiff a letter entitled "Cattle census". Casper and Pelz issued an order that a survey of cattle, pigs, poultry, and all animals be carried out in the parishes. The aim of the census was "The development of the cattle economy...I shall expect to have the results by the 1st of May 1942". Brée asked Dr Casper to defer the census until August when all "Agricultural Returns" were received. On the 24th April Pelz sent an "urgent" note to the Bailiff ordering that the census be completed and received by the 7th May 1942. The urgency was because the German Military Government at St Germain, Paris, had ordered a cattle census in France to be completed by the 1st May 1942. Therefore, Jersey had to complete the census without question. On the 7th May Brée sent the relevant figures to Field Command 515. The results were as follows.[1]

Horses	1,111
Cattle	8,875
Sheep	21
Goats	437
Pigs	1,192
Poultry	27,983

This census, however, was deemed unacceptable by Knackfuss. On the 20th December 1942, Knackfuss wrote a detailed letter to the Bailiff demanding exact information with regard to the increase or decrease in stocks of animals, meat production and requirements of feeding stuffs. This census was to be carried out on the 10th January 1943 with the final results submitted by the 31st January.

Knackfuss concluded his order with the statement "It is recommended that a file be kept of the farmers in which the dates of the animal census be entered. In this way the control of slaughtering for the black market, especially in regard to pigs will be facilitated. According to reports, the slaughtering of pigs under the eyes of the inspectors for the black market has reached such a pitch that deliveries to the slaughterhouse have sunk to a minimum". The DOA immediately passed the Livestock (Returns) (Jersey) Order, 1943, on the 4th January.

The livestock census was completed by the 10th January. The DOA Secretary was charged with delivering the results to Field Command 515.

On the 5th January the RJA&HS sent a recommendation to both the Superior Council and the DOA for an increase in the price paid to farmers for cattle sent to slaughter. The prices requested were as follows.

Type of Cattle	Price per lb, Liveweight
Calves	1/-
Maiden heifers	10d
Bulls under eighteen months	10d
Cows	8d
Bulls over eighteen months	8d

The RJA&HS also made a request to the DOA that the present system, whereby cattle brought in for slaughter at the public slaughterhouse were not weighed until the next day, should be modified in order that weighing took place not more than 6 hours after arrival. In addition, the RJA&HS wanted the vendors of cattle to be present at the weighing. The Superior Council, when considering these requests, "Declined to give effect to the recommendation in relation to the prices for cattle brought to the public slaughterhouses with the exception that farmers may bring in their cattle to the slaughterhouses in the late afternoon and the animals brought in will be weighed the following morning".

In the same week, a report submitted by the Milk Control Section stated that Mr J. F. Luce, St Lawrence, had informed the Foreman Milk Tester that he was fattening two animals for slaughter and sale to the Germans.[2] The DOA sent the report to the Attorney General.

In January, in response to several cases, all owners of "stolen livestock" were informed they had to swear an affidavit concerning the theft. No report of a stolen animal would be accepted without the appropriate affidavit.

On the 14th January the Calf Selection Committee, which had been set up by the DOA for the purpose of selecting calves to be exempted from the provisions of Article 5(i) of the Livestock (Jersey) Order, 1942, sent a letter to the DOA. The letter asked whether the DOA would be prepared to increase to one thousand in any one year the number of calves which could be exempted from slaughter. The DOA refused to modify its previous decision.

A report in January described that Mr W. Bouillier, St Brelade had allegedly refused to destroy a bull calf within fourteen days as ordered by the Livestock (Jersey) Order, 1942. In addition, he allegedly declined to milk his cow twice daily, the animal having recently calved. Bouillier was written to and ordered to send the bull calf to the abattoir for slaughter. He was also charged to appear before the DOA. A previous report by the Milk Control Section had instructed the Foreman Milk Tester, J. G. Malzard, "…to maintain a strict supervision on this man and report to the DOA immediately should he fail to send in the available supplies of milk".

Bouillier was also interviewed about his alleged refusal to slaughter his bull calf born on the 2nd January 1943. He was reminded of his obligation by the Milk Tester Mr J. F. Poignard. Bouillier replied he would only do so when the bull calf was one month old. At the interview Bouillier stated that he had already disposed of the calf but declined to give any information as to the manner of disposal.

The matter was referred to the Attorney General and the Connétable of St Brelade produced a further report. In view of the two reports, the DOA decided to withdraw legal proceedings. Instead, it requested the Department of Essential Commodities to issue a requisition order in virtue of Article 53(i) of the Defence (Jersey) Regulations, 1939, in respect of Mr Bouillier's cow. The requisition order was carried out by the State's Vet, who was also charged with submitting a report on the cow and informing the DOA whether the animal was worth retaining for milking purposes or whether it should be slaughtered. After examination the cow was slaughtered, and the carcass sold to the Department of Essential Commodities for £12-17-6.

On the 16th February Mr J. G. Beaugie, St Martin, who had failed to declare the death of a heifer calf, was ordered to appear before the DOA. He was not prosecuted, but Brée warned him to observe all his livestock in the future.

On the 23rd March the DOA met to discuss "The situation which has arisen in relation to supplies of meat for the civilian population as a result of the non-arrival from France of cattle destined to provide such supplies". During 1942, 1,747 live cattle had been imported from France to provide meat for the civilian population of the Island.[3] This was in addition to 485 local cattle slaughtered for meat supplies. Therefore in 1943 it would be necessary to slaughter approximately 1,260 cattle to meet the Island's civilian requirements. The DOA decided that this dilemma should be submitted to the RJA&HS and the JFU for discussion. Brée stressed the recommendation of these two bodies as "…the best means to be adopted in order to obtain from the local cattle the necessary meat for the civilian population in the event of any further failure occurring in the supplies from the mainland". A meeting between the DOA, RJA&HS and JFU was scheduled for the 30th March 1943, however it was cancelled at the last minute due to the discovery of warble fly in a herd of cattle owned by the Germans (and imported from the Continent) in the neighbourhood of St Peter's Barracks and the potentially catastrophic effect this could have on the Island's cattle.

On the 27th March, Brée met the twenty-seven leading dairy farmers to discuss the requirement for local meat. He took the chair and opened the meeting in a sombre tone. Brée explained that owing to the non-arrival of meat from France and the consequent cessation of meat rations, his department had been faced with the compulsory slaughtering of 40 to 50 head of cattle, which were required to provide a week's ration for the civilian population.[4] Brée asked the farmers to provide a means of selecting cattle, if and when compulsory slaughtering of local stock was ordered. E. C. Perrédès immediately retorted that farmers should be paid a fair price for meat. Brée diplomatically replied that the Superior Council would grant dairy farmers a meeting when a cattle selection process was ready.

Mr J. E. Gaudin suggested the setting up of a "Valuation Committee" which would put a value on cattle requisitioned for the civilian population. He furthermore suggested that the difference between the price obtained, and the real value of the animal, be subsequently paid when conditions returned to normal. The meeting recalled that such a Valuation Committee already existed. It was set up in early 1941 and existed until September 1941 when there was a weekly quota of 20 head of local cattle for slaughter. Perrédès proposed the reconstitution of that same Valuation Committee and the following dairy farmers were proposed and appointed: C. Le Gallais, J. B. Michel, F. Le Boutillier, P. Le Feuvre, R. W. Carson, H. Renouf, G. Le Masurier and E. C. Perrédès.

The meeting discussed various schemes for the selection of cattle to be slaughtered for meat. Mr J. H. Syvret proposed that the largest herds be drawn on first. Mr T. J. Ahier proposed an amendment that members of the Valuation Committee should act in their respective parishes in the selection of the animals required. This was carried by a large majority. A final amendment by Mr G. H. Le Rossignol asked all dairy farmers to notify what cattle they had that could be spared for slaughter.

On the 4th July 1942, a system of points had been agreed by members of the RJA&HS concerning the exemption of calves for slaughter.

Scale of Points – 4th July 1942

Points for cows in herds	1 or 2 cows – no points 3 and 4 cows – 1 point 5 to 7 cows – 2 points 8 to 10 cows – 3 points 11 to 14 cows – 4 points 15 to 20 cows – 5 points Over 20 cows – 6 points
Dam of calf or dam of heifer or bull highly commended	1 point
Dam of calf or dam of heifer or bull commended	Nil points

On the 30th January 1943 a new scale of points was suggested by the Calf Selection Sub-committee and circulated. It came into operation at the end of February 1943.[5]

On the 3rd February, a revised scheme for calf selection was produced with major amendments to the scale of points.[6] Those with lower points were more likely to have calves selected for slaughter, thus the larger herds were favoured.

Potatoes

In 1942, Pelz had held a meeting with Brée at which he had made it clear that the potato crop had to be more productive. Not only were 10,000 tons of potatoes required by Field Command, but also increased quantities for German export. The exact amount of seed potatoes was calculated by both men for the forthcoming potato season. A conference was subsequently held between Brée and merchants Messrs Falla and Bichard, concerning the reservation of potato seed for 1943.

On the 8th January 1943 Mr J. Mahé, St Lawrence, was ordered to deliver 3½ tons of potatoes, having failed to comply with his Cultivation Order. An inspection of his farm was carried out by Mr O. P. Gautier, and Mr Mahé was instructed to deliver within seven days two bags of ware and mid potatoes. In the same week two more farmers were also investigated because of failures to deliver potatoes. Mr A. C. Fiott, St Brelade was given a formal warning and Mr P. Jarnet, St Martin, was written to and informed that the DOA was not satisfied with the results of his 1942 cultivation. He was ordered to improve and increase his 1943 harvest. Mr R. Pirouet, St Peter, was handed a similar order.

The DOA now decided that, on farms where the Honorary Parish Inspectors had directed that French seed potatoes were to be planted, in place of failed cereal crops, the farmers would have to pay for the seed at a rate of £1-0-3 per vergée.

On the 26th January the DOA contacted Mr W. F. Labey, Grouville. Brée was dissatisfied with the results of Labey's 1942 potato harvest and warned him to improve the outcome for 1943. The same warning was given to Mr S. D. Blampied, St Lawrence; an Inspector was sent to his farm and a report produced on the quantity of potatoes in his possession. The result was that Mr Blampied's Cultivation Order for 1943 was changed and he was redirected to grow a larger area of cereals.

On the 16th February, 300 boxes of French seed potatoes were reserved for use by smallholders. These mids imported from France were sold at 10/6 per 50 kilo bag and a maximum of 50 kilos per smallholder was allowed. All applications had to be personally approved by Brée. In addition, a quantity of seed potatoes of the "Royal Kidney" variety arrived from France. These were distributed amongst farmers to grow as either a first or second crop and sold at £1 per 50 kilo bag. Brée decided that any farmer unable to pay for them could sign a bond allowing the DOA to deduct the value of the seed from the value of the crop sold by the farmer to the DOA, and he also stated that the minimum area for planting these potatoes was 10 perches. On the same day, the Field Commandant wrote with instructions for the method of payment for these seed potatoes, to the "Societé d'Importation et de Repartition des Pommes de Terre de Semence, 2 Chausée à Antin, Paris, 9E". On the advice of the Department of Finance and Economics, the DOA decided to make no payment until the full consignment had been delivered to it and a proper invoice submitted.

A month earlier, the President of the Department of Finance and Economics, Jurat Dorey, had informed the DOA that: "The occupied territory currency of the German army has, since the 16th January 1943, become invalid for the purchase of supplies in France. It has been decided that all payments due to the DOA by the German authorities in respect of the sale to the authorities of the island produce must be made at the Bureau des Changes in Paris so that the island may have at its disposal the necessary credit to make purchases in France". Therefore, although Reichsmarks were still valid in Jersey they were invalid in France. Field Command 515 representing the German Military Government in France henceforth would pay for its Island agricultural exports in francs. This in turn enabled the States of Jersey to purchase agricultural inputs and goods in France.

The removal of Reichsmarks in France had immediate consequences in Jersey. There was an immediate flow of Reichsmarks into the Island brought by barge crews from Granville and St Malo (there could be up to thirty barges a day). This did not go unnoticed by Field Command 515. The reasons for the removal of the German currency are not within the scope of this work, however there is one file relating to Reichsmarks which includes a letter from Pelz to the Bailiff entitled "Counterfeit money." Pelz wrote, "Cases with regard to counterfeit money being brought into circulation are continually taking place in occupied France territory".[7] In response, the Attorney General contacted the Connétable of St Helier requesting that any counterfeit German notes discovered in circulation be referred to him.

On the 18th February Colonel Knackfuss wrote to the Bailiff a letter entitled "Delivery of potatoes to the German armed forces". The letter stated that the remaining 150 tons of potatoes, part of a request from the 8th January, be delivered to the German Military Catering Service in Jersey. Another letter dated the 15th March followed up this request, the order having still not been executed; however, these potatoes were eventually delivered to the German Catering Service. They were initially sent to the Catering Office, where the delivery was checked, but immediately returned to the store of Marks and Riches Limited. The German Catering Service refused to accept the potatoes because they were sprouting shoots. After removal of the shoots, it was realised that this led to an unacceptable loss of weight and therefore some form of compensation was demanded from the DOA. Brée, in response and in the presence of Oberzahlmeister Mispel,[8] carried out a test on the potatoes and as a result delivered to the German Catering Office a total of 159.62 tonnes.[9]

In February, the Superior Council requested those farmers who had potatoes in store and surplus to their requirements, to place them at the disposal of the authorities for "...the feeding of the civilian population". In addition, an advertisement was placed in the local press prohibiting the sale or dispersal of potatoes, except under licence granted by the DOA, by any farmer or grower. Licensed retailers were exempt. Also in February, an Honorary Parish Inspector was sent to the farm of Mr J. Morin, St Mary who had been reported to have tons of potatoes in his possession and in the same week, Mr Emile Le G. Siouville, Grouville reported that his entire crop of greenhouse potatoes planted under a Cultivation Order had been eaten and destroyed by rats. Brée informed him to replant with tomatoes.

A report forwarded to the DOA by Mr C. W. Whitel, an Inspector employed by the Department of Essential Commodities, described "...the illicit selling of new potatoes". The report stated that a retailer at Millbrook had obtained new potatoes from Mr Felipe Ponzio, Castle Irwell Hôtel, St Lawrence. The report was referred to the Attorney General. The allegation stated that Mr E. G. Martin, St Brelade was "...selling potatoes at an exorbitant price to one of the foreign workmen in the island". The matter was forwarded to the Attorney General for investigation.[2]

On the 27th March, a letter from the Grain and Potato Controller to the Petrol Controller described "The unsatisfactory manner in which the French potato seed imported into St Helier harbour quay has been moved into the DOA store". The carter was Mr E. A. Allo. In response the DOA recommended to the Department of Transport and Communications that, due to his unsatisfactory conduct, the use of Mr Allo's licence to drive a lorry be withdrawn. The Department of Transport and Communications subsequently withdrew his licence. Mr Allo wrote to the DOA asking for its restoration, but the DOA refused.

The Warble Fly Infestation

On the 5th March 1943, Field Command 515 ordered the States Vet to restrict the movement of all cattle in and out of the harbour area and areas from Gloucester Street to the Victoria Pier. Three days later a verbal report by the States Vet to the DOA described that he had discovered foreign cattle around St Peter's Barracks that were badly infested with the warble fly. A notice was immediately sent to farmers warning of the presence of the pest and asking them to check their cattle. All the Connétables were written to, with advice on the actions to be implemented in their parish if warble fly was discovered.

The States Vet advised treatment for infected cattle should be given to farmers free of charge. This was passed on by the DOA to the Superior Council who accepted the idea. All cases, whether treated by the DOA, the States Vet, or vets in private practice, would be free of charge.

By the 19th March, and "…owing to the existing danger to be apprehended of considerable infection of the island by the warble fly" it was decided to pass an Order to combat the pest. The Superior Council meanwhile had accepted a scale of fees for those in private practice. On the 23rd March an entire herd of Jersey cattle was found to be infested by the maggots of the warble fly.

On the 30th March the Warble Fly (Jersey) Order, 1943 was passed.[10] On the 7th April the DOA wrote to the Connétables informing them that any farmer who discovered an animal infested with the warble fly maggot had to inform the Connétable within 24 hours. The DOA made it clear that the order did not arise from "Règlement pour combattre et éliminer epizootie qui pourrait envahir cette île"; however, this was the only means of combatting the pest as the reporting machinery provided by the Règlement was seen as the quickest method of dealing with the warble fly.[11]

Milk Supply

*"The Attorney General informed the DOA there would be a
prosecution for the adulteration of milk by the Royal Court who
were of the opinion that: It is not in the public interest that Mr Luce
should be allowed any longer to remain in personal control of his farm
or cattle".*

Attorney General's Report

Every month commencing in January 1943, as ordered by Field Command 515, the President of the Department of Essential Commodities delivered exact details of the Island's entire butter production and stocks. A detailed spreadsheet was sent comprising the following information.

Local Butter:
Production at the dairy.
Production at the farms.
Stocks – previous months in cold storage.
Stocks – previous months at wholesalers and dairies.

Imported Butter:
Total available for distribution.
Deliveries to German forces.

Deliveries to Department of Essential Commodities for distribution to the civilian population.

Stock in hand in cold storage.

Stock in hand at wholesalers and dairies.

These monthly spreadsheets were produced by the Jersey Civil Service until the end of the German occupation. The last was on the 23rd April 1945.[12]

On the 12th January Brée reported that, due to the poor quality of the fuel, the boiler fires at Don Street Dairy required constant attention. This meant the caretaker had to attend to the boiler each night and into the early hours of the morning. The DOA decided to pay him an extra 1/- a day.

On the 8th January Brée transmitted a report to the Attorney General, written by the Milk Control Section, regarding an alleged sale of milk to the German forces of occupation. The allegation was made against Mr J. F. Luce, St Lawrence, that he was acting in contravention of the Milk Control (Jersey) Order, 1940. Mr Luce was not the holder of a retailer licence as required by the order.[2] The purchase of agricultural commodities directly from farmers by members of the German armed forces was not allowed by Field Command 515. All such purchases had to be officially sanctioned and a permit issued by Pelz himself. In some cases, other Staff Officers would carry out this duty.

In the same week Mr W. E. Perchard, St Saviour, was called to attend an interview at the DOA. He was asked to explain alleged shortages in the quantities of milk delivered to the licensed retailer in whose register his name was entered. Brée simply gave him a warning that future compliance was required.

On the 22nd January Brée gave a lengthy talk to the DOA on the current position of penalties which could be enacted by the Milk Control Section. The talk was important as it marked a policy change in the surveillance of the Milk Control Unit, making it far more thorough in its control of milk production and distribution throughout Jersey. Brée's comments on Milk Control are therefore worth stating.

"Having regard to the fact that under the present circumstances in the island, milk is virtually the only source from which the population of the island can derive the fats necessary for its maintenance. The DOA is of the opinion that the penalties prescribed in the "Loi (1886) touchant la Falsification des Denrées [adulteration of commodities] are wholly inadequate in relation to offences in connection with milk, and accordingly, it was decided to recommend to the Superior Council that an Order should be made under The Defence (Jersey) Regulations, 1939, withdrawing offences concerning milk from the control of the "Loi" and in providing that persons convicted of such offences shall be liable to the penalties prescribed in the regulations for breaches of the Order made thereunder". Henceforth, farmers who broke Milk Control law would face a far heavier regime and penalties.

In January, Mr P. L. Gibaut, St Lawrence, was written to by Milk Control for failing to complete a registration for the supply of milk in respect of his child. He had previously been obtaining milk from various farmers. Mr Gibaut was warned of the consequences of any further infractions of the with Retailers) (Jersey) Order, 1940.

In February, the DOA received the balance sheet trading accounts for the Don Street Dairy for the year ending 31ˢᵗ December 1942. It demonstrated a final deficit of £7,659-12-1½. The Superior Council agreed, in an attempt to lessen the deficit, to increase the price of both skim milk and butter milk, however it refused to allow an increase in the price of butter. On the 30ᵗʰ March Brée reported to the DOA that in 1943 the Don Street Dairy would be run on a deficit.

On the 18ᵗʰ January Mr F. J. Luce, St Lawrence, applied for the deletion of his employee Mr J. G. Jehan from the list of persons to whom he was permitted to give milk. A report of the 11ᵗʰ February, following an interview with Mr Jehan, brought up a number of alleged serious discrepancies in the supply of milk by Luce to Jehan. Brée decided that "In view of the serious nature of the allegation, to refer the matter to the Attorney General". He also resolved that if the allegation was well founded the Attorney General was to institute proceedings against Mr Luce.[13]

After receiving a letter from his advocate that there was a possibility of legal proceedings, Luce on the 24ᵗʰ February voluntarily visited the Milk Control Office to discuss the matter with Mr Weeks. In his revocation of Jehan's name from his licence, Luce now decided to muddy the waters by giving the names "Varney" and "Odare" as recipients of his milk. In response, Weeks telephoned Luce's lawyer, Advocate J. F. Le Cornu to clarify the issue. It was evident that Luce had deliberately complicated the matter by stating these names.

Weeks' subsequent report to the Attorney General, concluded that Luce had deliberately taken insufficient notice of any communications from the DOA. In addition, he had become unsure and non-compliant of his legal obligations as a milk producer. The matter was left with Attorney General to consider. A week later he produced his report, which stated that Luce would be prosecuted for the alleged adulteration of milk. He informed the DOA that in the opinion of the Royal Court "It is not in the public interest that Mr Luce should be allowed any longer to remain in personal control of his farm or cattle".[2]

Brée discussed the matter with Advocate Le Cornu and suggested that his client take immediate steps to lease his farm and dispose of his cattle and horses. It was decided that Luce, Advocate Le Cornu and the DOA should meet again to discuss the steps which Mr Luce proposed to take to give effect to the wishes of the Royal Court. On the 9ᵗʰ March, Advocates Ogier and Le Cornu informed Brée that arrangements had been made to transfer all his cattle, farming implements and effects to his brother Mr F. E. Luce, who would rent the farm buildings and land up to Christmas 1943. The Royal Court accepted these terms.

On the 2nd March, Field Command 515 expressed its dissatisfaction with the lavatory accommodation at the Don Street Dairy. The States Engineer was ordered to prepare a report on the condition of the toilets and estimate all necessary work to "...meet the requirements of the German authorities". The subsequent remedial works were estimated at £30. The States Engineer was "without delay" charged to execute the work.

On the 13th March, two additional Milk Testers were employed as "The present staff is insufficient to deal with the number of checks of milk production which are, at present, necessary". The two men were Mr C. P. Biddle and Mr A. Hall at a weekly wage of £2.

In the same week the DOA accepted a recommendation from the Medical Board that, in view of the inability of diabetic patients to obtain eggs, the milk ration to such patients should be increased by a further half pint. The total quantity of milk which such patients were entitled to was one and a half pints.

On the 19th March the DOA recommended to the Superior Council that Reginald Weeks, Secretary/Accountant in charge of the Milk Control Section, should receive a "grant" of £25 as remuneration in respect of the extra work in administering, on behalf of the DOA, the Milk (Registration with Retailers) (Jersey) Order 1940, and the Livestock (Jersey) Order, 1942. Brée now rewarded Week's bureaucratic zeal in the discovery and investigation of farmers who had broken Milk Control Orders.

On the 23rd March, Le Gallais was given authorisation for a further twelve months for his milk retailer licence issued in virtue of the Milk Control (Jersey) Order, 1940. His original licence had been issued on the 7th June 1942 in order to supply, on a legal basis, fresh milk to the Staff Officers of Field Command 515. Le Gallais had been supplying the Staff Officers previously from Roselands Farm, without a licence. In consequence the DOA gave consent and issued a backdated licence. This was the only example during the German occupation that a backdated consent for a milk retailer licence was authorised.[14]

Also, on the 23rd March, the Department of Transport and Communications informed the DOA that they wished to convert all the lorries belonging to the Don Street Dairy, Jersey Dairies Limited and Victoria Co-operative Dairy, from petrol to gas consumption. The DOA agreed to the proposed conversion.

Watermills and Milling

On the 12th January 1943 Ernest Charles Gilley resumed work as a miller at Gargate. In the same week, Thomas A. du Feu, a private miller at Mont à L'Abbé Stores, St Helier, applied to the DOA for an increase in electrical power to four days, instead of two days a week, to crush and mill grain. He also asked to be allowed to purchase a new belt for an electric motor. The DOA agreed to both requests.

In February an application was received by the DOA from Mr M. Le Mottée and Mr W. N. Lucas of Gargate for an increase in salary. Both men had completed their probation period in a satisfactory manner. Le Mottée had his wage increased from £3 to £3-5-0 and Lucas from £2-15-0 to £3 a week. The same day Brée discovered that two milling staff at Grand Val were found to be "...in a neglected condition suffering from a lack of food and clothing". This was the first official mention in the German occupation of any DOA staff enduring any form of deprivation. Brée immediately informed the parish authorities, and the men were seen by Mr G. F. Mourant, Chef de Police, who forwarded a report.

In February the balance sheet was prepared for the costs of operating the Mills Control Section for the twelve months up to the 31st December 1942. The DOA requested the Department of Finance and Economics to open a credit of £1,830-10-9 to cover the costs during this period. The DOA also decided that it did not want the administrative costs of the Mills Control Section to be debited to the Trading Account but instead to be charged to the General Revenue of the States.

On the 16th February, Mr C. Le G. Lucas, Mr C. Vincent and Mr C. W. Le Clercq all completed their twelve-month probation period and were awarded a wage increase of 2/6 a week. During the same week, Mr Gilley at Gargate wrote to the DOA stating that his salary as a miller should be increased in line with the rate paid to other millers. Mr Gilley also stated that certain parts of the plant in Gargate Mill were his personal property. Brée replied that his salary would not be increased, however he could submit an application requesting that the DOA purchase from him the plant that was his property. The pleas for increased remuneration by mill staff continued. Mr J. Lewis, a mill's "clerk checker", requested an increase in salary "To cover the use of his bicycle in the service of the DOA". In addition, he stated that he had completed "considerable overtime" at his mill. It was decided to pay him an extra 1/6 weekly to cover the use of his bicycle. On the 23rd February Mr Day, the Mills Supervisor, had his salary debited through the Mills Trading Account.

On the 1st March, a report on the percentage losses at all DOA mills was completed. In particular, the losses at Grand Val were high. Brée ordered a further investigation of the workings of the mill in order to discover the reasons.

Cultivation Orders

On the 9th January 1943, following an inspection of a farm owned by Dr Charles R. Chichester, St Peter, the DOA sent him a letter criticising the standard of cultivation of his land. In addition, the Secretary of the DOA discussed the matter with the Honorary Parish Inspector, Mr E. Egré. The DOA decided that, in view of these reports and Dr Chichester's alleged failure to provide any supplies of foodstuffs for the requirements of the Island population, it would take possession of his farm under the Provisions of Article 5(1)(i) The Defence Regulations, 1939. Dr Chichester would be allowed to retain only his garden and meadows to provide pasture for his cattle.

On the 26th January tenders were advertised for the requisition of the land. On the same day, Dr Chichester wrote a letter to the DOA protesting against this requisition. Brée made it clear in his reply that his Cultivation Orders were rescinded and by the 5th February tenders for his farm had been received. A lease was given to Mr R. de Carteret, the arrangements being handled by the Greffier of the States.

On the 19th January Mr Charles Quenault, Honorary Parish Inspector for St Saviour, was ordered by the German forces to return to the DOA a cheque for £1 which had been issued for the use of his private telephone. Why Field Command 515 should not have allowed payment for the use of his telephone on DOA business is puzzling. No documentation was found to explain Field Command 515's refusal of payment.

The thirteen ploughing contractors hired by the DOA met on the 2nd February to discuss their remuneration for each vergée ploughed in the forthcoming season. After voicing their unhappiness with the amount they were to be paid, a compromise was reached. Three days later, the DOA granted a reduction in the amount of the refund paid by them to the DOA from 10/6 to 8/6 per vergée.

In January, Field Command 515 and Pelz purchased four seed drills from the Continent which were subsequently shipped to Jersey. In turn, the DOA purchased the drills from Field Command, to be used in the 1943 season. The machines were inspected and Brée decided that, because of their length and height, they were unsuitable for use. Brée was an intelligent and resourceful inventor with a capacity for design and fabrication of agricultural parts and machinery. He made a series of modifications to the seed drills, which were carried out successfully by L. C. Pallot, Central Motor Works, Trinity. Edwin Gibaut carried out a series of tests and reported that the purchased drills were satisfactory. They were subsequently hired out to approved contractors on very favourable terms: L. C. Pallot, J. G. Colback, C. W. Buesnel and J. F. A'Court. Increasingly, it was Field Command 515 and Pelz who, on behalf of the Island, were sourcing and obtaining agricultural inputs: seed, artificial fertiliser, chemical pesticides, agricultural machinery and parts, and fuel.

On the 28th January, Mr Pallot purchased the remaining Ford Ferguson tractor, requisitioned on behalf of the DOA from Dr Constantinos Mattas in December 1941, for the price of £208. The reasons for ownership of two brand new Ford Ferguson tractors by a Greek doctor born in Bulgaria, who had emigrated to Jersey in 1922 to work as a General Practitioner, remains a mystery. Dr Mattas was a resident of Jersey in the 1930s, but he also spent eleven months in Germany between 1935 and 1936.[15] Recently discovered correspondence has demonstrated that he visited Berlin in 1934, although this is not mentioned on his Alien's Card. As a result of a telephone line being cut and the production of an anti-German pamphlet, Dr Mattas was taken hostage in June 1942 along with nine local islanders, including a schoolteacher from Victoria College, Mr W. H. Kennet. Dr Mattas came through the experience unscathed, and no action was taken against him.[16]

On the 19th February the DOA recommended to the Department of Public Instruction that schoolboys should be released from school in order to assist in the planting of potatoes as from the 1st March 1943.

In March a report from Mr Philip Gallichan, Honorary Parish Inspector, St Saviour, stated that an authorised ploughing contractor, Mr H. Georgelin, had been ploughing land with petrol supplied by other farmers and replacing it with petrol obtained under the authority of the Parish Honorary Inspector. In view of the serious nature of Mr Georgelin's "improper action" he was removed from the list of ploughing contractors working on behalf of the DOA. Georgelin appealed but the DOA refused to alter its decision. In the same week the Petrol Controller informed the DOA that three contractors – G. Baudains, E. Hervé and J. W. Perchard – had used petrol issued by the Honorary Parish Inspector to scarify land prior to ploughing, whereas petrol was only to be used for ploughing. The DOA informed them that such use of petrol could not be tolerated, and they were warned that any further scarifying using petrol would lead to the termination of their appointment.

On the 9th March the Department of Transport and Communications placed 3,000 gallons of petrol at the disposal of the DOA to complete the 1943 ploughing season. One contractor, Mr S. F. Le Brun, was dismissed for using an excessive quantity of petrol which was under the control of the Honorary Parish Inspector, and he was replaced by Mr Francis Le Boutillier who used a Fordson tractor burning a new fuel mixture.

On the 9th March Brée approached Pelz in an endeavour to secure permission for farmers to cut the branches of trees which were harmful either to the growing of crops or to cattle. In the same week the DOA made preparations for the delivery of the 1943 Cultivation Directives. These were sent on the 23rd March under the heading "Direction under The Cultivation of Lands (Jersey) Order, 1942". It was emphasised that any non-compliance with the order was a punishable offence under the order in Council Regulations, 1st September 1939. Farmers were instructed to reply not later than the 17th April, indicating the areas they would plant with potatoes, mangolds, wheat, or cereals in fulfilment of these Directives. Pelz was aware of the crucial importance of sending out the Directives and busied himself with the logistics of their individual delivery to farmers.

Pigs

"Jurat Brée now informs me that between October to December 1942, Mr Huson sold 37 pigs to the German authorities, under permits from Field Command".

The Bailiff in correspondence with the Field Commandant

In early January 1943 Brée made one of his many visits to College House to discuss agricultural matters with Pelz. At the meeting the German authorities expressed dissatisfaction with "...the position regarding the pigs in the custody of Mr A. A. Huson, St Saviour". Brée informed the Field Commandant that, although he could not supply detailed information "à pied levé",[17] he was under the impression that the majority of the pigs were sold to the German forces. When Brée investigated the matter, he discovered that between October and December 1942 Mr Huson had sold thirty-seven pigs to the German authorities, against the production of permits granted by Field Command and Pelz.[18]

Fertilisers

During 1942, Pelz had written to the Bailiff concerning supplies of artificial fertilisers that were urgently needed for 1943. A definitive answer eventually sent to Pelz stated that in 1943 the requirements were:[19]

1,000 tons sulphate of ammonia
2,000 tons superphosphates
600 tons muriate or sulphate of potash
1,000 tons lime or chalk

A DOA report on the 19th January 1943 states that it had sufficient reserves of fertilisers to allow 3 hundredweight to be distributed per vergée for the 1943 potato crop. Three days later the DOA fixed the prices for artificial fertilisers which had recently been imported from France. These were sold to the merchants, who mixed them, for £14-10-10 per ton of ammonia and at £12-2-6 per ton of phosphates. In addition, merchants were invoiced 10/- per sack. If the sacks were returned no later than 31st March 1943 and in good condition, the merchants would be refunded.

Three groups made offers to purchase the entire stock of imported fertilisers – the JPMA, J. W. Huelin Limited and W. Dennis and Sons Limited. The JPMA was chosen as the sole handler of all imported French artificial fertilisers and was given strict formulae for mixing the chemicals, as prescribed by Mr Woodcock, along with instructions for selling only to farmers.

1. Payment to be made within one month of invoice.
2. Payment for future deliveries, due to be made, within two months from the date of delivery.
3. The above applied to ingredients for the 1943 season only.
4. The margins for sale to be approved by the DOA.
5. The price for mixtures made from these ingredients that were to be sold to farmers for cash would be subject to approval by the DOA.
6. The names of firms selected to mix ingredients had to be submitted for approval by the DOA.
7. The JPMA was made aware that the DOA would control the distribution of all fertilisers in virtue of the powers conferred upon it by the Fertilisers (Jersey) Order, 1941.

On the 2nd February the DOA met the President and Vice President of the JPMA, when the price of the mixture was set at 18/- per cwt.

On the 5th February, the DOA instructed the JPMA to furnish a return showing the quantity of potato fertiliser held in stock by each member of the JPMA. On the same day the DOA decided that all the "seedsmen" be authorised to supply fertilisers for "The use of small gardens at the rate of three lbs per box of seed potatoes planted at seven lbs per perch".[20] The maximum quantity allowed for any one person was fixed at 28 lbs and the price was set at 3½d per pound. Each seedsman was to keep a record of the persons to whom fertilisers had been sold, along with the quantity.

On the 8th February the Imports and Exports Advisory Committee wrote to the DOA asking for its view on an application from J. W. Huelin Limited for permission to import 300 tons of lime. The DOA made no objection but pointed out that all sales would be under its control under the Fertilisers (Jersey) Order, 1941. On the 21st March J. W. Huelin Limited wrote to the DOA that it had an offer of 500 tons of French agricultural lime. The company asked for support in obtaining an Import Licence, as required by the Import and Export of Goods (Control) (Jersey) Order, 1941. The DOA agreed and asked whether it intended to distribute the lime, when received, through various merchants. On the 30th March the company replied to the DOA and said that it "...declined to proceed with the purchase of this material under the conditions set forth by the DOA". It refused to distribute the agricultural lime through JPMA merchants under the auspices of the DOA, and simply wanted to sell the material itself, and thus retain the profit margin it had calculated would be forthcoming.

On the 2nd March, Mr Woodcock recommended that potato fertiliser be issued to the Jersey Allotment Council for the sole use of allotment holders at the rate of 5 lbs per perch. In the same week, the President of the JPMA expressed to the DOA his "...concern at the manner in which artificial fertilisers are being distributed by certain members of the Association". The

DOA requested that he "Furnish a return including the names and addresses of the persons to whom each of the members of the JPMA have supplied fertiliser together with the quantity of such fertiliser which has been supplied to each such persons".

On the 9th March Mr Woodcock authorised the preparation of 300 tons of fertiliser for the treatment of land which was to be devoted to hay and grazing in 1943. It was issued at half a hundredweight per vergée at a cost of 21/4 per cwt, the farmer having to supply his own bags. Woodcock also decided that, in the event of further supplies of chalk being imported, he would increase the quantity of fertiliser available for grazing land to 450 tons, an increase of 50% per vergée.

Agricultural Labour

On the 19th January 1943, the DOA recommended to the Superior Council that £1,000 be placed at its disposal to meet the cost of providing assistance with payment for agricultural labour, from the 5th October 1942 until the 30th January 1943, to those farmers whose applications had been approved by the Advisory Committee set up by Field Command 515 for that purpose. On the 12th February, the DOA asked Brée to propose to the Advisory Committee that it should deal with all applications for assistance in payment of agricultural labour. A notice would be sent to farmers, drawing attention to the possibility of obtaining assistance or, alternatively, the Honorary Parish Inspectors would be asked to make the scheme more widely known. Three days later the Department of Finance and Economics opened a credit of £2,500 to meet the cost of providing assistance for six months, until 30th July 1943.

On the 19th February the DOA again discussed the Agricultural Workers Bonus. It concluded that granting assistance with the payment of agricultural labour would result in "An injustice to farmers who are unable to obtain such assistance". Brée therefore decided to recommend to the Superior Council that the present scheme should terminate on the 31st July 1943 and be replaced by an increase in the prices paid for agricultural produce, to cover the additional cost of labour at the rates specified in a notice that was published in the local press on the 2nd October 1942, under the authority of an act of the same day. These payments would be made to those men already receiving the following weekly wage:

(i)   £2-0-0 to men without dependents
(ii) £2-10-0 per week to men with dependents

On the 25th May it was agreed that the scheme would terminate on the 31st July 1943.

Jersey Produce Merchants Association

In February 1943 the JPMA made an application to the DOA for an increase from 3/6 to 5/- per ton to cover the cost of removing shoots from potatoes. Brée agreed, provided that the charge would include sorting and bagging potatoes for distribution to the population, together with the removal of shoots. This concession prompted the JPMA to ask the DOA to receive a deputation, in order to discuss "Terms of payment to the members of the Association in relation to the handling, storing and sorting of potatoes of the 1943 crop".

A JPMA deputation subsequently met with the DOA when it was agreed that merchants would be paid 25/- per ton for bagging, storage and sorting the 1943 potato crop, payment to be made in two instalments. The first instalment of 75% would be payable on taking the potatoes into store, and the second of 25% to be payable at the conclusion of storage. The DOA in addition made it conditional that the potatoes be delivered in a proper manner and that all potatoes were marketable.

The DOA, furthermore, decided that it would pay 25/- in respect of each ton of potatoes shipped for export, to cover all services performed by the merchants in relation to those shipments. It also decided that the quantity of potatoes shipped on its behalf by merchants would be calculated based upon the quantity which the merchants held in store on its behalf.

Horses

In 1943 the need for horses for agricultural work greatly increased and there was a serious shortage of animals. As one farmer commented, "We had to rely solely on horses to do all the farm work. To the farmers they were more precious than a Rolls Royce".[21] A Grouville farmer commented in 2014, "Horses were the saviours of the Island during the German occupation". Increasingly, the States purchased horses from France.

In February a German officer, Zimmerman, purchased a local horse. It was subsequently offered by Field Command 515 to any farmer who had need of it for cultivating his land. Two farmers were written to by Brée, Mr A. J. Kempster, La Rocque and Mr G. A. Vautier, Egypt, Trinity, suggesting that they contact Field Command directly to make arrangements for the use of the horse.[22]

On the 19th February the horse that had been requisitioned in October 1942 from Dr H. G. Oliver (who had been deported to Germany in September 1942) was returned by two farmers to the DOA, being described as "unsatisfactory for farm work". The States Vet thereupon decided that the horse should be destroyed.

At the end of February, a large number of horses were imported from Granville and 18 hundredweight of oats supplied for their feed.

Tobacco

*"Herbert Minck has been authorised to cultivate tobacco on two to
three hectares
(12 to 18 vergées) of ground"*

Dr Casper in a letter to the Bailiff

In January and February the DOA instructed all farmers who had greenhouses that growing tobacco in them was not allowed.

On the 9th March Mr Walter Benest, St Brelade, made a formal application to the DOA for permission to grow 1 vergée of tobacco on his farmland as a first crop. His application was refused. Brée was resolved that it was not in the Island's best interests to allow tobacco cultivation to be officially sanctioned. He instructed all Honorary Parish Inspectors to report on any grower or occupier of any field, in which more than 1,000 tobacco plants were being grown as a first crop. A week later a second application was received from Mr P. V. Sarre, Bel Royal, to grow 19 perches of tobacco. Mr Sarre made it clear in his application that the land in question "...was not included in the Cultivation Directions issued to him for 1943". Brée decided to refer the matter to the Honorary Parish Inspectors for St Lawrence. Mr T. A. Pallot was charged with providing a report on the suitability of the land for growing tobacco and his subsequent report convinced Brée that he could not grant Sarre permission to cultivate tobacco. The Honorary Parish Inspector was ordered to inform Sarre that he was to devote his energies and land to the growing of vegetables.

It was certainly no surprise that farmers wanted to grow greater quantities of tobacco. It was a lucrative and easy cash crop to cultivate. Rationing of tobacco had become commonplace although the weekly ration varied from month to month. Tobacco became the cash crop for farmers and growers; it could be sold on any farm either straight from the ground or dried and cured, which gave it a value-added margin. Tobacco was an excellent bartering currency and could even be used as a form of payment to agricultural workers. German troops were also happy to exchange food, clothes and commodities. Joyce Le Ruez wrote in her private diary, "German soldiers came for toilet soap in exchange for tobacco".[23]

German soldiers themselves grew tobacco on a fairly widespread basis. Officers brought leaf tobacco into St Helier to be cut and were charged 2/- per pound weight. Much of their tobacco was extremely good quality and, when appropriate, it was mixed with locally grown poor-quality leaves at the tobacco factory in St Helier.[24]

The fact that German soldiers were growing and exchanging tobacco, for goods to send back to Germany, came to the attention of Pelz and

Field Command 515. On the 9th February 1943 OKVR Dr Casper wrote to the Bailiff a letter entitled "Herbert Minck tobacco grower". Dr Casper explained that Minck was capable of growing, drying and processing locally grown tobacco, and he had produced good results using uncultivated land near the airport. He furthermore suggested that a trial be established, using tobacco seed already available, to ascertain if tobacco growing could be profitable. Casper notes "If such is the case the cultivation must be undertaken by the States. The raw product would then be taken over by the Tobacco Company".

A conference was held at College House on the 16th March between the DOA and Field Command 515 on the subject of cultivating commercial quantities of tobacco. Both Brée and Pelz were in attendance. Dr Casper wrote to the Bailiff again on the 25th March. The letter made the Bailiff aware of six points concerning the establishment of a new tobacco plantation.

1. Herbert Minck has been authorised to cultivate tobacco on two to three hectares (12 to 18 vergées) of ground.
2. The ground will be supplied in the West by Herr Schirner of the Air Force [this was actually Herr Schöner].
3. The island administration is prepared to supply the necessary labour and machinery for the proper cultivation and care of the tobacco.[25]
4. The Jersey Tobacco Company shall purchase the dried leaves when ready from Mr Minck for the tanning of the tobacco.
5. The cost of cultivating the tobacco until such time as the dried leaves are delivered to the factory is borne by Mr Minck.
6. The work is to commence immediately.[26]

The "Experimental Tobacco" plantation at St Brelade proceeded. In April Knackfuss contacted the Bailiff complaining that Minck, "The tobacco planter" had hired a tractor and driver from the DOA and been invoiced "35RM for one day's work". Knackfuss was clearly convinced that Minck had been overcharged by the DOA. In a far more forceful tone than we normally see in his correspondence to the Island's Civilian Authority, Knackfuss demanded that no further costs be applied by the DOA on Minck's experimental plantation. On the 3rd May Brée replied, with an extremely detailed report, to the complaint that the ploughing contractor, J. Michel, had overcharged. The report, entitled "Experimental growing of tobacco" was written by the St Brelade Honorary Parish Inspector, Mr Herbert M. Gibaut.

Gibaut's report confirmed that Mr Michel informed Mr Minck (in his presence) that the cost of the tractor and driver, exclusive of petrol, would be £3-15-0 per day or 8/- an hour. This had been the same price that Michel had previously charged Field Command 515 for work done on several occasions and had always been paid without comment and was, moreover, the same as that charged by other contractors. Ploughing was carried out using "A very powerful German tractor over very rough land". Michel claimed this had caused damage to his farm implements and he found the work "unsatisfactory". Finally, he stated he did not really want the work!

On the 21st May a conference was held between OKVR Dr Casper and Jurat E. P. Le Masurier, President of the Department of Essential Supplies, Minck being present. The topic for discussion was the tobacco plantation. A few weeks later, the Attorney General and the Connétable of St Brelade visited the plantation, the aim being to inspect the quantity of leaves that had been stolen. This apparent pilfering of tobacco continued throughout the summer. On the 5th September, Knackfuss contacted the Bailiff concerning the latter's promise that the police would maintain surveillance of "Minck's tobacco plantation". Knackfuss curtly wrote "...tobacco is still being stolen" and insisted once more that "...a sufficient watch be kept". The Bailiff immediately conveyed to the Attorney General Knackfuss' request for increased policing of Minck's tobacco plantation.

Duret Aubin's reply to the Bailiff and to Knackfuss was a masterclass in the art of prevarication. He stated that the area of the plantation made it extremely difficult to supervise; part of it was in a German military area to which the civil police had no right of access. Duret Aubin advised that six men were needed night and day to ensure absolute protection of Minck's tobacco plants. He concluded by advising both the Bailiff and Knackfuss that Mr Minck should help the police, firstly by reporting where and when plants were stolen, and to give precise details.

The Order by the Attorney General to the Honorary and Full-time Police to Round-up OT Workers

In late 1942, Joyce Marie Le Ruez, Homestead Farm, St Peter, described in her diary events she witnessed around her father's farm. Joyce wrote about a new phenomenon that had appeared: foreign workmen wandering around the countryside. Her first diary entry had been in January 1942. "There are many foreign workmen here (all colours). They look very shabby and half starved". By August, she noticed that the plight of the OT workers had considerably worsened. "Some of the Russians working at the railway in St Peter came this afternoon barefoot. They are a pitiful sight. Russian workers have been to our potato crop. They are very hungry".

By September 1942, "A poor Russian was heavily beaten by the Todt when women were boiling potatoes for him were denounced by a Jerseyman. There are many instances of this". In the same week, "Russians and others came here for food today. Dad gave them some apples". In October, Joyce wrote "...poor Russians beaten by Todt today. John saw one half dead put in a lorry". The following week "...our little boy (Russian) of 15 years of age came and burst into tears. It is very sad to see these so young so far from home". Two weeks passed. "We are very pleased to see our little bandaged Russian again today. We had not seen him for a long time and thought perhaps he had gone. He had no bandages today, but his eye did not look very well. He had a friend with him. We gave them something to eat. Nikolai came from Kiev and had been struck in the eye by the OT. He gave me his photograph". Ukrainians were transported directly from Kiev to St Malo in railway wagons and shipped into Jersey. The train journey took three weeks. These Ukrainians were incarcerated in the wagons and cruelly mistreated on a continual basis for the entire journey. They were inadequately fed nor given water to keep them in a fit state and there were no sanitary facilities. When Nicolai reached Jersey in late 1941, he would have been physically and mentally traumatised.

By November and December 1942, OT workers were increasingly leaving their camps at night. The majority were starving and turned to robbing farm buildings and looking for any agricultural produce in fields and vegetable gardens. Joyce commented "There have been a lot of robberies lately. Still more robberies...it is usually within curfew time. They even skin rabbits on premises and cook them".

On the 1st December, Joyce was horrified by "A shocking tragedy. Poor Mr Le Gresley. Killed by a Russian in his sleep. He was given a blow on the head. Germans searching all day for Russians and caught fifteen". The next day, "The Germans are still hunting Russians. It's a very awkward situation for us".

The Le Ruez family was only one of many Jersey families who actively assisted OT workers, risking deportation to the Continent themselves, or death. Dennis Le Flem, Seaview Farm, St Helier, befriended an escaped Russian OT worker, a boy of his own age, Peter Bokatenko. The two boys looked similar and Dennis seriously put his life in jeopardy by giving his identity card to Peter. Dennis was arrested for hunting rabbits without the appropriate licence issued by Pelz. He was summoned to College House and questioned by a member of Field Command 515.[27] Dennis informed the officer that he had lost his identity card and was threatened with deportation to a camp as punishment. However, he was given a fine and warned to apply for a hunting permit.[28] Peter was subsequently arrested with the card in his possession.

At Springfield Farm, another Ukrainian boy, Mischa Ivanoff was hidden by Peter and Bertha Ireland. Mischa was sixteen years of age. He worked for the family from 1942 until the end of the German occupation. Mischa never spoke whilst outside the farm. The States Medical Officer of Health took a real risk by arranging for the surgical removal of Mischa's tattoo on his arm.

By early 1943 the numbers of escaped and starving OT workers had increased. This became anathema to the "OT Task Force West and the

Chief Building Supervisor, Julius, Workforce Office, St Malo". Instructions were sent to Field Command 515 that a large group of 25 OT workers was wandering the Island and under no effective control. In an attempt to take control of these foreign workers, the OT Einsatzgruppe West, St Malo, printed new OT identity cards. In addition, all foreign OT workers "under control" would not only be issued with the new cards, but they would incorporate a specially designed stamp. This was to distinguish them from foreign OT workers "who were not under control". In other words, those OT workers who had escaped. In addition to the new identity card and new stamp, another feature was placed on the document. This was a diagonal line across the bottom left-hand of the card on which the OT worker's photograph was pasted. If any of these features were not present, "The worker is not in order".

On the 7th January 1943 the Attorney General forwarded the above information to all the Connétables and that "The Field Commandant had requested that after 1pm on Tuesday, January 11th, 1944,[29] the police of the island, honorary and paid, will generally cause foreign workers to produce to them their identity cards and will immediately detain and convey to the police station, St Helier, any such persons found without the specially stamped identity card. The Field Commandant particularly requests that a specific control of all foreign workers' identity cards should take place after 1pm on each of the following days: Tuesday, January 11th, Friday, January 14th, and Saturday, January 15th. I shall be obliged to you if you will inform your police and make arrangement for the necessary control. The police are authorised by the Field Commandant to enter any restaurant or café regardless of nationality, for the purpose of this control. I have here, for your inspection if that will assist you, samples of foreign workers cards and as they should be stamped in order to show that they are in order".[30]

On the 8th January, Duret Aubin wrote to all concerned informing them of further variations in OT identity cards which had been issued by the German Air Force and Navy.

The above order is both interesting and informative. It demonstrates the chain of command concerning the corralling of escaped OT workers. The original order emanated from the OT Chief Building Supervisor. He, however, did not have the authority to order the Island's Civil Authority and administration, including the police, to expedite the systematic gathering of these unfortunate souls. The order to the Civil Authority had to emanate from the German Military Government in Jersey, Field Command 515, and then the order cascaded downwards to the Bailiff, Superior Council, Attorney General, Connétables and finally the Honorary and paid police.

By late April 1943, the pursuit by the Connétables and police of these OT workers had not proved successful. The reason was simple. Many of these young men had been assisted, and in a number of cases hidden, by extremely brave Jersey farmers and families.

On the 22nd April 1943, in an attempt to finally capture these OT workers and prevent thefts of agricultural produce, the Field Commandant and Military Commander ordered the Bailiff to commence, as from the 30th April, parish night patrols. The Connétables were ordered to issue identity cards to twenty men from each parish, to be taken on the night of the patrol and in agreement with their local Military Commander. These night passes were then returned at the end of the patrol to the Connétable. Night patrols were to be on alternate evenings. The Attorney General required each Connétable within six days to provide him with the full name, address, and identity card number of every night patrol officer.[31]

On the 17th May the Attorney General again wrote to the Connétables. He had received from the "Standortkommandant" the special permits and a list of instructions for the night patrols.[32]

It is interesting that Joyce Le Ruez notes in her diary that, on the 27th April 1943, Knackfuss met the Honorary Parish Inspectors at College House. At that meeting he demanded that the Jersey people provide a civilian guard to patrol their fields to prevent Russians from stealing produce.

Whatever happened to Nicolai from Kiev, Peter Bokatenko and Mischa Ivanoff from the Ukraine? Joyce recounts her last conversation with Nicolai on the 5th October 1943. "Our little bandaged Russian came to say goodbye. He looked much better than a year ago when he first came. He is going to work in France. All Russians are going away". Joyce never received any further news from Nicolai. Mischa Ivanoff worked on Springfield Farm for the entire occupation and lived as a member of the Ireland family. In effect, as Peter and Bertha Ireland had no children, he became their son. Although Mischa had no identity card, he lived an open life in the confines of the farm. Soon after Liberation Day all foreign workers were sent back to their country of origin. Mischa, however, slipped his Russian military escort and vanished into the French countryside. He married a French girl and they had two children.

Peter Bokatenko survived through the occupation, being helped by the Le Flem family and other farmers before his arrest. Peter's personal story of his brutal treatment by the OT and his betrayal by local informers was published in 1945.[33] After Liberation Day, he was sent to a rehabilitation centre at Newlands Corner, Guildford, Surrey. He thereafter went back to the Ukraine and corresponded with Dennis for the next thirty years.[34]

References

1. Jersey Archive. B/A/W41/20.
2. Jersey Archive. C/B/A1/8.
3. Jersey Archives. B/A/W31/20.
4. RJA&HS and JFU Joint Emergency Committee Minutes.
5. For a detailed list of the points scheme see Jersey Archive L/D/09/A10, p. 341.

6. *Ibid.* p. 338.
7. Jersey Archive. B/A/W50/15.
8. Most probably the Paymaster of the German Catering Service.
9. Jersey Archive. B/A/W31/2/73.
10. Jersey Archive. B/A/W31/2/77.
11. Jersey Archive. L/F/54/C/D/14.
12. Jersey Archive. B/A/W31/2/8-9.
13. Jersey Archive. D/Z/H5/141/2.
14. Jersey Archive. C/B/A1/7.
15. Jersey Archive. D/S/B1/1991.
16. Jersey Archive. Correspondence with Stuart Nicolle. 29th September 2020.
17. "speak off the cuff'.
18. Jersey Archive. B/A/W31/2/68.
19. Jersey Archive. B/A/W31/2/46.
20. The Island Seed Merchants.
21. John Labey. "Home Farm", Grouville. Address given to celebrate the 50th Anniversary of the liberation. 1995.
22. Jersey Archive. B/A/W31/2/71.
23. Joyce Le Ruez. Private diary. 14th January 1942. My thanks to Pam Laurens and her family for permission to read Joyce's diary and correspondence.
24. My thanks to Robert Germain, Managing Director, J. F. Germain & Sons Ltd.
25. Field Command 515.
26. Jersey Archives. B/A/W31/2/69A.
27. From Dennis' description of the officer in question it may well have been Dr Casper.
28. Gilson, A. RJA&HS Journal. 2019. Annual Report. p. 29. Also Jersey Rural Oct 2022 "A Farm under Occupation", pp. 58–59.
29. This should have read 1943.
30. Jersey Archive. L/F/54/C/D/12. Document dated 7th January 1943.
31. Jersey Archive. L/F/54/C/D/16. Field Command 515. Az. Pol. 0212. Document dated 22nd April 1943.
32. He was a German Military Officer in charge of the security for St Helier. His office was near the Weighbridge.
33. JEP. 18th May 1945.
34. JEP. 31st March 2014.

Chapter 12

April – May – June 1943

Milk Control

On the 6th April 1943, Brée announced that the Superior Council had agreed to an increase in the price of skimmed milk but had refused to increase the price of butter; the DOA informed the States that in 1943 the Don Street Dairy would run on a deficit and, in addition, Mr John de la Haye appeared before the DOA to explain alleged milk shortages to the dairy. He was given a warning that he had to send all the milk he produced, except for the quantity he was allowed to retain for his household. A failure to comply with this instruction would lead to legal proceedings. Brée gave a final warning that the improvement in his milk supply had to be immediate.

On the 9th April, the figure for the milk deficit for the year ending the 31st December 1942 was calculated at £10,115-14-3½. The next day, the DOA announced that skimmed milk would be available for sale every day. On the same day Mr G. A. Hamon, the Factory Manager of Don Street Dairy, made an application to increase the wages of his staff, H. Chevalier, F. Gray and J. Billot. Their salaries were increased by 5/- a week, and M. Noel by 10/-. The DOA decided that because of the increase in milk supplies being handled at Don Street Dairy and the longer hours the employees had to work, they would pay a weekly bonus of 7/6 from the 18th April until the 2nd October 1943 to the following staff:

- C. Wood — Stoker
- C. Hamon — Butter-maker and part-time stoker
- M. Noel — Weigher
- L. Le Dantec — Packer
- J. Billot — Weigher
- F. Gray — Weigher
- G. Haines — General hand
- G. Le Beuvant — Improver
- H. Chevalier — Weigher

In the same week, Mrs L. H. de la Haye, St Martin, was summoned to the DOA. She was instructed that an explanation was required as to alleged shortages of milk delivered to the dairy. The Milk Control Section was "...by no means satisfied with the explanations". She appeared before the DOA four days later. Brée expressed dissatisfaction with the explanations put forward. The producer was warned that in the event of any further shortages being discovered severe measures would be taken.[1]

On the 21st April, the Milk Control Section reported an allegation of "... an overselling during the month of March by Messrs Allo Brothers, 59 Great Union Road, who hold a retailer's licence." In view of the unsatisfactory nature of the explanations offered by the owners, the DOA wrote back expressing their dissatisfaction and warning that "A reoccurrence of such overselling would result in the DOA taking disciplinary action."

The end of April saw a spate of reported milk shortages. On the 30th April, Mr J. Le Masurier Junior, St Clement, appeared before the DOA to discuss certain alleged shortages in the quantity of milk delivered to the dairy. In view of the "unsatisfactory nature" of his explanation, he was given a warning. Brée was happy to take a lenient stance if he felt an offending farmer would not in future contravene agricultural directions.

A Milk Tester, Mr Hind, was replaced by Mr C. P. Biddle and Mr G. Paulain. It was also decided to call the Motor Traffic Inspector to Don Street Dairy to inspect the tyres of the bicycles used by the Milk Testers who were in the service of the DOA. A stock of cycle tyres was built up, to be used only by the Milk Testers.

Staff problems arose at the Don Street Dairy. The Factory Manager, Mr A. F. Hamon, summarily dismissed Mr Louis Le Dantec who had absented himself from work contrary to instructions. The Solicitor General was asked whether Le Dantec was due one week's pay in lieu of notice. He replied that the Milk Control Section, under the circumstances, was not under an obligation to pay Le Dantec one week's wages in lieu of notice. The circumstance for which he was summarily dismissed was "wilful disobedience" and this was reason enough. Mr Hamon found an immediate replacement. He appointed Mr Guy Wills as a butter packer and weigher at a weekly wage of £2-12-6 and a weekly bonus of 7/6.

On the 4th May, Mr D. A. McLinton was appointed on the staff of Don Street Dairy, in the place of Mr J. Firwin who had been deported from the Island in October 1942. His weekly wage was £2-2-6 after a four-week probationary period.

In May, further milk shortages were investigated. The first report concerned alleged shortages in the quantity delivered to the dairy by Captain J. S. McCann, St Saviour. Since the cow in the custody of Captain McCann had little value, in relation to the supply of milk for the requirements of the civilian population, the DOA charged the Cattle Slaughter Executive Committee to slaughter the animal.

On the 8th May, Miss N. Houillebecq was appointed at the Milk Control Section at a wage of £1-7-6 a week, after four weeks of probation. On the same day, Mr W. G. Le Ruez, Trinity, appeared before the DOA. It was alleged that he did not deliver all his milk to the dairy, less the quantity he was permitted to retain for his family. He was a given a written warning and the matter was closed.

At the same time, the DOA wrote to a number of dairy farmers concerning alleged problems when delivering their evening quota of milk to the licensed retailers in whose register their names were entered. They were: N.G. Renouf, St Martin, G. Le Boutillier, St Martin, J. R. Billot, St Saviour, F. R. Billot, St Saviour, and J. Morin, St Mary. Three of them had failed to deliver milk to their licensed retailer and were given one last warning. Mr Renouf and Mr Le Boutillier were called in for interviews concerning their evening deliveries of milk.

On the 28th May, a report alleged that Mrs P. Bonny, St Lawrence, had supplied milk to her ill daughter, in excess of that granted by the Medical Board. The cow which supplied this milk was eighteen years old. The DOA decided to refer this cow to the Cattle Slaughter Executive for slaughter.

On the 1st June, Mr Biddle resigned as a Milk Tester and was replaced by Mr J. T. Roberts who proved to be incompetent in his duties and who also resigned. Mr George Davey took over, but he too resigned five days later.

On the 12th June, the Cattle Slaughter Executive was instructed to slaughter a fourteen-year-old cow in the custody of Mrs L. H. de la Haye. The cow was no use for breeding and not producing enough milk for the civilian population.

At the same time, a report was sent to the DOA in relation to Mrs R. G. Dumotier, St Martin. She was a producer who it was alleged was not delivering the whole of the milk produced by her cow. Mrs Dumotier was called to appear before the DOA and, during the course of the investigation, it was ascertained that Mr J. B. Dumotier had left the Island and then come back. It was Mr Dumotier who was the legal milk producer under the Milk Control Order. After consideration of the report the DOA decided to ask the Attorney General to investigate a further allegation that milk was supplied from the farm to the German Forces. Mr Dumotier was ordered to send all his milk to the licensed retailer every evening.[2] The following week Dumotier continued to fail to deliver his full quota of milk and the matter was referred to the Attorney General.

Mr J. Ferry, St Mary, also appeared before the DOA to explain his alleged failure to deliver to the DOA "The whole of his milk produced by his cows other than the quantity which he is entitled to retain." The DOA decided that in view of "The unsatisfactory explanations offered by Mr Ferry and the strong suspicion which exists that the cattle are being milked improperly," they would report to the Cattle Slaughter Executive Committee. It examined two cows in his custody which produced very little milk and they were sent to the abattoir.

The following week, Mr A. Mauger, St Ouen appeared before the Connétable. When interviewed he was asked to explain alleged shortages in the quantity of milk he delivered. Mr Mauger was unable to supply a satisfactory account. He was warned that unless he curtailed his excessive retention of milk, drastic action would be taken against him. Brée decided that enough had been done to remedy the issue and the matter was dropped.

On the 21st June it was discovered through a routine audit that a large number of milk deliveries made by E. J. Paisnel, Grouville, to his licensed retailer had turned sour.[3] Paisnel was warned of the poor condition of his milk and that it was not fit to be sold to the public. In consequence the Milk Control Section reduced his milk payments by 6 pence a pot. A week later another producer, Mr W. C. Quenault, St Peter, delivered sour milk to his licensed retailer. He also received a reduced price per pot.

Watermills and Milling

On the 6th April, an investigation was carried out after an allegation that a carter had stolen wheat from Tesson, St Peter. On the same day, the tenancy for the Grand Val Mill was extended for a further year.

On the 16th April, Brée wrote to the Bailiff informing him that the German authorities were carrying out construction work in Grand Vaux which had led to all water supplies being cut off and Grand Val and Malassis Mills had to stop milling. A German construction unit, building a new road and culvert, had blocked the water supply to the mills. Brée's letter states, "It is essential that the water supply to the mills be maintained in order that flour required for the feeding of the population may be ground." He requested that the stream be passed through water pipes. The Bailiff subsequently wrote to the Field Command and within several days Brée's request had been implemented by the German engineer constructing the road.[4]

In June, the States Engineer and the Department of Public Health wrote to the DOA concerning rats at Quetivel. The letter suggested that the walls of Quetivel be rendered in order to make them "Rat-Proof." The DOA accepted the recommendation; however, it insisted that the fireplace on the ground floor should not be removed as "The retention of the old fireplace is necessary to enable the employees to cook their meals in winter."

On the 18th June Mr G. F. Josse, First Assistant Miller, Grand Val, was dismissed. The reason given was "…he for some time, had been very irregular in his attendance at the mill." He was given one week's notice and one week's salary. The following week, he was replaced as Assistant Miller by Mr F. J. Horton. He was paid £3 a week. Eric Horton, already employed at the mill, had his salary increased from £1-5-0 to £1-15-0 a week.

Tobacco

"Please grow and cure for me 100 Tobacco plants.
Signed W Le Blancq. Address, 41 Parade Place. Date, 1-6-43.
Please grow and cure for me 100 Tobacco plants.
Signed Alwyn Horace Fitch. Address 2 Bagot Avenue, St Saviour.
Date.1-6-43."

In the Société Jersiaise Library is an interesting notebook, the opening page outlines its purpose:

SEASON 1943-4
ORDER BOOK

TOBACCO PLANTS

J MALETROIT
FARMER AND GROWER
MONT COCHON
ST SAVIOUR
Phone, Millbrook, 123

Inside the book are over 100 written templates confirming tobacco orders for June 1943. During the period June to August 1943, Joseph Maletroit grew and cured 1,080 tobacco plants on his farm. He was expecting a total of 108 orders for tobacco.[5]

This important primary historical source is both interesting and informative for three reasons. Firstly, it clearly demonstrates that farmers grew tobacco as a cash crop; secondly, the ability of farmers to adapt to changing circumstances and to growing and marketing tobacco. And finally, that the cultivation of tobacco by farmers was an open enterprise – Mr Maletroit wrote the names of his customers in his order book. He, furthermore, wrote his own name, address, and telephone number. This was not a clandestine business.

The opportunity to obtain a cash income from cultivation of tobacco was seemingly not only taken up by farmers, but also by entrepreneurial islanders living in town. On the 18th May, Robert George Cornish, St Helier, appeared before the DOA. It was alleged that he had 30 perches situated at Francheville, Grouville and a second area of 30 perches at La Becquetterie, St Clement, which he had failed to declare as being in his custody, as required by the Cultivation of Lands (Jersey) Order, 1942, and on which it was alleged he grew tobacco.[6]

Mr Cornish, a pig breeder, admitted having in his possession the land in question at La Becquetterie, and further admitted having planted 900 tobacco plants without having obtained the Licence required by Article 8, Loi (1934) sur La Règie et le mode de Perception de l'Impôt sur la Tabac. Cornish denied he was in possession of the land at Francheville. The Honorary Parish Inspectors were ordered to investigate the matter thoroughly and report back to the DOA.

On the 4th June, the investigation and report was complete, confirming that Cornish had not cultivated tobacco at Francheville and that he leased the land at La Becquetterie. It was owned by the late Mr C. S. Bailhache, St Clement. The tenancy of the land was ascertained to be in the name of Mr William Edward George Truscott, an "agricultural foreman", St Helier. Mr Truscott had sub-let the land to several growers who cultivated tobacco plants, the total area being 20 perches. The DOA ordered the tobacco plants to be removed and replaced with imported seed potatoes.

In an obvious counter measure to deal with this large-scale tobacco cultivation, the President of the Department of Finance and Economics, Jurat Dorey, met with Brée on the 15th June. The Department had hitherto been issuing licences for the cultivation of tobacco plants.[7]

The decision was taken that licences for the cultivation of up to 100 tobacco plants would instead be issued by the DOA, and the duty paid for each plant would be 6 pence. Mr Herbert de Gruchy, a Harbour Inspector who was seconded to the DOA, was given a list of all growers and farmers who had paid duty on their tobacco plants. He duly inspected the area in tobacco cultivation and the relevant licences and cross-checked that all tobacco plants were duty-paid. Farmers who did not have a duty-paid licence had their plants confiscated and the leaves sent to the old cigarette factory in Providence Street.[8]

In addition to the above duty-paid licence, the DOA also issued a certificate to the applicant that it did not require him to grow any other crops on the land in which it was proposed to plant tobacco. The reasons for this modification were, firstly, it would cut down the amount of tobacco that found itself on the Black Market; and secondly, put a stop to fertile agricultural land being used for the cultivation of tobacco.

The DOA immediately wrote to all Honorary Parish Inspectors. They were informed that licences would be issued for 100 plants or less for the cultivation of tobacco and applications would only be granted if the Honorary Parish Inspectors had no objection. The DOA would authorise the licences to grow tobacco under the Cultivation of Lands (Jersey) Order, 1942.

At the end of June, the DOA met to consider the case of Mr E. de Chanteloup, Trinity. The Honorary Parish Inspectors had reported he was growing tobacco. After an investigation, it was ascertained that a number of persons were cultivating tobacco on 10 perches of land which was in his possession and was deemed suitable for food cultivation. The tobacco plants were removed and replaced with French seed potatoes.

A "Tobacco Plantation", of some 15 to 20 vergées in area, was suffering from large scale pilfering of tobacco leaves. The tobacco was grown under the sanction of Field Command 515, who put pressure on the Bailiff and the Attorney General to put a police guard around the fields. After a report on the security of the "Tobacco Plantation", Field Command was informed that the areas concerned were just too large to be securely policed.[9] This "Tobacco Plantation" was almost certainly that of Herbert Minck.

Potatoes

"Brée explained that this order that 350 tons of late variety potatoes should be planted throughout the Island was an order from the German authorities who originally had wanted 1000 tons planted."

Meeting of Brée with twenty-three important farmers

On the 3rd April Brée met with twenty-three farmers. An order he had received from Field Command 515 instructed him to ensure that 350 tons of late variety potatoes be planted throughout the Island. Many of these farmers were angry and severely criticised Brée. Philip Le Feuvre made it clear that planting 350 tons of late variety potatoes could only be achieved by breaking up good grassland or, if planted as a second crop, by reducing the area available for roots. The economic costs of growing these potatoes would be very high.

Brée responded by explaining that the order came from "...the German authorities who had originally wanted 1,000 tons planted." After further discussion, the assembled farmers proposed and seconded a resolution. "Considering that farmers are being compelled by the States to grow a crop of late variety potatoes against their better judgement – as being practical men and being convinced that they will sustain a loss in doing so, it would appear reasonable in the event of such being sustained, owing to factors beyond the control of growers, that the States should be asked to share responsibility for the anticipated failure." Brée was unhappy accepting this proposition and it was not submitted to the Superior Council.

At the meeting of the 3rd April, Brée and the farmers also discussed a new problem. "Whether the question of the pulling up of newly planted potatoes by foreigners could be stopped." The term "foreigners" was used to designate Russian or Ukrainian OT workers and other forced labourers from Europe. Brée replied that "...every effort had been made without success." This meeting made no reference to the plight of the "foreigners" - the destruction of their potato plants was the central issue for farmers.[10]

On the 6th April, the Superior Council approved an order that French seed potatoes could be sold to farmers on credit. On the same day, the DOA wrote to all Connétables asking if they would act as Parish Allocation Officers for the disposal of the 1943 potato crop. Some of the Connétables delegated a parish official in their place and the following were appointed.

St Brelade	J. J. Le Boutillier
St Clement	J. P. Le Masurier
Grouville	C. Le Huquet
St Helier	P. J. Mourant, A. Tarr

St John	P. J. Romeril Junior
St Martin	P. Ahier, J. N. Germain
St Lawrence	J. W. Baudains, Connétable
St Mary	C. Bisson
St Ouen	F. Le Boutillier
St Peter	J. du Val, Connétable
St Saviour	E. J. Mourant, Chef de Police
Trinity	J. E. Cabot

On the 13th April, on a recommendation of the Superior Council, greenhouse potato prices were fixed under the Vegetables (Maximum Prices) (Jersey) Order, 1941. These would be sold at a maximum of 6 pence per lb wholesale, and 7 pence per lb retail. The first allocation of greenhouse potatoes sold to the DOA was 28 tons on the 8th May 1943.

On the 27th April the DOA, in order to comply with instructions from the German Field Command, directed the States Draftsman to prepare a direction under the Cultivation of Lands (Jersey) Order, 1942. This required all persons who were not holders of Cultivation Orders, and who were growing 20 perches or more of potatoes, to declare to the DOA the area they had planted. Pelz had decided during the frequent visits he made in the countryside that too many farmers were cultivating potatoes outside the areas of the Cultivation Orders. This additional cultivation resulted in unrealistic production figures when calculating the total amount grown in the Island.

On the 5th May, new instructions were published concerning changes in the Cultivation of Lands (Jersey) Order, 1942.

1. Every occupier of more than 20 perches of land planted in potatoes shall, not later than 4 o'clock in the evening of the 29th May 1943, notify the DOA in writing of the area and the situation of the land so planted in potatoes.
2. These Directions shall not apply in relation to land planted in potatoes in pursuance of directions given to the occupier thereof by or on behalf of the DOA under the Cultivation of Lands (Jersey) Order, 1942.
3. Infringement of these Directions are offences against the Regulations made on the 1st September 1939 under the Order in Council, 25th August 1939.

At the end of April, Mr A. F. G. Jackson, St Helier, was called to appear before the DOA. It was alleged he failed to carry out Cultivation Directions to grow 12 perches of indoor potatoes. After hearing Mr Jackson's explanations, the matter was referred to the Attorney General.

On the last day of April, the DOA took the decision to purchase the entire 1943 outdoor potato crop. It also decided that the States would pay the cost of storing and marketing the crop and that a new direction would be issued requiring all potatoes grown in 1943 and sold to the DOA to be free of "chats" and "greens". On the 9th July the direction was amended to allow both "green potatoes and chats" to be delivered to the DOA, however these categories of potatoes had to be packed in separate containers and not mixed. The DOA decided it would pay farmers 13/- per cwt for these potatoes. They were issued to soup kitchens.

Also on the 30th April, Field Command notified the DOA of the prices they were prepared to pay for potatoes in 1943. The DOA decided to defer the matter until a later date.

On the 7th May, Walter Benest, St Brelade, appeared before the DOA to answer an allegation that having been directed to grow 18 perches of glasshouse potatoes, he had grown only 14 perches. Mr Benest's explanations were deemed unsatisfactory. The matter was referred to the Attorney General.

On the same day, Mr A. P. Mitchener, Grouville, was ordered to appear before the DOA. He had been directed to grow 15 perches of glasshouse potatoes, but he grew just 12 perches. Mr Mitchener confirmed he had planted 15 perches as directed. The problem was that "...a proportion of the crops had been devoured by rats." An investigation was made which confirmed his statement. No further action was taken.

On the 6th May, Mr F. T. Le Marquand wrote to the DOA complaining that the French seed potatoes sold to him were unfit for planting. He furthermore wanted them replaced and "an allowance" made in respect of these potatoes. The DOA decided that no allowance was forthcoming.

The following week, a report on a quantity of French seed potatoes demonstrated a large percentage of waste. Further investigation deemed them to be unfit for planting and it was decided to return them to store.

On the 18th May, the DOA altered the price paid to farmers for potatoes lifted during the year, but excluding those grown from French seed. The new price was 13/- per cwt and was implemented on the 21st May when the DOA passed the Home-Grown Potatoes (1943 Crop) (Maximum Prices) (Jersey) Order, 1943. Any farmer discovered selling potatoes beyond this maximum would be prosecuted.

On the 21st May, the Grain and Potato Section reported it had been unable to obtain payment from the German Field Command in respect of £600 for 6,000 potato sacks supplied on the 15th August 1942. After discussion within the DOA, it was decided that it was unlikely to receive payment from Field Command and wrote off the account.

On the 31st May Brée reported, from information received by Pelz, that the German authorities had discovered a Colorado Beetle in a field on Queen's Road, St Helier. The DOA immediately declared the entire Island a "Zone de Protection". This declaration authorised spraying of all potato crops with lead arsenate. All Honorary Parish Inspectors were ordered to carry out a search for Colorado Beetles in their respective parishes. They were also told to inspect all potato crops to ensure spraying was carried out.

The Attorney General wrote to all Connétables on the 31st May ordering them to appoint Colorado Inspectors under Article 3, Règlement pour combattre et eliminer le Doryphore. He concluded his letter: "The matter is one of very great urgency having regard to the discovery, on Saturday last, of the existence of that pest in the Island.[11]

The DOA ordered, under the Colorado Beetle (Compulsory Spraying) (Jersey) Order, 1943, the following:

1. Every occupier of land is to spray all his crops of potatoes between the 3rd and 10th of June with a prescribed mixture.
2. All spray mixtures are free of charge. It must be collected on the dates and at the depots specified.
3. The mixture is to be prepared exactly as appears on the packaging.

Colorado Beetle: Depots Open 9.00am to Noon and 2pm to 5pm

Parish	Depot	Date
St Brelade	Tabor Chapel and Schoolroom	2/06/43
St Clement	Jambart Farm	2/06/43
Grouville	Carteret Farm and Badminton Hall, Gorey Village	2/06/43
St Helier	31 Commercial Street	2/06/43
St John	Parish Hall	2/06/43
St Lawrence	Parish Hall	2/06/43
St Martin	La Poudretterie, and Homelea, Faldouet	2/06/43
St Mary	Old Parish Hall	3/06/43
St Ouen	St Peter's Destructors and Berry Brothers, Beaumont	3/06/43
St Saviour	Maison de Haut, Pigneaux	3/06/43
Trinity	States Experimental Farm	3/06/43

A second application was ordered under the Colorado Beetle (Compulsory Spraying) (No 2) (Jersey) Order, 1943 and completed between 24th and 30th June. The Connétables oversaw the distribution of the lead arsenate.

On the 1st June, the DOA received an application from the Greenhouse Growers Association for 350 gallons of petrol, needed for pumping water during June, July and August for the cultivation of potatoes.

On the 9th June, Mr Woodcock reported that a Colorado Beetle had been discovered at West Park; all potatoes growing at West Park were examined. On the same day, a quantity of imported sulphate of copper arrived on the Island. The DOA decided it would be issued together with caustic soda to be used as an anti-blight spray. It was made available from merchants W. Dennis and Sons Limited, A. T. Jeune and G. D. Laurens.

On the 11th June, the DOA decided that "In view of the prevalence of disease in the potato crop, and the chaotic conditions pervading in relation to the shipment of potatoes to the order of the German authorities at present in occupation of the Island, until further notice no potatoes shall be brought into the DOA stores."

In the same week, Le Gallais wrote to the DOA setting forth reasons in support of his contention that he was unable to comply with the directions of the Honorary Parish Inspectors requiring him to grow 1 vergée of French imported seed potatoes. The DOA, however, decided not to modify its directions. Le Gallais, never an individual to accept a decision if it directly conflicted with his opinion, wrote to the DOA for a second time asking for reconsideration. The DOA refused to modify its decision or to allow the Honorary Parish Inspectors to make alternative allocations.

In late June, the Trinity Deputy reported that Mr Ferry was allegedly digging potatoes and selling them to the German forces. The Parish Potato Allocation Officers also reported the allegation to the Connétable.[2] Brée wrote to the Attorney General asking for an investigation to be established as to the precise nature of the infringement.

On the 22nd June, in an attempt to deal with a severe shortage of potatoes for the civilian population, the DOA informed all farmers to deliver 3 tons in respect of each vergée allocated in their cultivation directions. The order was for early and late potatoes and excluded potatoes grown from imported French seed. Farmers were told that if they thought their crop was insufficient to provide the quantity required, they should see their Honorary Parish Inspectors who would decide the amount they should supply.

On the 29th June, the DOA received information from the German Military authority via the States Experimental Station, that a German soldier had discovered a Colorado Beetle at Three Oaks, St Lawrence. Mr Frank Le Maistre was sent to inspect the area but found no traces of infestation. He spent several days carrying out further investigations of the immediate area; the insect that eventually was found was not a Colorado Beetle.

Agricultural Labour

"The reason for Brée actively discussing the problem of agricultural labour with Dr Casper arose out the question of a local man Jean Robin, 22 Belmont Road, St Helier, who applied for permission to leave agricultural employment in order to work for the Todt Organization."

Correspondence between States of Jersey and Field Command 515

Between the 13th April and 12th June 1943, a total of £1,249-9-0 was paid out under the Agricultural Workers Bonus Scheme. The scheme worked well, with vouchers being reimbursed at the main Post Office by agricultural workers employed on the scheme.

On the 20th April, Mr E. P. Blampied, St Brelade, wrote to the Department of Public Instruction requesting an apprenticeship for his son Denis Francis Blampied who wanted to become a farmer and had applied for an apprenticeship grant. The Department of Public Instruction refused the grant; however it contacted the DOA regarding apprenticeships in agriculture for the purpose of a career in the industry. The DOA suggested a scheme be set up jointly with the Department of Public Instruction. It allowed a grant, for boys aged between fifteen and eighteen years of age, of 10/- a week. The grant was dependent on the boy being employed by an approved farmer. The farmer also contributed a minimum wage of 10/-.a week. On the 7th May, Denis was taken on as an apprentice by Mr J. H. Chevalier, St Brelade, on these terms.

On the 24th May the "Advisory Committee" on agricultural labour set up by the German authorities submitted a minute to the DOA recommending that all men who received the Agricultural Workers Bonus should be notified individually that the payment of such assistance would terminate on the 31st July 1943. The same minute was also sent to the JFU and to the RJA&HS. Assistance in the payment of agricultural labour would not be permitted as from August 1943.

The fundamental issue had been the shortage of labour for digging potatoes, which began in April and ended late July. The bonus had generally proved successful in alleviating the shortage of agricultural labour; however, it did not remedy the problem.

Within a week of the German order, the leading farmers met at the request of Deputy Le Quesne, President of the Department of Labour. Also present was Deputy John Le Marquand. The subject of the meeting was the question of farm labour and how much farmers proposed to pay men on the labour scheme for digging potatoes during the 1943 season. The meeting took place on the 29th May with some forty farmers being present.

The chair was taken by Le Gallais. He began the meeting by explaining that the DOA and Department of Labour were in touch with each other regarding the assistance needed by farmers during the potato harvesting season. Deputy Le Quesne stated that a registration had been carried out to identify who was available for agricultural labour. He wanted details from the farmers present how this labour would be used and what financial remuneration these men would receive. Perrédès urged that all men on the labour scheme who had been accustomed to agricultural work be told to return to farms. Mr J. H. Syvret suggested that workers be paid by the barrel.

It was made clear to the assembled farmers that the price paid to them for their potatoes was 13/- per cwt. It was fixed by the Field Command, who had refused to allow a higher price. The meeting discussed the payment that should be made to workers and a proposition by Messrs Perrédès and Michel was passed, agreeing that agricultural workers provided by the Department of

Labour would be paid at the rate of 1/- per hour. As the meeting progressed, and there was further discussion, a number of additional recommendations were agreed:

1. Working time for agricultural labourers to be reckoned from time of arrival to farm until departure from farm.
2. Employment in wet weather to be at the discretion of the farmer.
3. Labour to be drawn in the first instance from the parish.

Le Gallais suggested that a committee be formed to examine the Department of Labour's register and to select those men who were known to have been engaged in farmwork prior to 1940, and who were now employed in other types of work. Deputy Le Quesne welcomed the suggestion and the Committee was formed, comprising one representative from each parish.

O. C. Fiott	A. G. Houguez
J. E. Gaudin	E. R. Egré
A.J. Fair	T. G. Le Marinel
J. A. Pallot	E. W. Pallot
C. P. Journeaux	A. S. de Gruchy
N. J. Perrée	R. J. Labey

Men had been seduced to leave agricultural work by the extremely high wages offered by German construction companies and the OT, although the number who actually changed their occupation is difficult to document. The families of those who worked for German construction firms and the OT are reluctant to allow details to be made open. By early 1943, it was becoming an increasing problem for the civilian authorities. Large information posters were printed and displayed outside parish halls and churches, citing the Hague Convention, that Jerseymen should not work on projects for the German contractors.

In early May Brée discussed, with OKVR Dr Casper, the problem of young men leaving agriculture to work for German companies. The immediate reason for the discussion arose out of the question of a local man, Jean Robin, St Helier, who applied for permission to leave agricultural employment to work for the OT.[12]

At the end of May, Brée wrote to the Bailiff making him aware that "There is a lack of agricultural labour in the Island and I believe that, in the past, a number of agricultural workers have taken employment with the German services despite the notice published by the Field Command in May 1942. I am of the opinion that the position regarding labour would improve if the Field Command issued instructions to its various services that no workers should be employed."

The following week Colonel Knackfuss informed the Bailiff that "The Field Command will inform the German services and firms that agricultural labour may not be employed. The enforcement of the order concerning the prohibition of agricultural labour to change occupation is a matter for the States."

On the 1st June, the DOA made a request to the Department of Public Instruction that boys be released from school attendance from the 14th June to assist with the harvest work. It agreed to the request but added conditions to such releases.

On the 22nd June, the DOA requested the Department of Finance and Economics for a supplementary grant of £200 to cover the cost of the Agricultural Workers Bonus terminating on the 31st July 1943. This was "In conformity with the Advisory Committee set up by the German authorities in regard to the payment of agricultural labour."

Cereals

As a prelude to the 1943 threshing season, the DOA wrote to Raffray and Son, informing them that the 20-horsepower electric motor in their possession would be required, and asking for the terms by which the electric motor could be hired. Raffrays submitted an agreement for the electric motor to be hired at £2 a week or offering it for sale at £50. Le Gallais obtained a valuation from the Jersey Electricity Company, and after due consideration the electric motor was purchased.

On the 1st June, the DOA set out the organisation of the 1943 season.

1. All farmers who wish their cereal crops to be threshed on their farms are to stack their crops on a site which the threshing machine can easily access and work.
2. Farmers using horses must register for the privileged issue of oats between the 19th and 31st July 1943.
3. Instructions will be issued to Inspectors that the consumption of fuel at the threshing machines must be carefully supervised.
   a. The DOA will not, because of practicalities, allow a cheaper rate for threshing at depots. The DOA believes that saving the charge for moving the threshing machines, will be sufficient inducement to farmers to thresh at depots whenever possible.
   b. The DOA will charge based on the weight of grain threshed.
   c. A list of threshing depots will be published.
   d. The largest machine belonging to the DOA will only thresh at depots. The threshing sub-committee has arranged for a 25-horsepower electric motor belonging to Randalls to be used for this machine. It will also arrange for the 20-horsepower electric motor bought from Raffray to be used for its threshing machines.
   e. No binder twine will be issued by the DOA.
   f. The privilege of a farmer selecting a particular machine for working on his farm will be withdrawn. This previously caused an

inefficient use of machines. Instead, the Island will be divided into districts and one machine allocated to each district, which will only be available for work on the farms in that district. The requirement does not apply to farmers who transport their grain to the DOA depots.

g. The DOA will facilitate the electric operation of threshing machines, on condition that such machines do not travel from farm to farm.

4. All sweepings of the threshing machines working at the depots will be taken by the DOA.

5. All transport of the 1943 cereal harvest will be carried out with the Department of Transport and Communications.

6. Where necessary, grain can be stored overnight in country stores whilst in transit from the threshing machines to the DOA stores. All DOA stores in town will be required to remain open as late as the curfew. The public weighbridge will remain open to deal with the late-arriving loads and therefore a higher rate of overtime wages will be paid to DOA employees who are in charge of grain overnight. These employees will be held responsible for any loss of grain. To facilitate the work of these men, the DOA has applied to the German authorities for the issue of permits, to enable them to be out of doors later than the curfew.

7. To ensure that no DOA sacks are lost at the threshing machines, the sub-committee will carry out its own checks.

Observation was made concerning the existence of illicit threshing machines on the Island. Brée was given authority to immediately requisition any such machines that were discovered.

He met with the two farming associations on the 12th June to explain the DOA's proposals and the reasons for the changes being made for the 1943 threshing season. The farmers present referred to their own experiences of the 1942 season, when some machines had not operated perfectly. H. W. Maillard proposed that threshing charges to farmers be the same as for 1942, i.e., by the load at the depots, and by the hour on farms. This proposal was carried.

J. B. Michel and F. Le Boutillier wanted all the grain to be weighed at the threshing machines. Brée however made it clear that, although grain could be weighed at the machines, it had to be understood that the weights ascertained could not in any circumstances be accepted by the DOA in relation to payment; a ticket from the States weighbridge alone would be accepted. Brée concluded by stating that it had not yet been decided whether farmers would be allowed to keep a percentage of the grain, as in 1942.

Three days later, in view of the farmers' comments and views, the DOA and Brée agreed that the provision for charging based on the quantity of grain threshed would be dropped. As regards the recommendation that arrangements should be made to weigh all the grain at the threshing machines, the DOA wrote instructing them to secure, for the purposes of the recommendation, twelve suitable weighing machines. It was to be made clear that only weights obtained from the States weighbridge would be accepted for the purposes of payment. Finally, it was decided that the DOA, the RJA&HS and the JFU would jointly meet with the contractors, to agree the price to be paid by farmers to contractors for threshing their crops.

On the 20th June, the DOA received a report from the RJA&HS and the JFU concerning a sub-committee set up by them to make arrangements with the contractors. The report requested that a delegation from the DOA meet with both the contractors and the sub-committee, and it also contained a classification of the efficiency of the threshing machines operating in 1943. The classification, and the commensurate charges that the farmers wanted to pay to the contractors, basically put a spanner in the workings of the DOA's 1943 threshing season plan.

In view of these proposals the DOA appointed John du Val to act as Chairman of a "Classification Committee". The DOA wrote back to the sub-committee pointing out that, in view of their proposed threshing machine classification, the minimum charge for threshing at farms would be for 6 hours of threshing time, plus the cost of moving the machine.

On the 26th June, the DOA met with the farming associations with Philip Le Feuvre as Chairman. He stated that threshing charges would be the same as in 1942 and that the threshing contractors had agreed to this. He then stated that, during the 1942 season, the rate paid by farmers for threshing at their farms was less than satisfactory, because of the varying capacities of the machines. One farmer wanted the charges to be based on the number of vergées threshed. J. B. Michel wanted threshing charges to be on piecework, and not by the hour. It was agreed that the minimum area to be threshed would be 15 vergées, instead of last year's minimum of 6 hours threshing, and the DOA enquired how far the provision of the twelve portable weighing machines had progressed. A delegation was set up to meet with the contractors to discuss threshing charges. The members were J. B. Michel, F. Le Boutillier, P. Le Feuvre, G. M. Picot and E. C. Perrédès.

Jersey Produce Merchants Association

On the 6th April, the DOA decided it would make no further payments to the Jersey Farmers (Trading) Union after the firm neglected to care for the DOA wheat in its possession. The DOA had invoiced the firm £30 for remedial work on the grain but the firm refused to pay.

In early May, the President of the JPMA, J. M. Norman, wrote to the DOA asking Brée to arrange a meeting with his members to discuss "The terms of payment to the members of the Association in relation to the handling, sorting, and storage of potatoes of the 1943 potato crop". The meeting took place on the 11th May but Brée, after hearing what the JPMA wanted as remuneration, decided to defer a decision and convene a further meeting on the 14th May.

By the 21st May, the DOA had produced a report and a new contract for storage, sorting and bagging the crop. The DOA offered 25/- per ton, with payment in two instalments. The first instalment of 75% payable on taking the potatoes into store, and the second instalment of 25% to be paid at the conclusion of storage. All potatoes stored had to be kept in a marketable condition. In addition, the DOA would pay the merchants shipping costs of 25/- per ton. This was to cover all services performed by the merchants in relation to each shipment.

This contract did not satisfy Mr Norman and his members. He immediately wrote to Brée asking for a further 10/- per ton for his members. This was to also to cover potatoes sorted on behalf of the DOA since 1st March 1943. Brée, however, refused to modify his proposed agreement with the JPMA and on the 31st May the JPMA decided to accept the terms of 21st May.

The storage of grain by merchants on behalf of the DOA also became a cause for dispute between the two parties. In May, the DOA's sub-committee met with the merchants, some of whom demonstrated a large percentage loss of grain while it was in their stores. In January 1943, the DOA had decided it would deal individually with each merchant showing a shortage of grain stored on its behalf. Since no mutual agreement could be made with these individual merchants the DOA, on the 28th May, decided that, until a settlement had been made in respect of the shortages, no further business would be entered into with these firms. They were R. P. Amy, T. Davey and Company, Marks and Riches Limited, W. Nicholls and Sons Limited, A. C. Sarre, E. N. Pirouet and G. Touzel. Two weeks later the merchants had still refused to compromise. Brée, therefore, "purely as an act of grace" decided he would meet the merchants involved to give them an opportunity of settling the issue. He was adamant that, until all such discrepancies were satisfactorily dealt with, the DOA would maintain its decision to give no further business to these firms until a settlement had been reached. On the 9th June, the JPMA wrote to Brée requesting a meeting "...in order to negotiate a settlement".

The DOA met with the JPMA on the 15th June to deal with the question of shortages in the quantity of grain stored on behalf of the DOA. Agreement was made with all merchants except G. Touzel who still refused any liability for the losses. The other merchants were reinstated under their previous contracts.

In the same week the DOA decided that "In view of the presence of disease in the potato crop and the chaotic conditions pervading in relation to the shipment to order of the German authorities at present in occupation of the island that, until further notice no potatoes shall be brought into DOA stores".

On the 15th June detailed figures were submitted which established the quantity of potatoes of the 1942 crop stored on behalf of the DOA, and which were showing shortages. The DOA wrote to the JPMA and instructed that a delegation meet with the DOA on the 22nd June. After a detailed consideration of every case, the DOA decided to make no claim in respect of these shortages.

However, in view of the unsatisfactory conditions in the store of Le Rossignol and Company, and the very high percentage of shortages which had been found, it was decided that no further storage would be allocated to the firm.

Cultivation Orders

In early April the Department of Transport and Communications informed the DOA that the cost of 15,000 litres of petrol allocated by Field Command for agricultural purposes was 9 pence per gallon in excess of the price at which this petrol had been sold to the ploughing contractors. It asked the DOA to meet the loss involved which was £123-15-0. On the same day Mr P. J. Blandin was asked to explain the reasons for his very high consumption of petrol when carrying out ploughing. His explanation was not accepted, and his name removed from the authorised list of ploughing contractors.

On 9th April Mr J. F. Richardson, St Mary, was reported to have allegedly disposed of pigs and failed to make a declaration of sales, as required by the Pig (Control) (Jersey) Order, 1941. In addition, he failed to send in returns for the Livestock (Returns) (Jersey) Order, 1943. He was reported to the Attorney General.[1]

The following week the Honorary Parish Inspectors informed the DOA that Mr E. F. Taylor, St Lawrence had 4 vergées which he had allegedly failed to cultivate according to his directions. A report was produced which confirmed the allegation. The DOA decided that "In view of the unsatisfactory explanations offered, the DOA will refer the matter to the Attorney General with a view to the institution of proceedings in respect of the breach of the Order".

On the 20th April, Brée informed the DOA that the German authorities, and most probably KVR Pelz, had reported that Mr Edwin Le Seelleur, St Martin, had allegedly cultivated between 2 and 3 vergées of daffodils on his land. Brée instructed the DOA secretary to write a strongly worded letter to the Honorary Parish Inspectors expressing their view of "...the surprise that this wanton misuse of arable land should have been permitted and requiring this land forthwith to be ploughed and planted with imported seed potatoes". The following week, Mr Le Seelleur appealed to the DOA to modify its decision. This case of cultivating daffodils appears to be the only one where a farmer had been, contrary to cultivation directions, growing flowers. The question begs itself – where and to whom was Le Seelleur going to sell between 2 and 3 vergées of daffodils?

On the 30th April the RJA&HS questioned the fact that, although there was a maximum price for straw fixed by the Home-Grown Straw (Maximum Price) (Jersey) Order, 1941, and that the sale of straw was prohibited by the Price-Controlled Articles (Auction Sales) (Jersey) Order, 1941, sales by auction were still taking place. In consequence, the DOA wrote to H. W. Maillard and Son, Auctioneers, pointing out the prohibition. The auction house was ordered to inform the DOA for whom such sales had been made and to whom the straw had been sold. Several weeks later, the DOA wrote to A. Langlois, Auctioneers, in reference to an allegation that they had sold straw despite the prohibition order. The auctioneers were informed that these sales were forbidden, and within a week, they sent full details and particulars of clients of the straw auctions. The DOA carried out no further action.

On the 18th May Mr J. P. Paturel, St Saviour appeared before the DOA. He was asked to explain why, having been directed to sow 12 vergées in wheat, he had sown only seven. Brée issued Paturel with "A severe warning concerning future agricultural directions". On the same day, Mr L. H. Blight, St Saviour appeared before the DOA. It was alleged that his land was "in a neglected condition". After hearing his explanation, and in view of the confirmation given verbally by the Inspector, Philip Gallichan, the DOA decided to accept his explanations.

In June the DOA decided to grant its female staff, who had been in employment for not less than twelve consecutive months, an increase of 5/- in their weekly wage. A similar increase was made after each further period of twelve months. This would continue until women reached a wage of £2 a week. It is noteworthy that even with these increases, female clerical staff working for the DOA were still paid approximately half the wages of their male counterparts. This discrepancy remained throughout the occupation.

On the 22nd June the DOA was informed by the Royal Court that Mr G. H. Le Rossignol, St Peter had, at his own request, been released from his office as Honorary Parish Inspector. The release was granted by the Royal Court on the grounds of Mr Le Rossignol's failing health. Brée and the members of the DOA, aware of the valuable service he had given to the Island, expressed their regret at the reasons which made it necessary for him to resign from his duties. The Honorary Parish Inspectors were the lynchpin of the Island's agricultural inspectorate. For the DOA to lose one of them was a real blow. John du Val was asked to recommend a new person in place of Mr Le Rossignol. Within several weeks, he recommended Mr Henry P. Le Ruez. Brée immediately contacted the Attorney General and Mr Le Ruez subsequently went before the Royal Court and took his oath of office.

Cattle

In late March and April 1943, the DOA was forced to consider "The situation which had arisen in relation to supplies of meat for the civilian population as a result of the non-arrival from France of cattle destined to provide such supplies". Up to 1942, Pelz and the Field Command had, in an attempt to protect the Jersey pedigree herds, imported live cattle from France to provide meat for the Island's civilian population.[13]

In 1942, live cattle imports from France had been as follows, shipped in by barges from the French port of Granville.

January	237
February	89
March	–
April	91
May	91
June	192
July	164
August	202
September	202
October	181
November	175
December	123
Total	**1,747**
Bulls	48
Cows	1,699

The DOA had asked both farming associations to make "…recommendations… as to the best means to be adopted in order to obtain from the local cattle the necessary meat for the civilian population in the event of any further failure occurring in the supply from the mainland" (France). This led to the formation of the Cattle Slaughter Executive Committee. It comprised the top cattle breeders and owners of prize Jersey herds. It was run under the auspices of the Royal Jersey Agricultural and Horticultural Society. They now chose cattle from local herds for slaughter.

On the 9th April the DOA met to consider the scheme set up jointly by the RJA&HS and the JFU, relating to the provision of local cattle to ensure a meat supply for the civilian population.

1. The working of the scheme would be in the hands of an "Executive Committee" appointed by the joint councils of the RJA&HS and the JFU.
2. The Executive Committee (also referred to as the Cattle Slaughter Executive Committee) would be composed of Le Gallais, Michel, Le Boutillier, Le Feuvre, Carson and Perrédès.
3. H. G. Shepard would act as secretary to the Committee and keep all records of its proceedings, and also record the animals brought for slaughter from all twelve parishes.
4. The Executive Committee would be responsible for securing the animals to be slaughtered for the "public meat supply" as and when required by the DOA. In the performance of this task the Committee would pay "The utmost regard to the preservation of the best breeding strains of the Island stock and the maintenance of the public milk supply".
5. The selection of cattle would be undertaken by members of the RJA&HS in each parish with the aid, if necessary, of the JFU council members.

6. Parish Committees would name one of their number as the "reporting member" whose name would be communicated to the Secretary of the Executive Committee. The Parish Committees would be informed of requirements by the Executive Committee.

7. The first urgent call for sixty animals for one week's supply of meat would be filled by selecting five animals from each parish. The total population of cattle in each parish was to be ascertained and thereafter the number of animals required would be drawn from each parish, proportional to its cattle population.

8. The cattle population figures would be checked every six months using the records of the Milk Control Section of the DOA.

9. It would be obligatory for the parish representatives, in the event of their being unable to find the required quota of cattle at any time, to immediately inform the Executive Committee of the fact, and stating where sufficient animals to complete the quota would most likely be obtained but that the owners of such animals were "recalcitrant".

10. In the selection of cattle, the parish representatives would consider favourably "bona fide" breeders who kept cattle prior to 1st July 1940 and would draw the required animals preferably from those who had acquired cattle after that date.

11. The Milk Control Section of the DOA would supply the Executive Committee with information concerning producers who did not supply a reasonable quantity of milk in proportion to the number of cows in their herds. The parish representatives would therefore be enabled to select cattle from those producers, thereby leaving the better-milking herds to continue to supply the Island with milk.

12. The Executive Committee would act as an Appeals Committee in areas of dispute between cattle owners and the Parish Collecting Committees as to the exemption of any particular animal selected for slaughter. The decision of the Appeals Committee would be final.

13. On being informed of any owners who declined to provide the required cattle for slaughter, the Executive Committee would, in its turn, immediately acquaint the DOA which then would take the necessary steps to requisition the cattle from such owners.

14. Payment at official prices for animals selected for slaughter would be forthcoming at the RJA&HS office at 3 Mulcaster Street, approximately two weeks after the slaughter of the animal.

15. Henceforth all cattle requisition orders would be carried out by the DOA together with the Department of Essential Supplies. (They both also stepped in to purchase any barren heifers that farmers put up for sale at auction.)

On the 17th May 1943, the German Military Government of France held a conference in St Lô to discuss obtaining and delivering cattle from France to the Channel Islands. The total estimated requirement for meat imported from

France, for both the civilian and military populations of the Channel Islands, was 15,325 kilograms per annum.

On the 23rd May OKVR Dr Casper wrote to the Bailiff informing him that, in future, the Island would have to increase its own meat production by the slaughter of Jersey cattle.

Ten days later Brée wrote to the Bailiff about slaughtering local cattle to provide meat supplies for civilians. Brée stated, "My department does not anticipate that there will be any serious difficulty in providing from the island's livestock, the required monthly weight of meat, i.e., 15 tons."

On the 8th June Colonel Knackfuss wrote a letter to the Bailiff entitled 'Supplies of meat'. He ordered that, as from the 1st June, he required a detailed statement of meat made available from local production per month. This was to be broken down into a weekly statement showing:

1. Classification of animals and number
2. Live weight
3. Dead weight

"The meat supplies for the civilian population are to be carefully controlled. If you do not bring every pressure to bear to see that local meat production is used in a way I have calculated,......the civilian population will not be able to be supplied with the ration due".[14]

From the 5th June 1943 until the 20th April 1945 the slaughterhouse completed a detailed weekly return for Field Command, which was verified by the slaughterhouse director, Mr H. G. Gaudin. It was sent to the Department of Essential Commodities and checked by the President, Mr E. F. Le Masurier. He, in turn, sent it to the Bailiff who forwarded it to Colonel Knackfuss. A final check was an audit by Pelz on Gaudin's figures.[15]

These continual slaughterhouse returns proved Hauptmann Gussek's final statement to the Bailiff when he had departed from the Island in early September 1940 and the German Military Government, in the form of Field Command 515, took over. "I am leaving you, Field Command 515 will now begin the paper war".[16]

In April, it was reported that the number of cattle in the custody of Messrs P. Brée and O. Brée, Grouville, did not tally with the Milk Control Section. The Foreman Milk Tester, C. R. Mauger, visited the farm to investigate the matter. After enquiries failed to reconcile the number of cattle in their custody with the official DOA record, Oswald Brée was called to appear before the DOA to explain the discrepancy. After hearing his explanation, the DOA issued a warning concerning their future declarations, and amended their records after both men made new declarations. They were also given written warnings.

Le Gallais held RJA&HS meetings during April and May 1943 to discuss the cattle situation and cattle prices. He initially discussed this with the Superior Council. The latter made it clear that there would be no price increase, unless approved by the German Field Command. Le Gallais, as an alternative, wanted to go directly to the Field Command with a request to allow meat prices to increase. The Superior Council was firmly of the opinion that Le Gallais and the RJA&HS should not approach the German Field Command; he was informed that they would demand exact figures and specific reasons why meat prices should increase.

From April 1943, 60 head of cattle were slaughtered each month for the local civilian population, amounting to five per parish. Robert Carson recommended that returns of milk be obtained from the various herds to be used as a guide to select those cattle where the milk supply was below that which could reasonably be expected.

On the 30th April, the RJA&HS wrote to the DOA requesting that orders be implemented to prevent the sale by public auction of barren heifers or, alternatively, to provide that when such animals were offered for sale arrangements were made to requisition them. The DOA responded that the Cattle Slaughter Executive Committee already had sufficient powers to select these cattle and send them to slaughter. Cows not producing milk were referred to the DOA by the Milk Testers and subsequently the Cattle Slaughter Executive was informed. The animal was immediately requisitioned and sent to the abattoir.

On the 18th May the Meat (Maximum Retail Prices) (Amendment No 6) (Jersey) Order, 1943 was passed.[17]

On the 19th May, in compliance with instructions from Field Command 515, the DOA passed the Livestock (Amendment) (Jersey) Order, 1943.[17] Henceforth, all transfers of cattle or pigs had to be made in writing. Pigs born before the 10th January 1943 had to be sold to the Department of Essential Commodities. Any pigs born after the 10th January had to be offered for sale to the Department within nine months of birth. All farmers possessing a calf born after 1st June 1943 had to offer it for sale to the Department between the eighteenth and twenty-first day following its birth. All such animals were required to be delivered to the States' slaughterhouses. Any animals not offered for sale would be confiscated by the DOA.

On the 28th May, Mr D. F. Le Marquand, St Ouen, appeared before the DOA following allegations that he had failed to declare the birth of a calf within 48 hours of its birth, as required by Article 4 of the Livestock (Jersey) Order, 1942. Secondly that the calf, having been refused exemption from the provisions of Article 5(i) of the order, was not slaughtered within fourteen days of its birth. Thirdly, he refused to allow a Milk Tester to examine his herd, thus in breach of Article 6B(i) of the Milk Control (Jersey) Order, 1940. After hearing what Mr Le Marquand said and "...who adopted a truculent and deficient attitude", Brée referred the case to the Attorney General with a view to proceedings in respect of the breaches of the orders in question.[1]

On the same day, Mrs L. Rondel appeared before the DOA. It was alleged that she had retained a bull calf which had not been exempted from slaughter. Mrs Rondel admitted the offence and she further acknowledged that she had falsely declared, when signing the "Test Report", that the bull had died. The animal had been concealed and was only discovered because of a search of the premises carried out by a Foreman Milk Tester. Brée, "After very careful consideration of the case and in view of the fact that Mrs Rondel was a widow with a family of nine young children", gave "a serious warning" that any further cause for complaint would lead to proceedings against her.

On the 4th June the DOA considered a letter sent from Field Command concerning the supply of meat for the civilian population. The Field Command was informed that the DOA considered that, provided the Livestock (Jersey) Order, 1942, as amended, was carried out there would be no serious difficulty in securing, from Island livestock, the 15 tons required. Furthermore, it was pointed out to Field Command that in order to provide the required weight of meat it was essential that "The present practice of the German authorities in issuing permits allowing units of the German forces to purchase pigs (from the island farmers) shall be entirely discontinued".

References

1. Jersey Archive. C/B/A1/8.
2. Jersey Archive. C/B/A1/9.
3. Whether this was E. J. L. Paisnel, "The Beast of Jersey", who was convicted of a series of serious sexual assaults in 1971, is unclear. He would have been eighteen years of age in 1943.
4. Jersey Archive. B/A/W31/2/79.
5. Société Jersiaise Archive. LAN/A1/24. Tobacco plants order book season 1943–1944, J. Maletroit.
6. This totalled an area amounting to 1½ vergées, or 0.66 of an acre. 1 perch = 25 square feet.
7. "Jersey Tobacco Tokens" advertised on internet auction sites which purport to be of the occupation period were never issued. These "Tobacco Tokens" only began to appear in the early 1970s.
8. Jersey Archive. L/D/25/4/22.
9. Jersey Archive. B/A/W31/2/69A.
10. RJA&HS and JFU Joint Emergency Committee Minutes.
11. Jersey Archive. L/F/54/C/D/19.
12. Jersey Archive. B/A/W31/2/86.
13. Jersey Archive. B/A/W61/23.
14. Jersey Archive. B/A/W63/35.
15. Jersey Archive. B/A/W92/4. File is entitled "Lokale Schlachtungen auf Jersey". (Local Slaughtering in Jersey.)
16. Wood, A. and M. 1955. "Islands in Danger". p. 75.
17. Jersey Archive. B/A/W31/2/84.

Chapter 13

The Jersey Cattle Show of 1943
Collaborator or Competitor?

*"A determined effort was, indeed, made by the German Authorities
to force the Society to hold a [cattle] show in 1943, but your
officers tenaciously resisted the proposal. So many difficulties were
put forward that finally the Society was spared the mortification of
holding a show under the Swastika".*

RJA&HS Report

Two months before the arrival in July of German military forces to the Island,
the RJA&HS received a letter from the English Jersey Cattle Association. The
letter described the quality of Jersey cattle recently imported to the United
Kingdom for auction. The letter was to the point and self-explanatory.

"Dear Mr Shepard,
Some concern is being felt with regard to the quality of a number of
animals which are being offered at Public Auction Sales, and the Society
is considering taking steps in an endeavour to improve the general
standard of cattle sent to Sales.

In practice the undesirable type of cow is usually purchased by a
newcomer to the Breed or one who wishes to save one or two Jersey's to
improve the quality of milk, and when, as is often the case, such animals do
not give satisfaction, the purchaser is liable to think Jerseys are 'bad doers',
and thus a considerable amount of damage is done to the Breed in general.

I have been requested to communicate with you to ascertain whether
your committee will be kind enough to give the matter sympathetic
consideration, and it is hoped you may be able to co-operate with us
in some way with regard to the possible improvement of the quality of
island cattle imported into this country.

I am,
Yours sincerely,
(Signed) Edward Ashby, Secretary".[1]

Between 1920 and 1940 the leading cattle breeders, dairy farmers, merchants, and cattle agents sold and exported large numbers of cattle to the USA, Canada, United Kingdom, Scandinavia, Australia, New Zealand, and South Africa. This export trade was extremely lucrative and afforded excellent incomes for those involved. The two decades before the Second World War were regarded as "...the golden period of the cattle export trade in Jersey with just over 22,000 animals being exported all over the world".[2] Exports of Jersey cattle numbering up to sixty per shipment were by no means uncommon.[3]

This profitable export business invariably led to disagreements, personal rivalries and jealousies, and even threats of legal action amongst participants. It also led to a situation where some Island individuals were enticed into unscrupulous business practices. The 1930s witnessed increasing numbers of inferior cattle exported for auction.

Some of these cattle agents were men with big reputations. They included Carlyle Le Gallais, a leading breeder and agent for Paul Spann, the American importer, and two of the most important agents just prior to the German occupation were Robert Wilson Carson and George Courtman Breuilly. The latter was Manager of the Country Gentleman's Association Limited, 7A Esplanade and 6 Commercial Street, St Helier.[4]

In early April 1940 Le Gallais, who was President of the RJA&HS, guardians of the pedigree breed of Jersey cattle, warned his fellow members that, in order to protect their lucrative business concerning the export of cattle, they had to "...cull inferior stock and make every endeavour to weed out Jersey cattle considered unfit for exportation."[1]

The intense rivalry abated during the German occupation when the survival of the Jersey breed became the central concern.

Immediately after the "liberation of Jersey", on the 9th May 1945, these past rivalries were reignited and exposed. Individual breeders and agents, within days of the German surrender, were selected for denunciation as German collaborators. The number of collaborators was relatively small. However, the level of denunciation, coming immediately after liberation, was surprising.

The first cattle show in Jersey had been held in 1834, the original importance of these shows being to improve the breed by selection of the very best animals in the show. By the 1930s cattle shows had developed into providing "shop windows" for the world export market.

The breeders and farmers who entered their animals into these shows were at the top of the Jersey agricultural pyramid.[5] They were in effect an elite, not only exercising influence over the cattle industry but also politically and socially, and frequently acting as Honorary Police.

Visiting agents from the USA, Canada and elsewhere would attend the shows, carefully evaluating which animals to purchase. There was competition amongst the breeders to win awards and commendations to enhance the reputation of their herds and therefore to negotiate a better price. Island and parochial shows also became an important part of the cattle industry, by providing an opportunity for new ideas for increasing milk yields. Finally, the shows developed a worldwide reputation as a real spectacle and an exhibition of what was best about the Jersey breed.

The last show to be held on the Island before the Germans arrived was the 1940 Spring Show. The RJA&HS decided very soon after the military occupation that it was not desirable or practicable to hold any such events. The subject of either an Island or a parochial show completely disappears from any agenda immediately after the occupation. There is no record in the RJA&HS, JFU or DOA correspondence or minutes from 1940 to 1942 which allude to any consideration of holding a cattle show.

However, on the 3rd April 1943, at a meeting of the Joint RJA&HS and JFU Committees, Brée stood up and announced, "The German authorities want a cattle show to be held."[6]

In fact, before any official written orders had been sent to the Superior Council of Jersey, KVR Pelz had several days before spoken personally to his 'civilian counterpart", Touzel Brée, and informed him that an Island cattle show was to be organised for the summer.

The fact that Pelz informed Brée of the cattle show, before the Bailiff had received formal notification, need not surprise. Ever since Pelz's arrival in Jersey on the 9th August 1940, the two men had built up a 'structural relationship' in which they met and discussed agricultural policy details of mutual interest, such as cattle imports, agricultural production figures and cropping plans. In December 1940, Brée had given Pelz an alarm clock.[7]

In addition, Pelz, a university-trained expert and pre-war leading figure in the Austrian cattle industry, often discussed with Brée matters pertaining to the Jersey breed. When Brée gave a series of explanations to Pelz as to why Jersey cows were not bred for meat, Pelz wrote: "Only with great effort and serious admonition did I manage to make Brée supply Jersey cattle for consumption."[8]

On the 5th April the Bailiff received a letter from Colonel Knackfuss, entitled "Holding a Cattle Show". Knackfuss wrote: "In order to get a survey of the stocks of horned cattle in Jersey and to give the farmers and breeders an opportunity of once more taking an active part in breeding, I have decided to have a cattle show held in the autumn of this year. I request, therefore, that a suggested programme be drawn up and submitted, showing when the show will take place, who will be in charge, who will be allowed to take part and what classes of horned cattle will be shown. The Herd Book[9] shall commence immediately to choose the animals for exhibition so that the owners will have plenty of time to prepare their animals."[10]

On the 7th April, Brée informed the Bailiff that the matter of organising the cattle show had been referred to the secretary of the RJA&HS, H. G. Shepard. In addition, he would communicate all "...the necessary information for transmission to the German authorities." It appeared that the DOA and Brée expected a show to be held.

The DOA discussed on the 13th April the matter of the German request for a show. It was decided that the RJA&HS would "...make the necessary preparations...to give effect to the requirements of the German authorities in this matter."[11] The DOA saw no impediment to holding a show. On the 24th April the Jersey Herd Book Committee met with Field Command 515 and detailed the practical difficulties of holding an Island-wide show.

On the 3rd May, Brée, with delegates of the RJA&HS, met KVR Pelz in Room 20 at College House. The Society's delegates again emphasised, and gave specific reasons, why an Island-wide cattle show, under the present wartime conditions, would not be feasible. These problems were: transport and the lack of fuel; a dire shortage of agricultural labour; the stabling of cattle; interference with the Island milk supply; and the danger of spreading infectious diseases.

After a prolonged discussion – which was much to the irritation of Pelz – Le Gallais and the two Vice Presidents, Le Boutillier and Michel, were instructed to return to College House on the 7th May, Le Gallais being told to prepare a schedule for a summer show.

At this second meeting, Pelz reiterated his frustration with Le Gallais and his list of reasons as to why an Island-wide cattle show should not be held. Pelz knew Le Gallais well through the latter's position as an adjoint member of the DOA with responsibility for collections and deliveries of milk. Le Gallais' Roselands herd supplied the Staff Officers of Field Command with fresh milk, and it was Pelz who liaised with Le Gallais over the distribution and payment for this supply. Therefore, Pelz was in no way intimidated by Le Gallais' blustering concerning the setting up of an Island show, and he made it clear that these difficulties could be overcome.

At this point "...after further discussions, the Vice Presidents suggested, as an alternative, the holding of cattle parades in each parish or in groups of parishes". This would overcome the transport difficulty. The suggestion proved acceptable to the German authorities and the President and Vice Presidents were given to understand that "An order for the holding of these parochial cattle shows will be issued and transmitted through the normal channels."[10]

Immediately after the meeting was concluded and a joint agreement to hold parochial cattle shows had been accepted, OKVR Dr Casper wrote to the Bailiff, confirming the outcome of the "...several conferences with representatives of the Herd Book". He also confirmed that "The Field Command agrees, therefore, to the proposed combined show being split up into small shows in each parish, or two or three parishes combining together, as suggested by the representatives of the Herd Book."

Finally, Dr Casper, sensing the underlying misgivings of the cattle breeders, which Pelz would have explained to him, attempted to offer a justification for ordering parochial shows. Dr Casper made it clear, "In order to avoid misunderstandings special attention should be drawn to the fact that these cattle shows are purely in the interests of the breeders. The war situation has brought substantial changes in the conditions for keeping cattle in the Channel Islands so that it will be of great value to all farmers to get a survey of the present state of cattle breeding."[10]

George Courtman Breuilly and His Radio

On the 3rd January 1943, George Courtman Breuilly had been sentenced to six months' imprisonment by Field Command 515 for possession of an illegal radio and failing to surrender a radio-receiving set. His sentence was to be served in the local public prison from 4th June until 5th October 1943. On the 9th May the Attorney General received the necessary details from the German magistrate of Field Command 515 and he, in turn, wrote to the Connétable of St Helier, informing him of Breuilly's sentence.[12]

On the 8th May Le Gallais received a telephone call at home from Pelz's adjutant, Corporal Soeldner requesting an immediate meeting at Le Gallais' home.[13] Le Gallais "...having another appointment was unable to arrange this" and it was agreed that he would meet Corporal Soeldner in the boardroom of the RJA&HS offices on Tuesday, 11th May, at 2.30 p.m.

In Breuilly's post-war statement to his lawyer, Advocate P. N. Richardson, he explains that his association with German forces began on the 11th May 1943 when he met with Corporal Soeldner and accompanied him to the RJA&HS to meet Le Gallais and Shepard. Breuilly states that he had collected signatures from twenty-six Jersey farmers, many of whom were Society members, who wished to have a cattle show in 1943.[14] His reason for meeting Le Gallais and Shepard that day had been to hand them the petition, which was independent of any German interference. At the meeting, Corporal Soeldner explained to Le Gallais that he had been given direct orders from KVR Pelz to press the RJA&HS to begin immediate preparations for holding parish cattle shows in the month of July.

Le Gallais responded with the statement that "The official order had not been received". Corporal Soeldner, in turn, informed Le Gallais that Breuilly's petition demonstrated that farmers were anxious to participate in a cattle show. He stated that the signatures had been obtained by George C. Breuilly from Jersey farmers who were requesting this event.

Exasperated by having to repeat the very same issues that he had explained to Pelz at College House, Le Gallais pointed out that the Herd Book Committee had voted against an Island cattle show under present wartime conditions. A delegation of RJA&HS cattle farmers had placed its objections before the Field Commandant and, until the decision was reversed, he could do nothing.

In addition, Le Gallais suggested that those farmers who wanted to hold a show could take charge of the arrangements but that any cattle show organised by local farmers would not be a success, despite their apparent willingness. Corporal Soeldner insisted there had been a misunderstanding from the outset. A cattle show had not been ordered, but it was felt by Field Command that local farmers wanted a show to see the progress of breeding and, in an interesting comment relating to fears amongst cattle breeders and the associated community, that there was no intention of taking Jersey pedigree cattle out of the Island.

This last statement was a reference to October 1940 when a consignment of twenty-one Jersey pedigree cows and two bulls were shipped to the Kaiser Wilhem Institute at Dummerstorf, near Rostock. The animals had been sent to Germany as part of a Jersey-German livestock crossbreeding programme. In fact, the bulls were so highly prized by German scientists that they were subsequently sent throughout Germany and Austria in crossbreeding experiments with different varieties of indigenous cattle.[15] The export of these cattle caused widespread consternation amongst both Island breeders and the population.[16]

In May 1943 there was genuine concern that Jersey would be used as a repository for the export of cattle for crossbreeding programmes in Rostock and elsewhere. Le Gallais, and other members of the RJA&HS, almost certainly looked upon a cattle show, insisted upon by Field Command, as a ploy to select their very best bulls and cows which subsequently would be taken out of the Island. Shepard remarks on the large number of Jersey cattle bought by the Kaiser Wilhelm Institute for export to "...the Experimental Station at Rostock on the Baltic".[17] Just before they were shipped, these cattle were taken to the abattoirs near St Helier Harbour to await loading onto vessels, which led to the widespread rumour that "The Germans were taking all the cattle away".

As the discussion progressed between Le Gallais and Corporal Soeldner, the former insisted that all the members of the Herd Book Committee opposed holding an Island-wide cattle show. Corporal Soeldner concluded by stating that he would be present at the next meeting of the Herd Book Committee, fixed for Saturday 15th May. He explained that, as Major Pelz's adjutant, he would represent his superior with regard to the organisation of the show.

At that meeting, which took place as planned, Corporal Soeldner read a long statement in favour of holding a show. He read out the names of the twenty-six farmers who had signed the petition and who wished to exhibit their stock. He suggested that shows be held at the end of July (1943) and that the parochial committees should arrange these immediately.

Le Gallais, Le Boutillier and Michel, along with Philip Le Feuvre, Eugene Perrédès and Charles Quenault, questioned Corporal Soeldner as to how and from where these signatures had been obtained – they were the signatures collected by Breuilly.

The Corporal, feeling himself to be outnumbered and not receiving a positive response to Pelz's ambitions for holding a show, disclaimed "...any intention of the German authorities in ordering a show and, in the interests of the Jersey breed, a show should be held."

Le Gallais reiterated the reasons as to why "Parish Shows" had been put forward and "...read a letter from the DOA dated the 12th May 1943 embodying the order for these shows".

Philip Le Feuvre suggested to Corporal Soeldner that the twenty-six Jersey farmers who had signed the petition for an Island show should be called upon to arrange the show. Perrédès proposed that no cattle shows be held under present conditions, which Charles Quenault seconded, and it was carried unanimously. Corporal Soeldner said he would report the result of the meeting to Major Pelz, Head of Agriculture, Field Command 515. Lawrence Le Brocq, a newly appointed young clerk at the RJA&HS, witnessed Le Gallais coming out of the meeting room, and, seeing Breuilly alongside Soeldner, becoming extremely angry. This may have been because Pelz had sent his lowly corporal to the meeting, an affront to Le Gallais' pride. Also, and a more plausible reason, could be that he felt Breuilly was colluding with Field Command 515 and undermining the authority of the RJA&HS.

The question arises as to why Field Command 515, and Pelz in particular, were continually spending time and effort putting pressure on farmers (many of whom knew Pelz personally) to organise an Island show or, in its place, a series of parochial shows. This period, the summer of 1943, was in the middle of a war. The German Field Command was dealing with the Organisation Todt and the Island fortification programme; it was receiving constant construction applications from OT engineers and, in addition, over thirty vessels were arriving daily from the Continent. Fritz Todt was in Jersey supervising the building of fortifications and demanding resources from the Field Command. Holding an Island show was an unnecessary and time-consuming distraction for them.

The first possible explanation was that the Kaiser Wilhelm Institute may have requested more pedigree cattle to be exported for its crossbreeding programme at Dummerstorf. An Island show would have been an excellent means for identifying the best cattle. As had taken place in October 1940, these animals could easily be shipped to Germany and the export of Jersey cattle that had begun in August 1940 continued until May 1944. It only ceased in June 1944 after the Allied landings in Normandy, known as D-Day.

This explanation is unlikely. Edwin Lauprecht had visited Jersey for several months in 1942 and had researched and published a scientific report on Jersey pedigree stocks whilst investigating the RJA&HS Herd Book. He also examined milk production and fat levels in Jersey dairy herds. In studying Jersey cattle and milk production, Lauprecht was given full access to all the data he required by the RJA&HS. Indeed, Lauprecht felt "...very obliged to the [States of Jersey] veterinary surgeon Dr Blampied, as well as the gentlemen of the Jersey Herd Book in St Helier for willingly giving information."[18]

A second possible explanation for Pelz putting pressure on cattle breeders to hold a show is that he was fully aware of the crossbreeding programme at the Kaiser Wilhelm Institute. Pelz had assisted Lauprecht in 1942 with his scientific paper on the Jersey breed and milk production and, in fact,

Lauprecht acknowledged Pelz's help. Pelz was also aware of the problem of "Schlibet Fettlüke", or the "fat gap" concerning German milk. The reason Jersey cattle were exported to the Kaiser Wilhelm Institute was to bridge this "fat gap". Pelz, aware of this, sent tins of Jersey butter to his mother in Salzburg.

Pelz almost certainly pushed for an Island or parochial shows to be held as this would have forwarded his future career in the cattle industry. Between 1930 and 1940 Pelz had been an important figure in the Austrian cattle community, working in the Department of Cattle Breeding in the Federal District of Salzburg. He had also carried out research work at the Ministry of Agriculture in Vienna in the development of selective breeding, had introduced herd books and facilitated the movement of Austrian cattle for breeding purposes.[19]

As with many other German and Austrian scientists, the war was seen as a vehicle to promote their professional careers. Pelz had a degree in agriculture from the University of Natural Resources and Life Sciences, Vienna. He had a very good series of examination results and, as Dr Casper and Major Heider testified, he was scientifically extremely capable, highly regarded and an intelligent officer.[20] Pelz certainly realised that his post-war C.V. and career would benefit if he were to promulgate Jersey cattle shows.

The final reason why Pelz may have pushed so hard for holding a cattle show in 1943 was that he was ordered to organise the event by his superiors in Paris. German military propaganda units in Jersey were extremely active throughout the German occupation. Berlin units visited the Island to film on a regular basis – "Country Scenes in Rural Jersey" was a favoured topic for filming.[21]

The fact that Field Commandant Knackfuss, OKVR Dr Casper, KVR von Aufsess and KVR Pelz all became involved in the cattle show and pursued its implementation indicates that there was indeed pressure from headquarters in Paris.

On the 27th May, von Aufsess wrote to the Bailiff desiring a reply to Pelz's request for an Island show or parochial shows. He made the observation: "I am aware of the fact that the Herd Book has no very great interest in holding a cattle show". On the 2nd June Brée gave the Bailiff a detailed report of the meetings between Herd Book representatives and Field Command and on the 4th June the Bailiff replied to the Field Commandant. He summed up the outcome of the meeting on the 15th May that no cattle shows should be held, and that this proposal had been carried unanimously by members of the Jersey Herd Book.

On the 7th June the Field Commandant wrote to the Bailiffs of both Jersey and Guernsey. "After having received representatives from both islands that other more urgent work stands in the way of holding a cattle show, I have decided not to hold the proposed show this year. The breeders are to be suitably informed of this order."[10] The suggestion by Le Boutillier and Michel to hold a series of parochial shows was apparently dropped also. The year 1943 saw no cattle shows in any form.

The 4ᵗʰ June 1943 was also a significant day for George C. Breuilly. It was the first day of his prison sentence for failing to hand in a radio receiver to the German authorities, and on the 6ᵗʰ June Field Command informed the Attorney General that George Breuilly was to be kept in the public prison until his sentence ended on the 5ᵗʰ October 1943. Breuilly's attempts to promote a show by obtaining twenty-six signatures from farmers had failed.

However, on the 5ᵗʰ July Field Command's legal office decreed that Breuilly's sentence would be postponed from the 15ᵗʰ July until the 16ᵗʰ September 1943. The reason for his release from the public prison was in order that he could attend to his approaching cereal harvest. He was subsequently released at 7.00 p.m. on the 15ᵗʰ, in time to be back home before the night's curfew.[22]

On the 3ʳᵈ September, Brée met with the Field Commandant to discuss the case of an island farmer (Breuilly) who had been convicted of a radio offence and had served half his sentence and who Brée described as "a good farmer". This was indeed a highly unusual and exceptionally rare occurrence for the President of the DOA to meet the Commandant of Field Command 515 in order to discuss one individual, especially considering that, on the 22ⁿᵈ May 1942, Breuilly had already been fined RM500, or 100 days in prison, for "...selling foodstuffs whose sale was restricted" – in other words, black marketing.[23]

In his discussions, Brée emphasised that Breuilly had a large holding, that he supervised a second farm and was also the manager of the Country Gentlemen's Association Limited – which the DOA used to store its cereals. He did not mention that, early in the occupation, Breuilly had sold agricultural outputs at inflated prices – he was undoubtedly profiteering and had been officially reported and investigated.

Brée stated, "it would be an act of graciousness should the Commandant find it possible to substitute a fine in place of the remainder of his sentence. Should, however, it be ordered that the remainder of his sentence is to be served may I ask that the date of his return to prison be delayed for some two months to allow him time to complete his harvest and clean his ground."[24]

The Court of the German Field Command replied to Brée's request on the 13ᵗʰ September, stating that it would not approve of Breuilly's prison sentence being superseded by a fine; Breuilly was to complete his sentence. However, the court would allow an extension of his prison respite from the 16ᵗʰ September until the 31ˢᵗ October 1943. This apparent respite period was again an exceptional occurrence. The German Field Command was not at all in favour of mitigating sentences unless it was in their interests.

There appears to have been a period when correspondence between the Field Command, the Attorney General and the Viscount[25] demonstrated a high level of confusion concerning the alteration of Breuilly's sentence. The definitive and official position concerning him was eventually stated on the 5ᵗʰ November 1943.

The Attorney General made it clear to all parties involved in Breuilly's prison sentence: "I have been informed by the Court of Field Command

515 that, by decree of the [German] magistrate, further execution of the sentence against George Courtman Breuilly is postponed upon condition that he conducts himself in a proper manner. This decree has force from the 1ˢᵗ December 1943, and is revocable until the end of hostilities. Breuilly is to be released on the 30ᵗʰ November 1943 at 7pm."

On the 1ˢᵗ December the Viscount informed the Attorney General that "George Courtman Breuilly was released from public prison yesterday, the 30ᵗʰ Ultimo, at 7pm" and two days later the Attorney General informed Field Command 515.

The fact that Breuilly had attempted to facilitate an Island cattle show by organising a petition which was signed by twenty-six members of the RJA&HS had not gone down well with the Herd Book Committee – Le Gallais, Michel and Le Boutillier. That they themselves had suggested holding parochial shows, or parades, to the German authorities was immediately dropped from the records.

Breuilly maintained that the signatures he had collected were those of farmers who had approached him and who were in favour of holding a show. This, however, does not explain his involvement with Pelz's adjutant, Corporal Soeldner.

One explanation of the circumstances of Breuilly and the petition has been described by the son of the States of Jersey Veterinary Surgeon, who was twenty years of age at the time.[26] Thomas Le Quesne Blampied was not only the States Veterinary Surgeon, but he had also been a Vice President of the RJA&HS. According to Blampied's account to his son, Breuilly was charged and detained in February 1943 for not handing in his wireless to the German authorities, and he was also told that unless he cooperated in organising a cattle show he would be deported to spend his sentence in a German prison on the Continent. Breuilly, as a leading breeder and agent and manager of the Country Gentleman's Association, was ideally suited to collecting signatures for such an event. Whilst in the public prison, Breuilly was visited by Blampied. He informed him of the circumstances as to why he had collected names for the petition. He also told Blampied that farmers were indeed happy to participate in a cattle show.

George Amy Romeril

On 9ᵗʰ May 1945 Jersey was liberated by British forces. British Military Intelligence, on arrival, immediately went to College House. The majority of Field Command 515's files were removed and sent to England. A number of German files were left behind and were subsequently collected and kept by islanders.

On the 25ᵗʰ May, at a JFU Council Meeting, a proposition was carried unanimously that "Mr George Amy Romeril be expelled as a member of the JFU for having associated with the enemy during the occupation."[27]

George Romeril was the owner of one of the most important cattle stud farms in the 1930s, at Surville Manor, St Helier, and the breeder of many outstanding Jersey cattle. In addition, he was the Island agent for the American importer Wallace MacMonnies, exporting many successful bulls and cows across the Atlantic. Romeril bred "Surville Golden Designer", the sire that was so influential in the Island and in the USA when he headed the famous Vaucluse herd of Mrs Diane Ryan in Rhode Island, and he was the owner of the champion over Jersey in 1937.[2] The official records of the RJA&HS demonstrate that, along with E. C. Perrédès, he was the owner of cows with the highest pre-war milk yields.

On the 26th May 1945 there was a meeting of senior officers of the RJA&HS at which Perrédès proposed that members who had "helped the enemy" should be penalised.

On the 9th June, a meeting of twenty-seven members was also attended by the Society's legal advisor, solicitor W. S. Le Masurier. When Mr Le Masurier was asked about the possibility of expelling members who had collaborated with the enemy, he replied that the RJA&HS had "No power to expel a member unless it was a breach of its rules, trading with the enemy was a civil offence which would be punishable by law."

On the 16th June, 278 members attended a "Special General Meeting" held at the Town Hall, St Helier. The aim of the meeting was to discuss members' collaboration with the German authorities. Several members gave their personal view of "the best means of penalising collaboration with the enemy". The meeting was advised that, legally, it would be best to formulate a new rule to add to the existing rules, in order to provide for the expulsion of offending members who had worked with the Germans. It was stated to those present that "...any evidence of collaboration could be communicated confidentially and in writing to the President."

On the 4th August Mr J. E. Gaudin inquired what action, if any, had been taken on "a certain letter addressed to the President by Robert Wilson Carson with reference to the activities of two members [Romeril and Breuilly] in collaboration with the enemy."[14] Le Gallais answered that, in accordance with legal advice, punitive action could not be taken under the existing rules. It was decided that the RJA&HS would take advice from the Crown Officers and Mr Le Masurier would be informed of the course to be pursued. Perrédès concluded the meeting by instructing the secretary to write to the States of Jersey to express the Committee's displeasure at the fact that the Department of Public Health had made a contract for the supply of potatoes to the General Hospital with "...a well-known collaborator with the enemy."[14]

On the 17th November 1945, the members met again to discuss changes to the Fundamental Rules of the Society. It was agreed that a committee of twelve should be formed to examine the past conduct of members in relation to collaboration with the German authorities. It was agreed that this committee should carry out a full investigation and, if it was of the opinion that the complaints concerning an individual were founded and warranted expulsion, a "Special General Meeting" would be convened to consider the findings of the Committee. This Special General Meeting concerning collaboration would then, through a formal proposition, vote on the expulsion of an individual. If carried, the collaborator who had been a former member would have no right of appeal. In other words, once the resolution was passed by the membership the decision would be "definite and final".

There appears to have been a discussion as to whether this due process meant that principals of natural justice were being curtailed. Mr Le Masurier added that the allegations had been discussed in "long preparations with the Attorney General". This statement is interesting and informative. It demonstrates the close relationship between the breeders and the judicial branch of the Island's government. Many of these men were elected to the States of Jersey after the liberation. Francis Le Sueur proposed that this new addition to the Fundamental Rules be discussed at the forthcoming Annual General Meeting, and this was carried unanimously.

The first official AGM of the RJA&HS since 1939 was held on Saturday, 12th December 1945.[28] The meeting made clear that farmers and individuals who had collaborated with the German authorities would be identified.

On the 16th February 1946, the secretary, H. G. Shepard, read out to the assembled members a petition which was addressed to the President and signed by twelve members "...complaining of the conduct of George Amy Romeril and George Courtman Breuilly", both of whom had been important export agents just prior to the German occupation, and requesting that an investigation be carried out in accordance with Paragraph 2 of Rule 11 of the Fundamental Rules. Several members spoke of the "alleged misconduct" of George Romeril and George Breuilly. The committee, somewhat disconcerted by several vociferous supporters of the alleged collaborators, decided to take the advice of Mr Le Masurier and to withdraw the petition on technical grounds. Le Masurier stated to the assembled meeting that "...the facts provided in the statement were indefinite."[14]

On the 2nd March the petition was re-presented and read out to a full committee meeting by the President.[29]

"Sir,

We, the undersigned Members of the Society wish to draw your attention to the general conduct during the occupation of the Island of George C. Breuilly, a Member of the Society.

The said George C. Breuilly not only consorted with His Majesty's enemies during the period of occupation, but he did in fact, in collaboration with a member of the enemy forces, urge and induce other members of the Society to sign a Petition addressed to you, and did specifically on May 11th 1943, or about that time, in the Society's offices, Mulcaster Street, St. Helier, in collaboration with a Member of the enemy forces, attempt to induce you to agree to the proposal contained in the said Petition, in order to achieve an object, namely:- to hold a Show of Cattle in the Island of Jersey, which Show had it been held would undoubtedly have been for the benefit and the propaganda purposes of the enemy and which object, had it been achieved, would have been derogatory to and incompatible with the dignity, wellbeing and harmony of the Society, which enjoys the privilege of the Patronage of His Majesty the King. Fortunately, due chiefly to the firm stand taken by yourself, this catastrophe was avoided.

In view of the message of renewed loyalty forwarded to His Majesty after the Liberation of the Island, by decision of a General Meeting held on 15th June 1945, and consistent therewith, we respectfully request that this complaint should be investigated, in accordance with the provisions of Paragraph 2 of Rule 11 of the Fundamental Rules and that the said George C. Breuilly be expelled from the Society.

Yours respectfully,
(Signed)   J. B. Michel   C. Quenault
               J. E. Gaudin   Claude Godeaux
               C. P. Journeaux   P. C. Mourant
               A. W. Falle   P. L. Le Masurier
               T. G. Le Marinel   H. M. Gibaut "

The allegations were specifically aimed at Breuilly. It was clear to the leading cattle breeders of what he was guilty: firstly, he had collaborated with the Germans by asking farmers to sign a petition to hold a cattle show; and secondly, along with Corporal Soeldner, Pelz's adjutant, he tried to induce Le Gallais to organise an Island show aimed at benefiting the propaganda purposes of the German authorities.

The meeting agreed that a special sub-committee would investigate the allegations of German collaboration. The members who had made the allegations against Breuilly would not be allowed to sit on this sub-committee. J. A. Perrée opposed any precipitous action in view of the possible consequences which might arise. However, John Michel and Robert Carson were strongly in favour of prosecuting the matter.

Other communications concerning Romeril and his alleged "misconduct with the German occupiers" were discussed. It is worthwhile noting several points concerning the denunciation. Both Breuilly and Romeril were identified as collaborators by the Island's cattle-breeding elite, many of whom were also cattle-export agents. Both Breuilly and Romeril, prior to the German military occupation, were perhaps two of the most successful agents, exporting large numbers of Jersey cattle to the North American and UK markets. Romeril was also a top breeder and for the previous three years before the German military occupation had produced some of the best pedigree animals. Frigot's study of his pre-war business ledgers demonstrates that he was also a brilliant businessman when it came to the sale and export of Jersey bulls and heifers.[30] Romeril's ledgers show that he commanded prices that were several hundred pounds in excess of the average for bulls, and he also received a premium for the heifers he sold. In a small island where cattle breeders, farmers and agents knew each other well, intense rivalries and jealousies were often just below the surface. After the war, all these breeders, farmers and agents were looking forward to again exporting to their most profitable markets.

Both Carson and Le Gallais were not only successful breeders, but they also were export agents. Carson, in particular, sent very large numbers to the North American markets, with consignments of up to sixty heifers, like Breuilly, being not unusual.

It is therefore not beyond the realms of possibility that Le Gallais, Carson and others simply desired Romeril and Breuilly to be ostracised and boycotted in order to dominate the forthcoming post-war North American and world markets. After five to six years of war, many North Americans herds needed refreshing. They wanted both Breuilly and Romeril to be pushed out of the lucrative pedigree export markets.

In the petition presented on the 27th February, denouncing Breuilly, it was stated that he and Soeldner had collaborated together to force the RJA&HS to hold a cattle show. In addition, Breuilly had registered the names of twenty-six Society members in support of a show. The reason was simple: his petition had been put together to promulgate German propaganda.

The evidence, however, is clear. Although an Island cattle show was dismissed by Le Gallais and Michel, along with Touzel Brée, at the meeting with Pelz at College House on the 3rd May 1943, a compromise had been reached at the following meeting on the 7th May, between Pelz and the President and Vice Presidents of the RJA&HS. H. G. Shepard, in his notes, makes clear that "...the Vice Presidents [Le Boutillier and Michel] suggested, as an alternative, the holding of cattle parades in each parish or in groups of parishes...These suggestions proved acceptable to the German authorities." OKVR Dr Casper subsequently wrote to the Bailiff: "The Field Command agree, therefore, to the proposed show being split up into small shows in each parish, or two to three parishes combining together, as suggested by representatives of the Herd Book." In simple terms, the RJA&HS made it clear that due to practical difficulties – lack of transport, petrol and labour, and the possibility of spreading cattle diseases – an Island show could not be held under any circumstances; however, parochial cattle shows were possible. George Breuilly was not present at any of these meetings.

On the 16th March 1946, a sub-committee was established specifically to investigate all matters relating to the conduct of Breuilly and Romeril. The Chairman was A. J. du Feu, and the members were: J. Perchard, J. W. Le Gresley, P. B. Brée, A. Fair, R. J. Labey and E. R. Egré.

The sub-committee completed its report by the 24th April 1946. George Romeril immediately resigned from the Society; Breuilly was expelled. On the 22nd June, Breuilly's advocate, P. N. Richardson, met with the RJA&HS to discuss his client's expulsion. He stated that, under law, Breuilly's expulsion was retrospective and invalid. In consequence of the advocate's demand for a measure of natural justice, a "hearing" was set for Saturday 6th July. The purpose of the "hearing" would be to make a definitive decision concerning George Courtman Breuilly and any involvement or collaboration with the German occupiers. Both Advocate Richardson and Breuilly were instructed to attend.

Advocate Richardson, in response, wrote to the Society giving the names of four witnesses whom he wished to call in support of Breuilly. In addition, he sent a second letter concerning all allegations of collaboration made against Breuilly. The letter gave clear and concise reasons as to how Breuilly had conducted himself. Unfortunately, this correspondence has failed to materialise in any search of the archives.

At the hearing Advocate Richardson gave an account of what the German authorities had told his client and he called two witnesses – J. G. Le Main and Emile Thébault – who were questioned about Breuilly's association with the Germans. Mr Le Masurier questioned them about Breuilly's alleged visits to farmers to obtain signatures for a cattle show. G. R. Le Mière and F. C. Le Gros gave written statements that they had signed Breuilly's petition. Again, none of these statements have been found in any archive.

Le Masurier then questioned Breuilly about his visit to the RJA&HS office with Pelz's adjutant, Corporal Soeldner, and his visits to farms to see Claude Godeaux, J. J. Blampied, Clifford Le Vesconte and J. A. Norman with the object of obtaining signatures.

After the questioning, Richardson and Breuilly withdrew, and the written complaints of collaboration were considered by the sub-committee.

"After a full investigation and deliberation, Mr Philip Le Feuvre proposed and Mr H. J. Maillard seconded the following resolution:

July 6th, 1946

The Committee has this day taken into consideration the complaint against Mr George Courtman Breuilly and after a full investigation thereof are of the opinion that the said complaint is well founded and warrants the expulsion from the Society of the said George C. Breuilly under Rule 11, paragraph 2 of the Fundamental Rules."

The findings of the sub-committee were made known to the membership of the Society and it was decided that a full meeting would be arranged for Saturday 20th July at 3.00 p.m., at the Town Hall. The Committee, 200 members and some others, met to discuss the outcome of the sub-committee's decision to revoke Breuilly's membership. Philip Le Feuvre proposed that Breuilly be immediately expelled from the Society. This was seconded by A. J. du Feu. Advocate Richardson spoke in Breuilly's defence, and the meeting then proceeded to vote on the resolution, an "appel nominal" (roll call) being taken. The result of the vote was 101 in favour of expulsion and ninety-nine against. George C. Breuilly was expelled from the RJA&HS and condemned as a German collaborator by just two votes.

If Le Gallais and the RJA&HS committee thought that a final decision had been arrived at over the issue of Breuilly's German collaboration, they were very wrong. George Romeril had departed the Society quietly and without fuss; the very opposite occurred in the case of Breuilly.

On the 29th August the President received a petition covering major "irregularities" of the meeting and the vote on the 6th July, concerning Breuilly's expulsion. That special meeting was seen by the petitioners as unconstitutional and unsatisfactory. The petition read as follows:

"WE, the undersigned Members of the Royal Jersey Agricultural and Horticultural Society respectfully Petition you to call a Special General Meeting of the Society to be held at the earliest possible date to rescind and annul the decision of the Special General Meeting held at the Town Hall on Saturday July 20th, 1946 when on the proposition being put to the meeting you announced that the result of the voting was 101 in favour of the proposition confirming the Committee's recommendation to expel Mr G. C. Breuilly from the Society as against 99 votes against the proposition.

The reasons for our request that a further meeting should be convened are as follows:

1. Votes were recorded as being for the proposition which were clearly given against it.
2. Members were admitted to the Meeting without scrutiny of their cards.
3. Some Members who tendered their subscriptions during the week prior to the Meeting were refused Membership Cards, others were accepted.

In view of all these irregularities and the unsatisfactory way in which the vote was taken we unhesitatingly urge you to reconvene the Meeting and take the vote in a regular and constitutional manner.
(Signed)

Robert D. Holt	Mrs. Alice Blacker-Douglass	E. P. Romeril
H. Le Brocq	E. Thébault	D. C. Le Brocq
Emile Le Geyt Siouville	Alfred Dupré Renouard	J. E. Morcel
J. K. Kempster	A. Le Couteur	S. V. Pallot
T. S. R. Chamberlayne	J. C. Rondel	Ed. G. Pipon
G.R. Le Mière	F. C. Le Gros	A. J. Rolland
A. S. Pipon	R. P. Le Cornu	G. A. Luce.
E. C. Le Feuvre	F. J. Lucas	E. Pallot
Eton Le Brun	P. J. Groundsell	L. A. Le Breuilly
F. J. Hinault, Jun.	J. Le Masurier"	

The Society's legal advisor recommended that the best course of action would be to hold a further meeting to discuss the establishment of a "Rules Revision Committee". On the 9th November the RJA&HS wrote to Advocate Richardson asking for clarification of "reason three" of the petition of the 29th August. In addition, Richardson was informed that he had not furnished clarification of the three points described in the petition.

On the 13th December, Breuilly's advocate published a letter in the local press concerning the AGM that was due to take place the following day. He wrote "...it is hoped that members of the Society will attend in force to reject this utter abuse of power and control by an autocratic and arbitrary executive who wish to have control of the Society at their despotic mercy."[31]

The AGM was held on the 14th December, and the complicated issue of a series of amendments governing the Fundamental Rules of Membership, brought forward by the hierarchy, were discussed.

These discussions over membership had opened real divisions concerning Breuilly and his alleged role as a collaborator. The dichotomy of opinion also extended to the conduct of the farming elite, who had worked and interacted with Pelz and Field Command 515 during the German occupation.

The issue of Breuilly's alleged collaboration and, in particular, his role in collecting signatures for the cattle show, remained contentious throughout the 1950s. Several meetings and counter meetings were held on both sides, by those who continued to denounce Breuilly and by those who supported him. The meetings provided excellent news material for the local press.

The Committee kept stubbornly to their version of events. By December 1945 the official version of the episode was described as follows: "A determined effort was indeed made by the German authorities to force the Society to hold a show in 1943, but your officers tenaciously resisted the proposal. So many difficulties were put forward that finally the Society was spared the mortification of holding a show under the Swastika."[32]

The official version of the proposed 1943 cattle show remained intact. In 1968, H. G. Shepard wrote: "Efforts were made by the occupier to hold a show of cattle in 1943. These were successfully resisted, and the Swastika flag never floated above a "Royal Show."[17]

On the 6th July 1940, at a Special General Meeting of the RJA&HS Agricultural Department, a resolution had been passed empowering its officers to act as an Emergency Committee to conduct the affairs of the Department, of which the Jersey Herd Book was a part. The officers of the Emergency Committee were Le Gallais, Michel and Le Boutillier. The secretary was H. G. Shepard.

Three days later, on the 9th July 1940, the DOA had received a letter headed: "Gift of potatoes to Germans". The minutes describe "The Secretary [Colin Marie] was instructed to transmit to the German Commandant of the island, [Hauptmann Gussek] with the compliments of the Department, an offer of the RJA&HS to present to the said German Commandant a gift of two tons of potatoes". In effect, the Emergency Committee of the RJA&HS had gifted local produce to the German Commandant only nine days after the German military forces had invaded Jersey.[33]

Perrédès' denunciation of George Romeril as "A well-known collaborator" is particularly interesting. It can be seen in the context of their pre-war rivalry in both the export of high-value cattle to the USA and their outstanding records in breeding the foremost milk-producing cows. The competition between the two men in such a small society was intense.

In May 1945 a further reason perhaps influenced Perrédès to make accusations of collaboration against Romeril. This is the fact that, by the end of the occupation, Perrédès was almost certainly the owner of the largest dairy herd on the Island, if not in the Channel Islands. A draft letter dated 2nd June 1944 from Platzkommandantur I to the Army Command and Pelz, entitled "Shooting Range, Le Bourg, Grouville" describes: "Up to now the landowner Perrédès, Fairview Farm, St. Saviour, has grazed cattle on the firing range between Le Bourg and Francheville. The above person is the largest cattle owner in Jersey. His stock includes approximately 150 cattle of which 60 are cows and 90 are young animals."[34]

The JFU allegations of the 25th May 1945, recorded in the minutes, are that Romeril "…associated with the enemy during the Occupation" and that he also be penalised for "…helping the enemy", provided Perrédès with a fortuitous opportunity to eliminate his main competitor. In the turbulence of the immediate post-liberation period, when populist emotions were running high concerning German collaborators, it was a relatively simple process to merge the idea of "Collaborator" with "Competitor". Both the JFU and the RJA&HS had effectively banished Romeril. It was simple to lay open to the agricultural community the allegations of the two societies. George Romeril became the identifiable face of collaboration.

On the 21st May 1945 a farmer wrote in a letter to his family in England: "The following day [10th May] feelings were running high – mob-law prevailed for a bit but the Military have full control. The property of Informers was smashed…several Black Marketeers around St Ouen's have had to flee…black marketing has been terrible, prices fantastic but these people are known and will be duly punished. The person having the worst reputation is, I think, George Romeril who has disappeared at the moment - he was friendly and entertained the Gestapo."[35]

This letter is interesting for two reasons. Firstly, it names only twelve days after the liberation, a list of islanders who collaborated with the Germans and participated in the black market and states that retribution would occur. Secondly, and pertaining to Romeril, the accusations made against him were simply hearsay – "I think…" The writer's point that he "…entertained the Gestapo" was never legally proven and the notion that the Gestapo operated in Jersey is incorrect.

References

1. Jersey Archive. L/D/09/A1/10.
2. Frigot, D. 2017. Pioneers of the Jersey Breed. p. 82.
3. Jersey Archive. C/B/A1/3; C/B/A1/4 and C/B/A1/5.
4. George Courtman Breuilly also used alternative surnames: Le Breuilly, Brierly and Brailey.
5. RJA&HS. Annual Report. 1939, p. 39.
6. RJA&HS and JFU Joint Emergency Committee Minutes.
7. The biography of Hans Egon Pelz. Damals Erinnerungen, 2015. Compiled and published by the Pelz family.
8. Private letter from Pelz to Dr Josef Kratzer, President of the Munich Administrative Court. Dated 12th February 1957. Pelz family archive. Dr Kratzer served with Field Command 515 during the occupation of the Channel Island.
9. The Herd Book Committee comprised Carlyle Le Gallais, Francis Le Boutillier and John Buesnel Michel.
10. Jersey Archive. B/A/W31/2/78.
11. Jersey Archive. C/B/A1/8.
12. Jersey Archive. D/Z/H6/5/63.
13. Soeldner is wrongly spelt in RJA&HS records and is written as Seeldner.
14. Jersey Archive. L/D/09/A11.
15. Max Planck: Berlin I. Department 1a, Number 2858 and 2859.
16. Jersey Archive. B/A/W40/2/1.
17. Jersey Farmer and Grower. Vol 1. No 7. March 1968.
18. Lauprecht, E. Züchtungskunde. Vol XVII, pp. 369–386. Herausgegeben von Der Deutschen Gesellschaft Für Züchtunskunde, Unter Mitwirkung der Tierzuchtinstitute an Deutschen Hochschulen. Die Rinderzucht auf der Insel Jersey.
19. My sincere thanks to Dr Eva Rinnerthaler of the Landberg Salzburg, Salzburger Landesarchiv for her invaluable help in locating documents pertaining to Pelz. In addition, Andreas Riedl of the Amt der Salzburger Landesregierung.
20. Interviews with Dr Casper and Major Heider by Alan Allix.
21. Jersey Archive. Q/05/A/58. One Berlin propaganda unit was PK-Filmbericht, who filmed in 35 mm. One of their films can be seen titled "Englishe Kanalinseln".
22. The release of "G C Le Breuilly" was mentioned in a newspaper article, JEP 24th March 1994. The actual dates of his release were not mentioned in the article.
23. Jersey Archive. D/Z/H6/3/64.
24. Jersey Archive. B/A/W48/61.
25. An official of the States of Jersey and the Royal Court who serves summonses and legal documents; holds general court enforcement duties; acts as administering coroner and has bankruptcy responsibilities.
26. Interview with Nicholas Le Quesne Blampied on 27th November 2015.

27. JFU Minute Book. My thanks to Ms Maureen Rondel, former Executive Secretary, JFU, for allowing me access to the Minute Book files.

28. For a detailed description of the AGM see: JEP 12th December 1945.

29. Jersey Archive. L/D/09/A12. Only ten names appear on the petition. The petition document appears to have been trimmed and two names cut away.

30. My thanks to Derrick Frigot, MBE, for his assistance and description of George Romeril's ledger.

31. The Morning News. 13th December 1946. Letter to Editor. "RJA&HS - Despotic Move".

32. RJA&HS. Report of the Committee for the years 1940 to 1945. 8th December 1945.

33. Jersey Archives. C/B/A1/5.

34. Az.W:15-KO. Dated 2nd June 1944, private correspondence.

35. Letter from Vale Farm, St Peter, Jersey, dated 21st May 1945. The writer makes a mistake, almost certainly identifying the Field Police with the Gestapo, the latter having never operated in Jersey during the entire occupation.

Chapter 14

July to October 1943

Milk Control

In early July the Milk Control Section increased the salary of Mrs M. G. Perchard, a saleswoman at the Don Street Dairy, to £2-5-0 a week and Miss Iris Le Masurier was employed as a junior clerk on a salary of £1 a week. Two Milk Testers, Mr J. T. Roberts and Mr George Davy, resigned and were replaced by Mr J. P. Gicquel and Mr Q. H. Tirel. In addition, Mr Leslie Baker, Chief Clerk of the Milk Control Section, was awarded a wage increase of 7/6 a week. His revised weekly wage was £2-15-0.

On the 18th August, Miss G. Tomes asked the DOA for an increase in her weekly salary. Female employees were paid approximately half the wages of male employees in the clerical sections. After a report from the Head of Milk Control, the DOA decided that "While fully appreciating Miss Tomes' services it was unable to increase her salary".

Also in early July, a lift cable at the Don Street Dairy snapped, and a major accident was narrowly avoided. The State's Engineer was called to examine all the machinery. He reported back, pointing out "The lack of safety provision for the employees of the DOA, working amongst the machinery". The DOA told him to submit a report as to the "...best means to be adopted in order to provide for the safety of DOA employees". His subsequent report highlighted "The inadequate protection for the employees of the DOA working amongst the machinery at Don Street Dairy". In response, the DOA instructed the States Engineer to carry out all work necessary to safeguard the men working at the machinery. The safety work was completed by December.

Another report in early July discussed a letter sent by Mr Cyril R. Tanguy, Managing Director of L. J. Tanguy Limited, concerning his dairy's evening collection of milk from the Otago Cottage depot, St Martin. Many of the dairy farmers nearby had not supplied their milk in time for it to then be delivered to the public the following morning. As a result, Le Gallais carried out an inspection of the depot and two producers were written to for an explanation. Mr Y. Le Bouillennec and Mr P. Marrett were informed that after investigations of the evening milk delivery, it was satisfied that in the present circumstances it was not practicable for them to deliver to the depot twice daily. Since they had only one horse between them, an allowance was made for one delivery a day.

On the 30th July, Mr A. C. Allix, St Helier, a licensed milk retailer, appeared before the DOA. Mrs V. A. Rabet had alleged that Mr Allix had failed to deliver the quantity of milk to which she was entitled. He, furthermore, had failed to deliver to her certain additional quantities to which she was also entitled, by virtue of milk permits allocated to her.[1] After being interviewed Mr Allix was given a warning.

On the 12th August, the DOA made recommendations with regard to the distribution of skim milk.

1. The four distributing dairies shall be supplied with lists of all registered owners of calves and pigs.
2. Neither skim milk nor butter milk shall be distributed to producers who are not registered as being the owners of calves or pigs.
3. Available supplies of skim milk will henceforth be distributed 50% to members of the public and 50% to registered calf or pig owners. Any surplus of skim milk is to be made available to the public.
4. When supplies of skim milk are insufficient to maintain the proportions set out above, preference will be given firstly to owners of calves; secondly, to members of the public; and thirdly, to owners of pigs.
5. All supplies of skim milk to cafés and restaurants will be reduced by 50% on the 1st September 1943.

A report from the Attorney General dated 3rd September was discussed by the DOA. It concerned a decision by the Royal Court to convict Mr Alfred A. Allo, manager of Allo Brothers, for allegedly deriving cream from milk. The DOA decided to revoke the firm's retailer licence and the Attorney General was notified. On the 16th September Allo's advocates, Ogier and Le Cornu, asked for a delay in the revocation of the retailer licence until a new owner was confirmed. The DOA extended the period until the 21st September. On that day, the advocates confirmed that the Allo Brothers had disposed of their milk retailer's business to Jersey Dairies Limited.

On the 10th September a report discussed "...the shortage of 10½ pots of milk, or 43% in the quantity of milk delivered to the DOA". The allegation was made against Mr J. Le Pennec, St Ouen. He was called in to the DOA to offer to explain why his cows produced only a small amount of milk. Mr Le Pennec explained he did not have enough milk cans. He had been instructed to buy milk cans but had declined and was warned that he had to provide the necessary containers himself in order to fulfil his obligation to deliver milk to the licensed retailer. He was told that unless this legal obligation was forthcoming, he would be deprived of one of his cows.

On the 21st September Miss P. Gulliford, a Milk Control clerk, received a 5/- a week increase in her salary. As from the 27th September, milk collection times were altered to 8.30 a.m. and 5.00 p.m. but on the 23rd October the evening collection was terminated. A report of the 29th September described a continuing decrease in the supply of milk from dairy farmers. Therefore, the distribution of skim milk was restricted from four days a week to three.

On the 2nd October Mr H. Alexander resigned as a Milk Tester and Mr H. F. Le Sueur, St Lawrence, was appointed in his place. On the same day, Mr A. A. Voisin, St Lawrence, appeared before the DOA to provide an explanation as to why there were alleged shortages in the quantity of milk delivered by him to his appointed licensed retailer. The DOA, after hearing what Mr Voisin said and receiving an assurance that he had ceased supplying milk to his daughter-in-law and grandson, to which they were not entitled, warned him about future observance of the Milk Control (Jersey) Order, 1940. The matter was dropped.

On the 19th October the DOA "...taking note of an Act of the Superior Council, 13th October, decided to recommend that from the 1st January 1944 the salary of the DOA's secretary, Colin Cecil Marie, would increase from £300 to £350 per annum". On the same day Miss N. Houillebecq, Milk Control, received an increase of 2/6 a week. On the 26th October Mr C. Wood, the stoker at Don Street Dairy, retired.

On the 12th July 1943, Field Command 515 informed the Bailiff that dairy produce delivered to the following German establishments was to be increased.[2]

	Butter (kg)	Full Milk (litres)	Skim Milk (litres)
Soldatenheim I	4.5	15	25
Soldatenheim II	2	30	20
Soldatenheim III	4	10	20
Offiziershein	1.5	5	–
Total	12.0	60	65

The Bailiff immediately wrote to the DOA requesting "...necessary action please". On the 18th October the Field Commandant wrote again to the Bailiff concerning the opening of the new Soldatenheim IV at La Hougue, St Peter. He informed the Bailiff: "The daily milk delivery is to be arranged as follows. The farmer Le Rossignol, La Hougue, is to deliver 24 pints of fresh milk to the Soldatenheim IV against payment. This quantity is to be deducted from the supplies made to Soldatenheim II, St Brelade, until further notice. It is requested that the DOA be directed to reduce forthwith the daily deliveries hitherto made to Soldatenheim II, from 30 litres of fresh milk and 20 litres of skim milk to 20 litres of fresh milk and 15 litres skim milk. Le Rossignol is to receive permission to deliver 24 pints of fresh milk daily to Soldatenheim IV, La Hougue, against payment. Milk Control is to be notified".

Tobacco

On the 2nd July Mr W. Truscott, who had been growing tobacco plants, made a request to the DOA. He had been ordered to plant French seed potatoes to replace the tobacco and he requested to grow a crop of broccoli instead. The DOA refused to modify its directive.

In late July "...the German authorities now in occupation of the island reported that 30 perches of tobacco were being grown". The report was made by Pelz directly to Brée. The tobacco was allegedly being grown by Mr C. P. Mallet Junior.[1] He was immediately contacted and given seven days to remove the tobacco plants and replace them with a food crop. In the same week an allegation was reported that Mr H. Poole, St Lawrence, "... was growing a considerable quantity of tobacco". After an investigation had been carried out the DOA referred the matter to the Department of Finance and Economics.

A subsequent report dated the 7th August was sent to the DOA. Written by the Attorney General, it concerned the allegations that Mr H. Poole, St Lawrence, and Mr J. Maletroit, St Helier, were growing tobacco.[1] In view of the report, the DOA decided to request the Department of Finance and Economics that the "Loi (1934) sur le Règie et le mode de Perception de L'Impôt sur le Tabac" be amended so as to provide suitable penalties for breaches.[3] The DOA also wrote to the Honorary Parish Inspectors, instructing them to visit and inspect the premises of Mr Poole and Mr Maletroit, and also the premises of Mr L. Guillemet, St Lawrence. The report in relation to Maletroit was forthright on the quantity of tobacco grown. During the period June to August 1943, he had grown and cured 1,080 tobacco plants and had taken 108 orders for tobacco.[4] The Honorary Parish Inspector stated that Maletroit had not complied with directions issued to him under a Cultivation Order in that he had failed to grow 2 vergées of mangolds. Brée referred the matter to the Attorney General and requested him to institute proceedings against Maletroit for his failure to comply with the Cultivation Order.

A report from the Honorary Parish Inspector on the 22nd August concerned an allegation that Mr Guillemet was growing a large area of tobacco and that he had failed to grow 1 vergée of carrots as a second crop. The matter was referred to the Attorney General.

On the 1st October Brée reported to the DOA that the Royal Court had initiated actions against J. Maletroit and L. Guillemet in response to their failure to comply with directions under the Cultivation of Lands (Jersey) Order, 1942. Both men were instructed to sell their tobacco to the DOA. Maletroit received £46-7-6 and Guillemet £19-18-6. In addition, Brée reported that, in view of the purchase of this very large amount of tobacco leaf, he had made arrangements for it to be collected under the supervision of Mr Simpson, from the States Experimental Station, and an arrangement had been put in place with Jersey Canners Limited, Greve d'Azette, to dry the

13,000 tobacco leaves at a cost of £30. 10% would be added to the selling price of the tobacco to cover the additional labour by the factory.

On the 28th August, the DOA received a report from the Honorary Parish Inspectors that tobacco cultivation was taking place on land measuring 3½ vergées near West Hill, Mont á L'Abbé, St Helier. The field was rented from Mr E. W. Le Touzel, Trinity, by "...a man called Mr Fieldhouse". The field in question should have been planted with potatoes by Mr Le Touzel before "Mr Fieldhouse" had planted tobacco. It was noted that Le Touzel had delivered to the DOA only half of the 16½ tons of potatoes which his cultivation directions had required of him. Le Touzel was summoned and appeared before the DOA on the 3rd September. He was asked why he had failed to plant 30 perches of imported seed potatoes and had failed to comply with the requirements of agricultural orders. In specific terms, where growers had been unable to plant imported seed potatoes, they were obliged to sow an equal area of land in carrots or swedes as a substitute crop.

After hearing Le Touzel's explanations the matter was referred to the Attorney General for investigation. The DOA, in its submission, drew attention to the fact that Le Touzel had "...sublet 3½ vergées of land at West Hill, Mont à L'Abbe, St Helier, at a rental of £2 per vergée to a Mr Fieldhouse".

Watermills and Milling

On the 6th August the DOA requested the Department of Transport and Communications to procure a lorry powered by charcoal for carting grain and flour to and from the mills. It received a reply agreeing that a number of gasogene-operated lorries (an engine that converts wood into fuel) would be allocated to the DOA in connection with the transport of grain and flour.

The following week the Department of Transport and Communications suggested that, instead of lorries being placed at the disposal of the DOA for carting grain and flour, "A sufficient safeguard could be provided if an employee of the DOA travelled with each load to and from the mill". The DOA replied that the above suggestion would increase the already high cost of transport and would entail the employment of further men. This would push up the cost of flour to the public. The DOA therefore repeated its request that one or more gasogene-operated lorries be placed at its disposal.

On the 14th September the Department of Transport agreed to the original DOA request. It set forth the terms of hire for a gasogene-driven lorry to be placed at the disposal of the DOA for the cartage of grain and flour.

1. The charge for the lorry is 7/6 an hour.
2. The same driver will be at the disposal of the DOA at all times.
3. An additional man will be employed to load and unload the lorry.

On the 3rd September, on the recommendation of Brée, Mr P. A. Hervieu, Assistant Miller at Malassis Mill, was transferred to Quetivel Mill. Mr Hervieu took the position held by Mr C. Le G. Lucas who left the services of the DOA.

In September, the States Engineer informed the DOA that the millponds urgently needed cleaning; work was scheduled for the 13th September. In addition to the maintenance work, the DOA requested that the millstream at Gargate be straightened. The cost of all these works was £241-9-0.

On the night of the 21st and 22nd September, at Quetivel, a large quantity of clothing belonging to the millers was stolen. The millers' request for replacement clothing was refused by Brée.

Potatoes

In early summer 1943, Colonel Knackfuss wrote to the Bailiff. He criticised the expected total cultivation of potatoes and the resulting harvest - an issue which he had already discussed with Brée. He had made it clear to Brée that he wanted 1,400 hectares of potatoes cultivated, throughout the Island. Brée offered 1,222 hectares. In response to Brée's "...alterations...to which I did not agree", Knackfuss stated that "There may be difficulties with regard to the supplying of the civilian population". Knackfuss in simple terms was saying that any shortfall of potato cultivation would fall upon the civilian population, and not the German military forces.

Knackfuss indicated that he had been deceived by Brée's figures. He demanded that Brée prepare in one week "An exact estimate...to be submitted not only as a total statement but also divided up into parishes". All figures would have to agree with Cultivation Orders. He also claimed that the potato cultivation figures he had been given were opaque and underlined that "The estimate is...to include the determination of the size of all potato cultivation areas", including "...the later crops which...correspond to the actual areas planted".[5]

On the 28th June Mr J. F. Baudain wrote to the DOA concerning a delivery of imported seed potatoes. He had received a Cultivation Direction to plant the potatoes on 20 perches of his farm in St Clement. He refused to do so and demanded a refund. The DOA refused on both counts.

On the same day Mrs W. Wallard, Victoria Avenue, St Helier, discovered a Colorado Beetle which had flown into her house. A search was carried out in the area and a further beetle was discovered in "a quiescent state" at the foot of a lime tree at First Tower. Mr Frank Le Maistre was ordered to investigate the area of Mont Cochon where further sightings had been reported. After an extensive search, Le Maistre reported "Negative results". In response, Field Command 515 ordered that any appearance of the beetle in the Island had to be reported to them immediately. In addition, the DOA was ordered to be ready with "combative measures". Brée and the Attorney General informed all parish Connétables to make ready for immediate inspection of their fields.

Field Command also demanded that the DOA inform them of the number of knapsack and horse-drawn sprayers available to combat Colorado Beetle and, on the 9th July, all potato farmers were directed to spray against the beetle at the end of July and in early August.[6]

On the same day the DOA amended its former directions and orders, allowing green potatoes and chats to be delivered to the DOA, but placed in separate containers. The DOA would pay 13/- per cwt for these potatoes, which were subsequently sent to the Island's soup kitchens. Also discussed was the question of potato loads delivered by farmers which contained "cub potatoes". All farmers were warned that henceforth any such loads would be re-sorted and this would incur the farmers with an extra bill.

The summer of 1943 saw an increasing problem of farmers delivering sub-standard potatoes to fulfil their Cultivation Orders. Mr E. F. A'Court, St Ouen, having been instructed to re-sort a load of potatoes of varying standard, simply drove his load back to his farm "…in defiance of instructions". He was called to appear before the DOA on the 13th July and, after giving an explanation of the sub-standard quality of his potatoes, was given 48 hours to return all the potatoes to the DOA in the manner instructed. Mr A'Court duly delivered the load.

On the 17th July, Field Command sent a further letter to the Bailiff concerning potato yields in 1943. The Bailiff was informed that "A number of tests were carried out by the Field Command in order to ascertain the probable yield of the 1943 potato crop". Field Command again reiterated its "…dissatisfaction with the estimated figures of the crop submitted by the DOA". Indeed, Field Command, after a careful study of the figures, expressed "…the opinion that these figures could not be accepted as a reliable guide to the probable crop, nor did they make adequate provision for the quantities for the feeding of the civilian population". Brée was ordered to prepare new estimates for the 1943 potato harvest. He spent three days calculating the probable yield and by the 23rd July had made ready the terms of the representations which he proposed to make to "The German authority at present in occupation of the island".

Whilst Brée was making his calculations, a letter was sent to the DOA from Field Command. It required the DOA to bear the financial loss entailed due to "The importation into the island by the Field Command…of some 130 tons of seed potatoes which were either worthless or unreliable for seed owing to the fact that they were affected with dry rot". On the 24th September, Brée authorised the payment of £8,344-4-2 to the German Field Command in respect of seed imported into Jersey by the German authority.

A report of the 31st August described the delivery of five barrels of imported seed potatoes to Mr G. Dorey and Mr J. T. du Feu, Trinity. The latter refused to take delivery of the seed owing to its condition and it was deposited at the States Experimental Station. Both farmers put in a claim for compensation or a refund. They were instructed to plant swedes or turnips as a substitute and, at a later date, Mr Dorey was refunded the original cost of the seed potatoes.

The following week the Honorary Parish Inspector for Trinity reported that Mr J. H. Syvret was digging up his potatoes, grown from imported seed, although they were not yet mature. A report was prepared for the Attorney General. The same day Mr Billot, Maufant, St Saviour, made a complaint to the DOA on the poor quality of his imported seed. The DOA refused any form of compensation.

On the 20th August the Honorary Parish Inspector for St Ouen sent a report concerning the alleged "...deplorable condition of Rectory Farm".[1] The farm was held as a tenancy by Mrs J. R. Le Marquand. The DOA wrote to Mrs Le Marquand informing her of the nature of the report and warning that unless she took the appropriate action to terminate her tenancy in December, the DOA would enforce an order. On the 22nd September, the DOA received a letter from Advocates Le Masurier, Giffard and Poch, acting for Mrs Le Marquand. The allegation that their client's farm was in a bad condition was denied. In view of the letter, the DOA appointed a sub-committee comprising John du Val and Wesley Mallett to visit the farm and to write a full report. It was completed on the 1st October. The next day, Le Masurier, Giffard and Poch were informed that Mrs Le Marquand, the tenant of the farm, was to annul the lease by Christmas 1943.

On the 3rd September the Superior Council approved an Order that the DOA would pay farmers the sum of 13/- per cwt for potatoes grown from imported seed. In order to make this legal, the definition of "home grown" had to include the cultivation of French imported seed potatoes. The new Order was the Home-Grown Potatoes (1943 Crop) (Maximum Prices) (Amendment) (Jersey) Order, 1943.

On the 17th September Mr F. Le Lièvre, St Peter, was interviewed concerning his alleged failure to supply the quantity of potatoes he had been directed to deliver to the DOA. He was ordered to deliver not less than 10 cwt of mids in his possession. The Honorary Parish Inspector, Mr E. R. Egré, was instructed to enforce the order and the matter was dropped. Also interviewed was Mr L. Holmes, Trinity, whose potato deficit in 1943 was 13½ tons. After the interview, he immediately delivered the correct quantity to the DOA store.

On the 18th September, Field Command issued an order to the DOA requiring the delivery of 6 tons of seed potatoes to Sark. Brée expressed the opinion to the Field Command that "The insufficiency of the 1943 potato crop makes it impossible to export any further quantities of potatoes" and he reported back to the DOA after discussing the matter with the Superior Council. "The Superior Council has decided that an endeavour should be made to comply with the order of the German authorities now in occupation of the island that six tons of seed potatoes should be provided for the island of Sark". As a result of this decision a notice was put in the local press, inviting farmers to bring to the DOA for export to Sark the specified quantity of seed potatoes.

At the end of September, Mr H. Huelin, St Brelade, wrote to the DOA protesting against a requirement by Brée that he deliver 100 boxes of seed potatoes to the DOA. The order was directed at him because "Mr Huelin had delivered a quantity of potatoes to the DOA which were seriously short for the second year in succession". He was informed that any seed potatoes he may require in future to cultivate on his fields would have to be obtained from other sources. Wesley Mallet was appointed to value the potatoes which "...being of a very poor quality" he valued them at 9/- per cwt.

On the 1st October Mr Simpson reported that potato blight had arrived on the Island through imported potatoes. A notice was inserted in the local press that farmers had to spray their crops with the blight spray provided.

On the 4th October the Honorary Parish Inspector of St John reported that he had allocated to Mr Alexander S. Raworth, St John's Manor, 2½ vergées of imported potato seed to be planted as a first crop. Mr Raworth, however, had sown grass and allowed the field to become infested with weeds. The DOA sent the matter to the Attorney General in respect of his failure to comply with instructions issued under the Cultivation of Lands (Jersey) Order, 1942.

On the 5th October, Mr R. Labey, Grouville, appeared before the DOA to answer an allegation that he had sold a quantity of potatoes without a licence to Robert Henry Lawrence, St Helier. The DOA took into consideration that Mr Labey, several months previously, had delivered a load of potatoes in excess of that required by the Cultivation Order. It therefore decided to issue a licence to Mr Labey and he was given a warning to follow all future directions.

On the 19th October, eel worm was discovered at Mont Cochon, St Helier. An immediate order was issued to the occupier, Mr S. B. Sauvage prohibiting the sale of any root crop. He was also required to clean and inspect all his farm implements.

In October, the DOA considered a letter from Mr J. D. C. Ford, St Brelade. He asked for compensation, as the prices paid by the DOA for potatoes under the Home-Grown Potatoes (1943 Crop) (Maximum Prices) (Jersey) Order, 1943, did not cover the cost of cultivation. The land Mr Ford occupied was wholly in côtils. Mr Ford was informed that, in the absence of any evidence of financial hardship, the DOA was not prepared to make a recommendation for payment of compensation.

A week later, Mr Ford wrote "...pressing his claim compensation in respect of potatoes grown by him in 1943 as directed by the DOA". He made it clear that he had suffered financial hardship because of his compliance to agricultural directions. Brée was asked to interview Mr Ford and to report his findings, which he did on 22nd October. It was evident that Ford had been unable to meet his liabilities due to his losses in growing potatoes. The DOA decided that, under its Act of the 21st August 1942, it would not make a recommendation for compensation to be paid to Mr Ford.

Pigs

"Purchase of young pigs by troops. So far this year, approximately 70 young pigs
have been purchased by the troops from farmers. In this, no danger
to the local meat production for the civilian population can be seen.
Permits to purchase will continue
to be issued to the troops".

Letter from the Field Commandant to the Bailiff

By the summer of 1943, German military personnel stationed on the Island were permitted to purchase young pigs from farmers. Authorisation had to be formally applied for from the German Military Government, Field Command 515, and a permit issued, countersigned by Pelz, Head of Agriculture and Food Supplies for the Channel Islands. The purchase of young pigs increased to such an extent that the DOA wrote to the Field Command in June 1943 asking for the practice to cease.

On the 8th July Knackfuss replied to the Bailiff over the issue. "So far this year [1943] 70 young pigs have been purchased by the troops from farmers. In this, no danger to the local meat production for the local civil population can be seen. Permits to purchase will be continued to be issued to the troops".[7]

For Jersey farmers the reality was that selling young pigs to military personnel was extremely profitable and, in some cases, saved struggling farmers from pecuniary collapse. Also, the temptation for farmers to receive what they regarded as a commensurate and fair return for their outputs, instead of the DOA's fixed prices which they were forced to accept, was too much for some to turn down. Indeed, they were extremely willing to sell pigs to military personnel regardless of the permits issued by Field Command 515 and Pelz.

The problem of a diminishing level of pig production was brought to the Bailiff 's attention by Colonel Knackfuss. On the 22nd July, he advised farmers that "The keeping of pigs is to receive attention. The large quantities of pig potatoes and roots allows the keeping of pigs on every farm. It will serve as an example to you that the troops have several hundred pigs which are fed only kitchen and garden refuse".[8]

On the 20th August Brée referred the case of Mr R. H. Holt, St Helier, to the Attorney General for investigation. He was alleged to have in his custody "...certain unregistered pigs". Furthermore, it was alleged that Mr Holt "... proposes to sell to members of the German forces at present in occupation of the island".

At the same time the Commandant had written to the Bailiff. Knackfuss made it clear that he had seen young pigs being sold to German military personnel: "I have observed...[and] it has been established that pigs not fully grown (weighing 20 to 40 kilogrammes) have been slaughtered. It is uneconomic to slaughter...pigs of such small weight. This is at variance with the provision necessary for ensuring the proper feeding of the civilian population. You are therefore ordered to take steps which will make it impossible...[for] pigs of insufficient size to be slaughtered except by order of a veterinary surgeon".[9]

The Bailiff replied that the Cattle Slaughter Executive Committee and the States Vet had been notified concerning the slaughter of pigs of light weight. Indeed, the very same day Blampied contacted the Bailiff to say he would take all necessary action in conjunction with the DOA to stop the slaughter of underweight pigs.

On the 22nd August Mr J. W. Blampied, Inspector of Livestock, visited the premises of Mr L. Guillemet, St Lawrence. He found two four-month-old pigs which allegedly had not been registered. The matter was referred to the Attorney General.

A report of the 3rd September from the Attorney General to the DOA complained that "Mr J. W. Blampied, the DOA's Inspector for the purposes of the Livestock (Jersey) Order, 1942, has failed to carry out a proper inspection of the premises of Emile Thébault, St Helier, in relation to an allegation that Mr Thébault has in his possession certain unregistered pigs". Brée reported back that he had "...severely reprimanded the Inspector and warned him of his future conduct". On the 17th September, it was alleged that Mr L. Le Vannais, St Helier, had in his custody, and according to DOA records, five pigs. An inspection several days before had found only two licensed breeding sows. Le Vannais had made no return of pigs under the Livestock (Returns) (Jersey) Order, 1943. The matter was referred to the Attorney General.

Four days later, Mr P. de Caux, St John, appeared before the DOA and was asked to explain discrepancies which had been found between the number of pigs in his custody and the return submitted by him. "After hearing the further explanations of Mr de Caux, the DOA severely reprimanded him for his attempt to mislead the DOA's Inspector in relation to the number of pigs in his custody and warned him that should he fail, in the future, to comply with the Orders or Directions of the DOA, severe measures will be taken against him". Brée decided that the livestock infringement had been satisfactorily dealt with and saw no real need to follow with a prosecution. He therefore dropped the matter.

In the same week, Miss Adele Martret, St Ouen, appeared before the DOA to explain the apparent shortage of thirty-three pigs in her custody.[10] Miss Martret produced permits of sale signed by Pelz. She stated that they had been issued by the German authorities and allowed the occupying troops to purchase thirty-one pigs. Miss Martret also informed the DOA that she had in her possession a further permit for the sale of pigs. Brée ordered her to produce this further permit and he warned Miss Martret of the requirements of the Livestock (Jersey) Order, 1942, and admonished her to ensure that in future, such requirements were precisely complied with.

On the 23rd September Mr J. F. Langlois Junior, Grouville, was called for an interview with the DOA. It was alleged that there was a discrepancy between the number of pigs in his custody and DOA records. Mr Langlois produced a permit authorised by Field Command 515 to supply two pigs for fattening to the German forces. The DOA took no further action. Langlois, however, was warned of the requirement to obtain the necessary licence before transferring any livestock in his custody.

On the 28th September, an Inspector reported on the premises of Mr Eton Le Brun, St Lawrence, where four pigs were allegedly discovered which had not been declared. On the same day, "...as a result of information received" (a euphemism for an anonymous allegation), an Inspector was advised to visit the farm of Mr J. F. A'Court, St Peter. The subsequent inspection discovered three pigs. Both matters were reported to the Attorney General.

In late September, Mr R. D. Coutanche, Trinity and Mr A. P. Le Marquand, St Lawrence, both asked to send pigs to the public slaughterhouse as they were no longer able to feed them. The slaughterhouse, however, declined to accept them as they were not sufficiently large to be slaughtered. The States Vet, after examining the animals, recommended that they be slaughtered, but the following week he informed the DOA that "In view of certain instructions of the German authorities now in occupation of the island the slaughterhouse could not accept the pigs for slaughter". This, however, did not resolve the issue that these two farmers had no further means of feeding their pigs. Brée, having regard to the danger of the pigs losing weight rather than gaining weight, took the matter to the Superior Council.

A visit and inspection of the premises of Mrs L. Georgelin, St Ouen, discovered a pig in her custody. She had acquired the pig but when making the return prescribed by the Livestock (Returns) (Jersey) Order, 1943, she had failed to declare it. The matter was forwarded to the Attorney General for investigation.

On the 26th October, Colin Marie submitted "certain correspondence" concerning Mr J. O. Arthur, St John, in relation to an alleged discrepancy between the number of pigs found in his custody and the number shown in the records.[1] Three days later, Mr Arthur appeared before the DOA. After hearing his explanation and "...in view of the purely technical nature of the offence alleged," it was decided that no action would be taken.

Cereals

On the 3rd July the threshing sub-committee, which had been established at the end of June, met the leading contractors: T. G. Le Cappelain, W. T. Farrell, J. E. Richard, J. Priaulx, J. E. Colback, L. C. Pallot, T. R. Binet, S. J. Cabot and Mr Godel. On the 10th July the sub-committee met with JFU and RJA&HS members to explain the proposed costs and conditions which had been agreed. This was followed by a further meeting on the 17th July.

The agreement for the 1943 season was confirmed as follows.

1. Threshing contractors will to be paid RM8 per load for threshing at the depots.
2. A register will be kept of the capacity of each individual threshing machine. A joint committee of farmers and contractors will be set up to establish this.
3. The charge for threshing on farms will be a maximum of £2-10-0 an hour. (This meant that, for the farmer, threshing on the farm was more expensive than taking his grain to a depot.)
4. Agreements will be finalised for tying up bundles of straw on farms and at depots.

On the 22ⁿᵈ July a meeting was held between the DOA, JFU, RJA&HS and the contractors. The maximum working day at depots was agreed as being from 8.00 a.m. to 8.00 p.m. One hour was allowed for dinner. The contractors were instructed that they had to thresh and gather up the "siftings" after working hours and at their own expense. They were extremely displeased about this instruction, since the "siftings" were the property of the DOA. It was agreed that the Threshing Inspectors would assist in the work. A final amendment was added to the threshing contracts: the maximum charge for threshing on a farm was modified to £15 a day. A lesser charge would be made pro rata for a threshing machine of lower capacity.[11]

At the same time as these negotiations were being carried out, the DOA was considering tenders from contractors for the use of the two threshing machines imported from France. The DOA accepted one tender from James Edward Colback Junior, 13 Parade Road, St Helier and the other from L. C. Pallot, Central Motor Works, Sion, Trinity for, respectively, 6/6 and 6/- per working hour. Colback Junior, however, was informed that the DOA's acceptance of his tender was conditional upon his providing storage, from the end of the 1943 season until the opening of the 1944 season, for the machine hired to him. This imported machine was commented upon by Dr W. Casper in his autobiography. He said that "Pelz Dipl.Ing" wanted to begin the new threshing season by having an agricultural festival when the machine went into operation.[12] This would have been at the same time as the German propaganda units were in Jersey to film the planned 1943 cattle show, had it taken place.[13]

On the 9ᵗʰ July the Superior Council accepted the DOA's recommendation that cereal prices for grain from the 1943 harvest would be the same as in 1942. On the 16ᵗʰ July the DOA published its directions for the 1943 cereal crop.

1. In the directions "cereal" means wheat, oats, barley, or rye.
2. No cereal shall be stacked on stubble and, where it is intended to thresh any cereal on the site on which it is stacked, the site shall be one to which the threshing machine may have easy access.

3. No person shall order, permit, or effect the threshing of any cereal, except:
   a. under the accordance with the terms of a licence granted by the DOA; or,
   b. where the cereal is threshed by a threshing machine approved by the DOA.
4. Every person owning or having power to dispose of any cereal grain threshed before the coming into force of these directions is hereby required to offer the same for sale forthwith to the DOA.
   a. Delivery of cereal grain purchased aforesaid shall be made at the seller's prices.
   b. (i) Every person owning or having power to dispose of any cereal grain threshed after the coming into force of these directions is hereby required to offer the same for sale forthwith on threshing to the DOA.
      (ii) Delivery of a cereal grain purchased as aforesaid shall be made at the place of threshing.
   c. The "basic price" to be paid for cereal grain purchased shall be as follows, per cwt:
      a. Wheat £1-8-0
      b. Oats £1-2-6
      c. Barley £1-12-6
      d. Rye £1-19-6
   d. (i) The DOA may pay a price less than the basic price for grain of inferior quality.
      (ii) If any questions arise as to whether any cereal grain is of inferior quality it will be decided by the DOA.
   e. Where the price of any wheat grain is effected after 30th November, a price equal to 1% of the basic price multiplied by the number of months which have elapsed since that date (the month in which the sale is effected being considered as a month) shall be paid in addition to the basic price.
   f. Infringements of these directions are offences against Regulations made on the 1st September 1939, under the Order in Council 25th August 1939.
   g. These Directions shall come into force forthwith.

The DOA recommended, and the Superior Council agreed, that farmers who used horses for cultivating cereals would be granted a "privileged" issue of 13 cwt of oats for each horse. The price was the same as that at which the DOA purchased the oats. The DOA also recommended that farmers be allowed to retain, from grain grown by themselves, 7½% or one bag in thirteen, on condition that they take delivery of this grain at the threshing machine. The Superior Council changed this to 6% retention of grain.

On the 5th July Field Command wrote to the DOA concerning precautions to be taken to minimise the risk of the cereal harvest being destroyed by fire arising from acts of war. The DOA informed the Field Command of the Harvesting of Grain Crops (Fire Precautions) (Jersey) Order, 1941, which provided for the requirements of the German authorities. The DOA published a notice in the local press, and it was also sent to the licensed threshing contractors and to the threshing depots.

Mr George Messervy was appointed Chairman of the Grain Price Sub-Committee, which fixed prices for inferior grain, and on the 20th July three members were appointed to sit on the Committee: J. M. Norman, T. G. Le Marinel and H. G. Shepard. In late July, a notice was published in the local press calling for applicants for "Threshing Machine Inspectors". By the 3rd August the following appointments had been made:

Chief Inspectors at a salary of £4 a week:

Western District   J. C. Steel
Eastern District   O. P. Hamon

Sub-Inspectors at a salary of £3 a week:

R. Ching
C. A. de la Haye
P. G. Dubois
P. L. Gibaut
S. G. Guy
J. A. Huelin
E. Le Brocq
W. A. Pallot
G. F. Renault
R. C. Steel
H. Vautier

Assistant Sub-Inspectors:

P. W. Buesnel
E. J. Brochet
A. L. Gautier
F. A. Giquel
A. Gottard
E. W. Henstridge
H. Jehan
J. P. Langlois
S. J. Le Brocq
C. Le Cornu
G. R. Melville

The DOA now proceeded to fix the quantities and prices of seed to be sold to farmers for 1944. Per vergée, the allocations and prices were:

Wheat	90 pounds weight at 23/6
Oats	100 pounds weight at 20/3
Barley	90 pounds weight at 26/3
Rye	90 pounds weight at 31/6

The DOA wrote to the Honorary Parish Inspectors asking them to select wheat crops for providing seed for 1944, and to submit a list of these. The seed could only be selected where there was no presence of smut, to minimise the danger of the seed becoming infected.

On the 20th July Brée asked the Department of Transport and Communications for an issue of fuel for threshing an area of 10,600 vergées. On the 27thJuly, the Threshing Sub-Committee asked the DOA to carry out, without delay, a classification of threshing machines which would operate during the season, as threshing would soon commence.

The threshing depots were set up on the 23rd July.

Depot	Parish	Threshing Contractor
Jardin d'Olivet	Trinity	S. J. Cabot
La Grande Maison	St John	J. Richard
Petite Ménage	St Saviour	J. Richard
La Moie	St Brelade	T. G. Le Cappelain
St Peter's Works	St Peter	T. G. Le Cappelain
Grantez	St Ouen	W. T. Farrell
Opposite "Norwood"	St John	J. Priaulx
"Bel Respiro", Mont au Prêtre	St Helier	L. C. Pallot
Parish Storage Depot	St Martin	J. E. Colback Junior
Near Parish Church	St Saviour	T. R. Binet

In late July Mr Woodcock reported that smut had been discovered in several crops. These had to be stacked separately and were threshed only after all other wheat in that district had been threshed.

On the 27th July, the DOA issued threshing licences to the contractors. They received their directions under the Cultivation of Lands (Jersey) Order, 1942, which stipulated the following.

1. The price to be charged for the threshing of grain at a depot will not exceed 17/1 a load.
2. Threshing will only be carried out at the depot, or in the district allocated to the threshing contractor to whom the licence is issued.
3. All grain swept from the threshing machines working at the depots shall be delivered up each day to the DOA.

4. The straw is to be satisfactorily bundled.
5. Every threshing contractor is required to employ not less than 6 men in the operation of the threshing machine.
6. All threshing contractors must allow the DOA inspectors to check their bookings in order that inspectors will be in a position to arrange for the cartage of the grain.
7. The threshing contractor is required to produce his licence to any officer of the DOA on demand. The DOA reserves the right to revoke any licence issued, at any time. The DOA reserves the right to vary the conditions upon which any licence was issued, or to prescribe additional conditions, as considered necessary.

Licences were issued to the following contractors.

Name of Contractor	Address	Number of Machines
T. R. Binet	Les Côtils, Trinity	1
S. J. C. Cabot	Les Cateaux, Trinity	1
W. T. Farrel	Grantez, St Ouen	1
J. E. Colback Junior	13 Parade Road, St Helier	1
T. G. Le Cappelain	St Peter's Works, St Peter	1
L. C. Pallot	Central Motor Works, Sion, Trinity	1
J. Priaulx and Company	St Cyr, St John	1
J. Richard	La Grande Maison, St John	2
H. P. Godel	Les Pullières, St Ouen	1

On the 31st July it was reported that "Infection of the wheat crop with smut is widespread". The infected wheat was delivered to the DOA stores and treated with formaldehyde, which entailed the employment of further men. On the 6th August, the DOA ordered that wheat seed for the 1944 season should be selected only from farms where smut had not occurred.

Threshing began on the 9th August, with Edwin Gibaut in charge. On the 24th August the DOA authorised permits to members of the public, allowing them to thresh gleanings at machines under the control of the DOA. The grain could not be offered for sale. In the same week Field Command wrote to the DOA concerning "...certain agricultural requirements". The DOA inserted a notice in the local press informing the public of instructions, received from Field Command, which covered the stacking of cereals, the ploughing of stubble and the operation of threshing machines on Sundays. The instructions were forwarded to the threshing sub-committee in relation to the trial threshing of wheat, oats, barley, and rye, with the aim of carrying out tests on grain production and subsequently to submit a detailed report for transmission to the German authorities. In addition, Field Command ordered the public weighbridge to remain open until 7.00 p.m. in the evenings and, as threshing machines were ordered to operate on Sundays, the weighbridge to also operate on Sundays.

On the 27th August, one of the Assistant Sub-Inspectors was dismissed. Soon after, several farmers brought up the question whether they should be allowed to thresh grain arising from the rakings of their fields, and to retain it for their own use. The DOA decided that farmers should not keep the grain from rakings, and it was to be delivered to the DOA.

After making "repeated applications" to Mr J. T. du Feu, Trinity, to return 180 lbs of wheat seed which had been more than his requirements for sowing in the 1943 season, the DOA instructed him to immediately return the grain, otherwise he would be issued with a requisition order. A week later, a requisition order was made for "wheat seed...improperly retained". The excess in his possession resulted from a reduction in the amount which he had been directed to sow. The Crown Officers, however, stopped the requisition order and insisted that Mr du Feu present himself before the DOA to explain the reasons for his failure to return the seed.

On the 21st September, Mr P. J. Baudains, St Clement, appeared before the DOA to explain why he had delivered only a small quantity of wheat after cultivating 15 vergées. In the same week, Mr O. B. Fauvel was asked to explain why he had only cultivated 5 vergées when records demonstrated that he had been directed to sow 9 vergées of wheat. After hearing his explanation, the DOA administered a severe reprimand and warned him that, in future, judicial proceedings would be taken in respect of such failures. Two more farmers were called in for interviews to explain why they had delivered very small quantities of wheat. The DOA ordered the Threshing Sub-Committee to produce a detailed report on Mr G. Longstreeth, St Clement, and Mr V. C. Godel, Grouville, and the Senior Threshing Inspectors were instructed to assist in preparing the reports.

At the end of September, J. Richard appealed against the withdrawal of a licence for one of his threshing machines. After careful consideration, the DOA decided to restore his licence, on condition that he refund to each of his farmers 1/1½d, which was the amount he had overcharged on each load threshed. He was given eight days to make the refunds.

On the 15th October, the DOA issued a licence to Mr A. J. Falle, St Peter, to thresh by hand his own wheat which had been badly affected by smut. He was allowed to keep the grain, approximately ¾ of a hundredweight.

Jersey Produce Merchants Association

On the 9th July a delegation from the JPMA met the DOA to discuss payment for the storage of grain on their behalf, from the 1943 harvest. The merchants wanted to formulate whether payment would be at a fixed price, or a price based on a scale according to the length of time that the grain was stored.

The DOA proposed that storage charges be £1-1-0 per ton and that payment would be in two instalments: 75% upon the taking the grain into store and the balance of 25% payable at the conclusion of storage. Grain stores would be inspected and approved by the DOA and the manner of storage had to conform with its regulations. The JPMA was instructed to provide a list of stores where grain could be kept and the DOA would make the final decision. Recommendations were to be made as to which stores should be used for wheat. The JPMA, after receiving the DOA proposals, requested an extra 7/6 per ton for wheat storage. The DOA refused, but accepted the merchants' suggestion that, in due course, a permissible percentage of grain shrinkage could be agreed upon.

Between the 20th and 24th July, the Chief Inspector examined all the Island's cereal stores. There was a shortage of storage for wheat. Mr Simpson and Mr Woodcock were told to make a joint inspection of stores to check their suitability. After inspecting the stores, the following were selected for the 1943 cereal harvest:

R. P. Amy
George Blampied Limited
J. E. Baudains
E. Becquet (only for grain affected by smut)
W. Bird and Son Limited
Country Gentlemen's Association Limited
Jersey Co-operative Wholesale Society Limited
W. Dennis and Sons Limited
T. Dorey and Company Limited
P. J. de Gruchy
A. P. Falle and Sons Limited
Chas Gruchy and Company Limited
W. J. Gaudin
Guiton and Lucas
F. Giddens
Sidney Horman Limited
Job and Sons
O. J. Le Mottée Limited
Le Rossignol and Company.
Marks and Riches Limited
J. Martland Limited
C. Mossop
J. Spearman
John Terry Limited

The Chief Inspector oversaw the treatment of wheat affected by smut and gave instructions that all wheat saved for seed had to be stored in barrels.

By the 13th August the DOA decided that additional storage was needed. The following firms were contacted and asked whether they would be prepared to store grain from the 1943 harvest:

de Veulle and Company
Le Marquand Brothers
Le Riches Stores Limited
J. F. Pirouet and Son
Randall's Brewery

The DOA also formed a sub-committee comprising Brée, Gibaut and Le Gallais to discuss with the JPMA the fixing of a permissible percentage loss for grain held in storage from the 1942 harvest. The JPMA decided to ask for information as to the length of time during which grain storage would be required, and for concessions in relation to the height at which grain in barrels could be stored. The DOA's reply was that it could not give an undertaking as to the length of time members would be required to store grain; however, it did not anticipate that the average time would exceed twelve months. It would allow the stacking of barrels to a height no greater than two, subject to such storage being inspected and accepted as satisfactory by the DOA. The JPMA also requested that its members should be paid an additional 3/6 per ton, in consideration of storage of wheat seed. The DOA refused any additional payments.

On the 10th September, the JPMA met with the DOA to discuss additional payments for overtime worked, and the requirement for stores to be open on Sundays. The JPMA delegation comprised C. Gruchy, J. M. Norman and J. E. Becquet. The DOA made it clear it was unable to accede to their request but agreed to endeavour to inform the JPMA, on Saturdays, of the probable number of threshing machines working on the following Sunday, so that the number of stores which would be required to stay open could be estimated.

On 13th July the JPMA wrote to the DOA offering to ship potatoes which were ordered on behalf of the German authorities. These shipments would be "...in bulk from merchant's stores for 15/- a ton". The DOA replied that it reserved the right to ship potatoes direct from farms, should the circumstances render such a course desirable. Six days later, the JPMA informed the DOA that, when a shipment of potatoes was required on a Sunday, the declared rate of 15/- per ton did not apply. The DOA was also asked to pay the sum of £10 to cover additional expenses members had incurred as a result of "The abortive shipment of potatoes, to the order of the German authorities at present in occupation of the Island on Sunday 18th July 1943."

The DOA answered that the request for an additional payment in respect of a German shipment of potatoes on a Sunday would receive consideration; however this would take place only when the JPMA submitted detailed accounts of the shipment. Several days later, the JPMA protested at the methods adopted by the DOA when allocating bulk shipments of potatoes. When such shipments took place on weekdays, part of the quantity came directly from farms; whereas, when shipments took place on Sundays, the whole quantity was handled by their members. The JPMA expressed the view that far less inconvenience would be caused if potatoes shipped on Sundays were drawn directly from farms.

The DOA replied: "The very short notice given to the DOA concerning shipments of potatoes on Sundays by the German authorities now in occupation of the Island made it virtually impossible to obtain the required weight of potatoes from the country." It concluded that the uncertainty attendant upon such shipments rendered it necessary for the merchants to keep their stores open on Sundays, in order to supply potatoes as required by the German authorities.

The DOA also received accounts from the JPMA concerning the extra costs incurred, as a result of the abortive shipment on the 18th July. It was decided that the merchants would be paid the difference between the ordinary wage and the overtime rate in respect of their workers. Three merchants who sent insufficient accounts were not reimbursed.

On the 30th July, the JPMA wrote again in respect of the abortive shipment, the President stating: "As no potatoes had actually been shipped on the 18th July, the decision of the DOA was unfair." Brée refused to change his mind; however, as a gesture of goodwill he awarded a payment of £5 to the JPMA. In an attempt to end the matter of bulk shipments on Sundays, the DOA then decided to pay the JPMA 20/- a ton, which thus resolved the problem.

On August 20th the DOA approved Normans Limited and T. Mayo and Company Limited to store wheat seed for the 1944 crop.

On the 1st September, the DOA received letters from corn merchants E. N. Pirouet, 10 and 12 Cattle Street, and G. Touzel, 32 Halkett Place. Both had been sanctioned by the DOA because they had failed to provide compensation under claims filed in respect of unacceptable losses of grain stored by them in 1941. The following week, a meeting was held with both men "…in an endeavour to obtain a settlement in respect of the shortages which have been established in the quantities of grain of the 1941 harvest stored on behalf of the DOA." The two merchants agreed a full settlement of the DOA's claims and paid £20 and £17-10-0, respectively.

On the 22nd October the DOA made arrangements for imported wheat seed to be turned after treatment, by J. Martland Limited and A. P. Falle and Sons, at a cost of 3/- a ton.

Cultivation Orders

"I have ascertained…the DOA has done very little towards…the altered conditions of war. Farmers…do not show signs of having attended agricultural school."

Letter from Knackfuss to the Bailiff

On the 13th July 1943, the DOA considered the disposal of vraic gathered by men in the Department of Labour work scheme under instructions from the German authorities. Vraic would only be sold to farmers who had no cattle and who had a DOA permit to purchase. It was agreed with Deputy Edward Le Quesne, President of the Department of Labour, and Deputy John Le Marquand that:

1. All stacks of dried vraic will be sold by the Department of Labour through a public auction.
2. Given that green vraic will be sold to approved applicants at £2 a load, an allowance of four trips per farmer will be permitted, within a radius of 4 miles from the point of collection of the vraic in St Ouen's Bay.
3. Applications for this vraic must be addressed to the Department of Labour before the 1st December 1943.
4. All applications will be considered by a joint delegation of the DOA and the Department of Labour.

On the 24th August, to comply with the instructions from Field Command 515, a notice was inserted in the local press inviting applicants for the post of "Vegetable Inspectors" at a weekly salary of £3. On the 13th September, Mr F. V. Brée and Mr R. S. J. Pinel, both of St Lawrence, were appointed.

In the same week, a claim was sent to the DOA by Mr Edward Hacquoil, St Ouen, for compensation. He alleged the destruction by rabbits of 3 vergées of rye. The DOA instructed him to notify them of any severe financial hardship he suffered. In view of Mr Hacquoil's reply, which Brée decided was of "unsatisfactory nature", he was called in for a formal interview on the 9th September which clearly demonstrated that the farmer had indeed suffered a massive loss through the rabbit population destroying most of his rye harvest. Therefore, the DOA recommended to the Compensation Advisory Committee that he be awarded £8 per vergée compensation.

Surprisingly, a large number of farmers were issued "Hunting Licences" for the purpose of keeping the local rabbit population in check, and to protect their crops. These gun licences were relatively simple to obtain on the recommendation of either Pelz or Brée. They were issued from the beginning of October 1940. Certain well-known farmers, most probably through the auspices of Brée, were told they could apply for licences to keep shotguns or hunting rifles "...to combat rabbits...which caused appreciable damage to crops." Brée and Pelz met and agreed to allow retention of hunting rifles and shotguns. The records demonstrate that approximately twenty-five to thirty farmers were allowed to retain them.[14]

At the end of August, the Honorary Parish Inspector, St John, reported to the DOA an allegation that three farmers had privately sold oats that they had grown. The Inspector was instructed to visit the farms and warn all three farmers of the severe consequences of their actions.

Brée now endorsed the provision of 300 gallons of petrol for the "Glasshouse Growers Association" for the months of September, October, and November. Brée, himself a glasshouse agriculturalist of some repute, was keen to carry on this cultivation. Providing that the correct agricultural inputs were supplied, several crops could be harvested in succession,

On the 31st August Field Command wrote to the DOA asking for "The submission...of a draft programme for the cultivation in 1944." Brée responded by forwarding the areas allocated for 1944.

Crop	Area in Vergées
Wheat	10,000
Oats	4,000
Barley	150
Rye	400
Potatoes	7,200
Mangolds – first crop	3,000
Hay and Grazing	10,000
Vegetables	600

By the 21st September, Field Command had approved Brée's cropping plan. The Honorary Parish Inspectors were instructed to prepare Cultivation Orders for farmers in their parish, for the year 1944.

Alongside his 1944 cropping plan, Brée devised a more efficient control of land for the provision of hay and grazing and decided exactly what areas he would allocate. The basis of his calculations was as follows.

1. Farmers who have neither cattle nor horses in their custody and who occupy land measuring 10 vergées or more might be directed to devote not more than one-tenth of their land to the provision of grazing. Persons with less than 10 vergées will not devote any of their land for grazing.
2. Farmers having cattle or horses in their custody will be allocated hay and grazing on the basis of 1¾ vergées per head of cattle or horses.

On the 3rd September a letter from the Field Commandant to the Bailiff was read out to the DOA.[15] The letter was explicit in what was required; it bore all the hallmarks of Pelz's agricultural education and experience as a senior civil servant in the mid-1930s in the Federal State of Saltzberg, Austria.

Knackfuss made it clear that "The DOA is to arrange a press service which will publish an explanatory and an informative weekly article concerning the improvements in the conducting of agricultural economy. All agricultural orders and laws, price fixing, questions of export and import, the procuring of materials, agricultural planning, in short, everything for everybody and especially that which is of value to the farmers is stated...by the press.

The Press should issue and distribute memoranda concerning questions of increased production, the care of animals, systematic milk production, fertilizing and tilling the soil, as well as economic management.

I have ascertained...the DOA has done very little towards...the altered conditions of war. Expert advice to the farmers, who, as a rule, do not show signs of having attended an agricultural school and frequently only practice farming as a side-line or as amateurs...I therefore order...a printed memorandum for agriculture and explaining all the most important agriculture work for the current month is to appear monthly and is to be posted in all parishes near churches, at the parish halls and other important places. The DOA is to submit the first memorandum by the 1st October 1943."

The DOA, on the 9th September, charged Mr Simpson and Mr Woodcock to prepare all the necessary matters for submission to Field Command. By the 22nd September, the first monthly bulletin board and accompanying memorandum had been completed.

Knackfuss, however, when receiving the information for approval, informed the civilian authorities that it was "...quite inadequate." His frustration was clear: "I expect in the next memorandum to read something more of the things which have to do actually with practical conditions." Knackfuss was especially angry in respect of pig breeding, which he viewed with some disdain: "I expect practical illustrations as to show the breeding of pigs and the keeping thereof, which has sunk so low, may be raised with local farm feedstuffs or are your specialists of the opinion that the farmers are doing everything in their power to guarantee the population the meat ration due to increasing their own production? It is quite clear that the supplies of meat could be materially improved if farmers were made aware of their duty to keep more pigs. Official action in this direction and practical instruction have not been sufficient. Precedents are lacking."

On the 7th September, Field Command requested details of those tractors which were operated by petrol. A meeting took place two weeks later between the DOA and the Department of Transport and Communication to discuss petrol required for the forthcoming ploughing season. Mr B. L. Clift, the Petrol Controller, gave a full breakdown of the fuel needed. As a result, a meeting was held on the 6th November attended by the entire cohort of ploughing contractors, the full DOA committee comprising Brée, du Val, Gibaut and Secretary Marie, and the Petrol Controller.

The Ploughing Contractors who attended were:

St Brelade	P. Chevalier and J. Michel
St Clement	G. Blake and G. R. Le Gresley
Grouville	F. G. Buesnel and P. C. Le Cornu
St Helier	R. S. Langlois and A. V. Mundy
St John	E. Cotillard, S. W. de Gruchy, W. Laisney, A. H. Langlois, G. A. Luce
St Lawrence	A. A. Cotillard, P. E. Jean, C. H. Le Cornu

St Martin	K. G. Richardson and C. S. Rondel
St Mary	A. J. Barette, F. E. Rimeur, F. Le Boutillier, S. Le Gresley
St Peter	J. F. A'Court, A. F. Dauny, E. Gallichan, C. A. Jean, T G. Le Cappelain, T. G. Payn
St Saviour	C. W. Buesnel and W. Sutton
Trinity	R. Baudains, J. P. Godfray, Y. M. Gotel, E. W. Le Touzel, L. C. Pallot

Brée opened the meeting by stating that for the next season, 1943-44, he would reappoint all those attending, provided that each had ploughed not less than 100 vergées of land under the orders of the Honorary Parish Inspectors during the 1942-43 season. Those contractors who had ploughed less than 100 vergées would have to reapply for appointment.

A contract was agreed between the DOA and ploughing contractors. The conditions were as follows.

1. The Contractor undertakes to carry out all ploughing under instructions of the Honorary Parish Inspectors.
2. Ploughing is only to take place with the liquid fuel supplied by the Department of Transport and Communications. No scarifying is allowed.
3. The price to be charged for ploughing is £1-10-0 per vergée.
4. The allowance for liquid fuel is 1½ gallons per vergée.
5. The price to be charged to contractors for liquid fuel is 10/8 per gallon. Half of this (5/4) will be retained by the Department of Transport and Communications. This amount will take the place of the refund formerly made to the DOA in order to equalise the cost of ploughing as between the various types of power used for this purpose.
6. The costings by the DOA, per vergée, are agreed as follows:

Charge to farmers	£1-10-0
Cost of liquid fuel, 1½ gallons at 10/8 per gallon	16/-
Cost of liquid fuel for transport	6/-
Use of plough	2/6d
Wages of tractor driver	2/6
Wages of man to hold plough	2/-
Depreciation per vergée	1/-
Less margin for contractor per vergée	5/6

7. The vouchers enabling contractors to draw liquid fuel will be issued by Honorary Parish Inspectors to cover the fuel required to plough the allocated number of vergées during the week following the issue of the vouchers.

At the request of the contractors, a clause was inserted empowering them, in cases where extra liquid fuel had to be used for ploughing any land, to charge the farmer concerned with the extra cost of the fuel.

On the 22nd September the DOA, in agreement with the Department of Transport and Communications, approved tractors operated by "Aniche Gazosse" (gasogene) for use in the following 1944 season. These tractors were made available on the following terms.

1. Twenty converted Fordson tractors are offered to ploughing contractors at a weekly hire of £1 to cover the costs of depreciation and maintenance.
2. The owners of the converted tractors are in the first instance given the opportunity of becoming the contractor. If the owner does not wish to be the contractor, he has the option to nominate other men to operate these tractors.
3. There is no restriction on the consumption of "Aniche Gazosse" for agricultural purposes. These contractors are encouraged to undertake as much work as possible.
4. The price of the "Aniche Gazosse" will be adjusted to the price of petrol required to do the equivalent work; to which will be added the amount of the refund per vergée made to the DOA in respect of ploughing.
5. The cost of ploughing will be maintained at £1-10-0 per vergée and the profits made on the sale of "Aniche Gazosse", including the amount of refund included therein, will be credited to the "Gazogene" account of the Department of Transport and Communications against the costs of conversion of these tractors.

Field Command 515 was informed that, in addition to the twenty converted tractors, approximately 6,000 gallons of liquid fuel would be required to satisfactorily complete the entire 1944 ploughing season.

On the 23rd September, Field Command wrote to the DOA detailing information concerning land occupied by Mr J. M. Gouyette, St Saviour. The allegation concerned a field "in a badly neglected condition". A follow-up report made by the Honorary Parish Inspector summarised "…the very unfavourable condition of the field". The report made clear that both crops of potatoes and swedes were choked with weeds. The matter was sent to the Attorney General.

On the 26th October, the question of "financial credits" for the provision of assistance to farmers in 1944 was discussed. This scheme had been in operation between the years 1941 to 1943. A farmer who applied to the DOA for financial assistance would, on the execution of a bond and provided he was not indebted to the States in respect of financial assistance previously granted, be advanced money at the rate of £6 per vergée. It was payable in two instalments: the first after the 1st November 1943 at the rate of £3-10-0 per vergée and the second in

June 1944 at the rate of £2-10-0 per vergée. The interest was 3% per annum. The financial credit for the year 1944 would be advanced only for potatoes and cereals. It was to be reimbursed to the States after the crop was sold to the DOA.

On the 29th October Mr Godfray, the DOA's Chief Inspector, made a request for his salary to be paid monthly, instead of weekly, as were all Inspectors. His request was granted and the DOA then considered "The considerable amount of work carried out by A. V. Godfray on Sundays and holidays". The DOA recommended to the Superior Council that the Chief Inspector should be paid a bonus of £25 in respect of his additional work. The Agricultural Workers Bonus, paid to those entitled to claim on the scheme, totalled £953 for the period 19th June to 31st August 1943.

Horses

"It has proved unhygienic and inconvenient for the stable manure to remain for several days on the Victoria Pier and only removed once a week. It is requested that in future, the manure be removed regularly every two days at 10am".

Letter from Pelz to Brée

Between 13th July and 31st August 1943, Field Command 515 ordered a full muster of horses in the Island. The Field Command wrote to the Bailiff and informed him when and where the horses were to be registered and examined. The reason given for this was "...to inform themselves with the horses on the island".[16] There had previously been no discussion of this mustering of civilian horses. The Bailiff somewhat worryingly wrote to Brée, "I have no knowledge of what is intended". After discussing the matter with the Attorney General, he then informed Brée, "...there is no question of the requisition of horses".

The Field Command wrote again to the Bailiff on the 31st August. This new letter informed the Bailiff: "On Sunday, 5th September 1943, seven riding horses belonging to local civilians will be purchased by the German forces". Knackfuss gave specific details of the horses that were required.

No	Owner's Name	Address	Markings	Sex	Age
1	H. A. Flinn	Le Houmet, St Brelade	Chestnut	Mare	11
2	J. P. Vautier	La Vallette, St John	White	Mare	6
3	J. Taschke	Rozel Bakery, St Martin	Chestnut	Gelding	9
4	G. Kempster	La Sergenté, St Martin	Black	Mare	5
5	P. Bauche	Oaklands, St Peter	Brown	Mare	4
6	L. H. Blight	Cowley Farm, Maufant, St Saviour	White spots	Gelding	12
7	E. C. Perrédès	Fairview Farm, St Saviour	Brown	Mare	13

Field Command offered to supply seven substitute horses, that were no longer suited for military service, but which were considered suitable for agricultural work. The owners could purchase one of these horses offered as substitutes. Blampied, the States Vet, and Brée formed a committee to value the horses. All transactions were to be paid in cash.

At the same time, MVR Pelz wrote a letter to Brée entitled "Removal of the stable manure from Victoria Pier". Pelz brought to the attention of Brée the following problem: "It has proved to be unhygienic and inconvenient for the stable manure to remain for several days on the Victoria Pier and only removed once a week. It is requested that in future the manure be removed regularly every two days at 10am. An agreement with the Verpflegungausgabestelle BJ[17] with regard to this matter is to be arranged."[18] Several days later, Brée wrote to the Bailiff to inform him that "...the question of this manure does not concern my department and I have, accordingly, communicated to the States' Veterinary Surgeon the contents of the letter". On the 28th August, Blampied wrote to the Bailiff confirming "The necessary action is being taken by the Department of Transport and Communications concerning the removal of stable manure from Victoria Pier".[9]

The above incident is informative. Firstly, it demonstrates how issues brought up by the Field Command were dealt with. Secondly, from Pelz's initial letter to Brée, the problem of waste manure was settled in seven days easily and quickly during August 1943.

Cattle

The Island was now facing a serious shortage of hay, with most farmers finding it extremely difficult to obtain in any quantity. The DOA requested the Department of Essential Commodities to import as much hay as possible from France. It received the reply: "It has proved impossible to obtain a quantity of hay in France".

In April 1943, Mr E. J. Ahier, of the Parish Selection Committee, had visited Mr Edward Morgan Fox, Les Côtils, St Lawrence. Mr Fox was informed he would have to provide an animal for slaughter within several weeks. Mr Fox agreed he would submit a calf born in February. He was only sending to the dairy a small amount of milk each day. The Parish Selection Committee informed the Cattle Slaughter Executive Committee of this low yield and sent a list of cattle in Mr Fox's herd that were producing exceptionally low quantities of milk. The Cattle Slaughter Executive Committee decided that the calf should be slaughtered.

On the 24th June, Mr Fox was notified to bring in this calf to the abattoir. On receipt of the notification, Mr Fox replied that the loss "would be a hardship" because he had one dry cow that was about to calve and another due to calve in September. Mr Fox, therefore, was excused from sending the calf for slaughter until his next cow had calved. The calf was born on the 3rd

July. On the 10th July, Mr Fox made a formal appeal to the Calf Selection Committee for exemption of one calf. The RJA&HS Selection Committee refused to exempt Mr Fox's calf. It exempted calves which scored 6 points and above, whereas his calf scored only 4 points.

On the 16th July, the secretary of the Calf Selection Committee, Mr Shepard, wrote to Mr Fox. He was given a delay of three weeks to send the calf to the abattoir. On the 17th July, Mr Fox made a further appeal. The Committee refused to change its original decision of the 10th July, making it clear that there were no new apparent reasons to justify the calf's exemption. However, the fact that two vacancies for calf exemptions existed infuriated the Fox family. Their anger spurred the family into direct action. On the 20th July Mrs Ada Fox wrote a letter to Colonel Knackfuss asking for assistance against the judgement made by the Cattle Slaughter Executive Committee and their dismissal of appeals against the exemption of the calf.

On the 22nd July, Knackfuss wrote to the Bailiff (this is a good example of the confusion that arose amongst small farmers and the various cattle committees). The letter was entitled "Cattle held by E. Fox". The Commandant described "...that the wife of the above has informed me that of three cows, one had to be handed in for slaughter. The cow destined for slaughter after having calved for the second time was said to be full of milk. If the remaining calf is also to be slaughtered and the farmer's wife is correct, then this is a most undesirable proceeding. Of course, young breeding animals, especially if they are full of milk shall not be slaughtered. I take it that this is a misunderstanding and I request that you look into the matter and let me have a report.

The local administration must do everything possible to collect all the local meat production and prevent it from falling into the black market. Animals suitable for slaughter must not be taken from smallholders only but from where the greatest number is available. The supplying of meat shall not hit individuals especially, but the larger holder shall be included to the same extent".[19]

On the 28th July, in response to Knackfuss' letter, Brée informed the Bailiff of the decisions of both the Cattle Slaughter Executive and Calf Selection Committee's concerning the non-exemption of the calf belonging to Mr Fox. Two days later, the Bailiff replied to Knackfuss. He forwarded all the Calf Selection Committee's reports concerning Mr Fox's calf [wrongly written as "Cox" by the Bailiff].

On the 31st August, the DOA discussed the issue of "...a heifer not sent to the slaughterhouse". The DOA decided to send a formal letter ordering Mr Fox to deliver his calf to the slaughterhouse by the 8th September. On the 10th September, the slaughterhouse authorities informed the DOA that the heifer had not been sent. The DOA referred Mr Fox's breach of the order to the Attorney General who, a week later, decided to take legal action. On the 20th September Mrs Fox again contacted Field Command 515 concerning the forthcoming prosecution by the DOA and the Attorney General.

On the 22nd September, Pelz wrote to Brée directly. The letter was entitled "Mrs Fox, Les Côtils, St Lawrence. Letter from the Attorney General to the DOA". Pelz explained that the Field Command had discussed the matter and informed Mrs Fox to postpone the delivery of the calf until further instructions had been sent to her. He, furthermore, ordered the Bailiff to conduct an enquiry into the matter. Pelz stated that no further instructions, other than those from the Field Command, had been sent to Mrs Fox concerning the heifer calf. Therefore, Mrs Fox had been right in adhering to those instructions. In consequence, Field Command ordered that "no prosecution is, therefore, to be taken".

Pelz, in his review of the matter, was well aware that the heifer calf was no more than ten weeks old. He therefore decided to inform Brée that "A fresh examination of the case should be undertaken as to whether the slaughter of the animal appears to be necessary, taking into account breeding considerations". He concluded the letter with the order: "With regards to this, before Mrs Fox receives notification, I desire to have the opinion of the Jersey Herd Book and if necessary, a personal conversation with the department official".[20]

By the 30th September, Le Gallais had visited College House to discuss the matter of the Fox's heifer calf. The meeting took place in Room 20, Pelz's office. Pelz informed Le Gallais that Mrs Fox had been instructed to retain the calf. Le Gallais, however, informed Pelz that "...the calf must be slaughtered". Indeed, the importance of the matter was so great that Le Gallais would be "...at the disposal of the German authorities if an interview is desired".

On the 7th October, the Calf Selection Committee met to discuss the matter. The exemption of the calf was again refused. On the 13th October, Brée sent a detailed letter to the Bailiff, writing that he, the Bailiff, must make it clear to the German Field Command that there were a number of fundamental issues concerning cattle policy. The order requiring calves to be delivered for slaughter was to provide supplies of meat for the local civilian population. Indeed, the order itself was made on the instructions of the German authorities. The DOA policy was summed up as follows.

1. The indiscriminate retention of calves would result in a heavy drain on island milk supplies. Sufficient calves, however, were retained each month to maintain island cattle at numbers which can be fed.
2. Under the Livestock (Jersey) Order, 1942, the DOA is empowered to exempt a number of calves from slaughter and, for the purpose of selecting calves for exemption, the Calf Selection Committee, composed of the officers of the Jersey Herd Book, was set up by the DOA.
3. This Committee was composed of acknowledged authorities on the Jersey breed and the animals exempted from slaughter were selected with regard to the maintenance of the breed. In the case of Fox, the

breeding of the calf did not warrant its exemption from the slaughter provisions of the order.

4. The Calf Selection Order had been hitherto loyally obeyed. An exception made in the Fox case would make the order impossible to enforce. If Fox's appeal to the German authorities succeeds in evading the provision of the Livestock Order, the majority of farmers would act upon these appeals to retain their calves.

On the same day, the Bailiff wrote to Field Command. He stressed the importance of dismissing Mrs Fox's claim for exemption of her heifer calf, otherwise other Jersey farmers would request Field Command 515 to intervene and exempt their calves. The Bailiff was adamant that the order had to be strictly observed. On the 18th October Knackfuss replied to the Bailiff. He agreed with the recommendation of the Calf Selection Committee and the strict observance of all agricultural orders. Knackfuss concluded his letter with: "It appears commendable to observe also with the same strictness the collection of other agricultural produce including cereals".

On the 22nd October the DOA met to discuss the Fox calf. As a result, the DOA wrote to Mr Fox ordering him to deliver the animal to the States slaughterhouse by the 26th October 1943. It appears that the calf was slaughtered.

In August, the Cattle Slaughter Executive Committee reported that no cows from the Public Health Department at the Mental Hospital had been supplied for slaughter, despite the herd having non-productive animals. A letter was subsequently sent to the Mental Hospital, instructing that a cow be sent for slaughter within six weeks. Mr R. Kilmister, the Steward of the Mental Hospital, agreed to send one cow within the week.

On the 7th September, the DOA received a "verbal report" from Le Gallais that he had charged the Foreman Milk Tester to visit the farm of Mr P. Le Feuvre, Trinity, "...to verify the number of cattle in the herd and to report as to the age of each of the cattle. Also, as to whether the cattle so found agree with the declarations made by Mr Le Feuvre". The Foreman Milk Tester, accompanied by John Michel, visited the farm. Mr Michel was given all the "necessary authority and documentation", to enter both the farm and premises. He presented a report on the 10th October of the animals in the custody of Le Feuvre. A subsequent meeting was held with Mr Shepard and Mr Weeks.

Mr Le Feuvre appeared before the DOA on the 22nd October. Michel's report alleged that he had retained in his custody three calves, in breach of the Livestock (Jersey) Order, 1942. The calves were not exempted from Article 6 of the order. After hearing an explanation from Mr Le Feuvre, the DOA referred the matter to the Attorney General.[1]

Another report of the 7th September alleged the slaughter of two heifers by "unknown persons". The heifers had been in the custody of

E. C. Perrédès and had been reported as stolen or missing. Perrédès was requested to sign an affidavit confirming the loss of the two heifers. The DOA then reduced the number of animals in his herd in the official record.

In late October Mr H. E. Le Marquand, St Ouen, wrote to the Attorney General, making an official complaint that his calf "Rosebay's June", Folio 198, had been chosen for slaughter when in fact the calf came from a high-volume milk-producing lineage. He ended his letter by stating "...so it is not astonishing that farmers should hide their calves away so as to have some".

Perhaps it was no coincidence that the RJA&HS, under the advice of Carson, named a delegation to study and evaluate milk production on the Island. After investigation it was decided:

1. A card for every herd showing the average yield for the twelve months ending the 30th September. It would also show the average Island yield for the same period.
2. A sheet showing the production in each herd for the same period from which the average Island herd yield had been ascertained.
3. An abstract of the Milk Tester's report for each visit, from which the annual herd average can be calculated to the end of each successive month.

The information would be used by the Cattle Slaughter Executive Committee for the selection of low-yielding stock for slaughter.

The tattooing of cattle and pigs became an important issue of agricultural policy in 1943. The accepted historical interpretation is that the German Field Command ordered the tattooing of animals in 1943, as a means of preventing the fraudulent registration of those that had died. When animals had been registered as dead, the death certificate could be passed from one farmer to the next, to falsify DOA records of animals in the farmer's custody. The German authorities, therefore, ordered that an indelible tattoo be put on every animal to give an accurate description of the cause and date of death, with the DOA registration. This interpretation states that "The Germans instituted a series of spot checks, and anyone caught with a pig that had no tattoo was severely punished".[21]

However, the evidence regarding the tattooing of cattle demonstrates that this was an important and contentious issue, dating back to the 1930s. In early 1939, Le Gallais had suggested to the RJA&HS that the tattooing of all cattle should take place.

The issue of tattooing cattle, and Le Gallais' adamant call to pursue this policy, split the cattle breeders down the middle. There were three reasons why he wanted tattooing. Firstly, it would prevent poor-quality heifers and calves being sent from the Island to cattle auctions, purporting to be high-quality pedigree animals. The Jersey Cattle Society in England had pleaded with the RJA&HS to stop this practice. Secondly, it would prevent unscrupulous breeders selling to the North American export market pedigree cattle, including bulls, which were simply not what they were stated to be. Thirdly, calves could be identified by their owners as being of a certain parentage when in fact they were not and be given a mistaken pedigree as a result. This for example could occur when several calves were born overnight, and a genuine mix-up happened.

One such case of possible mistaken pedigree may have occurred with the animal "Lady Oxfordia".[22] She was bred by E. C. Perrédès and was "The famous cow of her time in Jersey and throughout the Jersey world. She was the only cow ever to be Supreme Champion over Jersey and also the Champion Producer over Jersey". She was exported to the USA in 1937 and in North Carolina she "...completed the highest record ever made in that state at that time".[23] However, the progeny belonging to the Oxford cattle had very distinctive white markings and Lady Oxfordia was completely monochrome with no white markings present.[24]

In 1939, Le Gallais had felt the issue of tattooing was important enough to set up a sub-committee which had reported back to the RJA&HS that it was "...convinced that such a practice is desirable and should be brought into effect". It suggested the immediate tattooing on the right ear, accompanied with a birth certificate.[25] On the 11th November 1939, the Jersey Herd Book Committee had met with Mr Perrédès who spoke fervently against any form of cattle tattooing. He described "...the repercussions the adoption of compulsory tattooing would have overseas". J. B. Michel supported the sub-committee's proposals, citing instances where the tattooing of calves would have saved much trouble. F. Le Boutillier described the measure as installing a high degree of confidence with members and with importers of Jersey cattle. Le Gallais, Michel and E. R. Egré proposed and seconded a proposition to immediately commence with tattooing. Perrédès proposed a deferment. Michel's proposition for tattooing received eight votes and Perrédès for deferment nine votes. The 1,000-word report by the Tattooing Sub-Committee was dismissed by the margin of one vote. Le Gallais, somewhat surprised at not getting his way on the matter, stated he was personally in favour of the tattooing of calves and then abruptly closed the meeting.

In the summer of 1943, Le Gallais, a non-voting member of the DOA and in charge of milk production and distribution, resurrected the proposition of tattooing. In early September, he made it clear that a quantity of Indian ink had been received which could facilitate tattooing. On the 14th September, a scheme for tattooing cattle was proposed in order to assist in the enforcement of the provisions of the Livestock (Jersey) Order, 1942. On the 28th September, the DOA discussed the question in detail and immediately prepared the necessary legislation. On the 5th October the DOA issued the following directions:

1. In these Directions "animal" means any bull, cow, heifer, calf, pig, or sheep.
2. The animal may be marked in such a manner and on such part of its body as the DOA thinks fit.
3. No person shall efface, obliterate, remove, or alter or attempt to alter any mark.
4. Infringements are offences against the Regulations made on the 1st September 1939, [emergency regulations] under the Order in Council, dated 25th August 1939.
5. These Orders come into force forthwith.

Calves born after the 1st October 1943, and which were exempted from slaughter under the provisions of Article 5 of the Livestock (Jersey) Order, 1942, were ordered to be tattooed. To begin with, the Foreman Milk Testers were tasked with tattooing these calves. The DOA wrote to the RJA&HS on the 8th October requesting them to inform the Calf Selection Committee to take all necessary steps to have calves which were exempted tattooed in the ear with a number. The RJA&HS, in accordance with the above order, approved "A record of earmarking to be completed by tattooing officials in respect of each calf tattooed." It was also decided that the serial number, without any prefix, should be tattooed on the left ear of each calf. It is worth noting that this method of identification was highly suitable for the Jersey cattle breed with its light skin colouring, making it easy to read tattoos.

On the 12th October the DOA authorised the Calf Selection Committee to employ one man to assist with the tattooing of calves. By the 30th October, the DOA had not been able to obtain the necessary equipment and Colin Marie wrote to Mr Shepard informing him: "The DOA requires tattooing instruments capable of marking cattle and pigs with both letters and numbers, and I should be grateful if you will inform me of any sets of tattooing instruments available in the island so that the owners thereof can be approached with a view to such instruments being loaned to or hired by the Department". The Calf Selection Committee immediately made enquiries as to the whereabouts of tattooing instruments and, at the same time, discussed the implications of the letter from the DOA.

The following resolution was passed and forwarded to the DOA: "After discussing the scheme of tattooing of cattle, the Selection Committee is of the opinion that unless the tattooing of all animals is carried out simultaneously with their identification with the Jersey Herd Book Certificate, the scheme would be unsatisfactory, and it is feared be detrimental eventually, to the tattooing of calves. The Committee considers, however, that herds under suspicion should be tattooed and, as far as possible, identified, unregistered stock being earmarked with a distinguishing prefix. The assistance of the Jersey Herd Book, in carrying out this proposal, is willingly offered".

The DOA, after receiving this letter, adopted the recommendation that all tattooed animals be issued with certificates by the Jersey Herd Book Committee so that animals could be fully identified.

The Requisition of Farms at Egypt, Trinity, by the German Military

"The performance of agriculture is just as decisive in war as that of the military".

Report by MVR Pelz on the requisition of farms and agricultural land, Egypt, Trinity, July 1943

In the summer of 1943, the German military decided that it needed extra land for training and for live fire ranges. All agricultural land requisitioned from farmers by the military had to go through an authorisation process with Field Command 515 which entailed a formal review from Pelz, as Head of Agricultural and Food Supply for the Channel Islands. The total area of Jersey requisitioned for military purposes amounted to some 3,500 vergées.

One of the largest requisitions occurred in July and August 1943. On the 30th June, von Schmettow, the Military Commander of the Channel Islands, made a request to the German Military Government in Jersey, Field Command 515, to requisition a large area of agricultural land and farms in the north of the Island. The area, known as "Egypt", was in the parish of Trinity. This land was requested by the German military for several reasons. The plans included an artillery firing range, an area for 24-hour military exercises and a training site for house-to-house fighting.[26] The formal military requisition comprised Egypt Farm, two neighbouring properties, and all the agricultural land up to the coast.[27]

Von Schmettow, in a "secret" letter to the Field Command, made it clear that the requisition was necessitated as there was to be change on the Island of military units. The Grenadier Regiment, comprising the Second Battalion I R 582, a Reserve Battalion, had been given orders to leave. Its replacement was the Ost Battalion 643, a volunteer Ukrainian unit. It was staffed with Ukrainian NCO's and Germans who spoke Russian. The senior officer was Hauptmann Dr Rannecke who, upon his arrival in the Island, was promoted to Major.[28] The Ost Battalion was to be deployed from St Peter through to St Mary and Trinity, mainly along the coastal perimeter.

The exchange of military units never took place. The Second Battalion I R 582 remained and the Ost Battalion, now on the Island, was renamed the Fourth Battalion I R 582 and it remained until May 1945.

On the 16th July 1943, MVR Pelz produced a detailed report on the requisition of the farms and land requested by the German military.[29] He described the farm at Egypt as 90 vergées in area, and a second farm as 33 vergées. In addition, he gave a detailed breakdown of the cultivation carried out there and a description and the number of animals on the farms. All in all, some 140 to 150 vergées were involved. The individual farmers were named: Mr Wesley Le Breton, Joan Le Breton, Frank Le Breton, Philip

Querée, Edna Le Feuvre, C. P. Ahier, A. R. Le Brun and Alfred Vautier. Pelz's report mentioned that the owners of Egypt Farm were "...the Rice family in England".

Pelz's report stated that the requisition of Egypt and its farms and land for military purposes could not be authorised. His reason was that such a large area of good agricultural land would be lost. He, furthermore, questioned the necessity of reducing the Island's area of arable land, as in his opinion arable land should only be destroyed in real battle and not just for military manoeuvres. Pelz commented, "The performance of agriculture is just as desired in war as that of the military" and he summed up his report by stating that, as the agricultural consultant for Field Command 515, he could not give his consent as long as there was a sandy area in the West of the Island. His recommendation to the Field Commandant was to turn down the request of the military for the requisition of Egypt.

Field Command 515, however, granted the military's request; it appears that the actual area requisitioned was reduced. Von Schmettow wrote to the Field Command sending back the map of the planned firing range, adding "After a thorough checking on the spot and because of the necessity to have a larger firing range on Jersey it is regarded an absolute necessity to plan the area". He added that a more precise map would be forwarded.

On the 28th July Field Command verified to the military authority that the area known as Egypt Farm would be requisitioned. It appears that Pelz's insistence that valuable agricultural land should not be lost had failed. The Field Command, however, made it clear that the tenant living and working at Egypt Farm had been an excellent farmer and deserved to be found a substitute farm to work. In addition, he was the father of eleven children.

On the 4th August, MVR von Aufsess wrote to the Military Commander of the area around Trinity, "Saf. Wölfe", to the Connétable of Trinity and the "Farmer Vautier". He stated which cultivated fields could or could not be harvested. Mr Vautier was given permission to carry on with the grazing of his herd, except when firing exercises were taking place. The Connétable was also ordered to locate a new farm for Mr Vautier.

Subsequently, the Connétable of Trinity, Mr Snowdon Benest, visited College House and discussed farms that were available and that could be assigned to Mr Vautier. The next day, Connétable Benest wrote to Dr Casper identifying two properties; the first was "La Ville Machon" 40 vergées in area, and the second "Diélament Manor", 36 vergées.

Negotiations were finalised with Mr Vautier and "An agreement was reached with the Field Command whereby Mr Vautier would move into the farm La Ville Machon as from Christmas 1943. Mr Vautier would make his own arrangement with the occupier with regard to the terms of the lease".

When the firing range at Egypt was completed and ready for use, the German Auxiliary Commander wrote and notified Field Command 515, who in turn contacted the Connétable with exact times of the start and finish of each firing exercise. This information was published in the local press.

On the 24th October 1943, Major Heider wrote to the Bailiff highlighting the danger to farmers of unexploded shells lying around the Egypt area. He forwarded a shaded map of the area where entry was strictly restricted and informed the Bailiff that any farmer who wished to enter this zone outside the times when live firing was taking place would have to contact Lieutenant Trager, Befehlshaber, Metropole Hotel, St Helier. All farmers entering this area took responsibility for their own safety. The Bailiff sent copies of the correspondence to the Connétables of Trinity and St John, S. Benest and J. Le Masurier, respectively.

References

1. Jersey Archive. C/B/A1/9.
2. Jersey Archive. B/A/W40/14/1.
3. My thanks to Mr Martin Huelin, Judicial Greffe's office for his assistance on tobacco legislation.
4. Société Jersiaise Library. Tobacco Plants Order Book Season 1943–44. J. Maletroit. LAN/A/1/24.
5. Jersey Archive. B/A/W31/2/87.
6. Jersey Archive. B/A/W31/2/24.
7. Jersey Archive. B/A/W31/2/93.
8. Jersey Archive. L/D/09/A10. Document, p. 398.
9. Jersey Archive. B/A/W70/1.
10. Jersey Archive. D/S/A/9/A3; D/S/A/9/B773.
11. RJA&HS and JFU Joint Emergency Committee Minutes.
12. Hans Egon Pelz post-war referred to himself as "Dipl.Ing." His university qualification was "Ing". Pelz was an "Ingenieur" abbreviated to "Ing". After the Anschluss of Austria by Germany, there was an edict which enabled an Austrian "Ingenieur" to become "Diplom Ingenieur" or "Dipl.Ing.". This was the equivalent nomenclature in Germany. Pelz could only call himself "Dipl.Ing." if his qualifying university in Vienna received a written request from him; the university has no record of confirmation conferring the change. Correspondence with Mr Tarik Gaafar, BOKU, Vienna, 28th August 2018 to 13th September 2018. Reference No: 2018083123000459. My thanks to BOKU University for allowing me a copy of Pelz's examination results.
13. Casper, Dr Wilhelm. Wir Menschen sind eine familie. Erinnerungen und Gedanken. 1994. p. 318.
14. Jersey Archive. B/A/W31/2/17.
15. Jersey Archive. B/A/W31/2/31.
16. Jersey Archive. B/A/W31/2/57.
17. Catering Office and Distribution Centre.
18. Jersey Archive. B/A/W31/2/100.
19. Jersey Archive. B/A/W31/2/95.
20. This almost certainly would have been Carlyle Le Gallais.

21. Lewis, Dr John, 1997. "A Doctor's Occupation. The dramatic true story of life in Nazi occupied Jersey". pp. 126–127.
22. Jersey Herd Book 40697.
23. Frigot, D. MBE. 2017. Pioneers of the Jersey Breed. p. 74.
24. My thanks to Derrick Frigot, MBE for his detailed assistance.
25. RJA&HS. The Jersey Herd Book Minute Book, entry for 28th October 1939.
26. JEP, 9th May 2014 and JEP, 30th June 2015.
27. JEP, 3rd July 2017.
28. My thanks to Mr Alan Allix for the benefit of his research.
29. KVR or Kriegsverwaltungsrat or War Administrator was changed to MVR or Militär Verwaltungsrat or Military Administrator sometime between May and June 1943. The same change in title was made to OKVR, which became OMVR. This was a higher rank than MVR in the German Military Government.

Chapter 15

November 1943 to April 1944

Milk Control

"The distribution of skim milk to members of the public shall be discontinued owing to the quantities available being barely sufficient to meet the requirements for the feeding of calves"

DOA Milk Control Section Report

On the 18th October 1943, Field Command made an order to the DOA that a supply of milk be made available to the recently opened Soldatenheim IV at La Hougue Farm, St Peter. The Commandant, Colonel Knackfuss, ordered that "The farmer Le Rossignol, La Hougue, St Peter, is to deliver daily, 24 pints of fresh milk to the Soldatenheim against payment. Le Rossignol is to receive permission to deliver 24 pints of fresh milk daily to Soldatenheim IV. The Milk Control is to be notified".[1] On the 2nd November, the DOA granted Mr Clarence Edward Le Cornu, also at La Hougue Farm, St Peter, a producer-retailer licence under Article 3(2) Milk Control (Jersey) Order, 1940, to supply 24 pints of fresh milk daily. A producer-retailer licence was also authorised to Mr John Blake, St Saviour. This licence was a renewal to sell milk to the German authorities, granted on the insistence of the Field Command. Then on the 16th December Field Command made another order, requiring Mr Blake to supply them with a further 8 pints of full cream milk. This presumably was on a daily basis and Mr Blake's producer-retailer licence was amended.

On the 9th November the temporary staff employed by the DOA to assist the Cattle Slaughter Executive Committee's appraisal of milk production were dispensed with. This group of DOA employees, along with the Milk Testers, had collated all the available data concerning the production of milk yields from the Island's herds. The entire process had taken six weeks.

In early November a report by the dairy collecting from Mrs B. Le Chanu, St Helier, alleged that the milk was in "...extremely dirty cans". The DOA subsequently paid only half the normal price for her milk.

On the 3rd December the DOA took note of a decision by the Medical Board that pregnant women should be entitled to a further half pint of milk, daily. Weeks voiced his immediate opposition. The DOA decided, "In view of the heavy drain on the milk available for butter making", it could not agree to the issue of this extra milk until it had met with the Island's Medical Officer of Health, Dr McKinstry. A week later the DOA met Dr McKinstry, Mr A. C. Halliwell, FRCP, and Dr H. J. Blampied, concerning the proposed extra ration. After discussion, the DOA decided to approve the additional milk but only on the assurance of the Medical Board that the extra milk to whooping cough patients would shortly terminate. It also agreed that the extra provision to pregnant women would be reviewed in January 1944.

On the 10th December, on the recommendation of the Milk Control Section, the supply of skim milk to the public was stopped. Weeks' reason to cease the supply was that quantities available were barely sufficient to meet the requirements of feeding the Island's calves. Brée, however, decided that every endeavour should be made to supply the public with skim milk at Christmas. On the same day, Weeks made a request to the DOA to install a telephone at his residence to facilitate dealing with applications for extra milk supplies on medical grounds, which were constantly submitted to him outside office hours. The DOA declined his application.

A report dated the 21st December sent to the DOA alleged "...certain shortages established in the quantities of milk supplied by Mr E. G. Laurens, St Mary, to the licenced retailer with whom he was registered." In view of the unsatisfactory explanations offered by Mr Laurens for the shortages, he was given a formal warning to observe the requirements of the Milk Control (Jersey) Order, 1940. No more shortages were reported, and Brée decided to take no further action.

The Milk Control Section received a report on the 24th January that consumers were allegedly receiving sour milk from the licensed retailer Mr G. W. Le Masurier, Val Plaisant Dairy, St Helier. The report also alleged that a number of registered consumers were receiving milk in excess of that to which they were entitled. Mr Le Masurier was instructed to appear before the DOA on the 1st February, accompanied by his legal representative Mr S. G. Crill. After hearing explanations from both, the DOA decided to defer the matter until Milk Control had evaluated delivery figures from the farmer to the licensed retailer. On the 16th February, the DOA noted a report "...on the explanations offered on behalf of Mr Le Masurier by Mr Crill in a letter of the 8th February". In view of this report, the DOA wrote to Mr Crill asking for further information on the points raised. On the 23rd February, Milk Control produced a further report based on the information provided by Mr Crill and in response, the DOA ordered Mr Crill to submit the copy of the milk registration certificate in respect of one of Le Masurier's consumers, Honorah G. Wilkinson. The solicitor was also informed that, should the DOA have any further difficulties with his client in relation to the distribution and control of milk, it would "...find itself with no alternative but to take severe action against Mr Le Masurier". On the 11th April the DOA noted a further report concerning the registration certificates issued under the Milk (Registration with Retailers) Jersey Order, 1940, in respect of a child named Honorah G. Wilkinson. The certificates were corrected and sent back to Mr Crill for forwarding to Mr Le Masurier.[2] It appears that the Milk Control Section had made administrative mistakes.

On the 26th December 1943, Mr Arthur du Pré Denning, St Brelade, wrote to the Attorney General alleging that he and six consumers had been given short measures of milk by their roundsman. These consumers left their milk jugs at the property Ocean View, to be filled by the roundsman, but they lived in an adjoining bungalow. One of the complainants, Mrs Appleby, stated that she and others had been "receiving short measures for some time past".[3]

The allegations of short measures were forwarded by the Attorney General to the DOA. The Milk Control Section put the matter into the hands of the Managing Director of Jersey Dairies, Mr Joseph Marie. In response, he carried out a detailed investigation of all deliveries carried out by the roundsman in St Brelade over several months, including the quantities of milk left by him at various points in his milk round.

A report dated the 18th January 1944 concluded that, although the roundsman may have been guilty of giving short measures in a few instances, it was certainly not proven that he made it a regular occurrence. The problem was due to the carelessness and negligence of the customers, some of whom admitted that, instead of using the official half-pint measures for a half-pint issue of milk, they gauged the milk in a full-pint measure. Some consumers also admitted not making provision for the froth produced by milk whilst others, who left their jugs outside the bungalow "Ocean View", judged the apparent shortage merely by eye. At no time was the quantity of milk checked with an authentic measure.

Colin Marie wrote to the Attorney General following the report. He stated, "I must stress that a milk roundsman's position in these difficult days is not a sinecure. It is my personal knowledge and experience that a certain section of consumers, probably in desperation, bribe the roundsmen in order to obtain extra supplies. With the strict control which we have to enforce over all roundsmen's quantities it is impossible for them to accede to these requests without resorting to dishonest methods".

On the 4th January 1944, Mr A. E. Le Lere was replaced by Mr Philip John Henwood as a Milk Tester. On the 29th February another Milk Tester, Mr G. Le Gros, was replaced by Mr D. Hamelin and Milk Control dispensed with the services of one of its clerical staff, Miss L. Houillebecq. On the same day the balance sheet for the Milk Control Section was completed for the previous twelve months, ending 31st December 1943. It demonstrated a loss of £8,956-15-10½.

On the 30th March, MVR von Aufsess wrote a letter to the Bailiff entitled "Butter for the Soldatenheim". He ordered that:

"On the occasion of this Easter Festival the following special allocation of butter is to be made at the Soldatenheim, Jersey:

Soldatenheim I	St Helier	35kg
Soldatenheim II	St Brelade	15kg
Soldatenheim III	Millbrook	<u>10kg</u>
	Total	<u>50kg</u>

The goods will, as usual, be paid in cash".

On the 28th April he again wrote to the Bailiff. This letter, entitled "Butter and milk allocations for the Soldatenheim", stated that "As from the 1st May 1944, the order concerning deliveries of butter and milk to the Soldatenheim hitherto in force is revoked and in accordance with the new regulations the following quantities are to be delivered daily:

	Butter	Fresh Milk	Skim Milk
Soldatenheim I, St Helier	6 kg	20 litres	40 litres
Offiziersheim, Fort Auvergne	2 kg	8 litres	10 litres
Soldatenheim II, St Brelade	4 kg	30 litres	25 litres
Soldatenheim, La Hougue	–	10 litres	–
Soldatenheim III, Millbrook	3 kg	20 litres	25 litres

The Soldatenheim, La Hougue will receive deliveries direct from the farmer in the neighbourhood as hitherto. Payment will be made in the same manner".[4]

On the 25th April the DOA decided to fix the times at which milk was collected from producers: the morning collection at 7.30 a.m. and the afternoon collection at 4.00 p.m. The four collecting dairies were: L. J. Tanguy Limited, Victoria Co-operative Dairy Limited, Fairview Dairy and Jersey Dairies Limited. A notice was published in the local press informing producers that these new hours had been fixed to meet the situation arising from the curtailment of the hours during which the supply of gas was available. The four collecting dairies were also advised that the order of the milk rounds should be reversed each month in order that the same producers would not always be at the beginning of each collection round. The DOA took into consideration a petition from a number of dairy farmers in St Ouen for the addition of petrol-driven vehicles to collect their milk. The DOA decided to subsidise the collecting dairies for this service.

At the end of April, in view of the increasing quantity of milk being processed by the Don Street Dairy and the longer hours which employees had to work, the DOA paid a bonus of 7/6 weekly as from the 1st April to all factory and engineering staff at the dairy. The bonus would terminate on the 30th September 1944. It was also decided to employ a temporary additional factory hand, Mr J. W. Benest, at a weekly wage of £2-10-6.

Pigs

On the 5th November 1943, the DOA interviewed Mr W. C. Le Herissier and Mr S. C. Syvret, both from St Mary, concerning "…an allegation that the former had sold to the latter "two pigs" and transferred the custody without first obtaining a licence as prescribed by the Livestock (Jersey) Order, 1942. Both men had also failed to complete the livestock return for animals in their custody as required by the Livestock (Returns) (Jersey) Order, 1943. Brée heard their explanations and discussed the matter with the Attorney General who, "In view of the purely technical nature of the offence alleged", decided to give them a written warning as to their future observance of Orders and Directions issued by the DOA. A third farmer, Mr J. O. Arthur, St John, was also given a formal warning to keep his Livestock Registration returns in order.[2]

On the 9th November the DOA interviewed Mr J. F. Rebindaine, St Brelade, who allegedly had been discovered by an Inspector to have in his custody one pig whereas, according to DOA records, he had none. A report concluded: "Mr Rebindaine failed to provide any satisfactory explanations as to the pig in question and, moreover, adopted an offensive attitude to J. W. Blampied, the DOA's Inspector, and threatened him with bodily violence should he again call at Mr Rebindaine's farm". The DOA referred the matter to the Attorney General under the Livestock (Jersey) Order, 1942, including the aggressive threats. The Attorney General decided that, before any action was taken, the Inspector be interviewed by Brée who felt that such an incident, if not swiftly dealt with, would lead to attacks and violence towards all his inspecting staff. Brée asked the Attorney General to also interview the Inspector and he forwarded another, separate, report by Centenier H. F. Le Rossignol that affirmed that Mr John Philip Huelin "…saw a pig in Mr Rebindaine's yard".

The Attorney General, reluctant to prosecute this case, discussed the matter with the Solicitor General and Law Officers. Although a conviction could take place, there appeared to be two problems. Firstly, there was a purely technical point arising out of the physical inspection of the farm and, secondly, there was a conflict of evidence which had become apparent as a result of the Centenier's investigation. The Attorney General, with the agreement of Brée, decided not to proceed.

This case was unusual, in so much as no prosecution was eventually sought. Many similar cases which had gone through the courts had been successfully prosecuted. Why was the case dropped even after Brée's intervention? The answer is that both the DOA and the Attorney General had far more important issues to investigate concerning the black market. When viewed across the spectrum of the black market and pigs, this was a relatively minor instance, involving only one pig. Brée felt that, although threats of violence had been made towards the Inspector, large amounts of time and resources had been spent on the case and nothing more could be gained. A formal warning was sufficient.

On the 26th November, a report alleged that a pig weighing 50 lbs, and for which no declaration had been made, had been found in a shed on the premises of Mr R. Vibert, St Ouen. On the same day, two unregistered pigs, each weighing 90 lbs, were allegedly found in the custody of Mr H. Vibert, St Ouen. They were referred to the Attorney General for investigation.

Also in November, Mr R. P. Le Cornu, St Mary, appeared before the DOA following a report from the Inspector which alleged that he had two unregistered pigs in his custody aged three months. The records indicated that no pigs had been registered by Mr Le Cornu since the 18th July 1943. The States Vet was instructed to check and confirm the age of the pigs.

On the 27th November a proposition was brought before the States by Jurat Labey to facilitate an increase in pig production and make pork more available for the civilian population. It was also an attempt to halt the ever-growing black market.

The proposal stated: "When a person has offered three pigs for sale to the Department of Essential Commodities, as required by Article 4a of the Livestock (Jersey) Order, 1942, the DOA shall release that person from his obligation to sell one (fourth) pig and the DOA grant that person an application, a licence under Article 3 of that Order to kill the fourth pig, it being understood that the breeder will be entitled to every fourth pig, irrespective of the total number of pigs produced by him." It is also proposed that: "The fat stock price be increased to 2/6 per pound".

Brée discussed these proposals at length with his committee. It was decided to report to the Superior Council that under the order, as amended, persons having the custody of pigs did, in fact, receive the equivalent of one pig in four in that, when pigs were delivered to the Department of Essential Commodities, the person having the custody of those pigs received 10% of the carcass and, in addition, the head of the animal which in all was equivalent to approximately 25% of the carcass.

The DOA took the view that to exempt every fourth pig from the requirements of the order would be inequitable as it unduly favoured persons who were able to raise large numbers of pigs, to the detriment of those who were only able to raise one or two and who, if the proposal was adopted, would have to wait many months before they were entitled to a percentage of pork. The DOA was convinced that it was more convenient for persons having custody of pigs to receive a percentage of each animal brought in for slaughter rather than to receive a whole pig at one time. Brée also decided, and recommended to the Superior Council, that Jurat Labey should approach Pelz and Field Command 515 with his request for obtaining an increase in the price of pork, as previous attempts to that end by the DOA had been unavailing.

On the 29th December, the DOA discussed a letter from Field Command 515 concerning the keeping of pigs by farmers. A letter was attached from Mr Henry du Val, St Helier, who suggested that every farmer should be allowed to rear two pigs each year for his own use. Brée made it clear to Pelz and Field Command 515 that this would not be practical in an island where the number of pigs on any farm was restricted, and it would not result in an increased quantity of pork becoming available to the public. He wrote to Field Command to endeavour to increase the wholesale price for pork to 2/- per pound, the retail price being increased correspondingly.

As a result of these discussions the DOA made the following Order on the 11th January 1944.

1. In paragraph (e) of Article 5c of the Livestock (Jersey) Order, 1942, as amended for 1/7 per pound deadweight, pigs (excluding boars) there shall be substituted 2/- per pound deadweight.
2. This order shall come into force on the 24th January 1944 and may be cited as the Livestock (Amendment No 2) (Jersey) Order, 1944.

On the 7th March the DOA again amended the order to: "pigs (excluding boars aged 6 months and over)".

On the 21st March, Mr Reginald T. de Gruchy, St Martin appeared before the DOA to explain an alleged discrepancy between the number of pigs in his custody and the records held by the DOA. "In view of the unsatisfactory nature of the explanations offered", the DOA referred the matter to the Attorney General.

On the same day the DOA's Tattooing Officers went to the farm of Mr N. R. Cope, St Martin to tattoo three pigs, however the pigs allegedly were not in his custody. Mr Cope explained he had sold them "...to the German forces in occupation of a part of the farm". Since Mr Cope had not made an application for a licence to transfer the custody of the pigs; had not surrendered to the DOA any permit issued by MVR Pelz and Field Command 515 authorising the sale of the pigs to the military unit concerned; and had failed to reply to two communications on the subject from the DOA, it was decided to refer the matter to the Attorney General for investigation.

Also on 21st March, correspondence was submitted to the DOA in relation to the alleged disappearance of a pig owned by Mr P. F. Baudains, St Martin. Colin Marie reported the "...illicit slaughter of a pig" and referred the matter to the Attorney General. In response, Mr Baudains telephoned Marie advising that seven pigs had been delivered to the slaughterhouse, and he was prepared to forgo the 10% of the carcasses to which he was entitled. "After consideration of the offer, the DOA decided that, provided Mr Baudains forfeited not less than 65 pounds weight of pork, this being the alleged weight of the pig illicitly slaughtered, it would recall the case sent to the Attorney General".

On the 28th March, Mr J. Richard, St John, and Mr C. G. Gibaut, St Lawrence, both appeared before the DOA to explain alleged discrepancies for a pig in their custody. Mr Richard was referred to the Attorney General. After hearing Mr Gibaut, the DOA decided that, provided he swore an affidavit in respect of the pig, his explanation would be accepted.

Cultivation Orders

On the 6ᵗʰ November 1943, the Petrol Controller, Bertrand Clift, summoned a meeting of the ploughing contractors. Also present were Touzel Brée, John du Val, Edwin Gibaut and Colin Marie. Two new ploughing contractors were employed for the 1943–44 season, Mr H. Lesbirel and Mr R. G. England. In view of the additional quantities of diesel oil that the Petrol Controller could make available for ploughing, it was decided to allow applications from the owners of Fordson tractors. Previously, these applications had been turned down because of the large quantity of fuel consumed by Fordson tractors. The newly appointed contractors using Fordsons were as follows:

W. Renouard	Pot du Roches	Trinity
L. Rondel	Beechwood	St Mary
C. H. Jarnet	La Pavillon	St Martin
C. W. Le Herissier	La Commune	Trinity
W. P. Le Seelleur	La Chenais des Bois	St Martin
H. J. Lesbirel	Le Pont	St Mary
R. G. England	Blanche Pierre	Trinity

The following contractors, using various models of tractors, were also appointed:

E. L. Henry	La Hougue Farm	St John
D. P. Larose	Le Huquet	St Martin
F. Boutillier & Son	Highfields	St Ouen
E. R. Le Cornu	Oak Farm	St Lawrence
J. C. Le Gresley	Valley Farm	St Lawrence
J. Georgelin	Beechwood	St Mary
R. S. Langlois	Stirling Castle Farm	St Helier
W. P. Becquet	Pièce Mauger	Trinity
J. R. de Caux	Dairy Farm	St Mary
L. Holmes	La Grande Maison.	Trinity
P. Binet	Clos du Buisson	St Saviour
E. R. Le Brun	Beaulieu	Trinity

H. J. Le Brocq	La Chasse	St Ouen
J. Le Masurier	Century House	St John
F. J. Nicolle	Oakfield	St Saviour
F. R. Ozouf	Highstead	St Saviour
T. A. Pallot	Lincoln House, Millbrook	St Lawrence
J. F. Pirouet	Fernside	St Saviour
G. Vasselin	Seaview	St Peter
J. Maletroit	La Place	St Brelade
J. Bouchault	Ouaisné	St Brelade
S. Hamon	Lowlands	St Brelade
J. E. Colback Junior	Sandown, Parade Road	St Helier

On the 5th November 1943, a letter was read from the Imports and Exports Advisory Committee with an attached application from Mr A. C. Sarre, the local representative of the Guernsey States, requesting permission to export 250 tonnes of straw to Guernsey. After consideration, the DOA decided to recommend that, in the first instance, permission should be granted for the export of 100 tonnes. On the 9th November over twenty of the leading farmers met to discuss the matter, the issue of exporting 100 tonnes to Guernsey having led them to great concern. Philip Le Feuvre stated that there was an Island-wide shortage of straw because of the "light crop" and H. W. Maillard confirmed that there was a huge local demand for the commodity.

Subsequent discussion amongst these farmers made it clear that both hay and root crops had not done well in 1943 and extra straw was needed for feeding cattle and horses. A unanimous decision recommended to the DOA that no straw should be allowed to leave for Guernsey. Straw held in store by Mr Sarre, and already acquired by him on behalf of Guernsey, would be purchased back by the DOA. Philip Le Feuvre and Francis Le Boutillier were asked to "...acquaint Mr Sarre with the action of the meeting".

At the meeting Le Gallais pointed out that, whereas the price of hay was controlled at a maximum of £20 per ton, the maximum price of straw had been £4 per ton the year before but since then, had been decontrolled. The DOA was therefore also asked to remove the price control on hay, as it had done with straw. Several individuals were mentioned who evaded the hay price, which "...often occurred".[5]

A letter from the RJA&HS and the JFU concerning the price of hay was sent, requesting that it be decontrolled. The DOA responded by affirming it would not revoke the Home-Grown Hay (Maximum Price) (Jersey) Order, 1941, stating that to revoke price control would not benefit the majority. The price for straw was also considered and it was decided to recommend to the Superior Council that an Order be made to fix the maximum price at £10 per ton.

On the 3rd December 1943, under the Cultivation of Lands (Jersey) Order, 1942, the following directions were issued.

1. Home-grown straw means straw of wheat, oats, barley, or rye sown in the island.
2. No person shall sell or buy home-grown straw at a price exceeding £10 per ton.
3. No person shall, in connection with a sale or disposal of home-grown straw, enter or offer to enter into any artificial or fictitious transaction or make or demand any unreasonable charge.
4. Directions come into force on the 6th December 1943.

The next day the DOA met with the RJA&HS and the JFU, and it was made clear by the members that they wished the export of straw to Guernsey to be prohibited as there was "...insufficient straw on the island for the requirements of its livestock". In response, the DOA decided to reduce the export to Guernsey from 100 to 80 tonnes.

Also on the 4th December, by virtue of a letter from Field Command 515, the DOA transmitted to the Department of Essential Commodities details of materials and spare parts required for the repair of agricultural machinery. As the occupation continued, Field Command 515 was becoming increasingly important in obtaining agricultural inputs: fuel, seed, artificial fertiliser, machinery, spare parts, pesticides and implements.

On the 9th November, Mr R. de Carteret informed the DOA that he did not wish to retain possession of the farm Woodville, St Peter, after December 1943. It had been requisitioned by the DOA from Dr Chichester and Mr de Carteret had farmed the land for one year. The DOA put the farm out to tender for one year, or to the end of hostilities. A tender from Mr W. C. Quenault, St Peter, for the sum of £14, was accepted on the 3rd December.

On the 28th October 1941 the farm of Mrs Mary Jane Perron, L'Etacq, St Ouen had been requisitioned by the DOA. On the 26th November 1943 the two farmers who had tendered for the land, Mr J. J. Le Cornu and Mr P. E. Amy, wished to remain in possession for a further year. Approximately one month earlier, Pelz and von Aufsess had both visited "...a nice farm in order to decide whether the tenant can stay against the will of the owner".[6]

As from the 1st March 1942, Mr Frank Le Maistre, Laboratory Assistant at the States Experimental Station, had received "A cost of living bonus amounting to 20% of his salary". He therefore received a supplementary credit of £57-12-0 to cover this "bonus" for the period 1st March 1942 to the 31st December 1943. When the bonus terminated Mr Le Maistre's salary was increased, as from the 1st January 1944, from £156 to £194 per annum.

On the 15th December the Medical Officer of Health sent a letter to the DOA recommending that a provision be made for growing sugar beet to provide additional sugar for the population. Brée replied that sugar beet had to be grown as a first crop, and as all cultivable land for growing first crops was allocated, it could not include the growing of sugar beet in its directions issued to farmers under the Cultivation of Lands (Jersey) Order, 1942. All crops had been allocated for the 1943–44 growing season and were essential for feeding the Island's population. The DOA, however, decided to recommend at Parish Agricultural Society meetings that farmers should attempt to sow as much sugar beet as possible in seed beds, with a view to transplanting them and growing on as a second crop. Brée made clear that this was the only means by which the DOA would accept sugar beet, i.e., when grown as a second crop.

In April 1944, in response to a letter from Jurat F. V. Le Feuvre concerning the Island-wide cultivation of sugar beet, the DOA stated that it had already made arrangements to raise seedlings so that smallholders could grow their own. Jurat Le Feuvre's letter was forwarded to a committee set up by the Superior Council to consider the question of growing and distributing sugar beet.

On the 14th January 1944, Mr Louis McDowall Sydenham-Clarke, La Moie Farm, St Brelade, wrote to the DOA concerning the damage and destruction of his crops by "...the foreign workmen now in the island". These "foreign workmen" had entered his fields, pulled up his crops and eaten them. He claimed that they had extensively damaged the crops, causing him severe financial hardship and compelling him to borrow money from Lloyds Bank Limited to enable him to carry on farming. He forwarded a compensation claim to the DOA and was sent details of the agricultural credits scheme granted to farmers to finance the cultivation of their land. He was instructed to prepare a more detailed claim, which was forwarded to the Department of Finance and Economics on the 18th January. However, on the 18th April his claim was rejected. Brée decided to intervene and recommended to the Department of Finance and Economics that "Compensation should be paid in respect of the damage suffered by his potato, vegetable and root crops as a result of the foreign workers in the island during the years 1942 and 1943".

On the 31st January, Advocates Le Masurier, Giffard and Poch wrote to the DOA concerning alleged losses suffered by the estate of Percy Alfred Le Rossignol, St Ouen, during the years 1941, 1942 and up to 30th August 1943. The claim was the result of cultivation by him under the Cultivation of Lands (Jersey) Orders 1940 and 1942. The DOA refused to recognise the claim and the law firm was told to file the claim for the alleged losses to the Department of Finance and Economics.

On the 16th February the DOA deliberated upon the question of making good agricultural land which had suffered damage because of occupation by the German military. It was decided that land released from military occupation should be fully cultivated. The DOA also decided that it would take no steps to fill up trenches or for the removal of obstructions. The farmers of this land would not be expected to cultivate any areas near the German obstacles.

On the 4th March Mr S. G. Le Couilliard, the Honorary Parish Inspector, Grouville, reported on the alleged "negligent cultivation" of Mr J. B. Godfray. On the 14th March Mr Godfray appeared before the DOA to offer an explanation. He was ordered not to sow the wheat seed that he had drawn from the DOA. The following week his brother, Mr A. J. Godfray, appeared before the DOA in relation to the cultivation of their farm. Since there had been a division of the farm due to inheritance, the DOA decided to issue new instructions to the estate under the Cultivation of Lands (Jersey) Order, 1942, and not simply to Mr J. B. Godfray as heretofore. The DOA then ordered that many of the fields should be rented to other farmers; all wheat seed drawn out by J. B. Godfray had to be returned to John Terry Limited before the 1st May; and on the 4th May the fields were leased to Mr A. Simon, Grouville.

On the 20th March, Mr Sarre asked for permission to purchase swedes in Jersey for "...the needs of the civil population of Guernsey". The DOA recommended to the Superior Council that permission be granted for Mr Sarre to purchase 50 tons, "It being a condition of the granting of such permission that swedes shall be purchased privately and without the publication of the local press". The DOA also recommended that the maximum price to be paid by Mr Sarre should not exceed £5 a ton, in order to prevent an excessive price being paid for these roots, to the detriment of local purchasers.

The question arises as to why the purchase of swedes by Mr Sarre on behalf of Guernsey was kept a closed issue. The answer can be found in the previous purchase of straw, which had met with unanimous opposition from leading Jersey farmers. Philip Le Feuvre and Francis Le Boutillier vehemently spoke out against sending any Jersey produce to Guernsey. Brée, therefore, wanted the purchase of Jersey swedes by Guernsey to be kept a closed issue in order not to antagonise these farmers.

A report of the 12th May from Mr Simpson described the presence of wireworm on the farm belonging to Mr J. B. Arthur, St Clement. The farmer was immediately directed to put his land under grass.

Watermills and Milling

On the 5th November 1943, the DOA increased the weekly allowance paid to Mr J. H. Lewis for the use of his bicycle; he was employed as a "checker" at the mills operated by the DOA.

On the same day, the States Engineer reported on the "...bad condition of the steam rollers now being used driving the Malassis and Grand Val mills". In response, Brée applied to the Department of Essential Commodities for a licence to use two motors of 25 and 20 horsepower, requisitioned from Randalls Brewery Limited at a charge of 15/- weekly. Brée also offered £5 compensation to the company as final settlement of any claims regarding the requisition order for the motors.

A report from Mr Richard Troy, a nightwatchman at Grand Val, alleged that coke belonging to the DOA was delivered to the home of one of the steamroller drivers. The driver was dismissed and a new man employed. Brée issued instructions that no coke or cinders were to be removed from any of the mills.

In an Act of 18th September 1940 Peter Philip Day had been appointed as "Supervisor of the Mills". Brée now recommended that the limits of his jurisdiction be defined more clearly. Mr Day was therefore reappointed as the "Mechanical Supervisor of the Mills" on the same salary and terms as previously, but with his responsibilities now also covering millstreams and storage ponds.

Early in December the DOA decided to look into the cartage of grain and flour to and from its mills. Brée decided to investigate the possibility of making use of the lorry belonging to the States slaughterhouse. The lorry was handed over to the DOA and Brée requested additional tyres from the Department of Transport and Communications, followed by permission to arrange for the conversion of the vehicle from petrol to gasogene operation.

On the 8th February 1944, the DOA met to consider the question of German military forces moving into a dwelling next door to Gargate. It was decided to have the communicating door between the mill and the dwelling house bricked up. The following week a letter from the Greffier of the States, acting on the advice of the Department of Public Health, asked the DOA to take steps to deal with what was described as "A rat menace". The DOA drew upon a sub-committee of Brée and du Val to visit the mill with a delegation from the Department of Public Health, the States Engineer and Mr L. Hammond, the States Sanitary Inspector. A report was produced on the 13th March with input from Mr Day. After reading the report, the Public Health Department advised that the brushings referred to were not to be used for human consumption and recommended that remedial works be carried out at the mill. The works were quickly completed.

On the 17th March the Senior Miller at Tesson, Mr Gilley, was certified as unable to work due to illness. Brée decided to pay him in full for two weeks, and thereafter two-thirds of full pay until the end of the medical certification of two months. In response to the miller's absence, an additional man was employed who also assisted in the transport of grain and flour.

Fertilisers

On the 25th January 1944, a delegation of the JPMA came before the DOA to discuss the price to be charged to farmers for lime "...which had recently been imported from France". The DOA authorised the JPMA to sell the lime at £8-15-0 per ton to those farmers holding a permit under the Fertilisers (Jersey) Order, 1941. The sale was only allowed on a cash basis and the farmer had to provide his own sacks. A notice to that effect was inserted in the local press.

On the 31st March the JPMA wrote to the DOA that, in view of information from the Granville office of the States of Jersey that the price of crushed lime had increased, it was necessary to increase the price to farmers to £10-7-6 per ton. From the 1st February, on the recommendation of Mr Simpson, the price of artificial fertilisers was increased: sulphate of ammonia to £20 per ton and muriate of potash £21 per ton.

On the last day of February, the JPMA and the DOA met to discuss the provision of artificial fertilisers for the 1944 season. The JPMA requested certain assurances for its members. Sacks were valuable and in very short supply and were provided by members for the shipment of fertiliser from France. The DOA indemnified them against any loss in the event of their sacks not being returned from France. Also, the price at which fertiliser was sold to farmers was often fixed before the cost price was known. The DOA indemnified members against any losses as a result of the cost price being increased after the sale price had been fixed. These guarantees were approved by the Superior Council.

On the 4th April the DOA informed the JPMA of conditions to be followed for the sale of artificial fertilisers for the 1944 season.

1. Payment for the first batch of fertilisers to be made within one month of invoice.
2. Payment for future deliveries to be made within two months from the date of delivery.
3. Fertilisers to be paid for by farmers in cash and subject to the Cultivation Orders issued by the DOA.

A memorandum was forwarded to the JPMA, reminding them of the directions of the Fertilisers (Jersey) Order, 1941.

On the 7th March, farmers cultivating wheat were reminded that chalk had to be purchased by the 15th May. To obtain chalk the farmer had to demonstrate a permit under the order. On the 4th April, the JPMA wrote to the DOA demonstrating a shortfall of 11 tons 6 cwt of chalk in a delivery from France. This had been due to "...certain unforeseen transport problems and freight charges". The Superior Council was requested to reimburse the JPMA £70-10-3. Ten days later the DOA decided that permits issued to farmers would henceforth have a validity of only fourteen days, and that all permits had to be taken up by the 29th April 1944.

On the 18th April 610 tons of sulphate of ammonia arrived on the Island. It was issued to farmers at the rate of 80 lbs per vergée for areas allocated to potatoes and paid for in cash. The following week the DOA approved terms for the JPMA to sell the imported sulphate of ammonia.

1. The rate was changed to 56 lbs per vergée on areas allocated to a first crop of mangolds, grain or potatoes.
2. The price for sacks was fixed at 25/- cash.
3. Basic slag at a rate of 110 lbs per vergée was allocated to first crop potatoes at the price of 13/6 for the 110 lbs. All sales were to be paid in cash and farmers had to provide their own sacks.

The sulphate of ammonia and basic slag was made available to farmers up to the 15th May and was to be used only for crops grown in the 1944 season. Supplies were sold on presentation of a current DOA cultivation direction. All merchants holding stocks of artificial fertilisers had to submit a detailed return showing the quantities still held by them by the close of business on the 15th May.

Horses

On the 5th December 1943, Field Command 515 wrote to the DOA concerning the provision of feeding stuffs for horses working in St Helier. In reply the DOA gave details of feeding stuffs that were available.

Following on from the last Island-wide muster of horses in November 1943, Colonel Knackfuss wrote to the Bailiff on the 21st February 1944 requesting information about horses to be reported back to Field Command:

1. All sales of horses including the names of the previous and the new owner, with a description of the horse.
2. Horses purchased from France were to be examined by the Field Command Veterinary Surgeon, Dr Kempt.
3. Horses that had been slaughtered or had died were to be reported, accompanied with a description and a certificate from the vet.

The Bailiff responded with the details on the 24th February. On the 1st April he also forwarded details of seven horses that had been sold by the Department of Transport and Communications to seven farmers.

On the 10th May, Brée, Major Heider and Miss Lillian White met at Samarès Manor. It was agreed by Miss White that two horses used at the Manor for riding and carriage work be employed for general economic purposes. The two horses had "...hitherto done no work and they are to be employed in a manner which their capabilities be used for the best advantage".

The two horses were subsequently purchased by the DOA in the presence of Miss White.[7]

Potatoes

On the 9th November 1943, a direction given to Mr P. C. Le Bailly, St Brelade, under the Cultivation of Lands (Jersey) Order, 1942, required him to deliver to the DOA 10 cwt of potatoes. Having allegedly failed to deliver them he was given one further week's grace. When Mr Le Bailly again failed to deliver the potatoes, the matter was forwarded to the Attorney General.

On the 1st December 1943, Brée reported to the DOA that the Superior Council had decided to issue "...a double ration of potatoes and butter to the civilian population at Christmas".

The following week, the DOA met to discuss the purchase of seed potatoes from France, as ordered by Field Command 515. The price was £2,003-4-1 in respect of 250 tons, equivalent to 375,000 francs. The money was deposited at the Comptoir national d'escompte de Paris (CNEP), Rue de Rivoli, 55, Paris.

On the 12th December, Brée referred in a meeting to the case of Mr T. Anthoine, St Saviour, who had in the past two years allegedly failed to deliver the quantity of potatoes prescribed in his directions.[8] As a consequence, the DOA reduced to 1 vergée the 1944 allocation that his mother, Mrs Anthoine, would be allowed to grow, plus 1 vergée of seed potatoes in 1945. She was also directed to increase the area grown in cereals. Finally, Brée wrote warning that, unless there was a considerable improvement in her cultivation in 1944, the DOA would find itself with no alternative but to have recourse to drastic measures. Mrs Anthoine was ordered at the same time to deliver 280 boxes of seed potatoes to the DOA stores.[2]

On the 11th January 1944, the Department of Public Instruction claimed payment for a quantity of potatoes "delivered from JCG" to the stores of W. Dennis and Sons Limited.[9] These potatoes had been grown on the lawn and grounds of the Jersey College for Girls. The potatoes had been weighed over the public weighbridge; however, the DOA decided that, as no weighbridge ticket could be found, no payment would be made to the Department of Public Instruction.

On the 1st February Brée reported that Mr J. F. Richardson, St Mary, had allegedly not delivered any potatoes grown from French seed imported in 1943. Mr Richardson informed Brée that "...not a single potato had resulted" from cultivation of the seed. Brée found it difficult to accept this statement and the Honorary Parish Inspectors were instructed to visit the farm and submit a report. On the 8th February the DOA took cognisance of the subsequent report concerning the alleged total failure of Mr Richardson's crop. He was instructed to appear before the DOA the following week but on the relevant day he informed them that he was unable to attend. He was ordered to submit an explanation and the meeting was postponed for a further week. After finally appearing before the DOA on the 22nd February, and giving his explanation, he was ordered to deliver 7 cwt of the Royal variety instead, not later than the 4th March.

On the 16th February the DOA was informed that a load of potatoes discovered in a store were unfit for human consumption. The reasons why a large quantity of potatoes had been left to deteriorate was not documented. The DOA decided to sell these potatoes for feeding to animals, at a price of 10/- per cwt, and a notice was inserted in the local press.

On the 14th April a large consignment of seed potatoes arrived from France. They were issued to farmers at a rate of 15 cwt per vergée and a price of £1-1-4 per cwt. These potatoes could be grown as either a first or second crop. In addition, smallholders were allowed to purchase up to 1 cwt on condition that the Honorary Parish Inspectors approved the cultivation. The DOA decided that farmers who could not pay for the French seed could do so by signing a bond. The DOA would deduct the value of potatoes supplied from the value of the crop subsequently sold by the farmer to the DOA. The Superior Council approved the scheme. The JPMA agreed to store the imported seed, with a handling fee for its members of 10/- per ton. The potatoes were then issued to farmers against DOA permits and the DOA collected payment.

In late February, Field Command 515 wrote to the Bailiff again, requesting details of the quantity of anti-Colorado Beetle chemicals available on the Island. On the 25th February Brée informed Field Command that "The quantity of arsenate of lime in the island for use as spray against the Colorado Beetle is 8½ tons. The quantity required to carry out three sprayings of the total crop is 7 tons. The stock of this material is therefore quite adequate for our requirements."[10]

In late April a series of meetings were held to discuss the price for potatoes, to be paid by the DOA to farmers. A "special meeting" held on the 5th May agreed to fix the price for potatoes grown under glass at 57/- per cwt. It was also decided that glasshouse potatoes would be put on the market on the 15th May.

On a recommendation of the Superior Council, it was decided that in order to compensate for the additional cost of cultivating côtil land, which owing to the steepness of the slopes had to be dug by hand, the DOA was empowered to pay 3/- per perch on all such land measuring 20 perches and over which was to be cultivated in 1944. The Honorary Parish Inspectors had to supply a certificate as to the correctness of the area for payment to be made to the farmer of the côtil.

Tobacco

In 1941 Germain and Sons Limited, one of the two tobacco factories on the Island cut approximately 170 lbs of locally grown and cured tobacco leaf. In 1942, this had increased to 13,244 lbs and by 1944 to 34,430 lbs – equivalent to 15,650 kilograms.[11] In real terms the actual figure for growing and curing leaf tobacco would have been far more than these figures because there was a second tobacco factory in St Helier.

By 1943, almost every farmer and smallholder grew tobacco, as well as German military personnel. One Luftwaffe officer, who had grown tobacco in Germany, brought excellent locally grown tobacco leaves into Germain's; the factory often mixed this with inferior quality tobacco before processing.

Locally grown and cured tobacco was cut into three varieties in the factory. The first was "fine cut" and cured for the manufacture of cigarettes. Secondly, a "Number 4" cut used for pipe smoking, and finally, a "Number 4 coarse". One pound of locally grown and cured tobacco made 320 cigarettes, or approximately sixteen packets. Germain and Sons charged 2/- per lb for the finished product. After 1943 a packet of twenty cigarettes could be sold for as much as 8/- to 13/- on the black market Therefore, there were tremendous profits to be made by any family that grew, cured, and produced tobacco.

On the 18th January 1944, Field Command wrote to the DOA in connection with the cultivation and sale of locally grown tobacco. The DOA then met with the Department of Essential Commodities and with Finance and Economics to discuss the letter, and on the 25th January new forms were printed for people to apply for a licence to cultivate tobacco in 1944. The forms were forwarded by the Department of Finance and Economics to the DOA.

Agricultural Labour

On the 9th November 1943, some twenty important farmers met to discuss shared problems caused by the German occupation. Philip Le Feuvre brought up the long-running and most contentious issue – that of agricultural labourers' wages and the perceived disparity between the hours worked by them and those in other work, especially on the States labour schemes. Edward Le Quesne's constant contradiction of the farmers' belief that the labour schemes were causing their workers to leave the countryside, had become anathema to them.

Le Feuvre began the meeting by giving an account of the problems faced by farmers due to increased labour costs, which he explained was having a serious and detrimental effect. The workers on the labour schemes were paid more than agricultural workers, they had a far shorter working week and benefitted from extra time off at the weekends. The issue was discussed again on the 18th March 1944, by the same group of farmers. It was proposed that a recommendation be made to the DOA to grant a bonus to agricultural workers in view of the longer hours of work and the extra costs of clothing and footwear. In the following discussion it was also revealed that men working for the Department of Labour drew sick pay, an allowance granted by the Superior Council.

At this point, Mr P. H. Renouf proposed that all agricultural workers receive a subsidy, either financial or in kind, paid for by the States of Jersey. Following its cancellation in October, the proposed renewal was to compensate for the extra hours worked and would make fairer the perceived imbalance between men working on labour schemes and those in agriculture. Mr Renouf explained that he wanted the financial benefits for labour scheme workers extended to agricultural workers. The resolution was accepted.

The meeting then discussed the earlier revelation that sick pay was a benefit to men on the Labour Schemes and "...expressed its astonishment at such a procedure being adopted to the detriment of agricultural and other classes of labour". It was proposed that a delegation should meet the Superior Council to address the issue of sick pay being paid to labour scheme workers. Messrs J. B. Michel, C. P. Journeaux and P. H. Renouf were named and mandated to ask the Superior Council for sick pay benefit to be extended to all classes of labour, or otherwise discontinued.[5]

Jersey Produce Merchants Association

On the 19th November 1943, the DOA leased the store at 16 The Esplanade, St Helier, belonging to Mr P. Hocquard, St John, for the storage of locally grown grain. The rental was 10/- a week.

On the 13th July 1943 the DOA had set up a subcommittee to discuss with the JPMA the fixing of an agreed percentage of "…permissible loss on the cereals of the 1942 harvest held in store on behalf of the DOA". The subcommittee comprised Brée, Gibaut and Le Gallais and they met with the JPMA on the 16th February 1944. A report was presented showing those merchants where losses exceeded 3½%. The JPMA accepted the report and the arrangements for settling the DOA's claims against those merchants who had exhibited an unacceptable loss in their storage of grain.

On the 25th April 1944, the DOA met to discuss the unsatisfactory storage of grain by the Jersey Farmer's (Trading) Union Limited and the cost of remedial labour to fix the situation. The DOA had authorised work to be carried out and, as a result, the DOA sent an invoice to the firm for £30-10-8 for turning and treating the grain held in store on its behalf. The JFTU wrote back offering a sum of £17-7-0 in full settlement of the claim, which the DOA refused to accept.

Cattle

"Please convey to officers and fellow members my grateful appreciation of their kind message of congratulations. My best wishes to all for 1944".

Red Cross message, 20th December 1943 from
Sir Daniel Alfred Edmond Cabot,
Chief Veterinary Officer, Ministry of Agriculture, UK
Sir Daniel (1888–1974) was knighted in 1943 and was a native
Jerseyman

"Your message received with pleasure. Glad to say all well and carrying on hopefully. Continued good wishes and kind regards from officers and members. Shepard".

Reply, 17th March 1944

On the 4th December 1943, the RJA&HS Calf Selection Committee met. It dealt with an exemption application from Mr Winter Poignard, St Brelade. The application had been successful and was accompanied by a permit issued by Field Command 515, allowing him an exemption from slaughter for another heifer in his custody.[12] Three days later the DOA received a letter from the Calf Selection Committee in relation to a statement made by Mr Poignard, to the effect that he had been instructed by Field Command 515 that he could retain a second heifer calf born on the 12th November 1943, but which had not been exempted. The DOA decided, since one heifer calf had been exempted from slaughter, it would not take any action until such time as Mr Poignard declined to deliver for slaughter the second animal.

In order to clarify the exact position in relation to Field Command issuing Calf Exemption Certificates, the DOA wrote to the RJA&HS stating: "It is noted that the document submitted by Mr Poignard is merely an authority from the Field Command 515 to purchase one heifer calf and makes no mention of any interference with the requirements of the existing legislation. In the event of Mr Poignard making an application for exemption of a calf which is not granted and then declines or neglects to deliver such animal for slaughter when required to do so, the DOA will, forthwith, upon notification make the strongest possible representations to the German authorities".[13]

The matter of Mr Poignard's heifer calf seemed to have been dealt with, however this was not the case. On the 21st December the Calf Selection Committee notified Mrs G. A. Lesbirel, St Mary, that a calf of "Pulsandene" had not been exempted from slaughter. Field Command 515, however, had issued a permit to Mr Poignard to purchase this calf. The Calf Selection Committee was informed that "Pulsandene" had been sold when she was in calf to Mr Poignard, who made it clear that he wished to retain the calf. In view of the German permit which exempted this calf, the Calf Selection Committee forwarded the matter to the DOA.[14]

On the 10th January 1944 the Committee wrote to Mrs Lesbirel (wrongly spelt as "Leshirel") ordering that the calf be delivered to the slaughterhouse by the 12th January. At this point the DOA decided to take no action unless Mrs Lesbirel failed to comply with the order.

By the 25th January, Mrs Lesbirel had still not sent the heifer for slaughter although it was not exempt - therefore she had failed to comply with the Livestock (Jersey) Order, 1942. In addition, since the custody of the calf had been transferred to Mr Poignard, and had not been authorised, the matter was referred to the Attorney General for possible proceedings. On the 1st February notification was received from the public slaughterhouse that the heifer calf belonging to Mrs Lesbirel had been delivered by Mr Poignard. The DOA therefore withdrew its legal proceedings against both individuals.

On the 10th December 1943, the Foreman Milk Tester, Mr C. R. Mauger, sent a report to the DOA in relation to a discrepancy between the number of cattle found in the herd of Mr E. C. Perrédès, St Saviour, and the DOA's records. On the 4th January, after hearing Mr Perrédès explanations, Brée decided to defer the matter until the 18th January to enable Mr Perrédès to prepare a list of animals in his custody, with particulars of the tattoo markings of each animal, and indicating which ones were missing from the herd. Mr Perrédès' herd of up to ninety cattle was the largest in the Island.[15]

A further report was written on the 15th January and Mr Perrédès appeared before the DOA three days later. The ensuing discussion between Weeks and Perrédès laid a portion of the blame for the alleged discrepancy upon a member of the Milk Control Staff. Brée, however, warned Perrédès as to his future observance of the requirements of the Livestock (Jersey) Order, 1942. The individual member of the Milk Control Section who had failed to correctly administer the records was handed a rebuke.

The following week, all corrections concerning the records for Mr Perrédès' herd were complete. One record in particular was modified, relating to the death of a calf which Mr Perrédès had allegedly failed to report to the Milk Testers. The correction was authorised in view of Perrédès statement that the carcass had been delivered to the public slaughterhouse for inspection by the States Vet. The result was that one Milk Tester was given a week's notice and was subsequently convicted by the Royal Court under the Livestock (Jersey) Order 1942.

On the 14th December, the DOA inserted a notice in the local press asking for applications for appointment as "tattooing officers and assistants". The salary was £3-10-0 and £3 respectively. On the same day, the DOA decided that all calves born between 1st January and 31st December 1944 should be tattooed with the letter "A" and, in each year thereafter, the calves born during that year would be similarly tattooed with a number pre-fixed with the succeeding letter of the alphabet but excluding the letter "L" and "O".

On the 20th December, the Calf Selection Committee wrote to the DOA recommending that the tattoo officers, when tattooing calves, should be instructed to verify the particulars of the dam. Brée decided to consult with the Law Officers before making a decision. The Law Officers reported back, recommending that this measure should not be put into effect.

On the 31st December tattooing offices and assistants were appointed and on the 4th January 1944, the DOA ordered each Parish to arrange a list of cattle so that the tattooing officers "...could proceed with the markings of the cattle in such a manner as to avoid loss of time in proceeding from farm to farm". The individuals in each parish ordered to facilitate the lists were as follows.

St Brelade	H. E. Le Rossignol
St Clement	D. Pallot
Grouville	A. W. Falle
St Helier	T. Le Q. Blampied

St John	J. Gartrell
St Lawrence	J. A. Pallot
St Martin	C. P. Journeaux
St Mary	C. Bisson
St Ouen	Connétable
St Peter	Connétable
St Saviour	C. R. Mauger, Foreman Milk Tester
Trinity	E. D. Gibaut

On the 15th January the DOA allocated assistants to each tattooing officer. These teams were directed to a "Western Marking Area", after which they presumably would cover the "Eastern Marking Area".

Tattooing Officer	Tattooing Assistant	District
R. Ching	P. L. Moses	St Mary
O. P. Hamon	P. G. Dubois	St Brelade
G. H. Le Rossignol	H. Vautier	St Peter
W. G. Le Ruez	J. Marett	St John
W. A. Pallot	A. L. Gautier	St Lawrence
J. C. Steel	W. J. Le Boutillier	St Ouen

Each tattooing officer was given their equipment and allocated "Identification Letters" to prevent any duplication of the numbers marked on the animals. The working hours were Monday to Friday, 9.00 a.m. to 5.30 p.m., and Saturday, 9.00 a.m. to 5.00 p.m. On the 1st February Mr A. J. Carter was assigned as a temporary clerk, with a salary of £2-10-0 a week. His job description was "The preparation of all records in connection with the tattooing of animals on the island". Le Gallais' herd at Roselands Farm was the first to be tattooed.

Whilst tattooing was taking place, Brée authorised a new direction prohibiting the movement of cattle. This measure was taken to prevent any clandestine attempts to hide animals from the tattooing officers.

As from the 23rd January 1944, the DOA amended the Livestock (Jersey) Order, 1942.

1. In these Directions, the boundary line means an imaginary line beginning at Bonne Nuit Harbour and extending thence along the middle of the main road via Le Brecquet ès Chats to the foot of Queen's Road and then along the middle of Rouge Bouillon, Elizabeth Place and Kensington Place and across the Esplanade to a point on the seashore opposite the middle of Kensington Place; cattle means any bull, cow, or heifer.

2. With a view to effecting the marking of cattle, the island shall be divided into two areas (each such area being hereinafter referred to as a marking area) namely:

   a. The part of the island lying on the Eastern side of the boundary line (hereinafter referred to the Eastern Marking Area).

   b. The part of the island on the Western side of the boundary line (hereinafter referred to as the Western Marking Area).

3. Where any farm or holding is situated partly in one marking area and partly in the other, that farm shall, for the purposes of these Directions, be deemed to be situated in the marking area within which the cattle kept on the farm are usually stabled.

4. (i) Except under the authority of a written permit granted by the DOA; no person shall, during the continuance in force of these directions, move any cattle from one marking area to the other. No person shall, in the period applicable hereunder or under any subsequent directions of the DOA to a marking area move any cattle into or out of any farm in that area.

   (ii) The period applicable for the purposes of the previous sub-paragraph shall begin at midnight on the 23rd January 1944.

5. The restriction on movement imposed by Article 4 of these directions shall not apply to the movement of an animal by the nearest available route from one part of a farm to another part thereof. Where a permit under these directions authorising the movement of an animal has been granted:

   a. The animal shall be moved by the nearest available route and without unnecessary delay to the place of destination specified in the permit and not elsewhere.

   b. The permit shall accompany the animal whilst it is being moved and shall, forthwith of the completion of the movement, be delivered up at or sent by post to the office of the DOA by the person to whom the permit was granted.

   c. Any person in charge of the animal during the movement shall, on demand by officer or police or by an official of the DOA produce the permit and allow a copy of an extract from it to be taken and shall, if required, give his name and address.

On the 7th March 1944, the DOA met to discuss the matter of Mr P. F. Genée and his son Mr C. R. Genée, St John. Both appeared before the DOA in relation to an allegation that the former had failed to report the death of a heifer on the 2nd February 1944 and had also failed to dispose of the carcass in line with the rules of the Department of Essential Commodities. In addition, he had "...distributed portions of the carcass to certain individuals". After listening to the two men the DOA referred the matter to the legal authorities. The Milk Tester who had dealt with the case was dismissed, the reason given being that his work was "unsatisfactory and inefficient". A new Milk Tester took up the matter and produced a report on the 3rd April, alleging that Mr Genée had transferred his herd of cattle into the custody of his son, of the same address, without having first obtained a licence, as prescribed by the Livestock (Jersey) Order, 1942. The Milk Control Section was instructed to put the case in order.

On the 6th March a report was forwarded concerning Mr E. Le Maistre, Egypt, Trinity, stating that grazing land and stables where certain of his cattle were kept were in fact requisitioned and occupied by the German military. After considering the statement, Brée decided to approach Field Command 515 requesting a permit for DOA Inspectors to carry out an investigation of the premises. Field Command 515 had an office which dealt with the requirements of the military and all interactions between the Island's administrative departments and civilians had to be sanctioned by this office. It was run by Major Demmler with his own team of ten administrators at College House, including two of the rank of Captain and two Lieutenants. As far back as 18th November 1940, Colonel Schumacher had made clear to the Bailiff that "All requisitioning and foodstuffs by individual units of the troops at individual shops or stores are immediately suspended. Requisitioning and reserving will, in future, take place only through Field Command 515."

The quota system for parishes to supply cattle for slaughter was stopped on the 8th January 1944, the scheme having been administered by the RJA&HS. The main reason for it to be abandoned was simply that several parishes had built up "waiting lists" of cattle that were suitable for slaughter. These cows were either producing little or no milk, were of an obvious inferior pedigree, or had simply reached old age. The Cattle Slaughter Executive Committee decided it would expedite its slaughter demands in the parishes that had "waiting lists". In 1944, the Committee called in first the very poorest examples of the Jersey breed and worked through a list of the next division of cattle of low standard. As a result, by the end of 1944, the pedigree stock was of an exceptionally high quality. Furthermore, in January 1944, the Cattle Slaughter Executive Committee was informed that the abattoir was in a position to take between twenty and forty cattle a week and it set up a detailed list of the owners of cattle which it deemed were suitable for slaughter.

Robert Carson stated that the Island had excellent and ample cold storage capacity which should be fully utilised. This, he made clear, would prevent cattle from losing weight whilst waiting their turn for slaughter. Pelz, in a private letter, commented on the ample freezer space at the abattoir, "My very good friend Mr Gaudin often, at the beginning of my island career, proudly showed me the rock-hard lumps of meat in the cold storage depot at the harbour".[16]

At the end of April 1944, the DOA decided that between June and September the number of exempted calves would increase to 100 per month, of which not more than three would be bull calves.

Field Command 515

*"The German Command for Northwest France in November 1943
sent a new Cultivation Plan for the Channel Islands. On the 29th
November 1943 this was relayed to the DOA. After taking note of the
German command orders from Paris, the DOA communicated
to the Field Command, the areas allocated to all island crops by the
Honorary Parish Inspectors".*

DOA Memorandum

On the 10th November 1943 Knackfuss wrote to the Bailiff a letter entitled "Soil Tests". It stated: "Few reliable tests have been made and there is little information with regard to the phosphorous, potash and lime content of the earth of the island. Therefore, for next month, soil tests are to be made on a large scale". An extremely detailed procedure was tabulated in this letter on how the tests were to be carried out.[17] The DOA charged Mr Simpson to undertake the tests, which were completed by the 31st March 1944. Twenty-nine Island-wide samples were collected and a full analysis carried out, the results being handed to Pelz to be checked by his team.

On the 15th November 1943, Field Command 515 made clear to the DOA that it required "...the holding of agricultural meetings so that farmers may be advised by experts of the DOA as to the proper cultivation of their land". The Connétables and Mr Simpson were informed and charged with making the necessary arrangements. By the 29th February 1944, a number of resolutions emanating from these meetings had been forwarded to the JFU and RJA&HS for discussion and consideration. Shepard, representing the two societies, wrote to the DOA submitting their recommendations.

One such recommendation was for the DOA to fix prices for all agricultural produce, and not the other State's Departments that were involved. The DOA responded that price fixing of all agricultural outputs by the DOA would involve an alteration in existing legislation and would necessitate the appointment of another Advisory Committee on pricing, in place of that nominated by the Superior Council. In addition, an "Advisory Committee" had already been set up to implement prices for the purposes of the Vegetables (Maximum Prices) (Jersey) Order, 1941.

Another recommendation made by the two societies was for the re-instatement of the bonus to agricultural workers. The DOA made it clear this was impossible, as Field Command 515 had ordered the previous agricultural bonus to be terminated. This was because Field Command wanted to keep local labour available for German construction firms working on the Island.

The final recommendation was an increase of 2 pence per lb in the price to be paid to farmers for cattle which were to be slaughtered. This recommendation was forwarded to the Department of Essential Commodities.

In November 1943, the German Command for Northwest France sent a new "Cultivation Plan" for the Channel Islands which was relayed to the DOA on the 29th November. After taking note of the letter, the DOA communicated to the Field Command the areas allocated by the Honorary Parish Inspectors for crops for 1944.

On the 14th January Field Command wrote to the DOA concerning "The alleged unsatisfactory cultivation of the fields in the island". In response, the DOA sent a letter to the Honorary Parish Inspectors and a memorandum was printed and posted on the noticeboards at all parish churches and halls. This dissemination of agricultural notes published by the DOA for viewing by farmers was questioned by the Field Command. On the 19th January, Heider asked the Bailiff how many copies had been made and where they had been sent. Brée replied on the 24th January that "Thirty copies of the agricultural notes were prepared and two copies are sent to each of the Connétables of the island for posting in the church boxes and at the parish hall. A copy is published in the press, and in addition, a copy published at this office, at the office of the RJA&HS and at the office of the JFU".[18]

On the 29th April, after an audit of milk and butter supplies by MVR Pelz, Brée wrote to the Bailiff to discuss the results of the audit. This correspondence is interesting for two reasons as it demonstrates that Pelz had personally discussed milk supplies with Reginald Weeks. Firstly, it is the only reference throughout the entire German occupation of Pelz discussing agricultural matters with Weeks, who oversaw the administration of the Milk Control Section. Secondly, it appears to demonstrate that Pelz could deal directly with a relatively minor individual in the chain of command of the DOA. Thirdly, it is noteworthy that Brée is still describing MVR Pelz as "Dr Pelz".[19]

Also in April 1944, Heider wrote to the Bailiff informing him that the pasture belonging to the house at Bel Air, Five Oaks, St Saviour, which was next to the site of the German Veterinary Hospital, was to be requisitioned for the horse hospital. The owner was to be notified.

In late December 1943, Pelz's pet dog, a black spaniel called "Herm", went missing. There is no record from where Pelz obtained the dog. Herm, however, appears to have been mistreated by its previous owner, and Pelz found him early in the occupation of the Island. Pelz's personal photographs demonstrate that he was extremely fond of Herm. The dog often accompanied him on his daily visits and inspections of farms; he would often jump in the back of Field Command 515 vehicles with Pelz, much to the annoyance of Knackfuss. Pelz was clearly an animal enthusiast. In the early 1930s, he was a prominent member of the Salzburg Committee Against Cruelty to Animals.[20]

On the 7th December 1943 Pelz inserted a notice in the local press. It read "Lost: Black spaniel answering to the name of "Herm". White chest, leather collar, incisor in upper lower jaw broken. Reward if returned to MVR Pelz, Field Commandantur".[21] Sadly, Pelz never found Herm, and no person came forward to obtain the reward.

References

1. Jersey Archive. B/A/W40/14/1.
2. Jersey Archive. C/B/A1/9.
3. Jersey Archive. D/Z/H5/141/2.
4. Jersey Archive. B/A/40/14/1.
5. RJA&HS and JFU Joint Emergency Committee Minutes.
6. Von Aufsess, H. M. 2020. Tagebuch aus der Okkupation zeit der Britischen Kandalinseln, 1943–1945, p. 88. This is the second diary of von Aufsess.
7. Jersey Archive. B/A/W31/2/57.
8. This almost certainly refers to Mrs Marjorie Clara Anthoine. Her husband, Leslie Thomas Anthoine, was a POW in Germany up to 1945.
9. Jersey College for Girls.
10. Jersey Archive. B/A/W31/2/24.
11. My thanks to Mr Robert Germain, J. F. Germain and Sons Limited. Mr Germain compiled these figures of locally grown and cured leaf tobacco from the original detailed ledgers kept during the occupation.
12. Jersey Archive. L/D/09/A10.
13. Jersey Archive. L/D/09/A10. Document p. 446.
14. Jersey Archive. L/D/09/A11.
15. Letter from German military to Field Command 515 concerning the use of Perrédès grazing land for use as a firing range four days a week. Private correspondence.
16. Hans Egon Pelz. Private letter to Dr Josef Kratzer, President of the Bavarian Administrative Court, Munich 22. Ludwigstr.14. Dated 12th February 1957. Salzburg. My thanks to the Pelz family for permission to use Hans Pelz's private correspondence.
17. Jersey Archive. B/A/W31/2/107.
18. Jersey Archive. B/A/W31/2/31.
19. Jersey Archive. B/A/W31/2/8-9.
20. Provincial Archive Salzburg, Rehri-Brief 1935/224.
21. JEP. 7th December 1943.

Chapter 16

May to November 1944

Tobacco

Island Grown Tobacco processed by J. F. Germain & Sons Limited

Year	Pounds Weight	Kilogrammes
1940	590	268
1941	170	72
1942	13,244	6,020
1943	34,430	15,650
1944	48,314	21,961
1945	12,846	5,839
Total	109,594	49,810

On the 2nd May 1944, the DOA approved applications for licences to grow tobacco, where the number of plants applied for did not exceed fifty. All fifty plants had to be grown at the applicant's home address. In cases where the application was for more than fifty plants, or where it was proposed to grow the tobacco at an address other than at which the applicant was domiciled, the matter was referred to the DOA and the Honorary Parish Inspectors. A note was published in the local press prescribing the last date for receiving applications for a tobacco licence, which would be the 20th May 1944. On the 16th May the DOA amended its act of the 2nd May and increased the number of plants from fifty to 100. Any applicant who wished to exceed 100 plants on one holding had to be referred to a DOA meeting.

On the 23rd May it was decided to appoint Tobacco Inspectors, under the Cultivation of Lands (Jersey) Order 1942, to check the Island-wide cultivation of tobacco plants. The following were appointed.

Parish	Tobacco Inspectors
St Brelade	J. J. Le Boutillier and H. M. Gibaut
St Clement	E. J. Malzard
St Helier	P. J. Mourant and P. L. Baudains
St Lawrence	H. W. Maillard and T. A. Pallot
St Martin	P. Ahier and G. Le Masurier
St Peter	E. R. Egré and H. P. Le Ruez
St Saviour	P. Gallichan and C. Quenault
Trinity	C. P. Ahier and A. R. Le Brun

When applications for a licence were received the DOA took advice from the Honorary Parish Inspectors before making a final decision. Over the next month, the DOA met almost weekly to discuss applications; several were refused.

On the 18th June Mr W. F. Poingdestre, Grouville, wrote to the DOA appealing against their decision to reject his application to cultivate tobacco for himself, his wife and son. In view of the contents of the letter the DOA changed its former position and approved the application. Further letters were received appealing against the rejection of licences. On the 28th June, Mr S. P. Falle of Messrs S. P. Falle and Son, 21 Commercial Street, St Helier, requested a full explanation for the rejection of his brother's request to grow tobacco at Douet de Rue, St Lawrence. The DOA subsequently reversed its decision and allowed a licence. A licence for Mr J. H. B. Sutherland, St Peter's Rectory for 100 plants was discussed. In this case, the decision was handed over to the Honorary Parish Inspectors who, upon inspection, allowed the issue of a licence.

For the remainder of June and July 1944, the DOA met for special consideration of the following applicants, and licences were subsequently issued.

Name	No of Plants	Parish
Mr E. L. Baynton-Roberts	200 plants	St Mary
Mr P. M. Rio	200 plants	St Brelade
Mr H. G. Le Hegarat	500 plants	St Mary
Mr P. L. Le Mottée		
Mr C. V. Cook		St Helier
Mr Sutherland		
Mr Starck	300 plants	Trinity

Potatoes

On the 9th May 1944 Mr Y. Rabet, St Clement, appeared before the DOA. He was asked "...to explain his failure to cultivate potatoes on the area of land which had been under glass". Similarly, he was asked to specify why he had allegedly failed to plant potatoes in 1944 on the area of land, not under glass, specified in the same direction under the Cultivation of Lands (Jersey) Order, 1942. After hearing Mr Rabet, the DOA found itself unable to accept his explanations and referred both matters to the Attorney General.[1]

On the same day, a report was received concerning Mr E. Le G. Siouville, Grouville, who had been directed to grow 4 perches of potatoes under glass. He had delivered to the DOA only 1 cwt 14 lbs of potatoes. Brée, himself a glasshouse grower of many years' experience, decided to examine the glasshouses and land to ascertain whether Mr Siouville had in fact planted any potatoes. An inspection took place which confirmed that "...a very small yield of the potato crop had been grown under glass in 1944". The DOA decided that in future no potatoes for growing under glass would be allocated to Mr Siouville.

In the same week, a report from D. Simpson described an area of 1½ vergées of potatoes grown by Mr L. H. Le Vannais, St Helier, which had been badly affected by eelworm. It was decided to sell the potatoes (approximately ten barrels) to the Food Distribution Department at the Sun Works, First Tower. The Department was advised that "The peeling or scraps thereof should be burned" and the potatoes then distributed among the local population.

Also on 9th May, the DOA released 100 tons of seed potatoes imported from France in 1944, at the price 15/- per cwt. These were planted as a second crop.

On the 15th May, Field Command 515 communicated to the DOA that the price of potatoes grown in 1944 must be fixed. In response the DOA recommended to the Superior Council that having regard to "...the reduced crop to be expected as a result of the climatic conditions recently prevailing in the island together with the serious shortage of artificial fertilisers", the maximum price to be paid to growers should be set at 14/- per cwt.

The DOA also informed the Superior Council that "The potato crop will be insufficient to provide any quantity for export as required by the German authorities". A final recommendation was, that in order to reduce the amount of subsidy payable in respect of potatoes, the retail price should be 2 pence per lb during the months of June to September 1944.

Brée, however, after detailed consultation with the Honorary Parish Inspectors as to the probable 1944 yield and in view of the anticipated small crop, decided to change the recommendation to the Superior Council and that the maximum price to be paid to growers should be 16/- per cwt (excluding glasshouse potatoes). On the 6th June the Home-Grown Potatoes (1944 Crop) (Maximum Prices) (Jersey) Order, 1944 was passed. Farmers were to be paid 16/- per cwt. The retail price was fixed at 2 pence per lb. Anyone selling potatoes had to keep accurate records of all transactions. Fictitious or artificial transactions, or unreasonable charges, were an infringement of the order and liable to prosecution.

On the 18th May, the Department of Education wrote to head teachers in relation to the exemption of boys from school attendance in order to assist with the digging of potatoes. Brée was very much in favour of the exemption and even extended the condition to cover a larger group of schoolboys for the specified period when potatoes were being dug. He also requested that the boys gave general assistance on farms.

On the 31st May the DOA authorised the opening of the market for outdoor potatoes grown in 1944. The Grain and Potato Section supplied the exact requirements of the civilian population and the occupying forces. These potatoes were collected from the twelve parishes based on the number of vergées which each parish had been required to grow.

The DOA, therefore, ordered the Connétables to appoint "Parish Allocation Officers" whose job was to collect their parish allocation of the 1944 crop.

Parish Allocation Officers

Parish	Name
St Brelade	J. J. Le Boutillier; H. M. Gibaut
St Clement	J. P. Le Masurier
Grouville	C. Le Huquet
St Helier	P. J. Mourant; A. Tarr
St John	P. J. Romeril Junior
St Lawrence	J. W. Baudains – Connétable; P. Ahier
St Mary	C. Bisson
St Ouen	F. Le Boutillier – Connétable
St Peter	J. du Val - Connétable, DOA member
St Saviour	G. J. Mourant – Chef du Police
Trinity	J. E. Cabot

A report of the 17th May alleged that Mr C. Boisard, St Saviour had failed to deliver to the DOA the potatoes grown by him under glass in 1944 under its cultivation directions. Mr Boisard stated in his reply that he had consumed these potatoes. The matter was referred to the Attorney General. On the same day, another report stated that Mr A. Poignard, St Brelade, having purchased 10 cwt of potatoes for feeding his livestock, had refused to pay for them. The reason he gave was that "The potatoes had to be thrown away and were of no use". A letter was sent to him demanding payment.

On the 30th May, the DOA met with all the Honorary Parish Inspectors. The issue discussed was the price at which the 1944 potato crop would be sold to wholesale distributors and therefore the price at which the wholesalers sold to retailers. The agreed prices were:

DOA to wholesalers – 14/10 per cwt.
Wholesalers to retailers – 15/2 per cwt.

The Honorary Parish Inspectors at this time were the following:

St Brelade	J. J. Le Boutillier, H. M. Gibaut
St Clement	J. P. Le Masurier
Grouville	S. G. Le Couilliard
St Helier	P. J. Mourant, P. L. Baudains
St John	J. Gartrell, C. Le Couteur
St Lawrence	H. W. Maillard, T. A. Pallot
St Martin	P. Ahier, G. Le Masurier
St Mary	E. J. Le Ruez
St Ouen	G. E. Huelin, E. G. Vautier
St Peter	E. R. Egré, H. P. Le Ruez
St Saviour	P. Gallichan, C. Quenault
Trinity	C. P. Ahier, A. R. Le Brun

On the 13th June, Brée reported that he had agreed with the JPMA to pay them for shipping potatoes in bulk on behalf of the German administration, at the rate of 15/- a ton. On the same day the DOA issued to all farmers, by virtue of Article 2, The Cultivation of Lands (Jersey) Order, 1942, directions to deliver to the DOA stores, by the 31st October 1944, not less than 2 tons of potatoes in respect of each vergée on which every farmer had been required to grow potatoes. In the same communication, farmers were also ordered to retain 1 ton per vergée of seed for planting in 1945. The area to be planted in 1945 was planned to be two-thirds of the area of 1944.

The DOA also decided that farmers who failed to deliver the correct quantity of potatoes would be required to provide, out of those remaining in their possession, such seed as the DOA may require for issue to farmers who had fulfilled the requirements of their directions. The requisitioned seed would be issued to farmers who had run out of seed potatoes and would be paid for by the DOA.

For the first time during the German occupation, there appears to be opposition from the Honorary Parish Inspectors to these directions. This was a concern to Brée as all agricultural policies and laws were totally dependent on the Honorary Parish Inspectors implementing and monitoring such measures. Therefore, on the 24th June, a full meeting of the Honorary Parish Inspectors was convened, "In order that the decision of the DOA in relation to the retaining of seed potatoes by growers for replanting in 1945 may be explained". Brée explained the decision that farmers would be allowed to retain seed from their 1944 crop, at the rate of 1 ton per vergée, for planting in 1945 on two-thirds of the area which each farmer had been directed to plant in 1944.

On the 15th July 1944, Dr Chichester wrote to the DOA. Although his farm had been requisitioned, he had retained some land. He stated that he was not in a position to deliver to the DOA the quantity of potatoes specified in his Cultivation Directions. Brée decided that, in view of the alleged unsatisfactory results of his cultivation, the matter would be referred to the Attorney General. The referral also included a further letter from Dr Chichester of "an abusive nature". Brée felt so strongly on the issue that he personally suggested to the Attorney General "It would be advisable to ask the Royal Court to visit the farm in the occupation of Dr Chichester".

On the 18th July a potato field belonging to Mr J. C. Vigot, Montpellier, Gorey Village, Grouville, was requisitioned by the German army. They also requisitioned the crop, after Mr Vigot had dug only 28 perches, and the land used as a minefield. As Mr Vigot had no potatoes left for the use of his family, the DOA allowed him to retain the twenty barrels that he had already dug.

On the 4th July the DOA ordered that all potato fields be sprayed between the 15th and 22nd July to combat the anticipated arrival of the Colorado Beetle. An invasion of the beetle began on the 25th July. Brée reported that a large colony had been discovered in a field grown by the German army at "Verclut", Grouville. A letter was immediately sent to the Connétables with instructions on combatting Colorado Beetle and a notice was published in the local press with the same information.

The Grain and Potato Control Section reported on the 21st July that "The sum being paid by the German authorities for the storage and transport to ship potatoes destined for Guernsey is only half of what they agreed upon with the German authorities who now decline to modify the price now being paid". In view of this alteration in price for exporting Jersey potatoes on behalf of the German authorities, it was estimated that a loss of 10/- per ton was involved, which had to be taken out of the public funds on all potatoes exported. The DOA decided to submit the matter to the Superior Council. On the 1st August Brée reported the problem and he made clear that the Island was subsidising the export of potatoes for the German authorities. The Superior Council decided to take no action on the matter. It made the decision to pay the 10/- a ton shortfall from monies drawn from the States Treasury.

The question of German potato exports is interesting. Exports on behalf of the Germans had begun almost immediately after military forces arrived in July 1940 and were still taking place in late July 1944. The official historical interpretation of the matter was summed up in 1993. "The export of the potato crop was halted immediately at the start of the occupation when the Esplanade was bombed and all shipping was stopped...with no shipping and England, the main market in turmoil, no potatoes were exported for the duration of the five years".[2] This was clearly not the case.

On the 1st August, Brée reported that he had obtained the sanction of the German authorities to spray against Colorado Beetle all potatoes growing in land under the control of the army of occupation. Brée considered that spraying fields which were cultivated by the Germans was so important that he obtained approval to personally engage the services of Mr F. W. Dobin,

Royal Jersey Golf Club, Grouville, at a weekly wage of £2-15-0, to assist Mr Frank Le Maistre of the States of Jersey Experimental Station to carry out the work. The German authorities provided both men with all the necessary permits "...to penetrate into such land in order to carry out the spraying of the potatoes therein".

Mr Dobin was employed by the DOA as a Colorado Beetle Inspector, and to spray potatoes grown on German military fields, for a further five months. Brée terminated his services on the 9th January 1945, making it clear to Mr Dobin that "...the need for this service was no longer existing".

On the 8th August the DOA interviewed Mr Philip Pirouet, St Peter, for failing to comply fully with his 1944 potato directions. He allegedly planted only 4½ vergées instead of a larger area amounting to 6½ vergées. After hearing Mr Pirouet's explanations the DOA refused to accept them and he was ordered to deliver to the DOA stores the full quantity of potatoes which he had been originally required to deliver, amounting to 8¾ tons.

A further order was made on the 8th August to again spray the potato crop against Colorado Beetle. The next spraying was set for the 19th to 26th August. On the 12th August Brée reported that a Colorado Beetle had been discovered in a household rubbish dump on Grouville Marsh. An intensive inspection was made in all fields and gardens in the neighbourhood. A further discovery was reported by Brée on the 22nd August. In fact, this was a much more serious outbreak, at Manor Farm, St Brelade, occupied by Mr J. Barette Senior. The farmland and immediate environs were immediately sprayed.

On the 22nd August, Mr C. W. Renouf, St Martin, informed the DOA that the German army had taken over all his outbuildings, including a store of 4 tons of potatoes. Brée immediately informed the Parish Allocation Officer to issue a permit for Mr Renouf to deliver the potatoes to the DOA stores.

On the 29th August further Colorado Beetles were discovered at Portelet, Noirmont, St Clement and Grouville. In view of these infestations, the DOA declared until further notice a 'Zone de Protection" covering the whole Island. This set in place a number of regulations: no crops were to be harvested, no agricultural work to be carried out and no public entrance or admission into infected areas. An area of 5 vergées at Noirmont was particularly badly infected. The field was fenced off and sprayed, along with all adjoining potato fields. A second outbreak occurred later on at Noirmont and the area was designated "An infected zone". This, however, did not stop unauthorised individuals entering the fields and removing potatoes.

Brée also "confided" to the Director of the States Experimental Station, the mission of arranging to carry out "...an examination of all crops of potatoes being grown by the army of occupation in order to ascertain whether the Colorado Beetle is present, such inspection being carried out prior to the spraying of such potatoes." The Director was empowered to engage the necessary labour for the work. Brée almost certainly meant, in the term "confided", that spraying anti-Colorado Beetle chemicals on German potato crops would not become public knowledge or be circulated to the Island's farmers.

On the 18th September the JPMA sold 295 tons 17 cwt of potatoes, and organised the shipment to Guernsey, "To the order of the German authorities now in occupation of the Island". The account was subsequently sent to the DOA. The DOA responded by informing the JPMA: "In view of the fact that the shipment of these potatoes was entirely undertaken by the German authorities, and the members of the JPMA only assisted to load the transport vehicles and loaned their barrels which were returned to them as each load was shipped, the DOA declines to accept the account".

In response, the JPMA sent a delegation to the DOA concerning this shipment and requesting payment of the account. After a considerable amount of discussion between the JPMA and the DOA, Brée advised that a compromise should be reached. An amended account for the order was produced which the JPMA reluctantly accepted.

On the 17th October Brée reported that potatoes in a field on La Rue du Genestel, Vingtaine du Rocquier, St Clement, and another in Vingtaine de Longueville, Grouville, had been removed by the German army. Both fields were infected with Colorado Beetle. The Director of the States' Experimental Station ordered that the plants be burned. The DOA advised that the fields be also sprayed with a solution of sulphuric acid, to reduce the danger of the beetle spreading to other fields or crops. Mr Simpson, however, advised Brée not to spray and instead any potatoes remaining in the ground should immediately be dug and delivered to the Jersey Canneries factory at Grève d'Azette. Brée made it clear to the Director that he was to ensure that those potatoes would not become a source of propagation of the beetle in the Island.

The year 1944 saw an alarming increase in the discovery of Colorado Beetle. This upsurge was due to "one reason" – the imported French potato seed shipped into Jersey by Field Command 515. As 1944 progressed, the DOA had to deal with a new problem. After October, Brée's requests to inspect and spray German fields were increasingly refused by the army. Pelz, who had always worked closely with Brée, was now on active duty in the Somme, France, repairing broken communications for the German army. The absence of Pelz was to have severe consequences for Jersey's agricultural output between October 1944 until May 1945.

On the 7th November the DOA, in compliance with the directions of the Platzkommandant and in pursuance of the Cultivation of Lands (Jersey) Order, 1942, made the following order: "Every farmer who has grown potatoes in 1944 and who has seed potatoes in his possession must furnish by 25th November 1944 a form specifying the number of boxes held by him".

On the 14th November a report alleged that Gerald Allen, Stonewall, St Helier, had failed to deliver 12 tons of potatoes, due on the 31st October, to the DOA stores. He was ordered to appear before the DOA.

He gave an explanation and Brée told him to deliver 3 tons of seed potatoes instead.

Brée, towards the end of November 1944, was in no mood to continually hear excuses from recalcitrant farmers as to why they were not fulfilling their cultivation directives. He made clear to all those who grew potatoes, whether early, main crop or late potatoes, that if they failed to deliver their specified quantities to the DOA stores, he would immediately remove or requisition the seed potatoes in their possession. This was certainly no idle threat.

Watermills and Milling

"As much wheat and rye as possible should be harvested at once. Four hundred tons of grain is required at the end of the month".

Touzel Brée, speaking to some thirty of the Island's cereal growers,
17th August 1944

On the 6th June 1944 Brée reported to the DOA that "...the German authorities now in occupation of the Island" required that Tesson Mill be converted to electric operation. He instructed the State's Engineer to proceed with the conversion and a 35-horsepower electric motor, which the OT had made available, was utilised for this purpose. At the same time, a German thermal generating station was established next to Tesson.

Early in August, Brée wrote to Major Heider, the Platzkommandant, to request the release from prison of one of the DOA's millers, Mr Philip H. Poingdestre and in the same week, the Bailiff wrote to Major Heider making it clear that "...the position has now risen in relation to the provision of flour for the island's requirement, which makes it necessary for me to ask that the serving of the sentence imposed upon this man may be deferred for a further period in order that he may be available to carry out his duties as a miller".[3]

The request was granted, and Mr Poingdestre was released by the German authorities on the 10th August. The rest of his sentence was deferred until the 11th October 1944. Heider, however, made it clear that a further deferment of the sentence could not be counted upon. In addition, Heider ordered that Mr Poingdestre "...instructed a substitute in the duties of his" (i.e. milling).

On the 2nd September the Jersey Electricity Company wrote to the DOA with regard to the German order which had caused them to cut electricity supplies to the population. The DOA discussed the effects on agricultural output. The curtailment of hours for which the supply was available had far reaching consequences on agriculture. Brée, therefore, made strong representations to the Platzkommandant pointing out the serious effects this action would have on the distribution of fresh milk, threshing the cereal harvest and the milling of grain.

In view of the curtailment of hours when electricity was available, and the consequent necessity of operating its mills during the night, the DOA decided to pay the men working nightly a bonus of 2/6d each for each shift. Mr W. H. Hawkins, in charge of Grand Val and Malassis, was also included in the receipt of this bonus.

On the 4th May 1944 Mr E. J. Horton, employed at Grand Val, requested an increase in salary of 5/- a week. This was approved, his wage now being £2. On the 9th October it was increased again, to £2-5-0 a week.

On the 17th October, in compliance with the directions of the Platzkommandant, the DOA made the following order:

1. (i) Except under and in accordance with the terms of a licence, no person shall carry on the business of a miller in cereals.
   (ii) The DOA may revoke or vary any licence granted.
2. The transference of a licence can only be allowed by a new application to the DOA.
3. No licence granted will authorise the milling for any one person a quantity of cereals exceeding 28 pounds weight.
4. The holder of a milling licence must allow any DOA official to enter any premises used in connection with business as a miller of cereals.
5. Infringements are offences against the regulations made on the 1st September 1939, under the Order in Council, 25th August 1939.
6. The Order comes into effect on the 25th October 1944 and is cited the Control of Mills (Jersey) Order, 1944.

In effect, Platzkommandantur had ordered the DOA to allow private milling by individuals and enterprises, such as shops. The licence now allowed an individual to take 28 lbs of cereals to be milled. The DOA had hitherto had a monopoly on all cereal milling. The change meant that the DOA now licensed and regulated private operations.

The reason for the Control of Mills (Jersey) Order, 1944 is not entirely clear. The first explanation could be that Heider and the German authorities saw that private milling of cereals was already taking place, which meant that not all Island-grown cereals were being milled under the auspices of the DOA. Cereal farmers had been simply by-passing DOA cultivation directions and, after threshing their cereal harvest, were using private millers to mill personal stores of grain. The second and most probable reason was that, after the 6th June 1944 when the Island was effectively cut off from French supply routes, imported French flour was no longer available. Therefore, increased capacity was urgently needed to mill the 1944 harvest. Brée, on the 17th August, convened a meeting of approximately thirty of the leading cereal growers. His instructions were "...as much wheat and rye as possible should be threshed at once, as 400 tons of grain is required at the end of the month".

The additional millers now authorised by the DOA to mill cereals under the new licences were as follows.

Miller	Address	Parish
E. W. Carré	St Ouen's Motor Works	St Ouen
T. A. du Feu	Mont à L'Abbe Stores	St Helier
The Jersey Farmers (Trading) Union Limited	70 The Esplanade	St Helier
H. W. Le Boutillier	La Gabourellerie	St Ouen
R. F. Le Huguet	Maufant Stores	St Saviour
Le Marquand Brothers	West Park	St Helier
H. E. Le Rossignol	"Trelawny"	St Brelade
J. F. Minchington	Mont Mado Mills	St John
E. N. Pirouet	10 and 11 Castle Street	St Helier
E. Slade	"El Hassa"	St Martin
J. C. Vautier	"Nil Solitaire"	St Peter

On the 17th October the DOA granted a licence to John Terry Limited, 9 The Esplanade, St Helier. On the 14th November, Mr Pirouet's licence was withdrawn at his request, and on the 21st November Mr H. P. Gould, Les Pallières, St Ouen, was granted a licence. On the 21st February 1945, Mr John C. Vautier, due to the cessation of the electricity supply, transferred his licence to Mr W. R. Le Marquand, Broadlands, St Peter.

In October 1944, Platzkommandantur ordered that oat flour be used in the making of bread. The DOA therefore authorised Brée to acquire additional milling plant to carry out a reorganisation of all the mills, as he considered expedient.

On 13th October, a letter from Platzkommandantur stated that they were "...taking over Grand Val Mill, St Saviour". In response, Brée asked the German authority "To requisition the mill outright from the DOA" and on the 2nd November the German authority responded by formally requisitioning the mill. Brée, therefore, decided to immediately cease all payments for the lease to the owner, Mr William Hunt Baxter.

On 14th November, Mr E. Gilley, the senior miller at Tesson Mill, was interviewed by Brée. Mr Gilley had been instructed not to mill cereals for members of the public for payment, but it was alleged that he had disregarded the warning. After hearing Mr Gilley, who admitted there was substance to the allegations, the DOA dismissed him on the 25th November. On 28th November Mr Gilley appealed against his dismissal, however the DOA declined to modify its decision.[1]

Horses

"Jurat Brée stated that the German authorities intended to requisition 350 horses for manufacturing sausages."

A meeting of the leading farmers with Brée

On 11ᵗʰ May 1944 Field Command 515 wrote to the DOA and informed them that all remaining horses belonging to Samarès Manor were to be requisitioned. The DOA was ordered to appoint the States Vet to value the horses and to write to Miss Lily B. White, who was in charge of the Manor in the absence of the proprietor.[4] Samarès Manor, early in the German occupation, had been requisitioned. It was used by the very senior Staff Officers of Field Command 515 and the German military forces as a quiet place to relax when not on duty. It was also where officers could have, out of the public gaze, assignations with local girls.[5] Miss White was also asked to appoint an independent valuer for the horses. On the 13ᵗʰ June, she wrote to the DOA and informed them that the horses had been acquired by the German military forces.

On 16ᵗʰ August Major Heider wrote a letter to the Bailiff entitled: "Delivery of Horses for Slaughter. Conference with Jurat Brée". Heider stated that, "After a conversation with Jurat Brée the following is ordered:

a) Approximately fifteen horses per week are, on instructions from the Veterinary Surgeon, to be delivered by the farmers for slaughter.
b) Valuations of the horses will be by a mixed commission.
c) In exchange, the troops will lend their horses to those farmers who have delivered their own for slaughter".[6]

On the 17ᵗʰ August Brée announced to a joint meeting of the JFU and RJA&HS, attended by approximately thirty farmers, that he had been informed that the German authorities intended to requisition 350 local horses for meat, for manufacturing sausages for the troops. The German order was to requisition old horses and, in exchange, farmers would have the loan of one of the horses owned by the German forces.[7] Brée stated that if any horse so lent be ill or met with an accident, the German Veterinary Surgeon, Dr Kempt, would relieve the farmer of any responsibility if death occurred.

The German Veterinary Hospital was at a requisitioned property called "Bel Air", La Pommeraie, St Saviour. It contained its own workshop and smithy to produce and repair horseshoes. Next to the house was a large field which was also requisitioned, for horses to recuperate. The statement by Brée to the farmers that Dr Kempt would take responsibility for any sick or injured horses, cross-references with the recollection of a farmer, Jack Le Sueur, who lived near the veterinary hospital.

During the occupation Mr Le Sueur found himself with a sick working horse. He was in a predicament as money was extremely short and he could not afford a vet. Mr Le Sueur thought to himself that, as a German veterinary hospital was just down the road, it might be possible for the German vet to help with treatment of his horse. He therefore decided to try his luck and went to see Dr Kempt. The vet received Mr Le Sueur with due politeness and treated his horse without charge. He told Mr Le Sueur that, should he have any future problems with the horse, he should return with the animal, and he would treat it again. In fact, he did subsequently return with the horse for further treatment.[8] It appears that Dr Kempt not only helped local farmers with veterinary treatment for horses but also was willing to treat other animals.[9]

On the same day that Brée informed farmers of the German order to requisition their horses, he met with his committee and advised them of the order.

On the 18th August Platzkommandantur sent the first notification to the Bailiff. "In accordance with the plan of the German forces, of which the DOA has been informed, old, chronically ill and worn-out horses of the civilian sector are to be taken by the forces for slaughter. As a substitute, the owners will be loaned horses by the German forces. The horses to be lent may be taken over as soon as the owners have supplied the horses for slaughter".[6]

The Bailiff immediately contacted Brée. He informed Brée that he wanted individual requisition orders to be made for each horse and handed to each owner. It is perhaps pertinent to ask why the Bailiff did not ask Platzkommandantur to issue individual requisition orders directly. He saw see this as a legal necessity under the Hague Convention. The answer is simple: Pelz and Brée had been communicating through meetings and informal discussion. It was certainly quicker and simpler for Brée to inform Pelz directly.

The following horses were requisitioned to provide sausages for the German army, beginning on the 18th August and continuing until 6th September 1944.

	Owner	Address	Description	Date of Requisition
1	W. C. Le Herissier	Oakwood, St Mary	Brown gelding. Wound mark, over 16 years.	18/08/44
2	J. P. Le Brocq	Le Potiron, St Mary	White mare. 11 years.	18/08/44
3	F. Morin	Le Rondin, St Mary	Dark Brown gelding. Three white feet, over 16 years.	18/08/44
4	J. Martret	La Planque, Trinity	Brown gelding. White spot. 12 years.	18/08/44
5	R. G. England	Blanche Pierre, Trinity	Dark brown gelding. Over 18 years.	18/08/44
6	L. S. Holmes	La Grande Maison, Trinity	Brown gelding. Over 18 years.	18/08/44
7	P. J. Lucas	Modderfield, St Martin	Reddish white mare. 15 years.	18/08/44
8	A. J. Kempster	Les Grandes Rues, St Martin	Brown gelding. 11 years.	18/08/44
9	T. G. Billot	La Ville Brée, St Martin	Dark brown mare. 16 years.	18/08/44
10	F. G. Billot	La Ville Brée, St Martin	White mare. 18 years.	18/08/44

	Owner	Address	Description	Date of Requisition
11	J. R. Perrée	The Oaks, St Peter	Brown gelding. Over 20 years.	18/08/44
12	Mrs Dauny	Alexandre Farm, St Peter	White gelding. 18 years.	18/08/44
13	P. H. Renouf	Petit Alva, St Peter	White mare. 16 years.	18/08/44
14	J. B. Laurens	La Chasserie, St Lawrence	Brown gelding. 18 years.	18/08/44
15	W. Querée	Le Rocher, St Lawrence	Brown gelding. 15 years.	18/08/44
16	C. Le Sueur	Six Roads Bakery, St Lawrence	Gelding. 14 years.	24/08/44
17	S. D. Blampied	Broadfields, St Lawrence	Mare. 18 years.	24/08/44
18	F. B. Romeril	Malorey Manor, St Lawrence	Gelding. 14 years.	24/08/44
19	J. R. Nicolle	Le Hurel, Trinity	Dark brown mare. 16 years.	24/08/44
20	S. M. Le Gros	La Vallette, Trinity	14 years.	24/08/44
21	R. A. Langlois	Pouclée Farm, St Helier	18 years.	24/08/44
22	B. Le Chanu	Rose Farm, Mont á L'Abbé, St Helier	16 years.	24/08/44
23	C. Vautier	La Davisonnerie, St Saviour	16 years.	24/08/44
24	J. P. Paturel	Clairfield, St Saviour	18 years.	24/08/44
25	J. Le Sueur	Clairval, St Saviour	20 years.	24/08/44
26	A.C. Sarre	Rue à la Dame, St Saviour	15 years.	24/08/44
27	E. Rabasse	St Matthew, St Peter	14 years.	24/08/44
28	J. Chevalier	La Haule Farm, St Brelade	16 years.	24/08/44
29	J. Michel	La Fontaine, St Brelade	18 years.	24/08/44
30	J. J. Le Boutillier	Beauvoir, St Brelade	Grey mare. 8 years.	24/08/44
31	C. D. Querée	Mare d'Angot, Trinity	Brown gelding. 14 years.	31/08/44
32	G. Dorey	La Chasse, Trinity	Brown gelding. 15 years.	31/08/44
33	S. G. de Gruchy	Carmel Farm, Trinity	Brown gelding. 18 years.	31/08/44

	Owner	Address	Description	Date of Requisition
34	E. R. Mourant	Mont Séjour, Mont au Prêtre, St Helier	Brown mare. 14 years.	31/08/44
35	F. Hinault	Greenfields, St John	Grey gelding. 15 years.	31/08/44
36	J. Rimeur	Meadow Farm, St Mary	Grey gelding. 15 years.	31/08/44
37	E. Le Cuirot	Boulivot House, Grouville	Brown gelding. 16 years.	31/08/44
38	S. J. Le Boutillier	Les Ormes, St Brelade	Black gelding. 15 years.	31/08/44
39	Mrs F. M. Huelin	Westview, St Mary	Black gelding. 18 years.	31/08/44
40	J. Mills	Mont Cochon, Bushy Farm, St Helier	Black gelding. 20 years.	31/08/44
41	M. Gibaut	Mon Plaisir, Grouville	Black mare. 14 years.	31/08/44
42	J. V. Mauger	Les Petits Capelles, St John	Chestnut mare. 16 years.	31/08/44
43	A. Holt	Radier, Grouville	Black gelding. 14 years.	31/08/44
44	I. J. Le Brun	Les Jardins, St Clement	Brown mare. 20 years.	31/08/44
45	S. M. Lemprière	Pigneaux Farm, St Saviour	Black gelding. 16 years.	31/08/44
46	P. Le Feuvre	Perry Farm, St Mary	Brown gelding. 18 years.	06/09/44
47	S. Le Brocq	Popin Farm, St Brelade	Brown gelding. 14 years.	06/09/44
48	S. Hamon	Highlands, St Brelade	Brown gelding. 15 years.	06/09/44
49	C. C. Pallot	Highview, St Lawrence	Black mare. 12 years.	06/09/44
50	H. Baudains	Le Hurel, St Lawrence.	Dark brown gelding. 18 years.	06/09/44
51	Mrs Gouédard	Avranches Farm, St Lawrence	White mare. 18 years.	06/09/44
52	S. Le Gresley	Uplands, St Ouen	Brown gelding. 18 years.	06/09/44
53	Mrs Amette	Morville, St Ouen	Brown mare. 6 years.	06/09/44
54	J. P. Vibert	La Villaize, St Ouen	Brown mare. 8 years.	06/09/44
55	C. G. de la Mare	Sandycroft, Grouville	Grey mare. 15 years.	06/09/44

On the 19th August Platzkommandandtur issued a "Loan Contract" for all horses that were the property of the German forces, and which were made use of by farmers. Heider delivered a copy of the loan agreement directly to Brée on the 22nd August.

Pigs

Between March and July 1944, the DOA discovered an alleged discrepancy of five pigs in the supposed possession of Mr H. Flinn, St Peter, and the actual number of pigs found in his custody. Mr Flinn wrote to the DOA describing the conduct of a German officer involved in the matter. The DOA ordered Mr Flinn to provide the name of the German officer in question in order that the allegation be investigated.

On the 1st August the DOA met to discuss the matter of a pig held by the States Experimental Station. The pig was the property of Mr R. P. Audrain, St Lawrence, and had been held at the Station from the 8th December 1943 to the 7th June 1944 whilst its owner was incarcerated. He, however, had failed to pay maintenance for the pig of 1 shilling a day. Brée decided to send the animal to the slaughterhouse. Mr Audrain was paid 19/9, being the difference between the amount paid to the DOA by the Department of Essential Commodities, namely £10-9-9, with £9-10-0 being the cost of keeping the pig.

In August Mr T. J. Le Gros, Trinity, applied for a licence to keep a sow purchased from Mr S. C. Syvret, St Mary, for breeding purposes. The estimated age of the sow was four months. The DOA records failed to show any record of the sow being in Mr Syvret's custody since the 30th July 1943. Mr Syvret appeared before the DOA when Brée "...was unable to accept the explanations which he offered". Syvret was instructed to appear again on the 5th September with the name of the individual from whom he originally purchased the sow, and the date upon which the purchase was made. At his next interview, Mr Syvret explained the circumstances and the matter was seemingly dropped by Brée.

Straw

On the 26th August Brée met with some twenty-five members of the two farming societies. He opened the meeting stating that, as members knew the situation of each individual farmer in their respective parishes, he looked to them to suggest ways and means of obtaining straw. Figures were produced stating the estimated tonnage of straw to be furnished by each parish, proportional to the area of cereals and the number of cattle.

After much discussion Philip Le Feuvre proposed that the quota of straw be worked out on the basis of the acreage of cereals grown, and that each parish be called upon to furnish the respective quota and be implemented by the formation of Parish Committees. The proposition was carried. Brée insisted that one person in each parish should be named to act in liaison with the DOA and further discussions continued as to the process of forming these Parish Committees. It was decided that the parish representatives of the JFU and the RJA&HS should form the committees, which would have the power to co-opt and name a reporting member to keep in touch with the DOA.

On the 9th September the DOA decided to increase the price paid by the German authorities, for straw which they required to be delivered to their forces, from £10 to £10-10-0 per ton. The 5% increase was "...to cover the losses by the Public Funds as a result of the German requirement that this straw shall be weighed over the German weighbridge, in addition to the weighing over the States weighbridge, with the certainty of a discrepancy between such weighbridges".

On the 10th September all applications to sell straw to the German authorities were handed to the Parish Allocation Officers. The following applications were received.

Name	Address	Type of Straw
C. L. Romeril	Cape Verde, St Lawrence	Wheat
J. Rebours	Royal Bay House, Grouville	Wheat
Mrs M. M. Langlois	Sugar Beet Factory, Bagot Road, St Saviour	Wheat
E. L. de Caux	Dairy Farm, St Mary	Wheat
J. E. Le Bailly	Portelet Farm, St Brelade	Rye
J. F. Poignard	Villa Miramar, St Brelade	Oat and rye
P. E. Renouf	Beau Désire, St Peter	Rye
J. P. Mallet	La Vieille Maison, La Moye, St Brelade	Rye
A. Jouny	Bouley Bay, Trinity	Wheat
J. C. de la Haye	La Valeuse, St Brelade	Wheat
P. B. Coutanche	Elmdale, St Lawrence. DOA referred application to the Parish Allocation Officers	Rye
E. F. Garrod	Les Cosmères Farm, St Saviour, DOA referred application to the Parish Allocation Officers	Wheat
A. Ahier	Ballymore, Gorey Village, Grouville. DOA referred application to the Parish Allocation Officers	Unspecified
G. and A. Hacquoil	The Gables, L'Etacq, St Ouen. Licence issued 26th September	Wheat
W. T. Le Saux	La Hougue Farm, St Ouen Licence issued 26th September	Wheat
P. Le Gresley	Quarry Farm, L'Etacq, St Ouen. Licence issued 26th September	Wheat

On the 19[10] September the DOA received a letter from Mr L. Guillemet, St Lawrence. He requested payment for a quantity of straw delivered by him to the requirements of the German forces. Mr Guillemet, however, had omitted to weigh the straw on the States' weighbridge. In support of his claim, he submitted to the DOA "...a paper purporting to be a ticket issued by the German controlled weighbridge".[10] The DOA authorised payment in his favour for the weight indicated on the German ticket.

The following week, Mr C. Le Sech, St Ouen, applied to the DOA for payment for a load of straw delivered to the order of the German authorities. This load again had only been weighed on the German weighbridge. The DOA made payment on the 27th and 30th September respectively to Mr J. F. Le Meltez, Trinity and Mr G. H. Le Cornu Junior, St Lawrence, who had applied for payment for certain loads of straw delivered to the orders of the German authorities. The straw had again only been weighed on the German weighbridge. The DOA authorised payment in favour of the two men for the weights "... shown on certain scraps of paper purporting to be weighbridge tickets issued at the German-controlled weighbridge". Further loads of straw were delivered by Mr J. L. Fossey, St John and Mr C.H. Le Cornu Senior, St Lawrence, in October and November. The DOA authorised all payments for deliveries to the German forces, although no official States weighbridge tickets were forthcoming.

Milk Control

On the 16th May, Mr Walter Channing was employed to assist in the distribution of curd. Three weeks later Mrs W. Bowra was also employed to distribute curd. Their respective salaries were £1-10-0 and £1-5-0 a week. Equal pay for women and men was obviously not an issue during the German occupation. On the 4th June, Miss Phyllis Ozouf, a clerk in the Milk Control Section, was given a 5/- a week wage increase. The following month Miss Marion Journeaux was also awarded a 5/- increase. After the head of curd distribution left the Milk Control Section on the 3rd October 1944, Mrs Bowra become head of sales for curd and another assistant, Mr R. Godel, was awarded a wage increase of 5/- a week.

On the 20th May a meeting was convened of the owners of the ten largest of herds. A letter had been received from the DOA requesting the RJA&HS and JFU to name a delegation to meet the Chamber of Commerce Dairymen's Committee, in connection with the milk collection hours during the summer. The Dairymen's Committee comprised: C. P. Tanguy, E. F. True, J. S. Marie, F. J. Le Saux and J. P. Le Garignon. The milk collection times were 7.30 a.m. and 4.00 p.m. However, the problem was that the afternoon collection time was extremely inconvenient, especially for farmers in St Ouen, St Martin and St Mary. The 4.00 p.m. collection necessitated farmers milking early in the afternoon which in turn disorganised field work, particularly in view of the difficulty in obtaining and keeping farm labour.

It was decided by both farming societies to accede to the DOA request and they appointed a delegation of representatives: J. B. Michel, F. Le Boutillier, A. G. Renouf, C. P. Billot, J. Le Brocq and G. Baudains. The consensus amongst them was that the summer starting times in 1943 of 8.00 a.m. and 5.30 p.m. had proved far more satisfactory for the collection of milk throughout the Island.

On the 27th May the delegation met with the DOA and the Dairymen's Committee. Brée began the meeting by stating he had received the farmers' concerns regarding milk collection times and fully understood that they were unsuitable. The farmers underlined their reasons, giving specific examples to Brée. Firstly, their labourers had to leave all field work early in the afternoon in order to milk the cows, and it then proved difficult for them to restart other work. Secondly, a number of outlying farms did not have the milk collected in the afternoon by their dairy.

In response, the dairymen explained that, with the water supply being cut off at 7.00 p.m., the milk could not be cooled or processed any later. Moreover, lorry drivers could not obtain warm meals owing to gas restrictions, and the gazogene lorries were unreliable in starting and running. As the discussions progressed a further problem emerged. The morning lorries were often overloaded, due to the additional milk that had not been received in the previous afternoon.

Suggestions were made to improve the milk collection times. Firstly, all milk rounds were reversed, allowing for the last collection to become the first. Secondly, farmers within easy reach of milk depots would be compelled to milk in the afternoons. Cases of individual hardship for some dairy farmers were investigated and exemptions duly made if necessary. The dairymen expressed their readiness to help farmers overcome difficulties. Brée closed the meeting by stating that the DOA would consider all matters in light of the discussions.[7]

Brée subsequently met the Dairymen's Committee separately to discuss milk collections. The dairymen gave a detailed account of just how difficult it was to process milk in relation to the supply of gas and water. Brée, after all the hours of discussion with all interested parties, finally decided not to alter the present prescribed hours for milk collection.

In early June 1944 the Victoria Co-operative Dairy Limited, a licensed retailer, sent a report to the Milk Control Section describing two problems. The first alleged that Mr J. Perchard, Trinity, was not delivering his afternoon milk. The dairy had communicated with Mr Perchard requesting his deliveries, however he had ignored the request. Secondly, he had allegedly delivered his evening milk the following morning, and in consequence the milk had turned sour.[11]

The DOA wrote to Mr Perchard, pointing out his failure to comply with the requirements of Article 5(5) of the Milk Control (Jersey) Order, 1940. He was warned that proceedings would be forthcoming unless he immediately complied. Mr Perchard again ignored all communications. Brée's frustration increased. He therefore decided to deal with Mr Perchard in a far more authoritative manner. Brée had become extremely exasperated that several milk producers had been continually reminded to fulfil their duty to deliver milk to the depot, in time for the afternoon collection by the dairy. He was determined to hasten legal proceedings against Mr Perchard and evidently use him as an example to other recalcitrant producers. Colin Marie telephoned the Attorney General with a view that proceedings be instigated.

As a result, Mr Perchard appeared before the DOA. He profusely apologised for his failure to comply with milk directions in relation to the delivery of milk and collection times. The licensed retailer confirmed that all milk collections were on time. In consequence the DOA wrote to the Attorney General "In view of the fact that this man has expressed his regrets at his failure to comply with the requirements of the DOA in relation to the delivery of his milk for the afternoon collection and further, that he is now so delivering his milk, the DOA has directed me to ask you be good enough to take no further action against Mr Perchard in this matter".

Brée now decided to deal once and for all with the ongoing problem of the non-delivery of afternoon milk to the collection depots. Victoria Co-operative, Jersey Dairies and L. J. Tanguy were asked to supply a list of producers who were not delivering their milk. Initially, their names were collated and a letter sent to each of them, pointing out the provisions of the Milk Control (Jersey) Order 1940 and ordering them to deliver their milk to the depots in time for the afternoon collection.

By the 11th July a number of producers were still failing to deliver milk from their afternoon session: E. R. Laisney, J. M. Larose, S. Laurens, C. Gallichan, F. A. Pirouet and J. G. Rondel. All were in Trinity and Brée decided to refer them to the Attorney General. Upon referral, Mr Laisney undertook to deliver all his afternoon milk to the dairy and the case was immediately dropped. As for the other referrals, these progressed to the Royal Court. The Royal Court, however, postponed all proceedings until the DOA had received further information which the legal authorities thought was pertinent.

On the 11th July Milk Control submitted computations of the "Average quantities of milk supplied over a period of 12 months per cow." Cows which were below average were referred by Milk Control to the Cattle Slaughter Executive Committee. Any cow that produced less than the average of 1¾ pots a day was pencilled in for slaughter. Cows belonging to the following farmers were therefore selected and slaughtered: H. Flinn and E. P. Roy, St Brelade, E. A. Jehan, Trinity and Miss A. Martret, St Ouen.

The following week more cows were identified as not producing a satisfactory quantity of milk. They belonged to Mr G. A. Luce and Mr J. M. Renouf, St Mary. Brée was adamant that, since the milk production of these herds was of little benefit to the Island, they should all be referred to the Cattle Slaughter Executive Committee. On the 19th September, Mr Renouf's cows all began to produce more milk, and there was a real increase in the farmer's deliveries. Whether or not the subsequent deferment of their slaughter, because of the increase, was deliberate or not, it sent an exceptionally strong message to dairy farmers. The message was simple: if you do not deliver all your milk under milk directions, or your yield is "very low" your herd will be examined by the Committee with a possibility they will be slaughtered.

On the 17th July the Department of Public Health reported farmers whose cattle were alleged to be yielding milk with a low average fat content. In consequence the DOA investigated two producers, Mr I. Kergozou and Mr E. J. Hacquoil, St Mary. Brée ordered that all Mr Kergozou's milk be sent to Don Street Dairy for the manufacture of butter, and Mr Hacquoil's herd be referred to the Cattle Slaughter Executive.

In late July Philip Renouf, St Peter, received formal instructions from the German forces to supply fresh milk to troops stationed on his farm. The order would have been sanctioned, and a permit issued, by Platzkommandantur I. In response to the German permit to obtain milk from the resident farmer, the DOA authorised a producer-retailer licence under Article 3 (2) of the Milk Control (Jersey) Order, 1940.

On the 25th July Milk Control submitted a list of producers who, despite being handed a formal warning, were still not delivering their milk in time for the afternoon collection by Jersey Dairies Limited. By law, these producers were not allowed to send or dispose of their milk to anyone else. Brée decided to take firm action once more on this issue. He immediately sent a letter to the Attorney General citing those famers who had failed to comply with the provisions of the milk order. The farmers alleged to have failed to deliver their milk were as follows.

Name	Parish
F. P. Durell	St Ouen
T. W. Durell	St Ouen
J. F. Bisson	St Ouen
L. P. de la Haye	St Ouen
A. B. Holley	St Peter
J. Le Blancq	St Ouen
P. Le Mottée	St Ouen
R. Querrée	St Ouen
B. Syvret	St Ouen
E. Syvret	St Ouen
W. F. Tomes	St John

Two other St Ouen producers, Mr W. J. Le Marquand and Mr P. L. Le Masurier, were sent a final warning.

In late July, a Milk Tester who had been appointed on the 17th January 1942 resigned. His position was taken by Mr F. G. Luce.

On the 29th July, Mr C. R. Mauger reported that a cow in the custody of Mrs Ada Balton, St Helier, had failed to produce an average quantity of milk. Brée decided that its preservation was no longer warranted; the cow was sent to the slaughterhouse. The following week Mr A. F. Guegan, St Mary, appeared before the DOA. He was instructed to explain the alleged "...exceedingly low yield of milk supplied by the cows in his custody during August 1943 and July 1944; namely an average of 0.69 of a pot per cow over the same period" (i.e., 12 months). Mr Guegan replied that he had insufficient pasture for the number of livestock in his custody. Brée decided to put the matter into the hands of the Cattle Slaughter Executive Committee, with a recommendation that three cows be selected for slaughter.

Early in August Mr C. Hamon, the caretaker for Don Street Dairy, requested Milk Control to pay for his electricity and gas as a partial payment for his extra duties of cleaning the offices. The DOA decided to pay him an extra 2/6 per week.

On the 22nd August the matter of Mr Gerald Wilfred Le Masurier was discussed. He held a Milk Retailers' Licence for the Val Plaisant Dairy but had recently been sentenced to a term of imprisonment by the German authorities. His son, Gerald Alfred Le Masurier, was issued a temporary licence until the release of his father from German custody. On the 12th September Le Masurier Senior was released and the temporary licence cancelled.

A report in the same month alleged that Mr S. de Gruchy, St Ouen, had delivered "...sour milk on a number of occasions despite a warning administered". Milk Control forthwith deducted 6d per pot from payment for his milk if it was found to be in a sour condition when received.

In the last week of August, Brée sent letters to Mr H.G. Le Quesne, St Saviour, and Mr G. A. Luce and Mr F. J. Perrée, St Mary, stating that he was dissatisfied with their milk yields. He made clear that unless a considerable improvement quickly took place, their cows with low milk yields would be slaughtered, as their production was insufficient to warrant their preservation.

Brée's increasing dissatisfaction with the low milk yields of summer 1944 continued into the autumn. He ordered the Milk Testers to scrutinise herds with low yields and forward reports directly to him. A report on the 1st September detailed cows belonging to Mr C. P. Genée, St John, where the average daily yield of each cow was only 0.58 pots. Brée wrote to Mr Genée, informing him that he was dissatisfied with the yield. He furthermore warned him that severe measures would be implemented unless there was an improvement. A further report by the Milk Testers on the 19th December described "...special additional tests" carried out by the Testers who had arrived at milking times agreed with Mr Genée. His milk yield increased. The DOA informed him that should there be any further cases of complaint in relation to milk supplies, it would consider "...depriving him of the cattle in his custody".

The States Vet reported to the DOA that, on the 4th September, Mr R. F. Hearn, St Ouen, presented himself at the slaughterhouse with a cow which he wished to exchange for a German horse. The States Vet, having protested to the German authorities that this was contrary to the Livestock (Restriction on Movement) (Jersey) Order, 1943, ordered the cow back to St Ouen. The matter was referred to the Attorney General.

A report of the 12th September described a cow in the custody of Mr Le Cornu, St Lawrence. The cow had reached ten years of age and its daily milk yield had recently dropped. Brée ordered that it be sent for slaughter.

On the same day Miss M. A. Journeaux, a shorthand typist in the Milk Control Section terminated her services. She was replaced by Miss Joyce Romeril.

The ongoing problem of herds that produced low milk yields was pursued unrelentingly by Brée for the next several months. He received a report on the 25th September detailing the quantities of milk delivered to licensed retailers. Brée noticed that the figures demonstrated an exceptionally low milk yield by two producers, Mr L. Holmes and Mr P. Tardivel, Trinity. Their milk yields were examined for the preceding twelve months. Brée, who was not only an excellent farmer but kept pedigree cattle himself, warned that their herds would be referred to the Cattle Slaughter Executive Committee. In addition, he ensured that both herds were scrutinised and tested weekly, and the reports immediately referred to him. In consequence of these checks, a letter was written to the licensed retailer asking why Mr Holmes had not delivered all his milk at the afternoon collection. The Victoria Co-operative Dairy's reply caused Brée to summon Mr Holmes for an interview. He gave him a final warning concerning his poor milk yields and ordered him to deliver all his milk for the afternoon collections.

On the 26th September Milk Control issued a producer-retailer licence to Mr J. F. Dallain, St Peter, to supply fresh milk as required by the German authorities. The milk was supplied to Colonel Emil Ziegler, Island Artillery Commander, A.R. 319, stationed at the Headquarters, Vine Park, St Peter. Photographic records demonstrate Colonel Ziegler was a frequent visitor to Samarès Manor and knew the guardian, Miss White.

On the 1st November von Aufsess, with two other German officers, visited "...a model dairy farm" to show them the best examples of the Jersey breed. From the description of the farm, it is almost certainly J. A. Perrée's, Oaklands, St Saviour. John Perrée's farm was far ahead of its time, with planned features for feeding and handling cattle and for storing manure.

Around the same time that Colonel Ziegler was ordering fresh milk from Mr Dallain, the DOA received a letter from Mr J. Stanley Marie, Managing Director of Jersey Dairies Limited, questioning the supply of milk to the German occupying forces in Jersey. It was decided that a reply should be sent from the Attorney General, who wrote directly to Mr Marie. He was informed that the civil authorities were required to supply "...reasonable demands in respect of the occupying forces". In addition, milk had to be supplied to the Germans "...to the extent to which such supplies are covered by requisitions".

In October all milk yields for the previous twelve months were examined. One herd was singled out, belonging to Mr H. W. Bexon, St Mary, where the average yield per cow was exceptionally low. In addition, Mr Bexon had refused to provide cows for slaughter, as selected by the Cattle Slaughter Executive Committee. Brée immediately ordered the States Vet to oversee the slaughter directions for the herd. In response Mr Bexon appealed against the requisition order, which was suspended for one month.

On the 6th November Mr Bexon wrote directly to the Bailiff appealing against the slaughter directions. On the 5th December a report was received from the States Vet stating that Mr Bexon had transferred the custody of his cattle without having first obtained a licence, as prescribed by Article 2 of the Livestock (Jersey) Order, 1942. In addition, he had disposed of an animal under requisition. The matter was referred to the Attorney General. The States Vet, on the 2nd January 1945, reported that all cattle requisitioned from Mr Bexon had been used to fulfil the meat requirements of the German forces.

In October an anonymous letter was received informing the DOA that Mr A. G. de Gruchy, St Ouen, was allegedly manufacturing butter and distributing the same, presumably at exorbitant prices, on the black market. A report stated, "My department is informed that the distribution of the butter takes place on Fridays after midday and I have been directed to suggest that the Honorary Police be asked to carry out a search of the premises in de Gruchy's occupation...in order to ascertain whether, in fact, the allegations have substance. For your information, the average milk yield in this man's custody per day during the twelve months ending 21st September 1944 is 1.457 pots daily, whereas...the very minimum yield over the period should be 1.75 pots and even the latter figure is very low".[11]

The DOA met to discuss the matter. The decision was made that in view of "...certain suspicions which exist as to the activities of Mr de Gruchy" it would ask the Attorney General to order the Parish Honorary Police to carry out a search of the premises.

On the 18th October the Attorney General wrote to Mr F. Le Boutillier, Connétable of St Ouen: "There is reason to believe that Mr A. G. de Gruchy is manufacturing butter and selling it illicitly...at extortionate rates...The distribution of butter takes place on Friday midday. The DOA also informs me, and it is a valuable piece of circumstantial evidence in this case, that during the 12 months the average yield per day was 1.457 pots. This would suggest that a substantial quantity of milk is being regularly retained. I should be obliged to you if you will have the matter carefully investigated. You may perhaps consider that a search of his premises on a Friday morning will be the most expeditious and effective way of testing the suspicions of the DOA".

The Connétable very unusually took just over three weeks to produce his report on de Gruchy and the alleged butter-manufacturing activities. The normal period for a report from a Connétable or Centenier to the Attorney General was two to five days. In fact, the Attorney General had to write to Le Boutillier on the 3rd November demanding: "May I please have a report?"

On the 9th November, Le Boutillier sent a brief reply replied to the Attorney General: "The police are making enquiries but up to now have found no incriminating evidence."

On the 11th October the German authorities wrote to the DOA requiring delivery of a further 5 tons of butter to the German troops, for the months of November and December 1944. The DOA asked Brée to personally intervene and make clear that: "In view of the serious effect which the supplying of these quantities will have upon the stocks of butter available, the President is asked to make energetic representations to the German authorities with a view to securing that these demands shall not exceed a reasonable proportion of the Island production."

Brée reported back to the DOA on the 24th October. He told them that he had protested in strong terms to the German authorities concerning the taking of butter stocks from the civilian population. In reply to his protestation the German authorities had threatened that, unless butter was delivered to them, they would order that the troops be supplied with full cream milk instead of skimmed milk, at a rate of one half pint per head. In view of Brée's report the DOA therefore made the decision that "The supplying of troops with full cream milk would be the greater mischief" and that being under duress, it was decided "...to supply the additional quantity of butter now demanded by the German authorities".[1]

On the 24th October 1944, Mr Jean-Marie Rimeur, St Peter, was ordered by the German authorities to supply them with fresh milk and in consequence the DOA issued a producer-retailer licence to Mr Rimeur, under the Milk Control (Jersey) Order, 1940. On the same day the Milk Control Section sent their Milk Testers to Mr E. J. Paisnel, Grouville, to carry out a check on the quantity and quality of milk produced by cows in his custody. Mr Paisnel's milk production was low. The DOA decided that a weekly check should be carried out whilst the cows were being milked.[12]

On the same day that Mr Rimeur was ordered to provide milk to the German authorities and Mr Paisnel was being investigated for low milk yields, the DOA received a letter from the Platzkommandant, Major Heider, ordering that the quantity of milk distributed to civilian hospitals and to the sick be reduced by half. The Chief Medical Officer of Health immediately sent a report to the DOA concerning the implications of this order. On the 2nd November the German authorities again wrote "...insisting upon the reduction of milk supplied on medical grounds".

On the 31st October, in an effort to reduce milk for the civilian population in order to supply the German request for extra butter, the following establishments had their milk licences revoked.

	Place	Address
1	Maison St Louis	St Saviour
2	Highlands College	St Saviour
3	The Convent, FCJ	Val Plaisant, St Helier
4	Saint Matthews Convent	St Mary
5	Waukrama Nursing Home	Roseville Street, St Helier
6	Woodlands Nursing Home	Grouville
7	Elizabeth Nursing Home	102 Great Union Road, St Helier
8	Newquay Nursing Home	Windsor Road, St Helier

In November the DOA approved the stopping of fresh milk which had been allocated to nursing mothers and to juveniles suffering from tuberculosis.

The German demand to requisition civilian butter escalated. On the 25th November Brée informed the DOA that the Germans authorities "...are now demanding that at least 8 tons of extra butter be manufactured during December 1944 and January 1945." Brée warned both the DOA and the Superior Council that this demand would consequently result in a situation where it was impossible to maintain the present ration of 2 ounces a week to the civilian population. This, additionally, would inevitably deprive civilians who were entitled to receive one pint of milk daily in virtue of directions of the 8th December 1943, issued under the Rationing (Jersey) Order, 1943.

The German demand for extra butter was read out at a joint JFU and RJA&HS meeting on the 28th November, with the DOA in attendance. The importance of the meeting can be gauged by the fact that all three secretaries were present: George Messervy, Harold Shepard and Colin Marie. The purpose of the meeting was "To consider the position which had arisen in relation to the supply of butter for the needs of the civilian population as a result of the commandeering by the German forces of 18½ metric tonnes from the Island's reserves". The DOA made it clear that butter production during December 1944 and January 1945 was insufficient to provide for the civilian ration. It therefore decided to take three measures to increase the quantity of milk available for butter production. Firstly, to suspend during December and January the operation of a number of provisions of the Livestock (Jersey) Order, 1942. Secondly, to recommend to the Department of Essential Commodities that the ration to persons entitled to receive 1 pint of milk daily be stopped for the months of December and January. And, in addition, the butter ration to be dispensed with during these months. Finally, the Department of Public Instruction was informed that milk supplies to schools were to be discontinued for two months. By the 23rd January 1945, the supply of milk to pupils at elementary and private schools had been resumed.

On the 18th December the DOA met to discuss the implications of the restrictions. The decision was made that milk retained by a producer, in respect of a child aged not more than two years, would be 1½ pints daily, and similarly for the children of servants of the producer. The Department of Essential Commodities and the Senior Medical Inspector were informed.

On the same day the DOA made a recommendation to the Superior Council that a bonus of £25-0-0 be paid to Mr Weeks. It was decided that he should receive extra remuneration for the work required to administer the Livestock (Jersey) Order, 1942, and the additional work given to him for the Milk (Registration with Retailers) (Jersey) Order, 1940.

Other staff in the Milk Control Section received salary increases. Mr M. Noel and Mr J.W. Benest had a 2/- a week pay rise, with both now being paid £2-7-6. Mr R. Godel was put on a permanent contract of £2-5-0 a week, and Mr M. Brée, who was ill, was given two weeks' salary and a temporary Milk Tester was employed. An employee at Don Street Dairy was dismissed for stealing a quantity of cream. The matter was put in the hands of the police and Mr J.W. Benest was employed to cover his work at a rate of £2-12-3 a week.

Two more farmers were summoned by Brée to explain low milk yields. Mr A. J. Henry, St Brelade, and Mr G. A. V. Kempster, St Martin, were told that their cattle would be referred to the Cattle Slaughter Executive Committee for selection.

On the 20th November the Foreman Milk Tester, J. G. Malzard, recommended that a number of cows belonging to Mr E. P. Rabet, St Peter, be referred to the Cattle Slaughter Executive Committee. The next day the Milk Control Section investigated the milk yields of the cattle in the custody of Mr C. W. Binet, Trinity. He had failed to deliver to his registered retailer 10 pots of milks. Brée ordered the cattle to be selected for slaughter for Binet's failure to comply with his obligations under Article 5(2) of the Milk Control (Jersey) Order, 1940, as amended.

The following day the registration of the Gas Works Metro Shop, as an establishment for the purposes of the Milk (Registration with Retailers) (Jersey) Order, 1940, was terminated. In addition, the milk retailer licence of Mr J. J. Le Marquand, Plaisance Dairy, St Ouen, was changed to the name of his wife, Mrs Helena Le Marquand. Mr Le Marquand was serving a term of imprisonment passed by the German military court. His wife was instructed to hold the licence until his period of prison ended.

On the 28th November the German authorities stated to the DOA that from the 1st December 1944 the hours of electricity supply would change. The new hours of supply were to be from 9.00 a.m. to 1.00 p.m. and from 6.00 p.m. to 11.00 p.m. In view of the repercussions which the absence of light in the early morning would have on the milk supply, Brée made energetic representations to have the morning supply modified so that electricity would be available from 7.00 a.m. to carry out the morning milking session.

Cereals

"Certain quantities of wheat were to be threshed forthwith and the threshing of oats was to be postponed until after these quantities had been threshed".

Major Heider, Platzkommandant, to DOA, 12th August 1944

"The following week the Platzkommandant informed the DOA that the German military authorities had placed 10,000 litres of petrol for the threshing of wheat and the requirements of the civil authorities".

19th August 1944

On the 6th June 1944 (D-Day) the German authorities ordered the DOA to lease additional cereal storage as a quantity of wheat imported from France was shortly to arrive. Whether or not this French wheat ever did arrive in the Island is not documented.

The Platzkommandant sent a letter to the DOA on the 4th July, concerning the threshing of the cereal crop. He made clear that the allowance (a percentage of grain which farmers could keep if they grew cereals) was to cease. The allowance of the privileged issue of oats distributed by the DOA for agricultural working horses was not included in the order.

On the 11th July the DOA set the prices that they would pay for the 1944 cereal crop. Six days later the threshing contractors and the Threshing Sub-Committee met "In order to discuss the operation of the threshing machines during the 1944 season".

On the 18th July the DOA met with Philip Cabot to discuss the 1944 purchase of cereal crops, legislation, and problems concerning the threshing season. The following directions were passed.

1. Cereals means wheat, oats, barley, or rye sown from 1st September 1943 and ending 30th September 1944.
2. No cereal shall be stocked on stubble and, where it is intended to thresh any cereal on the site, it shall be one to which the threshing machine may have easy access and on which it may operate without hindrance.
3. No person shall order the threshing of any cereal, except:
   a) made in accordance with the terms of a licence granted by the DOA.
   b) where the cereal is threshed by a threshing machine approved by the DOA.
4. (i) Every person having power to dispose of or owning any cereal grain threshed before the coming into force of these Directions is hereby required to offer the same forthwith to the DOA.

(ii) Delivery of cereal grain purchased aforesaid shall be made at the seller's premises.

5. The prices to be paid for cereal grain purchased shall be at the following rate:

Wheat	£1-8-0 cwt
Oats	£1-2-6 cwt
Barley	£1-12-6 cwt
Rye	£1-19-0 cwt

6. (i) The DOA may pay a price lesser than the basic price for cereals of inferior quality.
   (ii) The question of inferior quality will be decided by the DOA. Its price and the decision are final and conclusive.
7. Where the sale of any wheat grain is effected after the 30th November 1944 a price equal to 1% of the basic price multiplied by the number of months which have elapsed since that date (the month in which the sale is effected being considered as a month) shall be paid in addition to the basic price.
8. Infringements of these Directions are offences against the Regulations made on the 1st September 1939, under the Order in Council of the 25th August 1939.
9. These Directions shall come into force forthwith.

In late July a notice on the licencing of threshing machines was inserted in the local press and on the 8th August the DOA issued licences for the following machines:

Name of Contractor	Number of Threshing Machines
T. R. Benest	1
J. C. Cabot	1
J. E. Colback Junior	1
W. T. Farrell	1
W. P. Godel	1
T. G. Le Cappelain	2
L. C. Pallot	1
J. Richard	2
TOTAL	10

The DOA now decided that it would test the gazogene-driven tractors which were to be used for the 1944 season. Arrangements were made to thresh several loads of rye "...in order to carry out a practical test as to the capacity of gazogene-driven tractors to drive the threshing machines". It also decided, based upon the experience of the 1942 and 1943 threshing seasons, to employ extra temporary labour for loading, unloading, storage and treatment of the 1944 harvest.

On the 4th August the German authorities ordered the DOA that threshing was to be carried out on Sundays, until the end of the cereal harvest. In response the DOA put a notice in the local press to that effect.

On the 11th August a list of threshing depots was approved and published.

Depot	Contractor
La Grande Martin, St John	J. Richard
Le Hocq Marsh, St Clement	J. Richard
St Peter's Works, St Peter	T. G. Le Cappelain
Grantez, St Ouen	W. T. Farrell
Six Roads, St Lawrence	H. P. Godel
Parish Store Depot, St Mary	J. E. Colback Junior

In the same week the DOA decided to allow licences to individuals, to thresh gleanings at the various threshing machines.

Early in August a report from Mr G. E. Huelin, Honorary Parish Inspector, St Ouen, noted that a field of wheat grown by Mr A. Luce was not worth threshing. He was informed that the wheat had to be threshed, irrespective of its condition.

Between the 8th and 9th August, Threshing Inspectors were appointed, as follows.

Name	Address	Appointment	Wage Weekly
O. P. Hamon,	Glenroyd, La Rocque, Grouville	Threshing Inspector, Western District	£4-0-0
J. C. Steel	Sunnycot, La Moie, St Brelade	Threshing Inspector, Eastern District	£4-0-0
R. Ching	Rectory View, St Martin	Threshing Machine Inspector	£3-0-0
W. Farrell	Green Banks, Spring Grove, Bel Royal, St Lawrence	Threshing Machine Inspector	£3-0-0
E. Le Brocq	Southview, St Mary	Threshing Machine Inspector	£3-0-0
W. A. Pallot	17 Clubley Estate, St John's Road, St Helier	Threshing Machine Inspector	£3-0-0
R. C. Steel	Champ Clair Cottage, Trinity	Threshing Machine Inspector	£3-0-0
H. Vautier	Broadfields, St Lawrence	Threshing Machine Inspector	£3-0-0
P. W. Buesnel	Champ Clair Cottage, Trinity	Threshing Machine Sub-Inspector	£2-10-0
P. G. Dubois	Delmin, Mont au Prêtre, St Helier	Threshing Machine Sub-Inspector	£2-10-0

Name	Address	Appointment	Wage Weekly
A. Gautier	20 Clubley Estate, St John's Road, St Helier	Threshing Machine Sub-Inspector	£2-10-0
P. Gibaut	14 Verte Rue, St Lawrence	Threshing Machine Sub-Inspector	£2-10-0
A. Gottard	1 Cambrai, Gorey Village, Grouville	Threshing Machine Sub-Inspector	£2-10-0
J. P. Langlois	Les Varvots, St Lawrence	Threshing Machine Sub-Inspector	£2-10-0
E. W. Bertram	La Rosaye, St Martin	Assistant to Sub-Inspector	£2-10-0
E. de la Haye	Clayfield, St Peter	Assistant to Sub-Inspector	£2-10-0
J. Huelin	Les Six Boules, St Ouen	Assistant to Sub-Inspector	£2-10-0
G. R. Langdon	12 Coastlands, Greve d'Azette, St Clement	Assistant to Sub-Inspector	£2-10-0
W. Le Boutillier	Ellwyn, Mont à L'Abbé, St Helier	Assistant to Sub-Inspector	£2-10-0
G. R. Melville	Raynet, Le Bourg, St Clement	Assistant to Sub-Inspector	£2-10-0
P. Roberts	Rue ès Abbés, St Mary	Assistant to Sub-Inspector	£2-10-0
A. Taylor	Beau Sejour Cottage, St John	Assistant to Sub-Inspector	£2-10-0
F. F. Channing	25 Cleveland Road, St Helier	Assistant to Sub-Inspector	£2-10-0

Threshing Machine Sub-Inspectors and their assistants were employed on a weekly basis and no payment was made for overtime. They began work at 8.00 a.m. and finished at 8.00 p.m. There was a lunch interval at midday for 1 hour.

The DOA requested the Department of Essential Supplies that electric power be made available for the contractors at the threshing depots. On the 22nd August the DOA was authorised to use electricity for the operation of the threshing machines.

On the 12th August Platzkommandant Heider wrote to the DOA ordering that "Certain quantities of wheat shall be threshed forthwith and that the threshing of oats is to be postponed until after these quantities of what have been threshed". Brée immediately charged the Threshing Sub-Committee to arrange for the threshing of the specified quantity of wheat, to the exclusion of oats.

The following week Platzkommandantur informed the DOA that the German Military authorities "...had placed 10,000 litres of petrol for the threshing of wheat and the requirements of the civil authorities".

On the 29th August Mr G. Messervy, Clos Durell, Trinity, agreed to his appointment as Chairman of the Sub-Committee for Inferior Grain. Mr Messervy thereupon re-appointed the previous years' members to the sub-committee.

In the same week the DOA authorised the Grain and Potato Section to deduct 3½ lbs from the net weight shown on weighbridge tickets, in respect of wheat delivered to the German authorities. This was to allow for the average weight of each German sack in which the grain was contained, and which was ascertained by a trial weighing.

A report dated the 25th August from Mr Godfray described a loss of grain in transit between the threshing machines and the DOA stores. The DOA informed the Department of Transport and Communications that some form of action should be taken in the event of any future losses. The Threshing Sub-Committee was instructed to report as to the position concerning payment for grain lost in transit. It duly reported back on the 5th September and recommended that Mr C. L. Hamon, Trinity, be paid for sixty sacks of wheat which had been lost. The payment was only to be made if Mr Hamon applied for the missing sixty sacks. In the same week, a quantity of oats was also lost in transit between the DOA stores and one of their mills.

On the 30th August the DOA received a letter from the German authorities, insisting that all farmers carry out cereal threshing during the month of September. The matter was discussed and "The DOA decided to take no action in this matter". The tone of this response is interesting and perhaps informative for two reasons. Firstly, the fact that the DOA decided not to give any directions to farmers and contractors to take cognisance of the German order was the first time this had occurred. Secondly, the response to the German authorities, some ten weeks after D-Day, smacked of defiance.

Mr John Mallett submitted for payment a weighbridge ticket dated the 1st September, in respect of a load of rye, and demanded that an additional 2 cwt be added to the ticket. On examination, it was found to have been altered to show a weight of 2 cwt in excess of that originally shown on the ticket. Since the alteration had been made subsequent to the issue of the ticket by the public weigher, the DOA decided to refer the matter to the Attorney General. He replied instructing the DOA to settle the claim based on the correct weighbridge ticket.

On the 8th October the German authorities wrote to the DOA "...requiring inter alia the delivery of a further 570 tons of wheat. This quantity is required for the sowing of wheat in 1945". Two days later the German authorities sent a further letter to the DOA containing, according to minutes, an "...implied prohibition on the growing of early vegetables in place thereof". The German authorities were in effect demanding extra wheat be grown, in place of vegetables.

Brée was mortified by this order. He immediately replied: "The DOA, in view of its responsibility for ensuring the supply of food to the Island population and being of the opinion that compliance with the instructions of the occupying forces contained in these letters, will result in serious changes to the well-being, and indeed the life, of the Island population, decided to support the Superior Council that the subject matter of these communications be laid before the Protecting Power at the earliest possible moment to the intent that these instructions may be recalled as the DOA considers that the carrying out of these instructions would constitute a grave breach of the duty which it owes to the people of the Island."

A week later the DOA received a resolution unanimously adopted at a meeting of farmers held at St Peter on the 27th October, protesting against sowing cereals for the 1945 crop.

On the 21st October the DOA met with the Honorary Parish Inspectors to discuss the German demands. The Honorary Parish Inspectors present were as follows:

Parish	Name
St Brelade	J. J. Le Boutillier
St Clement	J. P. Le Masurier
St Helier	P. J. Mourant, P. L. Baudains
St John	J. Gartrell, C. Le Couteur
St Lawrence	H. W. Maillard, T. A. Pallot
St Martin	P. Ahier, G. Le Masurier
St Mary	P. Le Feuvre, E. J. Le Ruez
St Ouen	G. E. Huelin, E. G. Vautier
St Peter	E. R. Egré, H. P. Le Ruez
St Saviour	P. Gallichan, C. Quenault
Trinity	C. R. Ahier, A. R. Le Brun

Brée began the meeting by describing his response to the German authorities. He, however, was of the opinion that nothing further could be done at the present time. The DOA, in view of the German demands, published a notice to all farmers, calling upon them to attend meetings to discuss the cultivation of agricultural land in 1945.

During the summer and autumn of 1944, the Threshing Sub-Committee and the Inferior Grain Sub-Committee met on an almost weekly basis. They reported directly to the Grain and Potato Control Section.

Jersey Produce Merchants Association

On the 24th May 1944, a load of thirty-eight barrels of potatoes grown under glass was delivered to the DOA store of W. Dennis and Sons Limited. The firm, without calling upon the DOA's Inspectors, sorted the load and removed 97 lbs of damaged potatoes. The DOA decided that in view of "… the irregular action of the firm" in the matter, Mr Charles Gruchy, St Saviour the farmer who had delivered the potatoes, would be paid for them in full.

The DOA wrote to W. Dennis and Sons Limited and "...drew attention to the impropriety of the action taken by them". The firm was also instructed to dispose of the 97 lbs to one or more institutions in the Island, at the best possible price.

On the 27th June the JPMA wrote to the DOA. It offered to store the 1944 potato crop on the same terms as in 1943. The DOA agreed and subsequently asked the JPMA for its list of last year's members who had stored potatoes on its behalf. Upon receipt of the list the DOA approved the members of the JPMA who would store the 1944 crop, with the exception of A.C. Sarre.

A report of the 1st August described potatoes held in a number of JPMA stores on behalf of the DOA as being stacked to an excessive height. Brée then met with the merchants' representatives and made clear "The injurious nature of this practice." He instructed immediate arrangements be made to reduce the height of the stacks.

Between the 3rd and 12th August notices were inserted in the local press that, due to a shortage of storage space, farmers were not to transport potatoes to the DOA stores. On the 15th August the DOA suspended all further permits for the delivery of potatoes until new storage facilities became available.

On the same day the DOA informed the JPMA of its terms for the storage of the 1944 grain harvest. The terms were also sent to four merchants who were not members of the JPMA.

Merchant	Address
E. N. Pirouet	10 Cattle Street, St Helier
T. F. Pirouet	Union Street, St Helier
Randall's Brewery	Clare Street, St Helier
G. Touzel	Halkett Place, St Helier

The terms offered by the DOA to the merchants were as follows.

1. All persons holding grain on behalf of the DOA will be paid £1-10-0 per ton.
2. Payment will be made in two instalments.
3. 75% being due and payable upon the taking into store.
4. 25% being due at the conclusion of storage.
5. All storage of grain shall conform to the requirements of the DOA.
6. The DOA to decide whether grain will be stored in barrels or in bulk.
7. In barrels, grain must not exceed two in height.
8. Grain in bulk should not exceed 2 feet from the level of the floor on which it is stored.
9. Grain must be turned over at least once a week during the first month of storage and once a month thereafter. In particular cases, the DOA will ask for additional turning of grain.
10. A permissible shrinkage of grain will be allowed after discussion with the JPMA.

The JPMA was happy to accept these conditions for the storage of grain grown in 1944. The list of stores submitted was as follows:

R. P. Amy
C. P Bailhache
J. E. Baudains
E. Becquet
W. Bird and Son Limited
George Blampied Limited
Jersey Co-operative Wholesale Society Limited
Country Gentlemen's Association Limited
P. J. de Gruchy
W. Dennis and Sons Limited
T. Dorey and Company Limited
A. P. Falle and Sons Limited
W. J. Gaudin
F. Giddens
Chas Gruchy and Company Limited
Guiton and Lucas
Sidney Horman Limited
Job and Sons
A. E. Laurens
O. J. Le Mottée Limited
Le Rossignol and Company
Marks and Riches Limited
J. Martland Limited
T. Mayo and Company Limited
C. Mossop
Normans Limited
J. Spearman
John Terry Limited.

Le Rossignol, and Marks and Riches, were to be used when no other suitable storage was available.

Fertilisers

On the 23rd May 1944 the DOA decided that its stocks of sulphate of ammonia were to be used for the 1945 potato crop.

On the 25th September the DOA issued a notice to farmers that basic slag still held in storage would be supplied, at the rate of fifty-six barrels per vergée, upon production to the supplying merchant of the direction issued to each farmer under the Cultivation of Lands (Jersey) Order, 1942. The price was fixed at 7/- per 56 lbs and the slag could be drawn by farmers up to the 21st October 1944. After that date, the JPMA would be allowed to sell the material, under a general licence issued under the Fertilisers (Jersey) Order, 1941, to farmers without permits. The DOA made this conditional on the price remaining at the prescribed level and a notice to that effect was published in the local press.

Cultivation Directions

On 8th May 1944 the Petrol Controller sent a report to the DOA concerning ploughing carried out during the 1943–44 season by the gazogene-operated tractors. The DOA therefore recommended to the Department of Transport and Communications "...that every endeavour be made to secure early delivery of the 10 gazogene plants now on order and in addition that a further 20 such plants are to be ordered suitable for attachment to Fordson tractors with steel wheels".

In the same week, the DOA looked into the question of obtaining petrol for mowing hay. The Department of Transport and Communications was asked if it could provide petrol at one quart per vergée. In view of the request, it decided to approach the German authorities to obtain the release of the required petrol.

At the same time, an application for an increase in salary by Mr A. V. Bateman, a clerk in the Grain and Potato Control Section, was refused. However, three weeks later the DOA increased the wages of seven of its female clerical staff by 5/- a week: Miss Joan Picot, Miss Phyllis Ozouf, Miss Kathleen Picot, Miss Iris Le Masurier, Miss Marian Journeaux, Miss B. Keat and Mrs E. Gates. On the 10th June, Mr H. G. Brideaux, a clerk, resigned and went to work for J. Martland Limited. A junior clerk, Mr S. G. Carter, was promoted to the position with an increase of 5/- a week in his salary. Mr Ray Fauvel was appointed at a salary of £1-5-0 a week and Mr G. Godel received an increase of 5/- a week.

On the 3rd June a farmer appeared before the DOA. A report from the Honorary Parish Inspector, M. S. G. Le Couilliard, alleged that he had failed to declare in his occupation 3 vergées of agricultural côtils. On the same day, Miss Beryl Enid Mourant also appeared before the DOA. She was the administrator of her brother's farm, him being absent from the Island. It was alleged she had failed to declare 4 vergées of agricultural land and was in breach of Article 3, the Cultivation of Lands, (Jersey) Order, 1942. Miss Mourant delivered an explanation to Brée. He, however, was not satisfied with her arguments and referred to the Attorney General. After investigating the matter, the Attorney General decided that, since she was the administrator of the agricultural land in question, and the actual owner was serving with the armed forces of the Crown, no action should be taken against Miss Mourant. However, as the alleged infraction concerned Miss Mourant only, and not the actual owner of the land, Brée asked for proceedings to be instigated.

The DOA on the 20th June decided that, in view of an increase in the salary of Mr Frank Le Maistre, the laboratory assistant at the States Experimental

Station, the Department of Finance and Economics would be asked to open a credit of £35 for his salary.

On the 27th June the situation concerning the employment of Mr Charles Le Cras, of the Grain and Potato Section, was discussed. Mr Le Cras had been absent from his duties because of appendicitis. He had been on full pay. The DOA decided to pay him two-thirds of his salary for two weeks and subsequently half for a further two weeks. On the 29th July the DOA received a further medical certificate excusing Mr Le Cras from fulfilling his duties. The DOA notified him that it would continue to pay half his salary until 12th August 1944 "...after which date his services will terminate".

On the 5th September, Edwin Woodcock, the chemist at the States Experimental Station, died. The DOA requested the Department of Finance and Economics to place at its disposal, for half a day weekly, the services of Mr Francis Crumpton, a staff member of the States Analyst Section. This arrangement operated until the end of the occupation.

On the 6th October the RJA&HS and the JFU met to discuss a suggestion from the JPMA that a scholarship in agriculture be established, as a memorial to the late Mr Woodcock, in recognition of his work to both merchants and farmers. The members present at the meeting decided to set up a scholarship, with their financial backing, with a capital sum of £3,000 and to be made to Jersey-born boys of agricultural descent. Initially, it was decided to award the scholarship for attendance at an English agricultural college. The general opinion was that a subscription should be made from all farmers belonging to the two societies.

On the 28th October the two societies met again to discuss the Woodcock Scholarship. The JPMA voted £400 and individual contributions amounted to a further £150. The societies then decided that the States should be asked to provide instruction in agricultural chemistry, possibly at Victoria College. It was also finally agreed that, to obtain £3,000 to provide the capital for the scholarship, the RJA&HS and the JFU should appoint "Parish Collecting Committees" to take responsibility.

On the 12th September Brée produced the cropping plan for 1945. Copies were circulated to all DOA members and to the Honorary Parish Inspectors.

In the same week, a report from Mr J. Gartrell, Honorary Parish Inspector, described the failure of 3 vergées of rye grown by Mr E. L. Henry, St John. The rye had been sown instead of wheat and oats and was "...a total failure and not worth harvesting." The DOA allowed Mr Henry to graze his cattle on the rye field.

On the 13th October the DOA recommended to the Superior Council that, as from the 1st January 1945, the salary of its secretary, Colin Marie, be increased from £350 to £400 per annum. At the same time, the expenditure for the DOA for the year 1945 was estimated to be £10,620.

The question of the manufacture of sugar beet syrup now became an issue for the two societies, as it had become an increasingly "valuable commodity" as the occupation progressed. The town population did not receive an adequate or fair ration of sugar beet syrup and were asking why it was so difficult to purchase. It was pointed out at a meeting of the societies that the shortage of fuel made it impossible to manufacture the syrup. It was alleged that the branch wood intended as fuel was being burnt at tree-felling sites, instead of being utilised.

Two weeks later Brée appealed to the Honorary Parish Inspectors to provide, from each of their respective parishes, 5 tons of sugar beet for the manufacture of syrup for the public institutions. They were also asked to provide particulars as to the depots established in each parish for the collection of sugar beet. The DOA prepared and had printed receipt books so that farmers delivering sugar beet to these depots could be paid. Deliveries were made in 80 lb non-returnable barrels and payment to farmers was made by Messrs de Gruchy and Brasford (Jam Manufacturers), 4 St Clements Road, St Helier. The Department of Essential Commodities provided the transport from the depots to the premises where the syrup was manufactured.

On the 18th November Major Heider wrote to the Bailiff. The letter was entitled "Preservation of the oat fields". Heider made clear, "I request that the farmers be ordered to preserve all crops arising from oats strewn wild where these are in good condition and where, in the meantime, grass seed has not been sown. A conference has already been held with Jurat Brée. Further, I request that you will order that the turnip leaves are not to be ploughed in, as is often done, but that before harvesting the turnips for feeding the cattle, are washed and used as additional cattle food".[13]

Cattle

"In fulfilling the German demands, no fewer than 1,000 head of cattle were slaughtered between December 18th, 1944, and May 5th, 1945, an average of 40 head a week. Besides this number, the Germans requisitioned 200 head for shipment to Guernsey, over half of this number being, however, still alive in Alderney. There is no doubt that, had slaughtering at this rate continued for some months longer, great injury would have been done to the breed on the Island."

RJA&HS Report, December 1945

In May 1944 the Calf Selection Committee was informed by the DOA that for the months of June, July, August and September, an exemption of 100 heifer calves and three bull calves would be permitted each month.

On the 13th May, George Breuilly sent in an appeal to the Calf Selection Committee for the exemption from slaughter of his calf "Poppy of the Priory" born 2nd May 1944.[14] His appeal was rejected but on the 10th June he sent in a second appeal. This again was dismissed on the same grounds as before. The Calf Selection Committee ordered Breuilly to immediately send the calf to the abattoir. However, on the 24th June Breuilly made a third appeal. The response to the third appeal was clear. "After considerable discussion the Committee maintained its previous decision that the appeal and re-appeal cannot be granted as to do so could cause a precedent."

The official records demonstrate that "Poppy of the Priory" was exported from the Island in March 1946 and that she was born on 27th May 1941, therefore it could not be the calf born on 2nd May 1944. This begs the question as to why the calf was named "Poppy of the Priory" when an animal was already registered with that name. Secondly, why was the calf not sent to the slaughterhouse? It was highly unusual for a calf that was not exempted to be allowed a dispensation. Furthermore, it was unprecedented that after three failed appeals, the calf was still not slaughtered. There are no official sources as to why and there can be only one realistic answer. Breuilly must have received a Calf Exemption Certificate from Pelz and Platzkommandantur I after asking them to intervene. In view of Breuilly's involvement with Pelz and the 1943 Cattle Show Petition, it would have been relatively simple to obtain the required certificate. This was another reason why George Courtman Breuilly was singled out as a collaborator, immediately after the liberation, by many of the Island's elite farmers.

On the 10th June the Cattle Slaughter Executive Committee met with the reporting members of its Parish Committees. These were:

Parish	Name
St Brelade	C. Fiott
St Clement	E. G. Norman
Grouville	A. W. Falle
St Helier	P. J. Mourant
St Martin	C. Le Vesconte
St Lawrence	H. W. Maillard
St Mary	N. J. Perrée
St Ouen	P. H. Le Masurier
St Saviour	C. Quenault
Trinity	A. S. de Gruchy
St Peter	E. R. Egré

The members of the Cattle Slaughter Executive Committee, in June 1944, were:

C. Le Gallais – President
J. B. Michel
F. Le Boutillier
Ph. Le Feuvre
E. C. Pérrèdes
R. W. Carson

At the meeting, it was reported that there were too few cattle being offered for slaughter. Therefore, to maintain a supply to meet the abattoir's requirements, a new "Parish Quota" system was organised. This would call in 30 head, as from the 17th June, to fulfil the German quota demanded. The Parish Committees were ordered at their discretion, to draw cattle from those who were "Not genuine farms and only kept cattle since the occupation".[15] This obviously was a real advantage to the larger well-established cattle farmers who ran the two farming societies. However, in order to allow a modicum of fairness in the selection of cattle for slaughter, a limit was placed on smaller herds on the number of cows that could be selected.

On 1st June Major Heider wrote a letter to the Bailiff entitled "Cattle census". It ordered: "A cattle census is to be carried out on 15th June 1944 in both islands...The Island Administration is to supply by 25th June 1944, three copies of lists showing a summary of the results of the cattle census arranged according to Parishes".[16]

The DOA met on the 6th June to discuss the order. The next day it passed the Livestock (Returns) (Jersey) Order 1944 which was submitted by the Bailiff to Platzkommandantur and approved by Heider and Pelz on the 10th June. On the 28th June, Brée sent the results of the cattle census to the Bailiff for transmission to the German authorities.

On the 18th June, Heider informed the DOA and all civilian authorities: "On account of the military situation a supply of goods from the Continent cannot be guaranteed over the next few months. In order to conserve the present stocks of cereals until the next coming harvest and the supply of meat as long as possible the bread and meat rations are fixed as follows. No meat ration will be available in the week, June 19th to 24th, 1944, and in each alternative week thereafter, but in these weeks the butter ration will increase by 2 ounces".

Heider again wrote to the Bailiff on the 20th June; the letter was entitled "Meat Rationing. Ref: Conference with Jurat Le Masurier and Mr Henry Gaudin of the Slaughterhouse." Both Jurat Le Masurier and Henry Gaudin produced for Heider and Pelz detailed statistics, all written on cards and based on weekly slaughter figures, of the monthly consumption of meat, totalling 20 tons, and the amount of meat rations issued by them three times a week. Computations demonstrated that one Jersey cow provided 120 kilogrammes of meat which meant that 170 head of cattle had to be slaughtered per month to feed the population. Heider, furthermore, made it clear to the Bailiff that, from mid-July 1944, the German forces required a further seventeen to 20 head of livestock weekly from the civil administration. This amounted to an additional 70 head monthly to be taken from herds. The total number of cattle slaughtered amounted to 5% of the total number of animals giving milk, corresponding to a reduction of 30,000 litres in annual milk production.

Platzkommandant Heider, under advice from Pelz in whom he had total confidence, instructed the DOA and the Department of Essential Commodities to consider five points as regards the new demands for meat.

1. The supply of meat with bones.
2. The cancelling of the meat supply to soup kitchens, pointing out that vegetable soup could be prepared in sufficient quantities and in more nourishing form for the poorer part of the civilian population. (Pelz took an active role in procuring more vegetables for the soup kitchens.)
3. Platzkommandantur I had a store of hard cheese. This could be used in place of meat. A ration of hard cheese equal to the food value of meat could be issued once a month.
4. Although Heider's first cattle census had not yet been completed, a further return was required covering the next three months and showing the quantity of livestock intended for delivery and slaughter. Heider wanted this second return by the 1st July 1944. It also had to account for the 2 tons of meat required each week by the German troops. Finally, under directions from Pelz, Heider made clear that the return had to demonstrate the extent to which young cows and heifers could be slaughtered in order to preserve the milk-producing herds.
5. Heider completed his points by emphasising that in times of war great restrictions were required of everyone. He therefore wanted fish to be included in the consideration of meat rationing. He finally instructed both the DOA and the Department of Essential Supplies that a further conference would be held with them in early July.[17]

Brée produced a detailed reply on the 29th June. He based all Heider's and Pelz's points on a civilian population of 38,782. The details of animals that would be available for weekly slaughter were forwarded to Heider and Pelz.

	Weight
30 cows, average weight 230 lbs each	6,900 lbs
100 calves, average weight 37 lbs each	3,700 lbs
Pigs	1,000 lbs
Total Weekly	11,600 lbs

Several meetings took place between the 6th and 8th July, Brée calculating that 36 head of cattle would have to be slaughtered every week, approximating to 150 head monthly. The Bailiff met with MVR von Aufsess and "Dr Pelz" to discuss Brée's figures. The Bailiff stated that a basic ration of 4 ounces of meat each fortnight, together with other allowances mentioned in Brée's figures, could maintain the number of cattle without any reduction in overall herd integrity. This satisfied both von Aufsess and Pelz. The DOA then discussed meat requirements for the Germans. The possible outcomes of issuing meat rations to both German and civilian populations were evaluated. Brée put forward detailed plans and was authorised to conduct all negotiations with the German authorities: "The number of cattle which it was possible to slaughter had to be negotiated without causing damage to the Island milk supply."

After these meetings Pelz asked Brée to produce a list of the number of herds in each parish.[18] His request was for two reasons. Firstly, he wanted to cross-reference the previous animal census with Brée's figure of there being 1,199 herds. The second reason was explained by Heider's letter to the Bailiff dated 1st July, entitled "Livestock census: Repetition Order dated 1st June 1944." Heider wrote: "The returns of the livestock census are incomplete and therefore useless compared with last year's census, there is a reduction of 2,000 in the herds of cattle, although in this period only 1,600 head were slaughtered. Both Jurat Brée and Jurat Le Masurier contest the accuracy of these returns and state that the farmers make a return of fewer cattle than they actually own, in order to avoid delivery. In addition, a sector of the farmers had not sent in the forms. In fact, Pelz had visited six farms on the 6th June and discovered that three had made no cattle returns."

In consequence, Heider ordered another census and that the DOA direct and take responsibility for the census and to use the Honorary Parish Inspectors and Milk Testers to verify the figures. In addition, he ordered special passes to be produced in English and German for the census takers and a list of dairy farms for every parish. This census took place between the 6th and 9th July 1944. The returns were with Heider by the 13th July.[16]

It is interesting to note that between the 1st June and 13th July 1944, the number of cattle on the Island confirmed by a census varied between 6,938, 7,812 and 9,092. Therefore, within seven weeks, the head of cattle increased by 2,154 – if we are to believe the official census figures! They demonstrate that in the period June–July 1944 dairy farmers were extremely reluctant to comply and to cooperate with the successful completion of any German cattle census.

On the 14th October the Cattle Slaughter Executive Committee met with the "Reporting Members" of the Parish Committees. The secretary was H. G. Shepard. The meeting began with correspondence which stated, "It was reported that the German authorities had ordered a meat ration every week in future and that thereafter a minimum of 25 head weekly would be required for slaughter." After a period of consternation amongst the members, Shepard explained the procedure that "On receipt of information from the DOA cattle from certain herds where milk production is below average should be selected for slaughter". The Committee agreed that this, as a policy, was acceptable.[15]

On the 24th October the DOA met to discuss the case of Mr H. Dorey, Trinity, who had alleged the theft of a heifer. He was called before the DOA and Brée instructed him to produce an affidavit to that effect. The stolen heifer was eighteen months old, but it had not been slaughtered within fourteen days of birth as required by the Newly-Born Calves (Jersey) Order, 1941. Brée decided to refer the matter to the Crown Officers. The Solicitor General investigated the case. He decided that any legal action was unlikely to succeed. Brée, therefore, "...administered a severe warning to Mr Dorey." As a result, the Livestock (Jersey) Order, 1942 was amended on the 1st November 1944, the amendment stating: "In the event of the theft of any livestock, the person having the custody of the animal, shall within 24 hours, give notice in writing to the DOA."

On the 14th November the German authorities wrote to the DOA "... intimating that they require certain quantities of meat for the requirement of the troops and such meat to be provided from the Island cattle".[19] The DOA decided "To safeguard as far as possible the Island breed of cattle, the selection of the animals should be placed in the hands of the Cattle Slaughter Executive Committee". The Committee met on the 24th November. Carlyle Le Gallais opened the meeting stating, "It was reported that the occupying forces required almost immediately 7 metric tons of meat weekly from Island cattle representing 50 to 60 head, this with the civic requirements of 35 head weekly would absorb in 3 months, 1,000 animals or about 10% of the cattle population".[15]

The Committee decided that, firstly, the requirements of both civil and military authorities had to be considered together. Secondly, that the selection of cattle for slaughter to meet these requirements had to be carried out by the Committee working with the parochial slaughter committees. Thirdly, that payments to farmers, whether it be meat for civilians or Germans, should be made at the RJA&HS offices, as a separate organisation. Le Gallais believed that if cattle farmers dealt directly with the DOA over slaughter payments, confusion would prevail.

The Committee, whilst discussing the selection of cattle for slaughter, and with a view to finding bulls that were redundant, decided to obtain from all owners of stud bulls, lists of the services by their bulls for the past twelve months. It furthermore suggested that parishes which had not supplied their quotas should immediately make good the deficiencies. It was also agreed, and not for the first time, that herds where the milk supply was below average would be called upon to supply the cattle.

The RJA&HS was determined that this was an excellent opportunity to cull and decrease the number of animals that were poor milk producers. Shepard submitted a detailed scheme for dealing with herds, in alphabetical order, omitting those which had supplied cattle during the last six months. The parochial slaughter committees were advised to work upon these lines.

On the 25th November a conference was held between the civilian authorities and societies to discuss the increasing German demands for meat. Present were Brée, du Val and Gibaut of the DOA, plus the two "adjoint" members, Le Gallais and Mallet. Also present were the RJA&HS and JFU councils and the three secretaries of the DOA, RJA&HS and JFU namely, Marie, Shepard and Messervy. The meeting was attended by approximately thirty farmers.

Brée chaired the meeting. He firstly read in full the translation of the letter sent by German Platzkommandantur I, dated the 14th November 1944. It demanded that the Island supply 7.2 metric tons of meat weekly from the 10th December 1944 to the 31st January 1945, and 8.2 metric tons weekly thereafter, for feeding the German troops in occupation of the Island. Brée stated that the Germans would accept cattle at live weight, and that with local civilian requirements he estimated that between ninety and 100 head of cattle would be required weekly. The Germans would also accept a proportion of horse meat.

It was unanimously agreed that only the RJA&HS Cattle Slaughter Executive Committee would select and authorise the requisition of cattle. John du Val stressed that there had to be uniformity in selection amongst all parishes. Brée urged that only horses not of any use be released for slaughter. A discussion was also held on the knock-on effects on the provision of fresh milk and butter.

The official RJA&HS report on the matter states the following: "In fulfilling the German demands, no fewer than 1,000 head of cattle were slaughtered between December 18th 1944, and May 5th 1945, an average of 40 head a week. Beside this number, the Germans requisitioned 200 head for shipment to Guernsey, over half of this number being, however, still alive in Alderney. There is no doubt that, had slaughtering at this rate continued for some months longer, great injury would have been done to the breed on the island".[20]

In the period between March and April 1944, Colonel Knackfuss was ordered by Headquarters in Paris to leave the Island. Shortly before Knackfuss left to go to France, he purchased a bull and a cow and he left Jersey with the two animals. The purchase and expenses were remitted to College House. However, no payments were made by the German authority and, in consequence, Brée wrote to the Bailiff in November 1944 with a request for an approach to be made to the German authorities for payment which had been left outstanding.[21]

What became of the Jersey bull and cow? Their fate was summarised in the following report.

"Strangest story is that of the German Commandant's souvenirs. Early in 1944 the erstwhile Commandant of Jersey received orders to move elsewhere in occupied territory. To remind him of his sojourn in Jersey he decided to take a Jersey cow and a Jersey bull. These were duly bought, paid for, and shipped to France. Not many months after, came D-Day. The tide of battle rolled along the Cotentin peninsula and the Brittany coast and died away as the German armies were rolled backwards toward their homeland. A year later V.E. Day liberated the Island and contact with the outside world restored. In 1946 news came from the Syndicat des Eleveurs de la Race Jersiaise (the French-Jersey breed Society) that, in a Normandy village, had been discovered a Jersey cow and a Jersey bull, with, strangely enough, some documentary evidence that the animals were indeed the Commandant's souvenirs. Where he went or what became of him, we do not know. Possibly when at last the German forces were in retreat superfluous belongings, such as Jersey cattle, had to be abandoned, and our poor Commandant had perforce to leave his souvenirs in charge of a villager, to await collection".[22]

Field Command 515: Change in Status

In March 1944 the decision was made to turn the Channel Islands into a "Festungen" (Fortress), the reason being that it had become obvious that the Allies would invade Europe sometime in 1944. This invasion would include a possible attack, or siege of Jersey, as well as the other islands. In the summer of 1944, the Island came under the control of Oberst Siegfried Heine, who was now the senior military officer in Jersey having originally arrived in 1943. From this point Field Command 515 was overridden by the army.

Therefore, in the event of an Allied invasion of Europe, the German Military Government at St Germain, Paris, decided to reduce the Feldkommandantur to a Platzkommandantur. It therefore withdrew Oberst Knackfuss and a number of senior staff to St Lô, in order to fill the need for experienced experts on the Continent, and placed Stabchef (Chief of Staff) Major Wilhelm Heider in charge as the Platzkommandant of Platzkommandantur I, Channel Islands, as of May 1944.

In post-war interviews Heider was clear that Heine was content for Platzkommandantur I to carry on operating as they had before as Field Command 515. There was, however, one major difference: Platzkommandantur I was no longer responsible for court cases. From here on all court cases were held by the Festungkommandant, Oberst Heine.[23]

Hans Egon Pelz was ordered by von Schmettow, sometime between the 10th and 16th June 1944, to serve in France. Pelz, however, did not leave the Island until the very end of August or early September 1944. His next deployment was in the Somme region where he become responsible for the repair of communications. In October he wrote a letter to his comrades at College House informing them that he was well. At the end of the war, Pelz was in Italy and was captured by Italian partisans. He returned to Salzburg a month later.

References

1. Jersey Archive. C/B/A1/10.
2. Le Ruez, Elisabeth. The Jersey Cow and its Island Home. RJA&HS. c.1993, p. 7.
3. Jersey Archive. B/A/W31/2/124.
4. Elizabeth Lady Knott.
5. A. Allix and A. Gilson. November 2000. Société Jersiaise Photographic Archive. Éditions Emile. Occupation at leisure 1940–1944.

6. Jersey Archive. B/A/W31/2/125.

7. RJA&HS and JFU Joint Emergency Committee Minutes.

8. Interview between the late Mr Jack Le Sueur, cattle farmer, Clairvale Farm, La Rue de Mannelier, St Saviour and Mr Alan Allix, a co-founder of the Channel Island Occupation Society. My thanks to Mr Allix for allowing me the use of his notes.

9. Anecdotal evidence suggests that Dr Kempt was happy to treat Island cattle, free of charge, a service taken up by farmers.

10. To date it has not been possible to discover where the German weighbridge was sited.

11. Jersey Archives. D/Z/H5/141.

12. The farmer was almost certainly Edward John Louis Paisnel. He carried out a series of thirteen serious assaults during the years 1960 to 1971 and became known as the "Beast of Jersey" in the national press.

13. Jersey Archive. B/A/W31/143.

14. RJA&HS Herd Book, No 53114.

15. Jersey Archive. L/D/09/A11.

16. Jersey Archive. B/A/W41/20.

17. Jersey Archive. B/A/W31/1/113.

18. Jersey Archive. B/A/W31/2/122.

19. Jersey Archive. B/A/W40/2/3.

20. RJA&HS. Report of the Committee for the years 1940 to 1945, presented to the Annual General Meeting. 8th December 1945, p. 7.

21. Jersey Archive. B/A/W31/2/140.

22. The Jersey at Home, Vl.4, No 2, August 1954, p. 3.

23. Interview with Heider by Alan Allix, a founder member of the C.I.O.S.

Chapter 17

December 1944 to 8th May 1945

Milk Control

*"The supply of liquid milk to the civilian population...shall cease,
in place of such liquid milk, the members of the civilian population,
shall be issued with ten grams of butter per day provided that the
requirements of the army in occupation in relation to butter
first shall be satisfied."*

Letter from German authorities to Brée

After the Allied invasion of Europe had taken place and the Channel Islands were effectively cut off from mainland Europe, the German forces ordered that 23,000 litres of full-fat milk a month be requisitioned from the Don Street Dairy. In late autumn 1944, Heider modified this order so that German troops henceforth be allocated 20,000 litres of skimmed milk and 3,000 litres of full-fat milk. The latter allocation went to German military hospitals. The order to change to skim milk was to allow the manufacture of an extra 1,000 kilos of butter a month which was ordered by Platzkommandantur. It was delivered by the dairy to the Verpflegungausgabestelle, which also paid for it.[1] This metric ton was in addition to the butter the German Forces were already requisitioning. Heider made clear that butter delivered to the German military hospitals had to be in fresh condition.[2]

It was only a matter of weeks before a new requisition was ordered. This was the collection of eggs from all farmers. The German authorities ordered that the Connétables be empowered to issue egg requisition orders. The reason that the Connétables were singled out to expedite this order "...in the event of the holder of fowls not being inclined to supply the eggs voluntarily" was that it was unlikely anyone would contradict their Connétable.

The Bailiff was informed by the German authorities that, unless the eggs were supplied, an order would be issued to slaughter all fowls. This order had already been carried out in France by the German Military Government. The Connétables were disconsolate at the prospect of entering their parishioners' farms and removing eggs.³ Several of them personally made representations to the Bailiff not to have to carry out these requirements but were ordered to undertake them.

Several weeks later Heider ordered that the numbers of eggs be increased. He made clear this was necessitated by the numbers of wounded German soldiers arriving at Island military hospitals. The Bailiff, worried about the increasing agricultural requisitions, wrote to the President of Essential Supplies: "In the present state of food supplies, I think every effort should be made to have this increase cancelled or modified."

On the 30th November 1944, the Bailiff agreed to the following measures to save 4 tons of butter for December 1944 and January 1945.

1. A discontinuation of the weekly butter ration to all farmers.
2. The reduction of milk to farmers to feed and raise their calves.
3. A discontinuation of full-fat milk to all school children.
4. The reduction in milk allocations to civilian hospitals and individuals with medical certificates.
5. A reduction of the milk allocation to all normal civilian consumers of 7½%. This equated to one milkless day in every fourteen days.

These deprivations forced upon civilians and carried out by the Jersey administration did not satisfy the German authorities. On the 1st December the DOA received a letter demanding that immediate changes be made to the Milk Control (Jersey) Order, 1940. These amendments concerned the Adult, Child and Juvenile Milk Registration, respectively cited as MR1, MR2 and MR3 certificates. These certificates were issued by the DOA under the Milk (Registration with Retailers) (Jersey) Order, 1940.

The major amendment ordered by Platzkommandandtur was that the maximum amount of milk supplied by all licensed retailers to their customers should not exceed "one half pint per day" for holders of the Adult Milk Registration Certificate and "one pint per day" for holders of the Child and Juvenile Milk Registration Certificates. This amendment came into force on the 11th December 1944.

Within a few weeks the Platzkommandant made another order. He demanded that the frequency of the adult ration change from 1 pint a day to 1 pint every three days. This later order was implemented by the DOA on the 15th January 1945.

On the 5th December the DOA decided that, in view of the hours during which the electricity supply was not available, making it impossible for milk to be processed, the dairies themselves could not be held responsible for sour milk. The DOA also informed the dairies to take every precaution to guard against "dirty milk" supplied to them by farmers. It was also decided that henceforth registered consumers would not be allowed to transfer from one licensed retailer to another, the only exception being when a consumer changed their residence.

On the 12ᵗʰ December, Milk Control reviewed the daily milk yields per head of the Island's herds. Four herds stood out as producing low milk yields. These belonged to G. de la Haye and Mrs Le Sueur, both in St Helier; F. R. Billot, St Saviour; and H. Le Brocq, St Ouen. All were written to and informed that their herds would be recommended to the Cattle Slaughter Executive Committee for slaughter. Mr de la Haye wrote back arguing against this measure. Brée, however, was determined not to modify his decision.

On the 19ᵗʰ December, following the reduction of the milk supply to civilian adults, the DOA changed the amount of milk retained by a producer in respect of a child aged two years and above. This was amended to 1½ pints a day and extended to the children of servants. The amendment was communicated to the States Medical Officer.

On the same day, John du Val requested Brée to arrange a meeting with the German authorities. He wanted to ask them to provide a quantity of diesel oil "For issue to farmers so that light be made available for the morning milking."

The dairies were also struggling to process milk without an adequate supply of electricity. Brée personally intervened and hired a dynamo from the Parish of St Helier at 10/- a week. This was used to supply light at the Don Street Dairy when public lighting was discontinued.

On the 2ⁿᵈ January 1945, the DOA called in for an interview H. G. Shephard, Secretary of the Cattle Slaughter Executive Committee, and D. Buesnel, a Milk Tester. An allegation had been made that cattle ostensibly in the custody of Captain Guy Janvrin Robin, were in fact in the custody of Mr E. N. Pallot, St Saviour. In consequence, it was alleged, Captain Guy was drawing milk to which he would not normally be entitled. The final allegation was that Mr Pallot had supplied milk to Captain Robin, the latter not being a member of the farmer's household nor employed by the farmer in tending his cattle. The DOA decided to refer the matter to the Attorney General.

These allegations went back to December 1944 when Captain Robin was notified by the Cattle Slaughter Executive Committee to send in a cow for slaughter and he had replied that he owned no cows. The Slaughter Committee, however, obtained on the 30ᵗʰ December 1944 all Captain Robin's transactions on the sale and purchase of cows. The last sale was a cow to George Amy Romeril on the 23ʳᵈ November 1944. This led to a discussion as to whether Robin actually owned any cattle.

On the 5ᵗʰ January 1945 Colin Marie wrote to the Attorney General. The letter stated, "The DOA directed me to refer to you certain information concerning the cattle of Mr E. N. Pallot and Captain Guy J. Robin." On the 10ᵗʰ January the Attorney General, after carefully examining the DOA's transfer of animal documentation between Captain Robin and Mr Pallot, ordered the Chef de Police to thoroughly investigate the matter.[4] The Chef de Police concluded his report on the 25ᵗʰ January. He replied to the Attorney General, confirming that the animal in question, which it was alleged belonged to Mr Pallot, had in fact been sold to George Amy Romeril in

November 1944. The report also confirmed that Mr Pallot's and Captain Robin's cows were milked separately.

On the 29th January the Attorney General wrote to Brée, who had referred the case to him as being identical to that of J. B. Michel on the 28th April 1942. The Attorney General, however, disagreed and noted several differences with the Michel case. Firstly, Captain Robin's and Mr Pallot's properties were on one estate. Secondly, the persons to whom Michel had claimed to have transferred the custody of his cows lived on entirely separate properties and were not Mr Michel's tenants. Thirdly, Captain Robin's cows were always milked separately from Mr Pallot's, and the milk records were signed by him. In Mr Michel's case, all the cows were milked with his cows, the milk placed in the same containers, and all the milk reports, covering not only his cows but also those whose custody he claimed to have transferred to other persons, were signed by him. Finally, the Attorney General made clear that all milk reports were consistent with Captain Robin's claim. Therefore, there was little chance of any prosecution succeeding.

On the 31st January, the DOA wrote to the Attorney General. The DOA made it clear that, in view of his detailed assessment of the case, it would no longer ask for any action to be taken.[5] The following week the Cattle Slaughter Executive Committee discussed again the issue of the cow that Captain Robin had refused to send for slaughter. It was reported to the Committee that Robin had sold the cow to Pallot, who was therefore ordered by the Committee to provide two cows for slaughter.

In early January 1945 the Milk Control Section carried out an investigation of all milk yields. This would show the daily average milk yield per head of cattle during the previous twelve months ending the 31st December 1944. Five farmers were highlighted, and four named, as having herds which consistently produced low milk yields. These four were J. A. Dallain, E. Le Cornu, C. Simon and G. A. Vautier. The latter had also "...purposely ignored communications from the DOA as he found them very tiresome." Brée advised the Slaughter Committee that cattle for slaughter be selected from these herds as "The milk production of these herds is of little value to the Island." The four producers were informed in writing directly by Brée of the consequences of their low milk yields. Mr Simon appeared before the DOA to argue against the slaughter of his animals. Brée refused to modify the decision.

On 9th January a Milk Tester, C. Henry, became ill. An authorisation was made to pay him two-thirds of his salary. On the same day S. C. Baudains resigned and was replaced by R. Le Masurier.

On 16th January, the DOA referred the entire herd of S. M. Le Gros, St Martin, for slaughter. Brée had looked at the very low milk yields and decided that the herd was of little value to the civilian population.

The same day the Milk Control Section sent an enquiry concerning the prices to be charged to the German authorities "...for the butter supplied against the demands of the occupying forces." The German authority had made a further demand for butter from civilian stocks, dated the 9th January 1945. Brée replied stating that, since this was a requisition order, no charge was to be made for the butter. Milk Control was ordered instead to notify the Department of Finance and Economics of the quantity and prices of the butter delivered, "...so that the value may be entered in the costs of the army of occupation." On the 6th February, the DOA directed Milk Control to inform the Department of Finance and Economics that the price of butter requisitioned by the German forces was 4/2¾ per pound weight.

The issue of the continued maintenance of the Island's milk supply was discussed by the RJA&HS early in December 1944. The Cattle Slaughter Executive Committee, alongside its Parish reporting members, all agreed that "In selecting cattle for slaughter every consideration must be given to the maintenance of the public milk supply and the preservation of the best specimens of the breed." The leading dairy farmers were clear in their policy that milk supply from herds that gave consistently below average milk yields, or that farmers who had illicit dealings on the black market in milk or butter, would result in cattle from those offending herds initially being called upon for slaughter.

The milk supply problems were the central issue for a meeting called by Brée on the 13th January 1945. The importance of the meeting can be seen from the fact that twenty-five of the Island's leading farmers gathered to listen to Brée. These were farmers with the largest herds and who were without question the largest landowners.

Brée began the meeting by stating that the question of milk supply had been discussed with Red Cross officials and that the Germans had ordered that no butter rations were to be issued at present to the civilian population. In addition, they had ordered adults to be given only 2 pints of milk a week. Children and those with medical certificates, along with famers, were allowed to keep their full ration. Brée informed the meeting that he would obtain a supplementary quantity of skim milk in lieu of the civilian butter ration stopped by the German forces.

On the 17th January Heider wrote a letter to the Bailiff entitled "Collection of milk." On the previous day, the Department of Transport had reported that "The production of gas wood for the gazogene milk lorries had dropped from 14 to 6 tons per week." The reasons were the ending of the electricity supply and lack of coal for drying wood for the gazogene lorries. Heider pointed out that milk collection lorries each needed 9 tons of dried wood per week and the lack of it was seriously endangering the Island-wide milk collections for both the civilian and military populations.

Heider, in response to the problem, allocated petrol from the German Military Command of the Channel Islands. He, however, insisted that economies were to be made in the petrol consumption of other forms of civil transport. This extra allocation for the lorries was taken from the 14,000 litres of petrol per month which the civilian administration received from the German Military Command. Furthermore, he insisted that petrol supplies for civilian ambulances be discontinued, and horse-driven carts used instead. This transportation, he added, was to be used for the removal of corpses from the hospitals.[6]

On the 23rd January, the DOA recommended to the Superior Council that the supply of milk to elementary and private schools should resume. A week later, in view of German orders, producer-retailer licences were issued for the supply of milk to military forces to: Edmund P. Romeril, P. Tréhard and, several weeks later, Carlyle Le Gallais and Albert J. Henry.

This increase in fresh milk supplied from producer-retailers to the German forces led to a shortage of milk cans. Heider, in an attempt to clear up this "matter" ordered that 100 milk cans be made available from the DOA to provide the extra milk to German forces.[7]

Brée now decided to request a new investigation into the milk supply and, on the 6th February 1945, the report was completed. It was not pleasant reading for Brée and the DOA Committee. It stated that "Considerable quantities of milk are being received in town in a condition making it unfit for distribution to the public." This was the most distressing aspect of the report, in relation to the public milk supply. A notice was inserted in the local press stressing the absolute necessity of milk producers taking every precaution to ensure that milk was received in a hygienic condition for distribution to the public. All producers were warned that, if milk was received at the collecting dairies in an unfit condition, they would receive a drastically reduced price of 6 pence per pot. The law already existed to carry out this threat, under the provision of Article 5(4) of the Milk Control (Jersey) Order, 1940.

Two weeks later a follow up report stated "...considerable quantities of milk are being received sour from producers." This problem now reached a point where Brée decided he must act decisively. He appointed men to travel with the milk collecting lorries who were to examine all milk containers and liquid milk at the collecting depots before they were sent to the dairy. These men were initially given the title "Examiners". They were instructed to report to Milk Control any milk which they found to be sour, or in a dirty container. This then led to an immediate reduction in the price paid by the DOA to the producer.

On the 27th February these "Examiners" were subsequently referred to as "Inspectors of milk and milk containers" to distinguish them from "Milk Testers". They were paid 10/- a week more than the Milk Testers. The first Inspectors employed were: N. Balleine, C. de la Court, A. Hall, and W. Tirel. About the same time, D. Buesnel resigned as a Milk Tester and Mr P. A. Nicolle and Mr C. J. Le Brocq were subsequently employed as Temporary Milk Testers.

On the 10th February the DOA received a letter from the Platzkommandant requiring that Milk Testers give to "...the German troops in control of milk such information as the troops required." On the 6th March, the German forces ordered from the DOA further supplies of milk for their troops. The following producer-retailer licensees were authorised to supply fresh milk to German troops: Mr P. du Feu, St Peter, Mr C. J. G. Lair, Trinity, and Mrs K. Payn, Grouville. The number of producers authorised to supply fresh milk kept increasing. The German authorities, however, were convinced that producers were holding back milk that should have been sent to the German troops. Heider wrote a letter to the Bailiff entitled "Delivery of milk". He demanded that a report be sent to him detailing the average milk yield per cow for January 1945, for those farmers who had delivered milk to German forces.[8] These were as follows.

W. J. Vibert	Douet de Rue	St Lawrence
A. S. Barette	Raworth Farm	St Lawrence
E. H. Vibert	Midlands Farm	St Lawrence
H. N. Renouf	China Quarries	St Lawrence
H. A. Pipon	Oaklands Farm	St Lawrence
A. S. Pipon	Highlands Farm	St Lawrence
J. B. Laurens	La Chasserie	St Lawrence
P. E. Jean	Les Noyers	St Lawrence
E. M. Guerin	Le Coin Farm	St Lawrence
G. W. Honvre	Carrefour Selous	St Lawrence
B. Bichard	Beechlands	St Lawrence
J. Priaulx	St Cyr	St John
J. Arthur	Les Ruettes	St John

The problem of farmers sending dirty milk to the collecting depots reappeared again in March. On the 5th March, Milk Control reported that dirty milk cans from two producers had directly led to a distribution of milk unfit for the public. When dirty milk was added to a lorry's collection, in effect the entire collection went bad. Brée recommended that the herds of two producers, Mrs L. de la Haye and Mr W. Lucas, St Martin, have cattle selected for slaughter. He gave the reason that these two farmers had "...twice been penalised in respect of dirty cans."

The issue of dirty milk had become a matter of increasing exasperation and annoyance to Brée. The problem had surfaced almost from the beginning of the German occupation, and he was determined to deal with it. The two farmers were given a fortnight to find a solution to their problem of "dirty milk cans." On the 20th March, a follow up report concerning these two milk producers made it clear that, while no further reports had been received as to the cleanliness of Mrs de la Haye's milk containers, further reports had been received in relation to Mr Lucas. He was summoned to appear before the DOA the following week.

On the 27th March Mrs Lucas, representing her husband, appeared before the DOA. She was informed that "The milk cans of Mr Lucas are frequently found to be in a dirty condition." Brée gave her a warning that "Any further reports of dirty cans being received, the DOA will feel obliged to require that cattle for slaughter shall be drawn from the herd of Mr Lucas."

On the 7th March Brée spoke to Pelz's friend and fellow administrator, Pokorni, who was in charge of the Island's public utilities. He informed Pokorni that, as from the 11th March, the Don Street Dairy would run out of fuel from its civilian sources and therefore cease production. This in effect would put an end to the supply of milk and butter to the German forces. In response Pokorni released a quantity of coal to be used by Don Street Dairy. The coal however was of such poor quality it could only be used mixed with tar. The Platzkommandant ordered the Bailiff to release stocks of coal from the Gas Company to Don Street Dairy.[9]

On the 8th March the new Platzkommandant, von Cleve, wrote to the Bailiff. The letter was entitled "Milk deliveries to Soldatenheim." He ordered that the quantity of skimmed milk delivered to Soldatenheim I be increased by 10 litres daily to 50 litres. In addition, La Hougue Soldatenheim's delivery of fresh milk by Mr Le Rossignol, La Hougue Farm, St Peter, increase to 20 litres with immediate effect.[10]

This was soon followed by a further letter from von Cleve, entitled "Ceding a room for the manufacture of curd." For technical reasons von Cleve wanted a room at the back of Don Street Dairy to be used to manufacture curd. He therefore requisitioned the sheds there. Von Cleve called the manager of the dairy, A. F. Hamon, and the technical expert J. Pluck, to discuss the technical details of manufacturing curd. Both men were appalled at having to spend long periods with von Cleve discussing and assisting the establishment of a curd-producing factory on behalf of the Germans. In fact, after several weeks of assisting the German authorities, they were both genuinely worried of future reprisals if they were to be perceived as German collaborators. The manufacture of curd required von Cleve to requisition the stomachs of slaughtered calves. These were collected and paid for by the German forces and taken to Don Street Dairy.[11]

Early in March 1945 the German authorities issued further instructions to the Superior Council concerning civilian milk supplies. These included the retention by milk producers of only half a pint of milk daily for themselves and their servants. Children were still allowed to retain their previous ration. The previous act of the DOA from December 1944 was amended and this new order came into force on the 13th March 1945.

On the same day, a report reached the DOA concerning "The dirty condition of the milk containers used by R. Y. Thérin, St Mary." He was summoned to appear before the DOA and on the 18th April a further report on the milk delivered by him stated "Once again milk was delivered in filthy containers." However, he did not actually appear before them until the 1st May. This non-appearance after being called in by the DOA was highly unusual. Brée referred Thérin's herd to the Cattle Slaughter Executive Committee.

On the 20th March, the German authorities ordered the DOA to issue producer-retailer licences to three farmers: John Philip du Val, St Helier; Peter Francis Allo, St Lawrence; and Mr Joseph Kerhoat, St Martin. These licences gave them "...authority to supply milk to the German forces as required." Two weeks later the German authorities instructed the DOA that more milk supplies were required. The DOA authorised another producer-retailer licence, to Mr John Douglas Arthur, St John, to provide milk to German forces.

On the 19th March, Weeks wrote a detailed letter to Brée. He begins his report by stating in stark terms the challenges faced by his department concerning milk production and collection, the effects of cattle slaughtering, butter manufacture, and the increasing control on all of these by the German military. The letter is of immense historical value as Weeks details all the problems faced by Milk Control since 1940. The report is highly reliable, written by the person who dealt directly with all milk orders and who was administering and scrutinising the Milk Testers and their reports.

Weeks states that he was appointed Secretary-Accountant of the Milk Control Section, in February 1940 and then Manager of the Don Street Dairy. His two primary responsibilities were to run the provisions of the milk order and to maintain a supply of milk to the civilian population. He saw the period 1940 to 1944 as a time when, although the German Field Command increased their orders, he carried out their directions with "...as good a grace as possible...without causing much inconvenience." It is interesting to note that these were the years Pelz ran his department, "Agriculture and Food Supplies", for Field Command 515.[12] However, the Allied invasion of France had caused the Germans to tighten their control and since January 1945 "The German Agricultural Office had taken over Milk Control." Weeks makes clear this had "...rendered my efforts futile." He also states that he has lost his dignity. The effects of the German occupation are summarised.

Firstly, he describes milk production: "Although the DOA have their official Testers, German inspectors are working in each parish. They are to be found testing, in addition to our men, or waiting at the farms to watch them at their jobs; in fact, prying into everything being done. They ask the same questions our men do, and they do not hesitate to call on our Testers at their homes. The Constable of St Ouen [Francis le Boutillier] was recently asked by the Germans to convene two of our Testers in order that our men supply certain information."

"The German inspectors do not hesitate to demand of the producers information as they require and their appearance in uniform carries more weight than our men in civilian clothes. German and local Testers are calling in on our producers, the same work duplicated, the same questions asked. All this is making the DOA's work look ridiculous. Some producers openly boast of keeping back milk because such milk would find its way to Don

Street to be used for butter-making for the Germans. Little use talking to them [Germans] about sick people, children and the possible restoration of milk on milkless days if the surplus is increased."

Weeks' next topic is milk collection, describing German efforts "...to cut down the territories covered by the collecting dairymen" and that the new "Naval Control" had added extra difficulties.

The distribution of milk is then described. "The adoption of the German proposal to institute three milkless days per week for adults has led to a relaxation in control over retailers. The four collecting dairymen [dairies] particularly have been subjected to frequent German inspection and questioning." Weeks, furthermore, explains that the 3 milkless days had led to extra work for Milk Control which resulted in "...whatever quantity of milk is saved means more butter for the Germans."

In addition: "The recent adoption of the German proposal to reduce the amount which a producer be allowed to retain from the produce of his herd is bound to make our control appear more futile than ever. The average producer will do nothing about it except go on taking the same amount (and more) as before, whilst the DOA keeps up the show of checking the milk yield each month. The producer is always thinking that more milk for Don Street Dairy means more butter for the Germans."

"The adoption of the German order to cut down milk consumption by the sick, in their homes and in institutions, led the DOA to write to some of the institutions concerning the over consumption of milk. In some cases, the persons written to were seriously concerned that they are wondering why we are trying to increase the surplus to Don Street Dairy [in German hands]."

Weeks' description of the German takeover of Milk Control was covered by the next section entitled "Butter Production." He begins: "Herein lies the root of the evil, the requisitioning of butter turned the Don Street Dairy from a factory assisting our country men into one assisting the enemy...As manager of the Dairy, the Germans constantly refer to me for all sorts of information. Queries by telephone and in person are frequent occurrences as well as inspections and questionings. In fact, as time goes on, I am becoming no more than a collaborator...It is useless to tell outsiders that we are sticking to our jobs simply to ensure the supply of skim and curd to the public. We are told that the taking over of these two commodities by the Germans is only a matter of time."

He completes his report by stating, "You will see that all this brings me more and more into daily collaboration with the enemy. I am a public servant, paid with the public's money and the public is getting nothing in return; in fact, I am being paid to do work which is helping the Germans. My position is, therefore, impossible and I beg the DOA to release me of my responsibility at an early date".[13]

On the same day as Weeks' letter of the 19th March, Mr A. F. Hamon, the Factory Manager, and Mr J. Pluck, Factory Engineer, of the Don Street Dairy also submitted their written resignations to Brée. Their reason for resigning was that whilst assisting in the supply of (milk) by-products to the public, they were principally assisting the enemy in the manufacture of butter. Both men were extremely worried that after the war an enquiry would examine the reasons as to why they had assisted the Germans. They believed this could eventually have an adverse and important effect on their careers.

It, however, appears that the Bailiff, Superior Council and Brée collectively asked Messrs Weeks, Hamon and Pluck to withdraw their resignations for two weeks. Brée stated to them, "That some plan was being formed by the enemy which might cause the resignations to be swallowed up in a more serious action." The three men temporarily withdrew their resignations.[14]

On the 21st March, the German authorities wrote Brée a six-page document containing new demands. He viewed this as calamitous. The letter was entitled "Supply of milk for civilians and the forces".[15]

The German authorities ordered that "The supply of liquid milk to the civilian population, with certain conditional exceptions therein specified, shall cease and that, in place of such liquid milk, the members of the civilian population, other than those still entitled to receive liquid milk in virtue of the exceptions aforesaid, shall be issued with ten grammes of butter per day provided that the requirements of the army of occupation in relation to butter first shall be satisfied." Brée immediately understood that there were no guarantees that any butter existed that could be available to the civilian population. He was most of all concerned that the supply of milk for children, adolescents and the sick would not be forthcoming.

In response to the above order, on the 26th March 1945 the Bailiff informed Brée that he had communicated with the German Commandant that he had no knowledge of any such arrangement. Brée made clear to the Superior Council that he and the DOA were not prepared to fulfil the requirements of the German authorities. In response, therefore, he personally submitted a series of counter propositions to the German authorities. These were as follows.

1. That the German authorities requisition the entire Don Street Dairy, together with the machinery, plant, and utensils from the Jersey Co-operative Dairy Company Limited.

2. That the DOA would guarantee a minimum quantity of 4,900 pots of whole milk to be supplied to the dairy each day for the next six months. This quantity of milk was sufficient to enable the German authorities to manufacture 19 tons of butter each month. This fulfilled the requirements of all the German troops. The resultant quantity of skim milk, 2,250 pots per day, was sufficient for the manufacture of 15 tons of curd.

3. That the deficit of 10 tons of butter and 30 tons of curd, the German requirement being 29 tons of butter and 45 tons of curd per month, was to be made up to the German authorities with 80 Island cattle per month, in addition to the present quota of cattle requisitioned by them in the letter dated 14th December 1944.

In order to preserve the Island's breed as far as possible, Brée decided that no meat whatsoever would be supplied to the civilian population.

On the 3rd April Brée met with the German authorities to discuss their milk demands and his counter proposals. He made clear to them that Jersey cows only produced 2 pots of milk daily. The German response was that in reality the Jersey cow produced 3 pots of milk daily.

As a result of these discussions on milk yields, the Germans postponed putting into effect their requirements in the letter of 21st March 1945. The German authorities now decided to initiate immediate trials over the entire Island to establish the actual daily average yield per cow. Therefore, that very day Brée instructed all Milk Testers to visit all milk producers in their districts in order to acquaint them with the latest German initiative in relation to "milk and cattle".

Brée also made clear to dairy farmers exactly what the German intentions meant. He explained that the greater the quantity of milk delivered, the fewer would be the number of cattle, in excess of the quota for slaughter, called for by the German requisition dated the 14th November 1944.

At the same time, the JFU and the RJA&HS met to discuss the supply of milk to the civilian population. They agreed upon the following resolution: "That according to circumstances which may arise it is expedient that every effort be made for the civil population to obtain supplies of milk. All Island farmers are to be made fully aware of their responsibility to provide as much milk as possible."

The Island-wide shortage of milk, and the question of its equitable distribution amongst the civilian population, did not prevent some producers from participating in a highly lucrative black market. In late March the DOA received information that Mr C. Ollivier, St Brelade, was allegedly a black marketeer. The allegations originated from Mr A. J. Boucault, Ouaisné, St Brelade.[16]

Mr Boucault alleged that Mr Ollivier had sold seed potatoes on the black market and on Wednesdays and Saturdays also allegedly sold black market milk and butter. Ollivier owned a herd of seven cows. The DOA carried out an analysis of his daily milk yield delivered to the depot, and this was seen as insufficient. In addition, a computation was made of the average milk production of his herd for the previous twelve months. The results demonstrated a "...very low average milk yield, and in some measure, substantiates the allegation that Ollivier is a trader on the black market in respect of milk or its derivatives." Mr Boucault then went on to make a further allegation of another black marketeer.

On the 10th April 1945, the DOA "In relation to the milk situation arising from the German milk demands" dispensed with the services of the Milk Testers. Their contracts were immediately terminated. Each Milk Tester was given a week's wages in lieu of notice. The four Inspectors of Milk Containers were also dismissed. The dismissal of these Testers and Inspectors threw the entire milk control system – production, collection, manufacture, and distribution – into total chaos. The German forces, as well as the civilian population, were immediately deprived of all fresh milk and milk products. For whatever reasons their contracts were abruptly terminated by Brée and the DOA, it appears that the action brought about a more responsive dialogue with the German authorities.

On the 17th April the German authorities made new and "certain arrangements" over their milk demands. The DOA immediately re-engaged the Milk Testers and Milk Container Inspectors. A letter from Plaztkommandantur was received by Brée, ordering the requisition of more buildings at the Don Street Dairy site for the purpose of increasing the manufacture of butter for the troops. Brée decided that "In view of the very uncertain position now prevailing in relation to milk...no action in this matter would be taken until the major issue has been settled."

In view of the imminent requisitioning of Don Street Dairy by the German authorities, Brée and the DOA decided that, once the dairy had left their control, dairy staff would be handed one week's notice with pay and endeavours made to secure some other form of employment for them.

Brée also informed the DOA that, in accordance with the provisions of International Law, the German authorities required that Mr Hamon and Mr Pluck, the factory manager and the engineer, would remain on the premises at Don Street Dairy for a period of "a few days" after requisition of the premises. The DOA also appointed Mr Charles Hamon, the former caretaker at Don Street Dairy, to weigh the surplus milk delivered in order that producers were paid. Mr Hamon's wage was £2-12-6 a week.

Also, on the 17th April, Brée met with the members of his committee and rather tentatively announced, "In view of certain arrangements which have been made with the German authorities at present in occupation of the Island, its Act of the 10th April 1945, dispensing with the services of the Milk Testers, is recalled."

On the 18th April Platzkommandantur took control of the Don Street Dairy. On the same day, the Milk Control Section circulated a change in collection times to all producers. As from the 23rd April the new collection times would be 8.00 a.m. and 4.30 p.m. The requisition of Don Street Dairy also led to the removal and relocation of the Milk Control Section to 31 Broad Street, St Helier. The weekly rental was £1-10-0.

Also on this day, the Military Commander of the Channel Islands sent a telegram to the Bailiff entitled "Milk":

"The collection of milk in Jersey is, according to reports submitted to me, not yet sufficient and in the last few days has shown, in spite of the expected increase owing to the season of the year, a tendency to decrease. It is appreciably lower than in previous years. The required quantity of 20,000 litres per day has not hitherto been reached by half. I hereby charge you to take with expedition all suitable measures required to supply the civil population with the basic ration of 8.6 gr. of fat per head per day as recognised by the German government and to ensure the delivery of milk for the forces. If the delivery has not reached the quantity of 20,000 litres per day by 25th April 1945, I shall take suitable measures to guarantee the supply for the population and the troops."

The next day the Bailiff convened a meeting with the Superior Council. In addition, the Presidents and Vice Presidents of the JFU and the RJA&HS, along with Brée and the DOA, and finally the most important dairy farmers, were summoned. The meeting was held in the Bailiff's Chambers. The Bailiff made a lengthy statement on the position arising from the ultimatum of the German authorities that the milk supply must increase, or they would take over farms and cattle.[17.]

Brée then addressed the meeting. He stated that the German military forces would take 21 tons of their meat demands in milk products, thus saving forty-two cows per week from slaughter. This amounted to 9,000 pots of milk daily. At present only 4,000 pots were being secured. It was therefore necessary to increase the supply of milk by 5,000 pots a day to meet the German demands and to provide milk for the civil population. The meeting then discussed at length "...ways and means of increasing the supply of milk."

The next day, the 20th April, a further meeting was held at the RJA&HS offices, convened by both farming societies and some thirty-five leading farmers, to discuss and address the issues of the previous day's meeting with the Bailiff and the DOA. The farmers were handed a detailed statement from the DOA on the present state of the milk supply.

Le Gallais opened the meeting by stating that the Germans knew that milk was available on the Island. The meeting had to take important decisions on the future of this milk supply. He explained the realpolitik of the Island's position in respect of the German demands. Le Gallais had a natural ability to explain causation and its various effects, and the farmers listened attentively.

It was agreed that a large amount of milk was wasted by feeding to calves. It was therefore recommended that the Department of Transport speed up the collection of calves for slaughter. A further suggestion by Pérrèdes that calves be slaughtered at one week and not three was agreed. The DOA, however, subsequently rejected this proposal. It was also agreed that one method of saving milk would be to allow no calf exemptions up to the 30th April, and then only fifty a month. This was subsequently changed to 100 a month.

The meeting then discussed how best to collect the required milk supply and particularly how those who "...black marketed their milk and butter could be dealt with."

At this point in the meeting Brée walked into the room. He interrupted with a message from the Bailiff which was clear and unequivocal. The Bailiff had been informed by Admiral Friedrich Hüffmeier that an increase of milk must appear immediately, or punishments would be inflicted on the inhabitants of the Island. Brée also stated that he had been informed that, if the names of illicit suppliers of milk to German soldiers were supplied, those Germans would be dealt with. Brée then withdrew from the meeting. A number of suggestions were made. School milk for children should be discontinued and "School Committees" formed to collect 2½ pots of milk daily from farms.[18] A final suggestion called for all private sales and auctions of cattle to cease.

On the 21st April, in an attempt to evaluate where all the milk was ending up, the Cattle Slaughter Executive Committee requested from Milk Control that "Milk production figures for all herds in the Island during the past year be placed at their disposal." In addition, the Committee would subsequently choose for slaughter the poorest quality of milk-yielding cattle. Brée, however, decided to recommend that the RJA&HS and the JFU should sit together and jointly name several men to check the quantity of milk produced by all herds. Brée wanted this group to select cattle from herds whose milk production was exceptionally low. He also decided to check the figures for milk delivered to licensed retailers. These figures would be reported back to the Cattle Slaughter Executive Committee and the herds for which milk production figures did not correlate with milk delivered to licensed retailers would be taken for slaughter "...without causing prejudice to the milk supply of the Island."

The DOA transferred two clerks from the Grain and Potato Control Section to Milk Control to compute the figures required by the Cattle Slaughter Executive Committee.

On the 23rd April 1945 Brée wrote to every farmer. The gravity of the Island's situation as far as milk supplies were concerned was detailed and is worth repeating.

STATES OF JERSEY – DEPARTMENT OF AGRICULTURE

(Milk Control Section.)
Milk Control Office,
31 Broad Street,
Jersey,

23 April 1945

The Occupying Authorities recently demanded that the supply of milk to Don Street be immediately increased to 10,000 pots per day, otherwise they would slaughter at least 750 animals per month, use military measures to insure a supply to meet their requirements and take control of the milk distribution.

The Superior Council ordered a reduction in the consumption of whole milk by cutting out the supply to the schools, placing persons over fifteen years of age on the same basis as adults (two pints per week instead of seven) and cancelling medical extras to persons over sixty-five.

In addition, through representatives of the R.J.A. and H.S. and the Jersey Farmers Union, producers were appealed to increase their supply.

A milkless day for adults was ordered last Sunday, so as to increase the surplus to Don Street, in the hope that producers would also swell the total in response to the appeal made to them. The result was that, whilst the unfortunate consumers affected went without, the response by the producers was negligible.

DO YOU REALISE THE GRAVITY OF THE SITUATION? Keep back only that quantity which you are lawfully entitled. (See below.)

If more milk does not come in, your herd is threatened, the Occupying Authorities will take control, and the sick, babies, pregnant women, and those in Nursing Homes etc will suffer.

T. J. BRÉE.
President, States Department of Agriculture.

1½ pints per person under 2 years of age
1 pint per person from 2 to 15 years of age.
½ pint per person from 15 years and upward.
Plus medical extras as authorised.
For exempted calves – 2 pots per day for the first month.
1 pot per day following 3 months.
For non-exempted calves – 2 pots per day for 3 weeks after birth.

Brée was in a desperate situation as regards milk supplies to the civilian population. He was concerned that adults, children, the sick and the elderly had now had their milk supplies cut to the very limit. Any further cuts would undoubtedly lead to malnutrition. His letter was perhaps the last throw of the dice to persuade dairy farmers to send in their milk.[19]

On the 24th April, the DOA, JFU, and RJA&HS met to discuss the milk supply. Robert Carson urged that all farmers take action in increasing their milk production. At this point the representatives of the Island's dairies entered. The main decision taken was that Carson and Francis Le Boutillier would check the milk deliveries of several producers and report back information concerning "low milk deliveries". Both Carson and Le Boutillier were empowered to co-opt any individuals required in the performance of this duty. They were also instructed to call upon the parish collection committees to call in or take cattle for slaughter from herds that were not producing milk.

On the 1st May 1945, the Milk Control (Jersey) Order, 1940, was amended. All adults now received one half pint per day of milk (excluding three days in every seven). All children with medical certificates were to receive 1 pint of milk a day. On the same day Brée reported that "In view of the serious situation which has arisen in relation to the demands for milk by the German authorities" he had ordered "The whole or greater part of the herds of cattle in the custody of the following persons to be delivered to the public slaughterhouse". The herds belonged to Mr L. Cole, St Martin; Mr R. Langlois, St Saviour; and Mr J. M. Le Brocq, St Ouen. A requisition order was sent, and the Attorney General consulted.

On the 8th May the Milk Control order was again amended. As from 9th May all adults were entitled to 1 pint of full milk a day. On the same day, a report was received stating that Mr A. Camiot, St Mary, had delivered milk that was dirty and on one occasion "...containing straw". The Cattle Slaughter Executive was informed and told to select cattle from his herd for slaughter. Also, that day Mr C. Hamon, the Caretaker at Don Street Dairy, resigned. He stated in his letter of resignation he was not prepared to carry on the role. The reason was almost certainly that he did not wish to be associated with the German control of the dairy.

The German requisition of Don Street Dairy and fresh milk supplies led to considerable local anger focused on the States of Jersey and the DOA. On the 9th May, Dr Chichester wrote to the DOA. He stated, "It is of no interest to me to know that the Germans seek to justify their demands of 18,000 litres, nor am I convinced in any way with what the "occupying" authority states about the guarantee it gave the British government. I know that the population gets no fat save what is contained in the 1½ pints of milk which it gets weekly from the civilian government...this amount of fat is so small that it may well be said the population gets no fat.

The Civil Government...is under no obligation to feed soldiers...it should resist any demands for milk to supply the [German] garrison. It also knows that it is starving the population; that it has been supplying the military with food...and allowing our people to die from malnutrition.

I find that the Civil Government has been supplying the garrison with 5 pints of milk per man per day whilst it has been giving its own people 1½ pints – to some less – per week. I know that farmers have been deprived of their herds on the grounds that the owners were not supplying the milk demanded; what authority has done this; what has the Civil Government done to protect their owners. I request that this letter be shown to the Bailiff".[20]

Cattle

"As regards the requisition of Island cattle called upon by the German authorities, no indication shall be given to cattle owners as to whether their cattle are required for civil or military purposes."
DOA meeting, 5th December 1944

On the 14th November 1944, the Platzkommandant, Heider, wrote to the Bailiff. The letter, entitled "Meat requirements for troops", was short and to the point: "As from 10th December 1944, the troops' requirements of meat will have to be covered from the civilian sector as from that date there will be no more troops' horses available for slaughter. The competent military authorities give the requirements as 7.2 metric tons per week until 31st January 1945. As from 1st February 1945, the requirements will increase to 8.2 tons per week".[21]

The Superior Council met to discuss the demands. On the 25th November, the DOA approved the selection of cattle to provide meat supplies for the demands of the German authorities.

One week later the Cattle Slaughter Executive Committee and the leading milk producers met to discuss the arrangements for fulfilling Heider's demands. The Slaughter Executive, along with the RJA&HS, agreed that "The Cattle must be called in without indicating to the owners whether they are a civil or military requirement and that the apportioning of the animals to the respective authorities be done at the abattoirs."

In other words, cattle for slaughter requisitioned from farmers would be handed to the German authorities without the owners being informed. Le Gallais and the senior members of the RJA&HS thought it highly unlikely that a dairy farmer would have been willing to hand over his animals had he known it was for German consumption.[22]

The Slaughter Executive and the RJA&HS also agreed that a previous decision be implemented. The first call for cattle to be slaughtered to fulfil the German demands would be made from those islanders who had started to keep cows after the 1st July 1940, the first day of the German occupation. Also, that in selecting cattle the fundamental consideration would be the maintenance of the public milk supply and the preservation of the best specimens of the Jersey breed.

The overriding factor to be considered when selecting cattle for slaughter would be the DOA's information highlighting that milk supply from a herd was consistently below average, or that black market dealings in milk or butter had taken place. The Slaughter Executive approved a parish quota for the selection of cattle. This was made subject to any adjustment where parishes had fulfilled their quotas to date. The quota per month was as follows.

Parish	Head of Cattle
St Brelade	5
St Clement	3
Grouville	6
St Helier	6
St John	10
St Lawrence	10
St Martin	10

Parish	Head of Cattle
St Mary	7
St Ouen	10
St Peter	10
St Saviour	10
Trinity	13
Total	100

On the 14th December 1944 Heider wrote to the Bailiff confirming that the first delivery of 7.2 tons of meat was to be made in the week 18th to 23rd December. Heider had already discussed the delivery of the meat with the States Vet, Thomas Blampied, and he made it clear that meat deliveries to the German authorities had to be spread out during the week and not the whole amount in one delivery.

On the 19th December the DOA met to discuss the cases of two farmers who refused to hand over cattle for slaughter: Mr E. P. Rabet, St Peter, and Mr J. C. de la Haye, St Brelade. On the same day, the German authorities notified the DOA that Mr Rabet was "...not to be required to deliver a cow." Brée decided to send the Slaughter Executive to Mr Rabet and to requisition another animal. Rabet made it clear upon their arrival that he had already sent a cow for slaughter and would not allow another to go the same way. Mr de la Haye, who had previously been notified in a requisition order to provide a cow for slaughter, produced a German exemption order. When asked a second time to fulfil the order he refused.

At an RJA&HS meeting, Le Gallais explained to members that cattle brought in for slaughter for German consumption would be weighed on arrival at the abattoir and payments made on that weight. He also reported that the German authorities required, in addition to the cattle, five horses weekly for slaughter.

On the 2nd January 1945, the Slaughter Executive recommended to the DOA that the movement of cattle from the custody of one person to another be prohibited, unless a licence had been obtained under the Livestock (Jersey) Order, 1942. The licence was to be carried, for checking, on the person who was moving the animal. This was somewhat confusing as there was already an order in place which prohibited the movement of cattle between parties. It appears that a concession to move cattle in the case of auctions had led farmers to circumvent the order. In response the DOA, in an attempt to deal with this loophole, instructed all auctioneers to submit a list of cattle sold at auction. In addition, the DOA decided that it would prohibit the sale at auction of an animal listed for requisition and slaughter.

On the 10th January Brée sent the Bailiff an invoice for £1,588 to be forwarded to Platzkommandantur I for cattle slaughtered in December 1944 on behalf of the German military. Brée asked that the account be settled with the States Treasurer. The invoice, however, was not met with the approval of Platzkommandantur. On the 23rd January, MVR von Aufsess wrote a letter to the Bailiff entitled "Accounts for livestock. Conference with the DOA and States Greffier." Von Aufsess made it clear that all cattle accounts had to be made out in kilograms and in German currency. He also ordered that cattle accounts should not be sent to Platzkommandantur, but that two copies should be sent to the Verpflegungsausgabestelle, 13–14 The Esplanade, St Helier.[22] Finally, he ordered cattle accounts to be sent weekly, not monthly, and that cattle were to be weighed over the German weighbridge.

On the 10th February the Cattle Slaughter Executive Committee held a meeting. Shepard reported to them that the German requirements had now increased to fifty-three head of cattle weekly. Two weeks later a number of dairy farmers complained to the RJA&HS that they had not been paid for their cattle, which had been sent for slaughter for the German military. Le Gallais answered he would take this matter up with the DOA. He commented that the Germans were now taking working horses from farmers who had need of them and he would also take this up with the Superior Council.

The above issue of non-payment for cattle was caused by the Verpflegungsausgabestelle declining to recognise any price other than 6 pence per lb live weight for all cattle supplied. The DOA had sent accounts based on prices for bulls and cows of 6 pence per lb, and heifers 8 pence per lb live weight. Only 6 pence per lb would be paid, irrespective of whether it was heifer meat.

Brée, however, refused to concede the issue of cattle prices. He responded that the German authorities had previously always paid for cattle at "…the ordinary ruling prices." He informed them that "I would like to point out that the price prescribed for heifers is higher than that provided for bulls and cows, having regard to the fact that the meat of the former is superior to that of the latter."

On the 27th February the DOA met to discuss the non-payments. It was decided to accept the price of 6 pence per lb live weight for all animals. The Treasurer of the States was authorised to pay farmers on this basis and the RJA&I IS was informed. On the 6th March the Germans made the payments.

Also on the 27th February, the DOA discussed a letter received from the Slaughter Executive. The letter asked the DOA to immediately bring to the notice of the Superior Council that the Germans were requisitioning horses capable for farm work. This had resulted in a number of farmers being unable to carry out the necessary operations to produce food for the civilian population. Brée took the matter to the Superior Council. He asked the Bailiff to endeavour to have these requisitions immediately stopped. In addition, Brée made a further personal intervention by going to College House and speaking to the Staff Officers of Platzkommandantur. As a result, the German authorities "…agreed to suspend such requisitions and in place of such horses to take 50% of the pigs in the Island for the feeding of the occupying forces."

The Slaughter Executive also recommended to the DOA that "In order to curtail to some extent the number of cattle required for slaughter, farmers and their families entitled to receive one pint of milk daily shall be deprived of the ration of meat to which they are entitled under directions dated 20th December 1944, under the Rationing (Jersey) Order, 1940." Brée refused to accept the recommendation calling it "Inexpedient".

On the 10th March there was a meeting between the Cattle Slaughter Executive and the Calf Selection Committees. A bull calf born on 1st February 1945 named "D-Day Daydream" was refused exemption from slaughter.[23] Once the process of calf exemptions and appeals had been dealt with, Shepard reported that he had been interrogated by an "Official of the German Secret Police." The reason was that Mr E. P. Rabet and Mr J. de la Haye had claimed that they had been exempted from supplying cattle for slaughter after having received requisition orders. (These slaughter exemptions were presumably from the German authorities.) Shepard informed the meeting that he had given the German Secret Police such information as was necessary. In addition, he had been summoned to College House and told by German officers that "The system of selecting cattle for slaughter was not satisfactory in that milk supply was not taken into account." Shepard advised them to communicate their criticisms to the DOA and he also made clear to them that the Cattle Slaughter Executive Committee was only the servant of the DOA. Finally, Shephard was ordered by the officers at College House to provide 120 head of cattle within several days for shipment to Guernsey. Shepard immediately went to Brée and passed on the order directly.[22]

The DOA subsequently discussed the serious situation arising from the German demand for cattle to be sent to Guernsey. It was agreed that it had to make a concerted effort to avoid a further depletion of Jersey's cattle population.

On the 21st March Le Gallais reported to the Slaughter Executive that, on the previous day, the German authorities had issued the Connétables with an order to supply 100 head of cattle, for shipment to Guernsey on the 22nd March. Le Gallais met with the Bailiff and with Brée. They agreed that, as the requisition order to the Connétables originated from the Germans, they were deemed to be "ex officio" and would be allowed to proceed. The RJA&HS offered the Connétables the assistance of the parish collecting committees.

The German requisition of cattle for Guernsey laid down the order that the animals supplied would be at the "Controlled Price". The RJA&HS decided that it was an opportune moment for farmers to be forced to weed out the remaining "...poor stock in their herds", and that they would carry out a valuation of those animals which were to be purchased by the Germans. Le Gallais proposed that RJA&HS representatives should meet the Connétables in two days and make a formal protest to the German authorities. He was also adamant that, whilst cattle farmers were now having their poorest quality animals weeded out and the inferior stock removed, any new requisitions would have to be professionally valued.

The RJA&HS also agreed, regarding the shipment to Guernsey, that farmers would not only be paid the controlled price but that the cattle would be valued on arrival at the quay in St Helier on the 22nd March. Subsequently the DOA would register a claim with the proper authorities on behalf of the farmers for "The difference between the controlled price and the valuation figure of each animal." The "Valuation Board" was to be E. C. Pérrèdes, R. W. Carson and P. C. Mourant. Furthermore, it was agreed that this new procedure would be adopted for both local military and civil population cattle requirements.

On the same day Le Gallais wrote, on behalf of the Slaughter Executive, to each of the twelve Connétables. The letter put on record the RJA&HS's profound alarm at the Connétables' requisition of 100 head of cattle to be sent to Guernsey for slaughter. He emphasised: "This requisition you are carrying out on the order of the Occupying Authorities."

Le Gallais, furthermore, made a passionate plea on behalf of the RJA&HS and its Slaughter Executive. "The Royal Jersey Agricultural Society has, during its existence of over 100 years, devoted itself to the improvement of the Breed and, as representing it, this Committee cannot but view with great apprehension the continued depletion of the breed, which is an Island asset and cannot be replaced from elsewhere. The Committee would therefore beg of you to use your best endeavours to convince the appropriate authorities of the great danger to the inhabitants of the shortage in milk and butter supplies which is bound to occur if the slaughter of Island cattle is continued at the present rate".[24]

The Connétables sent a copy of Le Gallais' letter to the Bailiff. The Bailiff in turn forwarded it to the Platzkommandant, Captain von Cleve.

On the 16th April 1945, von Cleve responded to the Bailiff, the Connétables and the RJA&HS. He stated that the German authorities shared the apprehension of all parties that the further slaughter of cattle would endanger milk supplies and butter production and that the Island breed was an asset. The German authorities, however, had a carefully worked out plan. This plan had been devised by a special expert who had taken measures so that herds would only be encroached upon to a degree which could be borne.

Von Cleve made it clear that: "This plan can, however, only by carried out if the actual milk available is delivered in full. Only then from the milk and milk products obtained, by the substitution of cheese, will meat be available for the civil population and troops without endangering the breed. It is, therefore, in the interests of the Agricultural Society and the Farmers' Union to support the plan submitted and appeal to the producers, controllers, collectors and distributors of milk. The plan is the only way in which a substantial depletion of the breed can be prevented."

What exactly was von Cleve's "plan" is not documented. However, by the 12th March 1945, he had instigated a team of "Commandos" whose primary aim was to supply cattle which were desirable for slaughter for German meat requirements. In fact, von Cleve had written to the Bailiff pointing out two herds where animals were in poor condition, and which made exceptionally bad deliveries of milk. Von Cleve ordered a detailed examination of these herds by his Commandos. Subsequently a number of cattle were removed by the Germans for slaughter. The two farmers whose herds had been visited and examined were Mr John Priaulx, St Cyr, and Mr J. Arthur, Les Ruettes, St John.[25]

On the 27th March the German authorities reported that several accounts rendered to them "...would not be accepted as the weights of the cattle invoiced were in excess of the weights ascertained over the German weighbridge". Brée, in a discussion of this matter with the DOA, made clear that, having regard to the principle approved on the 5th December 1944, "No indication shall be given to cattle owners as to whether their cattle are required for civil or military purposes". In accordance with this principle all official notification to cattle owners to deliver cattle for slaughter specified that the animals destined would be weighed over the States weighbridge. Brée decided to recommend to the Superior Council that the States Treasury receive authorisation to pay farmers whose cattle had been delivered to the requirements of the Germans, the weight ascertained over the States weighbridge; and to accept payment from the German authorities on the weights of such animals as ascertained over the German weighbridge.

On the 3rd April, Brée reported that the Superior Council had approved the RJA&HS request that all cattle selected for slaughter should be valued. Brée put together a number of suitably qualified men to act as a new "Panel" to carry out the valuations. This was also referred to as a "Joint Valuation Committee". The proposed panel refused to value cattle for slaughter on behalf of the German forces. Brée, therefore, asked others to run the valuations: Mr W. G. Le Ruez and Mr T. Renouf, with Mr F. P. Le Quesne appointed as Chairman. Le Ruez and Renouf would represent the States of Jersey. In addition, two RJA&HS representatives joined, Carson and Pérrèdes.

On the same day, an order was made to requisition a cow for slaughter from the Richomme Brothers, Grouville. By the time the requisition order was sent to the brothers, the German authorities had already taken the cow for slaughter.

The following day the Slaughter Executive requested the DOA to write to a number of farmers who refused to send their cattle for slaughter. They were warned that, unless the cattle were delivered between 10.00 a.m. and noon on the specified day, a requisition order would be applied without further notice.

On the 17th April, a requisition order was delivered to Miss A. Cross, Grouville, however the cow in question had already been taken by the German authorities. On the same day, the DOA received a petition from several farmers in St Martin "...taking exception to the method of selection of cattle for slaughter by the delegates of the Cattle Slaughter Executive Committee." The signatories of the petition were asked to attend a meeting with the DOA on the 20th April.

The month of April saw increasing numbers of farmers refusing to hand over their cattle. On the 10th April R. W. Le Sauteur, Grouville, refused a requisition order from the States Vet. The matter was referred to the Attorney General and a further order was issued. In the meantime, the German authorities had taken possession of the cow.

On the 20th April the DOA, the Slaughter Executive Committee and the Parish Selection Committee for St Martin met with farmers who had petitioned with a series of complaints in relation to the selection of cattle for slaughter. The petition read:

"We, the undersigned, definitely decline to furnish any more cattle for slaughter until a more equitable distribution of the burden of the levy is made. We feel that until a new committee is named in the parish to make the selection, justice and fair play will not be achieved to represent fairly all interests. It appears to us that farmers should not be appointed particularly if they have their own herds at heart and keep bulls for public service, as they are likely to have thoughts before them protecting the herds that cross their bulls.

Signed,

B. P. Amy
J. N. Germain
D. N. Fauvel
G. R. C. Le Brun
W. G. Bartholomew
O. G. Ahier
G. A. Carrel
S. G. Godel
J. Daffains
J. W. Messervy, Junior
J. M. Robert
D. P. Larose"

Of the signatories, the following did not attend the meeting: Messrs Fauvel, Ahier, Daffains and Larose. Mr Godel wrote asking for his name to be withdrawn, as he had decided he did not wish to be associated with the petition. After hearing all the petitioners who were present, Brée and the DOA decided they had not made a case for a change to the Parish Selection Committee. The petition was rejected.

On the 24th April the DOA passed the Livestock (Amendment No 3) (Jersey) Order, 1945. This essentially prohibited any person from buying, selling, or disposing of cattle, except under a DOA licence. The licence would be granted only to the person proposing to dispose of, and the person proposing to buy, the animal.

In the same week the Platzkommandant, Captain von Cleve, wrote to the Bailiff. The letter was entitled "Settlement of prices for livestock." The letter made clear that a new arrangement regarding the prices paid for cattle delivered to the troops had been agreed with the DOA on the 15th April. All future German payments were now based on two categories: "Category S", cattle for slaughter, and "Category Z" for breeding animals. Henceforth farmers were to be paid directly by the Verpflegungausgabestelle immediately after delivery of the cattle.[26] The actual prices agreed between the DOA and Platzkommandantur were:

Category S – 10 pence per pound live weight
Category Z – 1/3 per pound live weight

In view of the increased prices being paid by the Germans, it became increasingly difficult for civilians to find meat at the prices prescribed by the Livestock (Jersey) Order, 1942. Farmers obviously wanted to sell their cattle to the German authorities at the new premium price rather than the lower civilian price. Brée, therefore, recommended to the Superior Council that the Article be amended to conform with German prices. This decision to amend cattle prices seems to have caused confusion. The following week the DOA asked that cattle prices for civilians be set by the Cattle Valuation Committee.

Reports were now increasingly reaching the DOA from its Milk Testers that calves not exempted from slaughter were being kept by farmers. In addition, John du Val forwarded two reports of farmers who had not slaughtered their calves. These cases were forwarded to the Attorney General.

On the 4th May, the Platzkommandant wrote a letter to the Bailiff entitled "Valuation and payment of cattle."

"Following on the interview between the Platzcommand and the Bailiff of Jersey with Jurats Dorey and Le Masurier the following agreed recommendations are submitted for your consideration:

1. All cattle purchased from the farmers for slaughter, whether for German or local consumption, will be paid for by the Treasurer of the States according to the valuation placed on each animal by the Committee set up jointly by the States of Jersey and the Royal Jersey Agricultural Society.
2. The Treasurer of the States will render, for payment by the German Authorities, weekly accounts for the amount of cattle taken by the German Forces charged at the rate of 1 R.M. per kilo, live weight, over the German controlled weighbridge."

On the 5th May, the day after von Cleve's letter to the Bailiff, Le Gallais, on behalf of the RJA&HS, wrote to the President of Finance and Economics. He stated, "The farmers in Jersey approve the arrangement made by you with the Platz Command that all cattle taken for slaughter for Local or German consumption, should be paid for by the Treasury of the States in accordance with the valuation placed on each animal by the joint committee set up on the 4th April last. The responsibility for payment from the German authorities on a weight basis of 1 RM per kilo rests with the Treasury of the States." Le Gallais ended the letter by stressing that farmers were to be paid not on a weight basis but according to the valuations.

On the same day, Le Gallais met with more than twenty elite cattle farmers, all of whom were members of the RJA&HS. He assured them that payment for cattle for slaughter was on a valuation basis. He stressed this had been agreed with the Superior Council after meetings with the Departments of Finance and Economics and Essential Commodities, as well as the German Occupying forces, and included cattle shipments to Guernsey, specifically the second shipment. The meeting decided that further efforts were to be made to obtain payment of the difference between the weight price and the valuation, in respect of the first shipment of cattle to Guernsey. The Germans had already paid farmers at the rate of 6 pence per pound live weight.

One week later, on the 11th May 1945, the Bailiff wrote across von Cleve's letter: "File for Records. Not dealt with".[27] The Joint Valuation Committee set up to value cattle sent to slaughter lasted up to the 12th May 1945, ensuring that all owners received any payments due to them.

Cereals

In November 1944, Platzkommandantur issued a far-reaching order entitled "The Blocking of Stocks". The order was promulgated firstly, to prevent thefts; and secondly to prevent black market dealings in the community. All farm stocks were now blocked by the German forces and were not to be disposed of by farmers, except with the authorisation of Platzkommandantur I. The stocks listed in the order were potatoes, seed potatoes and cereals. They were subsequently checked by German "Commandos" who visited and inspected every farm.[28]

During the month of November 1944, German agricultural Inspectors (probably these Commandos) carried out an inspection of all the wheat fields. The subsequent report confirmed an excellent wheat crop which contained good quality seed and the Germans ordered that where good quality seed was evident, those fields were not to be used for grazing.[29]

On the 1st December 1944, Heider ordered the Bailiff that blocked grain stored on farms must be transported on the 4th December to the Verpflegungsausgabestelle. Each parish had to provide a vehicle. The farmers who supplied the grain would be paid immediately. The Bailiff arranged a conference with von Aufsess and informed him that the grain requisition could not be carried out by the Superior Council; it would have to be done by the Connétables. In addition, the Bailiff informed von Aufsess that there was insufficient time to organise the requisition. Von Aufsess agreed to both proposals and the grain requisition was postponed to the 6th December.[30]

On the 5th December the DOA discussed a further German order to sow 100 tons of wheat. The DOA then issued wheat seed to those farmers who had in their custody less than 10 head of cattle. The quantity issued was 25% of the area grown by the farmer in 1944. The DOA also decided that in view of the existing war time conditions it was inexpedient to undertake the purchase of the crop. On the same day, a sub-committee was set up to supervise the threshing of the 1945 cereal crop.

On the 12th December, in view of the German order to sow wheat, the DOA decided it would sell the wheat seed to farmers at £1-0-3 for 70 lbs, the weight prescribed by the German authorities for sowing 1 vergée. It was also decided that farmers who did not grow wheat in 1944 could be allocated seed in 1945.

On the 11th January 1945, Brée wrote to the Bailiff informing him that the German army had taken away from Mr T.W. Avrill, St Ouen, thirteen barrels of wheat and forty-four barrels of oats. Brée requested the Bailiff to contact the German authorities and demand the fifty-seven barrels be returned to the owner.

Two days later Platzkommandantur I ordered the sowing of 50 tons of oats. It issued oat seed at 90 lbs per vergée. The price was set at £1-1-4 per bag and only for a cash sale. Brée decided that he would endeavour to obtain new supplies of cereal seed through the International Red Cross.

Throughout January 1945 the Feldgendarmerie made checks on grain stores.[31] One check by the German police on Philip John de Gruchy, 19 David Place, St Helier, found a barrel of oats. In consequence Heider wrote to the Bailiff that this was suspiciously looking like black marketing. Brée investigated and informed the Bailiff that this was not the case. The barrel of oats was in the custody of the firm.[32]

On the 13th March von Cleve wrote to the Bailiff to ensure that all threshing machines, portable steam engines and tractors were serviced for the coming season. He also requested a report on the condition of the threshing machines and requisitioned a number of drive belts and connections used by threshing operators.[33] He asked that the account be sent to Platzkommandantur. Brée, however, made clear that it should be forwarded to the Department of Finance and Economics so that the amount was debited to the account of the army of occupation. The report on the condition of the machines was forwarded to von Cleve.

Threshing Machines, 1945

Contractor	Drive	Capacity/Hour	Condition
T.R. Binet, Les Côtils, Trinity. 1 machine	20 hp semi-diesel engine	3 loads	Good working order but belt and tank required
St J.C. Cabot, Les Câteaux, Trinity. 1 machine	Tractor or steam engine	3 loads	Good order subject to minor repairs

Contractor	Drive	Capacity/Hour	Condition
J. C. Colback, 13, Parade Road, St Helier. 1 machine	Tractor	3 loads	Good, subject to overhaul
W.T. Farrell, Grantez, St Ouen. 1 machine	Tractor	¾ loads	Appears to be in good order
H. P. Godel, Les Pallières, St Ouen. 1 machine	Tractor	¾ loads	Good
T. G. Le Cappelain, St Peter's Works, St Peter. 3 machines	1. Electricity 2. Tractor 3. Tractor	Le Cappelain cannot supply any information	Fairly good
L. C. Pallot, Sion, Trinity. 1 machine	Heavy oil engine	¾ loads	Considerable repair required
J. Priaulx, St Cyr, St John. 1 machine	At depot: electricity At farm: tractor	¾ loads	Good
J. Richard, La Grande Maison, St John. 2 machines	1. Steam engine 2. Tractor	3 loads.	Good

Potatoes

"The DOA should allocate the quantity of [potato] seed which every farmer shall be required to deliver to the occupying authorities and that each farmer shall be responsible for delivery of the quantity of his allocation at a central depot in each parish for collecting by German forces which would be responsible for payment for the potatoes so delivered. This payment to be a transaction solely between the individual farmer and the German authorities."

RJA&HS and JFU Joint meeting

On the 6th November 1944, 1,100 tons of potatoes from the 1944 harvest were allocated to the civilian population. Eleven days later, Heider informed the Bailiff that whatever remained of this civilian allocation, and any other late potatoes, was to be delivered to the stores where the Germans kept their requisitioned potatoes.

On the 22nd November the Bailiff and Brée met with von Aufsess to discuss this requisition. It was agreed that it would be temporarily withdrawn until after the Superior Council had met on the 27th November. Heider's initial requisition order was the forerunner of five months of continual and extensive expropriation of civilian stocks of potatoes by the German authorities.

On the 1st December Brée requested the German authorities to sanction the unblocking of seed potatoes for planting in glasshouses. Heider agreed to release this seed but demanded it be planted as early potatoes. On the 4th December, Platzkommandantur requisitioned DOA potatoes and the next day additional potato stores were taken over. Heider asked that the accounts for these requisitioned potatoes be sent to himself.

Within 24 hours the Bailiff wrote to Heider and made an official protest. He firstly stated that the requisition of these additional potatoes was in excess of those already taken and this was irrespective of German payments made to the States. Secondly, the quantity of extra potatoes requisitioned from DOA stores would result in a deficiency for the civilian population. Thirdly, the blocking of potatoes on farms also deprived the Island of potatoes that could be available. Finally, he cited Article 52 of the Hague Convention that requisitions had to be in proportion to the resources of the Island and therefore this was a breach of the Convention.[34] The Bailiff had his own typed copy of the Hague Convention, to which he referred in dealings with the German authorities.

On the 7th December Heider replied to the Bailiff, stating that his protest had been forwarded to the Befehlshaber of the Channel Islands. This, however, did not affect the removal and requisition of the stores of DOA potatoes that had already taken place.

On the 12th December, a Colorado Beetle was found in the field "Clos de la Mare", Leoville, St Ouen. An immediate response was the building of wire fencing and posts around the field.

Within a few days of another outbreak Brée requested a meeting of the RJA&HS and JFU Joint Emergency Committee. He asked them to issue more information concerning potatoes. Brée chaired the meeting which comprised the DOA Committee, the Presidents and Vice Presidents of the two societies, and twenty-six important farmers. He began the meeting stating that the German forces had demanded 1,000 tons of seed potatoes.[16] This particular requisition had been stated to Brée verbally by Heider, but as yet he had received no written order. He had convened the meeting "… in order that suggestions might be made as to the best means of complying with the order."

Brée stated that he would ask the Germans to "unblock" the seed potato stores which they had blocked in the course of their farm inspections in November and December 1944. Philip Le Feuvre suggested it be agreed to source the potato seed, provided that this was a final German demand. (The word "German" was subsequently crossed out after the meeting.)

Brée also stated that the seed potatoes had to be carted by the farmers themselves to central depots where the Germans would collect them. Mr P. H. Renouf pointed out that seed potatoes were stored in potato boxes.

Any payments forthcoming by the German authorities, therefore, should be invoiced by the box and not the barrel.

Le Gallais advised the DOA to arrange the "unblocking" of farmers' seed potatoes and for a census of all Island stocks to be carried out. This would allow each farmer to hand over a proportionate quantity from his store of seed potatoes. Brée added that farmers who had brought in their full quota of eating potatoes in 1944 for the civilian population would be protected. Farmers, however, who had failed to do so would be the first to provide seed potatoes for the Germans.

On the 16th December Brée informed the two agricultural societies that "...without any official information on the subject, he understood from conversations with the occupying authorities that they would demand the delivery to them of a quantity of potatoes which had been reserved for seed." The DOA accepted the recommendation of the two societies that "The DOA should allocate the quantity of seed which each farmer shall be required to deliver to the occupying authorities and that each farmer shall be responsible for delivering the quantity of his allocation at a central depot in each parish for collection by the German forces which would be responsible for payment for the potatoes delivered, such payment to be a transaction between the individual farmer and the German authorities."

At the end of December, a number of farmers requested information as to whether the subsidy for planting potatoes on côtils would be available in 1945. The DOA's answer was short and to the point: "The DOA have decided that the conditions in relation to the cultivation of land in 1945 are not sufficiently clear to enable it to arrive at a decision on the matter."

On the 17th December the German authorities wrote to the DOA instructing Brée to provide details concerning the planting of potatoes in 1945. He forwarded the letter to the Superior Council who replied to the German authorities that "No action is to be taken until the question has been submitted to the Commission of the Protecting Power."

On the 9th January 1945, Brée reported that he had secured from the German authorities the unblocking of seed potatoes, but they required 776 tons of these to be sent to Guernsey. In addition, they had ordered a further 1,200 tons to be planted for the requirements of the German forces. The remainder of the Island's seed potatoes were released to the Civil Administration for planting the 1945 crop for the civil population.

The DOA now instructed farmers who had not complied with 1944 directions to deliver their allocated potatoes, or they would be used for feeding the civilian population until the 1945 harvest was ready. In addition, they would provide potatoes for Guernsey. Finally, farmers were told that under directions from the Cultivation of Lands (Jersey) Order, 1942, they were to plant for 1945 the seed potatoes they had been authorised to retain for this purpose.

On the 12th January Heider wrote to the Bailiff. The letter was entitled "Cultivation 1945". He informed the Bailiff that 3,000 tons of seed potatoes were to be planted. In addition, all farmers were to sow vegetables and cultivate root crops in all remaining fields. It was made clear that if any civilian fields were left fallow the occupying military forces would cultivate these fields.

The next day Brée and the DOA met with the two farming societies. He informed them that there were 5,000 tons of seed potatoes on the Island, that the Germans had unblocked 776 tons for immediate transport to Guernsey and they had ordered 1,200 tons to be planted for their own troops. He said the Germans had claimed output should be between 1½ and 2 tons per vergée, but he had told them that this was not the case. In addition, Brée indicated that he wanted 1,500 tons to be planted, to provide potatoes for the civilian population. He had made available between 1,500 and 1,600 tons for this purpose. He informed the meeting that the German military would take over any fields that were left uncultivated. Finally, Brée told the farmers that he would persevere in order to obtain various agricultural inputs through the International Red Cross the next time they were in the Island.

On the 23rd January the DOA directed farmers that all planting of potatoes in open ground was prohibited. The reason, on an order from Heider, is not known. On the same day, the DOA requested the Superior Council to give a ruling as to whether farmers should or should not be paid for seed potatoes recently requisitioned by the German authorities and sent to Guernsey. It also requested that the Connétables provide transport for potatoes to be sent to town (required for feeding the civilian population) if the farmer had no means of transport.

On the 28th January Heider wrote to the Bailiff concerning seed potatoes. He stated that the Island had 3,000 tons and, in addition, there were 50 tons under glasshouse cultivation. Heider ordered that in order to feed the civilian population up to the 31st March 1945, he would further release 700 tons of seed potatoes. He also revoked the prohibition order of the 23rd January.

The Bailiff immediately convened a conference with von Aufsess. The Attorney General attended. The Bailiff and Attorney General both protested against the departure from the initial verbal arrangement previously made which guaranteed a potato ration to the Island's civilian population.[35]

Between the 21st and 26th January the JPMA wrote to the DOA requesting to be paid 10 pence per ton for 91 tons of potatoes shipped to the order of the German authorities between the 4th and 6th December 1944. This amount being "The extra cost of transport of the potatoes caused by the delays occasioned by the action of the German forces." The DOA accepted the request and paid £3-15-2 to the JPMA.

On the 2nd February, the Platzkommandant wrote to the Bailiff. The letter was entitled "Planting potatoes. Conference between MVR Aufsess, Captain Ambacher and the Bailiff, dated 25th January 1945." The letter sanctioned the issue of potatoes to the civilian population up to the end of April 1945. The 1,200 tons of potatoes previously sanctioned for the civilian population was reduced to 1,000 tons. The Bailiff was ordered to tell the DOA to provide a list of farmers and the quantities collected from each one. Heider also ordered that once these 1,000 tons had been collected all farmers were to sow the 1945 potato crop on the most fertile soil.[36]

Between the 2nd and 17th February, 980 tons 11 cwt of blocked potatoes were collected by the DOA for the civilian population. Heider wrote again to the Bailiff on the 16th February, wanting details of the Island's plan for the supply and distribution of these potatoes, and making it clear that this was the Bailiff's responsibility. A breadless period had been ordered for the civilian population and this distribution of potatoes was to make up for the cessation of the bread allowance. In addition, Heider stated that any further lack of potatoes would not be made good. Red Cross flour, however, was expected to arrive soon.

On the 20th February the DOA directed farmers to plant potatoes. The seed was distributed at eighty boxes per vergée. They were planted 18 inches apart with a similar distance between the rows. On the same day, a further Colorado Beetle outbreak was discovered in the east of the Island, and the DOA re-engaged Mr F. W. Dobin to inspect fields and identify any colonies.

On the 22nd February the Bailiff wrote to the Platzkommandant making it clear "…that no responsibility can rest upon the civilian administration for any shortage of potatoes…due to military requisitions."

On the 27th February the DOA decided that farmers who had failed to deliver the quantity of potatoes required of them, as specified by their June 1944 Cultivation Directions, would be ordered to provide, out of the potatoes still in their possession, seed potatoes for issue to farmers who had fulfilled their requirements and were without any seed potatoes.

On the 2nd March the Bailiff, von Cleve and von Aufsess met. The conference discussed civilian supplies. The following points were agreed.

1. The potato allowance would be decreased to its previous amount of 2,250 grammes.
2. A continuation of the meat allowance could no longer be counted on.
3. The fat allowance for juveniles and children would be reduced.
4. The 40,000 litres of milk fixed for hospitals was reduced to 30,000.

The Bailiff responded by stating:

1. That he and the Attorney General had no authority to agree to these proposals.
2. That a previous conference on the 14th February was binding on all sides.
3. That the conference of the 2nd March made clear that "…the responsibility for the feeding of the civil population rested upon the occupying forces."

By the 18th March the German forces were requisitioning and removing potatoes and grain from DOA stores. This included, on the 18th March, 100 tons of potatoes and grain.[36]

The Chief Medical Officer of Health became involved in the German requisitions. He wrote directly to von Cleve informing him that he believed there would be serious consequences of these actions on food stores, seriously affecting children.

Von Cleve, in an effort to counter the Bailiff's arguments, wrote to him. The letter was entitled "Rejection of the protests with regard to requisitions." He refuted that the requisition of potatoes constituted a breach of Article 52 of the Hague Convention. He stated that the German government in the autumn of 1944, through the Protecting Power, had explained to the British government that there would be a food crisis at the end of the year, and he listed the rations sent by the Red Cross as from 1st January 1945. He, furthermore, made clear that the applicability of "Military necessity" was undisputed in International Law.

This "Military necessity" allowed for the provision of the laws of war to be disregarded if the disregard is the final and only possibility of saving oneself from destruction or for the successful execution of an undertaking decisive to the outcome of the war. He wrote "The protests are therefore rejected and not based on reality."

Von Cleve terminated his letter with the following: "The occupying authorities have granted considerable quantities of flour, potatoes, meat, fat, and other foodstuffs in excess of this minimum since 1st January 1945. They have even gone so far that they have jeopardised the health of the troops more than that of the civil population. Moreover, they have of their own accord done everything to hasten and make effective in all spheres the assistance by the International Red Cross. Also, in the future they will continue their exertions to assist the civil population as far as possible".[34, 36.]

The Bailiff replied on the 12th April. He refuted von Cleve's assertions and reiterated that the army of occupation had a duty in International Law to feed the civilian population.

On the 8th May 1945 new legislation was enacted to deal with a now far more serious Island-wide outbreak of Colorado Beetle. Over thirty infected areas were found, many of these on or near potatoes grown by Germans. It took two subsequent years to fumigate these infected areas and clear the problems. All UK potato markets were closed after the war until the problem was eradicated.

Watermills and Milling

On the 11th December 1944 the DOA granted a licence to Mr R. A. Deffains, Le Rondin Stores, St Mary. He was authorised to mill cereals under the Control of Mills (Jersey) Order, 1944.

A week later reports were sent to the DOA that there was no local grain for milling. The only mill that was working was Tesson, St Peter. The rest were idle. In December 1944 and January 1945 two senior millers fell ill, Mr F. J. Horton succumbed to pleurisy and Mr R. Le Marchand to acute gastroenteritis. Both millers worked at Malassis.

On the 18ᵗʰ January, Platzkommandantur requisitioned 50,235 kilograms of flour. This included 50 tons to be sent to Guernsey.[36]

By the end of January, the German authorities had requisitioned almost all the remaining flour belonging to the civilian population. The flour requisitioned for Guernsey was for the civilian population who were "... in a desperate situation in relation to the supply of bread." The milling of wheat for Guernsey was regarded as a loan, which the DOA hoped would be returned from the flour which Guernsey would receive from the International Red Cross. The flour, however, was not finally shipped to Guernsey as a "loan" but as "a military requisition."

On the 23ʳᵈ January Brée requested from the German authorities the steamroller and equipment from Grand Val Mill. Heider released the steamroller but retained most of the other equipment.[37]

On the 30ᵗʰ January the German authorities requisitioned Malassis. On the same day, Heider informed the Bailiff that the water power and drive at Gargate would for certain periods be required by troops to drive an electric plant. He, however, made clear this was not to encroach upon the mill or milling for the civilian population.[38]

In February, the milling licence of Mr John C. Vautier was transferred to Mr W. R. Le Marquand. In the same week milling licences were granted to Mr J. R. Le Quesne, St Clement; Mr V. M. Baudains, La Rocque; Mr J. F. C. Langlois, Longueville, St Saviour; and Normans Limited. The following week a further licence was granted to Mr D. P. Wilden, Vauxhall Street, St Helier, to carry out milling at Tostevin's Garage in the same street.

Fertilisers

On the 30ᵗʰ December 1944, a meeting was held to discuss the distribution of fertilisers for the following year. On the 16ᵗʰ January 1945, the JPMA and the DOA discussed the prices for the sale of fertilisers. At this meeting, the DOA authorised the issue of 1½ lbs of muriate of potash and 1 lb of sulphate of ammonia per perch for planting greenhouse potatoes.

On the 3ʳᵈ April, all farmers who held Cultivation Orders were issued with permits under the Fertilisers (Jersey) Order, 1941, to purchase fertilisers for the 1945 season. Muriate of potash and sulphate of ammonia were issued at 7 lbs per vergée.

In the same week, Platzkommandantur ordered the DOA to supply a list of the stocks of fertilisers held in the Island. Brée responded with a full list on the 11ᵗʰ April.[39]

Straw

The German forces from September 1944 had begun to requisition large amounts of straw from the civilian population. On the 6th December Brée formally protested to the German authorities on this continued commandeering of straw. Ten days later Heider replied to Brée's protest and modified the German army's requisition, reducing the weekly quantity by 50 tons.

On the 19th December, the DOA wrote to the "Straw Allocation Officer", St John, requiring him to order in "...for the use of the German forces the whole of the straw in the custody of Mr E. P. Allo and Mr E. Henry, St John". On the same day authorisation was given to pay Mr Cyril Renouf, Trinity, for a quantity of straw delivered to the German forces "...as shown by a certain document purporting to be a weighbridge ticket issued by the German controlled weighbridge."

On the 2nd January 1945, Mr Edwin Le Marquand, St Peter, was authorised to receive payment for an account in respect of 4,800 kilograms of straw delivered to the German forces "Provided that the Grain and Potato Control Accountant has received from the German forces the necessary funds to cover the value of the straw supplied."

In the same week, further authorisations were given to pay the accounts of Mr W. P. Becquet, Trinity, Mr W. E. Le V. dit Durrell, St Helier, and Mr E. Henry for straw delivered by them for the requirements of the German troops. All these accounts were based on straw weighed by the German-controlled weighbridge and not over the States weighbridge. This annoyed Brée, however, unusually, he seemed not be in a position to rectify the problem.

Jersey Produce Merchants Association

In January 1944, the DOA had met the merchants to discuss shrinkage for the 1943 harvest. On the 19th December 1944, a report demonstrated the shrinkages established in the 1943 grain harvest stored by merchants. Those involved were C. S. Bailhache, Country Gentlemen's Association Limited, T. Dorey and Company Limited, Le Rossignol and Company and Normans Limited. Shortages had been established at all these firms, up to December 1944.

The DOA, as a result of subsequent discussions, decided to take the following course of action. The firm C. S. Bailhache had 25% of payment for storage withheld until the question of their grain losses had been satisfactorily explained. The Country Gentlemen's Association Limited offered to pay the DOA £41-5-5 in consideration of their grain shortages. The DOA replied to this offer that "...in view of the seriousness of the losses involved the DOA is not prepared to accept any offer less than £50." The firm subsequently paid

£80. T. Dorey Limited and Le Rossignol and Company did not settle their losses until after the liberation. No agreement could be made with Normans Limited as Mr J. M. Norman was recovering from an illness. The losses were too great in value, so the matter was left until he was available for a full discussion.

On the 23rd January 1945, the DOA discussed the storage of potatoes for the civilian population. The chosen JPMA stores were:

R. P. Amy
W. Dennis and Sons Limited
Chas Gruchy and Company Limited
Job and Sons
A. E. Laurens
Marks and Riches Limited
John Terry Limited.

A meeting was held with these firms on the 30th January to discuss payment for the transportation and storage of potatoes brought into St Helier. The DOA agreed to pay the full costs for the storage and distribution, while the issue of sorting the potatoes was left to a later date.

In April 1945 the German forces took 100 tons of these potatoes. The merchants immediately asked the DOA for payment in respect of the potatoes taken, based on the agreement of July 1944. The DOA agreed; however, it refused to make any payment for sorting Jersey Royals from the 100 tons taken by the German forces. Further requisitions were made by the Germans from stores owned by P. J. de Gruchy.

At the end of the January the DOA ordered Marks and Riches to find separate storage accommodation for potatoes stored by them on behalf of the German forces. They were also instructed to keep separate all potatoes brought into St Helier for the civilian population.

In April, the German forces requisitioned the potato stocks of A. Giddens and of the Country Gentlemen's Association Limited.

On the 8th May 1945, the DOA decided to "...endeavour to purchase 500 tons of late seed potatoes from the United Kingdom."

Cultivation Orders

The last six months of the German occupation forced the DOA to spend more time and effort dealing with the ever-increasing food requisitions by the German authorities, rather than dealing with agricultural policies. These requisitions were taking eggs, butter, milk, potatoes, flour, cattle, and tobacco.[40]

The Germans were especially good at finding and requisitioning large stores of tobacco products. On behalf of Platzkommandantur, von Aufsess requisitioned 2,000 tobacco plants from H. G. Le Quesne, St Saviour and E. P. Allo, St Helier. He ordered that the tobacco be harvested, dried, and delivered to the Jersey Tobacco Factory. The Bailiff was ordered to instruct the Jersey Tobacco Factory to deliver the finished tobacco to the Verpflegungausgabestelle.[41]

In December 1944 and onwards the DOA increasingly made direct pleas to Heider and von Aufsess to allow temporary releases for farmers who were in prison, for them to carry out urgent glasshouse cultivation and to tend to their herds. Some pleas were successful, but others were not.[42]

On the 12th December the huge number of wooden Dutch trays, not used in the 1940 export of tomatoes and stored at W. Dumosch Limited, were disposed of and given to the civilian population.

That very day, Dr Chichester wrote to the DOA, requesting that his land which had been requisitioned be returned to him. This included a number of fields which had been leased by the DOA to another farmer. Dr Chichester's request was refused. He wrote again on the 13th February asking for the return of his land. Brée replied "...having regard to his husbandry in the past it was decided it would be in the interests of the community not to grant this request."

The matter, however, took a new turn in April 1945. The tenant of Dr Chichester's fields complained that Dr Chichester was turning his cows out to graze on the requisitioned fields that he farmed. Brée sent the matter to the Attorney General, who in turn placed it in the hands of the Connétable. Brée then made it clear to Dr Chichester that if the intervention of the Connétable failed to resolve the issue, he would requisition his cows.

On the 18th December Heider wrote to the Bailiff. This letter, entitled "Thefts from farms", clearly demonstrates his real irritation with farmers. Heider writes: "Recently the reports of thefts made by farmers has reached me to such an extent the positions cannot in future be borne...The constant allegations that the offenders...are the troops of occupation must be decisively refuted. In all cases reported the thefts could have been committed by the civilian population or else there was no theft and the farmer concerned employed this method in setting aside, in some cases a considerable quantity, of foodstuffs. As the alleged thefts...are potatoes...This makes a cultivation plan impossible. The farmers are to be informed...they are responsible for the safe custody of their stocks".[43]

Heider, furthermore, made several recommendations concerning the security and storing of agricultural stocks. He finally threatened that any investigations of alleged farm thefts which were shown to be caused by negligence on the part of the farmer would result in severe penalties.

Heider's threat was well founded. In the same month Mr Emile Henry, St John, allegedly reported that 30 head of poultry had been stolen from him. The farmer was investigated by the German police and subsequently sent to a German court and sentenced to three months' imprisonment. In response to Henry's imprisonment the Bailiff sent an official objection to the sentence.

On the 23rd January, Heider replied that the German prison sentence was not for the theft of the 30 head of poultry, which had been blocked by the German forces. The reason for the imprisonment was that the Police and Feldgendarmerie had investigated the matter and the farmer had intentionally deceived the authorities, which was a criminal offence.[44]

Brée discussed the issue of agricultural thefts with the DOA. It was felt that these matters could only be dealt with by the police. The Attorney General was requested to take such steps as he considered to be proper. This however did not stop the ever-increasing number of thefts from farms. Most farmers now kept a continual guard on their produce and even brought livestock and poultry into their farmhouses at night.

On the 29th December Mr J. B. Arthur, St Clement, reported that German troops had requisitioned his potatoes. He was given a chit by a German NCO for 600 kilograms which stated that each barrel of potatoes was 50 pounds in weight when in fact it was 100 pounds in weight. Brée informed the Bailiff who wrote to Heider. On the 10th January Heider replied, stating: "The complaint made by J. B. Arthur is unfounded as the potatoes delivered by him were to a large extent bad. Further, as the potatoes were just harvested there was much earth adhering to them. The calculation of 50 pounds weight per barrel corresponds, therefore, to the inferior value of the potatoes".[30]

In early February James Gartrell, Honorary Parish Inspector for St John since 1940, passed away. Brée's eulogy described the huge amount of valuable work he had rendered to the Island in relation to the production of food during the German occupation.

On the 27th February Mr P. Pomar made representations to the DOA on behalf of the Spanish workers on the Islands. Although they had been issued ration books to enable them to obtain Red Cross boxes, they had received no tobacco allowance from any source and therefore were applying for such.[45]

On the 30th April von Cleve sent an order to all merchants who had vegetables in their stores informing them, along with the Bailiff, that all vegetables were to be immediately requisitioned by the German forces.[46]

The last few weeks of the German occupation saw a rapid deterioration in the health of German military personnel. Malnutrition was becoming an increasing problem for the German forces. Both Joyce Le Ruez and Betty Agnès commented on the large number of German soldiers who went from farm to farm begging for any food available.[47.] However, there were surprisingly few incidents of German troops stealing Red Cross parcels from the civilian population.

References

1. Army Requisition and Rations Store.
2. Jersey Archive. B/A/W40/5/3.
3. Jersey Archive. B/A/W40/5/2.
4. Jersey Archive. D/Z/H5/141/2.

5. *Ibid*. Document 1/6/8/M/Le M. See Jersey Archive, L/F/54/C/D/1 for details of J.B. Michel's case. File contains correspondence of Attorney General and John du Val about alleged breaches of milk control.

6. Jersey Archive. B/A/W91/43.

7. *Ibid*.

8. Jersey Archive. B/A/W31/2/165.

9. Jersey Archive. B/A/W31/2/167.

10. Jersey Archive. B/A/W40/14/1.

11. Jersey Archive. B/A/W40/5/9.

12. Pelz arrived in Jersey on the 9th August 1940. He was ordered to go to France by von Schmettow between the 10th and 16th June 1944. Pelz appears to have left the Island in late August. In October 1944 he was in the Somme Region, France.

13. Jersey Archive. B/A/W40/5/7. Document: States of Jersey – DOA – Milk Control Section. Dated 9th March 1945.

14. *Ibid*. Document: States of Jersey – DOA - Milk Control Section. Dated 21st March 1945.

15. Jersey Archive. B/A/W40/5/7. Document: Wi/15/F. Dated 21st March 1945.

16. Jersey Archive. D/Z/H5/141/2. Document : 2/2/1/M/LeM.

17. RJA&HS. Joint Committee of the JFU and RJA&HS. Minutes.

18. School milk for primary students. My thanks to Kaya Camara, States Greffe, for sending me details of the milk withdrawal proposition.
Students' milk was discontinued by the States of Jersey in January 2011. This was carried out as a financial saving. The amount of public money actually saved was derisory. This perhaps is ironic when compared with the lengths the Superior Council and the DOA took to supply children with milk during the German occupation. Jersey was almost certainly one of the few German-occupied areas where children received full-fat milk for the entire war.

19. My thanks to Mrs Pam Laurens and the trustees of Miss Joyce Le Ruez's estate, and the late Mr Dennis Edward Le Flem, who provided me with copies of this letter.

20. Jersey Archive. D/Z/H5/141/2. Document dated 9th May 1945.

21. Jersey Archive. B/A/W40/2/3.

22. Jersey Archive. L/D/09/A11.

23. RJA&HS Herd book 48974.

24. Jersey Archive. B/A/W40/5/8.

25. Jersey Archive. B/A/W31/2/168.

26. Jersey Archive. B/A/W31/2/172.

27. Jersey Archive. B/A/W31/2/177.

28. My thanks to the late Miss Joyce Le Ruez who kindly gave me a copy of her father's Blocking Order placed on his St Peter's farm.

29. Jersey Archive. B/A/W31/2/141.

30. Jersey Archive. B/A/W31/2/145.

31. German Field Police.

32. Jersey Archive. B/A/W31/2/161.

33. Jersey Archive. B/A/W31/2/169.
34. Jersey Archive. B/A/W40/5/5.
35. Jersey Archive. B/A/W31/2/159.
36. *Ibid.*
37. Jersey Archive. B/A/W31/2/162.
38. Jersey Archive. B/A/W31/2/163.
39. Jersey Archive. B/A/W31/2/171.
40. Jersey Archive. B/A/W40/5/10. See also, B/A/W31/2/178.
41. Jersey Archive. B/A/W40/5/4.
42. Jersey Archive. B/A/W31/2/148.
43. Jersey Archive. B/A/W31/2/154.
44. Jersey Evening Post, 19th January 1945. Article "Too Clever".
45. Jersey Archive. B/A/W91/45.
46. Jersey Archive. B/A/W31/2/175.
47. My thanks to Elizabeth (Betty) Agnès (née Valpy), December 2014 and Joyce Le Ruez for providing me with clear and excellent accounts of German soldiers begging at their parent's farms.

Postscript

The Liberation

Immediately after the liberation the DOA ensured that children, juveniles and the sick again received a full ration of milk. A newspaper article made the observation, "It is worthy to note that of all places under German occupation, Jersey was the only place where the population had full cream milk all the time. She kept a population of 40,000 plus thousands of Germans supplied with butter".

The DOA revoked all milk-producer licences of those who had supplied units of German forces. This was in combination with a revocation of nine of the most important occupation agricultural directives. A large quantity of butter held by the Germans was discovered in a store. It, however, was "... not fit to be issued to the civilian population". All German stocks of cereals were mixed up and given to farmers as pig meal. In addition, farmers who held German horses in their custody were allowed to keep them.

The greatest problem facing Island agriculture in May 1945 was a massive Colorado Beetle infestation. There were thirty infected zones across the Island. Inspectors observed that these were fields where potatoes had been grown by the German forces. The UK authorities made it clear that no Jersey potatoes would be allowed to be imported into the country until the entire infestation was completely eradicated. This took two full years to accomplish.

In response to the UK refusal to import Jersey potatoes, the States made formal representations to the British authorities for permission for Dr Thomas Small and Mr Ernest G. Ing to return to the Island. They were, respectively, the former pre-occupation States mycologist and horticulturalist, who had previously specialised in combatting both Colorado Beetle and eelworm outbreaks. The official record states that "...they had left their posts at the evacuation". Dr Small returned, but Mr Ing declined.

In September 1945 Brée chaired a meeting with the major farmers to discuss the Colorado Beetle problem. He informed them that potato fields would be sprayed by an English firm, flown over to carry out the work. The firm had power spray machines which were made available to Jersey farmers to use the following year. The timeframe for spraying all the fields was two years. It was completed on time and eventually covered approximately

16,000 vergées. By 1950, the value of Jersey potato exports to the UK was £2 million. (This is the equivalent of £55 million in today's terms.)

On the 29th May 1945, the States decided that any employees of the DOA, who had been deported by the Germans in 1942, would be paid for the period during which they were absent from the Island.

On the 19th June 1945, it was decided to cease milling Island-grown cereals. The mill's Supervisor, Mr Day, who had been appointed on the 13th September 1940, was given one month's notice. Brée thanked him for his services in maintaining the mechanical efficiency of the mill's during the German occupation.

In August farmers met to discuss their labour problems; in particular, how much they would pay their agricultural workers. A meeting on the 16th August of the two major societies, attended by thirty-four of the most important farmers, agreed upon a minimum wage of £3 a week, based on a 50-hour working week.

The first post-liberation meeting of the RJA&HS took place on the 26th May 1945. It was attended by Sir Daniel Cabot, Chief Veterinary Officer for the Ministry of Agriculture, UK, and himself a Jerseyman. Sir Cabot entered the room flanked by Brée and Le Gallais. The members decided that all Jersey cattle which had been exported to the other Channel Islands would be returned and slaughtered. In addition, all cattle that had come into contact with German-imported or German-owned cattle would also be sent to the abattoir.

The RJA&HS spent the remainder of 1945 attempting to identify, and remove from its membership, anyone whom it deemed had collaborated with the German authorities. Major changes to the society's fundamental rules were suggested. This led to a great deal of ill feeling between RJA&HS members and lasted until 1950.

On the 6th June 1945 the "US War Shipping Administration" made an enquiry to the States about the export of cattle for shipment to the United States. The DOA decided to allow between 120 and 160 head of cattle to be exported. This decision to allow the export business to resume led to a veritable bonanza for Island cattle breeders and agents. It was almost certainly the reason behind the denunciation of two Jersey breeders, who were also agents, as German collaborators.

The first cattle breeders to receive export licences were John Buesnel Michel and Carlyle Le Gallais. In the period June to December 1945, twenty-two export licences were issued.

On the 23rd May 1945, exactly five years to the day since the last cattle show, a show was held at John Perrée's farm, Oaklands, St Saviour. The standard of all the cattle was exceptionally high. The reason was, that over the period of the German occupation, the Cattle Slaughter Executive and the Calf Selection Committees had weeded out and culled the poorest specimens of the breed. After May 1945, the animals that were left were of the highest quality and much-improved milk producers.

This fact was quickly noted by American, British, Australian, and South African cattle breeders. The post-war export business saw a rush of buyers and agents arriving to purchase bulls and heifers. These cattle were highly sought after and commanded a premium. A price of 1,000 guineas was not unusual for a good bull and one was sold for 10,000 guineas.

For the first time cattle were flown to North America, rather than being shipped. These were three pedigree bulls sold by Mr T. F. Le Ruez, and Mr W. G. Perchard. At the same time, two bulls were sold to members of the English Jersey Cattle Society for £2,500 and £3,000. Large numbers of cattle were exported over the following years, leading to concerns that too many of the best animals were leaving the Island.

On the 16th July 1945, the RJA&HS requested the DOA to re-tattoo all herds. The original wartime ink that had been used was defective, identification marks were fading and were no longer legible. The DOA agreed but it was not possible for the Herd Book staff to complete the task with their existing equipment. The problem was solved by the States Vet and George Breuilly purchasing new tattooing equipment.

In October 1945 the question of artificial insemination of cattle was discussed for the first time. This had been accelerated in the UK in response to the war effort. It had enabled the more widespread use of superior breeding bulls, thus increasing milk supply. The DOA made its policy clear. "The DOA considering it essential in the interests of the island that the purity of the island breed of cattle be maintained unimpaired and considering further that the uncontrolled use of the practice of AI will be prejudicial to that purity, charged its secretary to arrange a 'Project de Loi' to control this practice for submission to the States".

The post-occupation period saw a resumption in tomato exports. This provided an excellent return to farmers. Prices in the UK market were extremely high and remained buoyant for several years. This high return tempted a number of farmers with cattle to specialise in both indoor and outdoor tomatoes, at the expense of their herds.

Touzel John Brée, President of the DOA, received an OBE. He sadly died whilst on a motoring holiday in the Pyrenees, on 25th July 1951, aged seventy. In post-war Austria Hans Egon Pelz went on to achieve a successful career in the cattle industry. In 1949 he became Director of the Salzburg Cattle Marketing Company, making "an extraordinary contribution to the farming community of Salzburg by great knowledge and personal commitment".

Brée's contribution to the history of the German occupation, as well as that of Pelz, has never been fully recognised and evaluated. It appears both men have been whitewashed from the official occupation record. The reason for their apparent lack of recognition is interesting and certainly a topic for future research and discussion.

Appendix 1

Field Command 515 Headquarters, College House

```
FELDKOMMANDANTUR   515.

1941..........1944.

                    Feldkommandant.
                    Col.Fr.Knackfuss.

Stabschef           Adjutant           Oberkriegsverwaltungsrat
(Chief of Staff)    Leutnant Kolb.     (Chief of Administration)
Major W.Heider.                        KvR von Aufsess.
                                       DR. WILHELM CASPER K.V.O.R.
                                       1941 to NOV. 1943

Soldatenheim                           Verpflegung u.Landwirtshaf
Hauptm Koppelmann.                     (Food and Agriculture)
                                       Dr Egon Pelz.
Uffz Zimmer.
                                       Offentliche Versorgungs-
Stabarzt.                              betrieb.(Public Utilities)
Chief Medical Officer                  Inspektor Pokorni.
Dr Blackwenn.
                                         Arbeits Abt.
Kriegsgerichtsrat                        (Labour Dept.)
Senior Court Judge                       Sec Ruhnka.
Dr Segar.
                                       Textilware u. Verwaltung.
                                       Textiles and Administratio
Geheime Feldpolizei                    Sonderfuhrer Bleul
Secret Field Police
Dr John.                               Auslander,Reisepass u.
                                       Zenzor.(Rote Kreuz)
                                       Foreigners,leave passes and
                                       Censor.
Tierarzt                               Sonderfuhrer Herm.
Veterinary Surgeon.
Dr Kempt                               Zahlmeister
                                       (Paymaster)
                                       ? Schumacher.
Propaganda.
Sonderfuhrer Hohle.                    Dolmetcher
                                       (Interpreter)
                                       ? Wolchen

Room 1, Hauptgeschaftzimmer  Feldwebel Hassfulln
ROOM 17, Geschaftzimmer,Gefreiter Layohol
```

The plan was drawn by Karl Greier, an interpreter for the German Military Government from the 12th August 1940 to the 15th September 1943.

Feldkommandant – Room 24
Food and Agriculture – Room 20
Public Utilities – Room 16
Chief Paymaster and Paymaster of the Catering Services, Arnst and Patzer – Room 19

(Courtesy of Alan Allix)

518

Appendix 2

Firing Range, Egypt

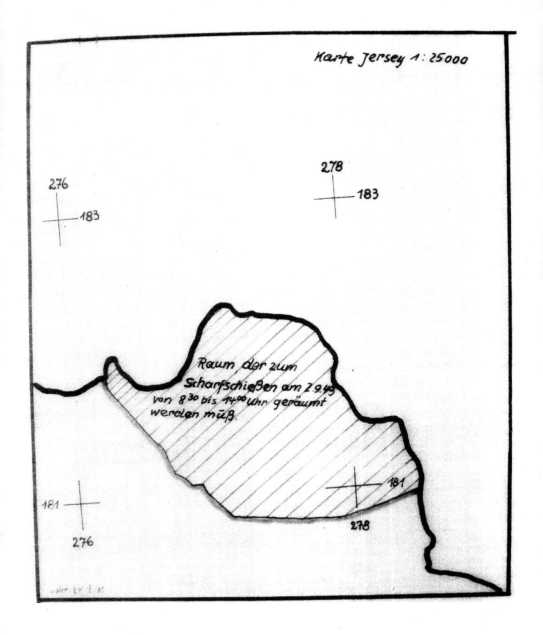

The area shaded had to be cleared for sniper firing practice from 8.30 a.m. to 2.00 p.m.

Appendix 3
Firing Range Requisitioned by the German Army, Egypt

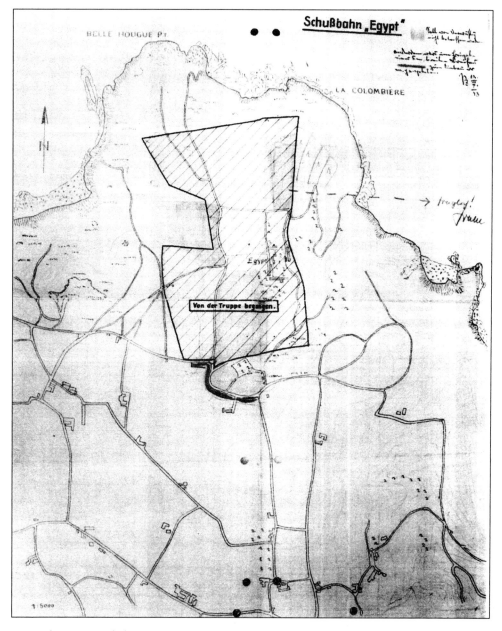

Pelz requested the army not to cause any damage to the land shaded darker.

Appendix 4

Map of the Proposed Requisition of 23 Farms by the German Military in August 1942

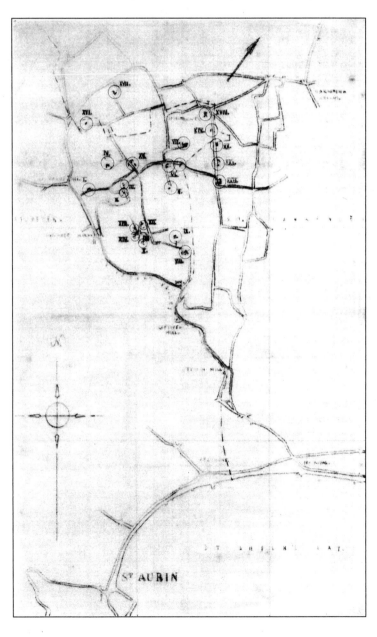

Glossary

The names of individuals written came from a variety of primary sources and different provenances. The editor, when reviewing the final manuscript, noted variations in names, initials and spellings. As a result, all names were cross referenced with the official record in the Jersey Archive. In consequence and for the sake of consistency only the name appearing in the official record was used.

● States, Civil Service and Inspectors

NAME	TITLE/POSITION
CROWN OFFICERS AND CIVIL SERVICE as at May 1942	
Le Couilliard, Sydney George	Agricultural Marketing Board
Le Marinel, T.	Agricultural Marketing Board
Perée, J. A.	Agricultural Marketing Board
Coutanche, Alexander Moncrieff	Bailiff
Le Gallais, Carlyle	Department of Agriculture, Adjoint member
Mallet, Wesley John	Department of Agriculture, Adjoint member
Godfray, Archie Vivian	Department of Agriculture, Chief Inspector
Hubert, Philip	Department of Agriculture, Deputy Chief Inspector
Brée, Touzel John, Jurat	Department of Agriculture, President
Marie, Colin Cecil	Department of Agriculture, Secretary
Gibaut, Edwin Denize, Deputy	Department of Agriculture, Vice President

NAME	TITLE/POSITION
du Val, John, Connétable St Peter	Department of Agriculture, Vice President
Le Masurier, Edwin Philip, Jurat	Department of Essential Supplies/ Commodities
Mourant, Thomas Philip	Department of Essential Supplies/ Commodities
Labey, Ernest George, Jurat	Department of Finance & Economics
Dorey, Edgar Aleck, Jurat	Department of Finance & Economics, President
Le Quesne, Edward, Deputy	Department of Labour, President
Pepin, Stuart Philip	Fuel Controller
Aubin, Charles Walter Duret	H.M. Attorney General
Giffard, John Francis	H.M. Receiver General
Harrison, Cecil S.	H.M. Solicitor General
Blampied, John Wesley	Inspector of Livestock
Bois, Francis de Lisle	Law Draftsman
Brée, Philip Ernest	Lieutenant-Bailiff
McKinstry, Robert Noel, Dr	Medical Officer of Health
Weeks, Reginald Oswald	Milk Control, Secretary/Accountant
Le Masurier, Joshua Philip	Price Advisory Board
Sutherland, James B. H.	Price Advisory Board
Bailhache, Vivian John	Price Advisory Board, President
Michel, John Buesnel	Price Advisory Board; Agricultural Marketing Board
Norman, John Mallet	Price Advisory Board; Agricultural Marketing Board
Le Quesne, Frank Philip	Price Advisory Board; Joint Valuation Committee
Hammond, Leonard	Sanitary Inspector
Rice, C. W.	States Engineer
Crumpton, Francis	States Experimental Station, Chemist
Woodcock, Edwin J.	States Experimental Station, Chemist
Simpson, David	States Experimental Station, Director
Gréard, Jules Pierre	States Experimental Station, Foreman

NAME	TITLE/POSITION
Le Liard, Yves Marie	States Experimental Station, Foreman
Mourant, P. E.	States Experimental Station, Foreman
Le Maistre, Frank	States Experimental Station, Lab assistant
Ing, Ernest George	States Experimental Station, Microbiologist
Blampied, Thomas Le Quesne	States Veterinary Surgeon
Ereaut, Herbert Frank	Treasurer of the States
Le Gros, Charles Sydney	Viscount

INSPECTORS

Le Couilliard, Sydney George	Grouville. Honorary Parish Inpector
Siouville, Emile Le Geyt	Grouville. Honorary Parish Inspector
Gibaut, Herbert Marett	St Brelade. Honorary Parish Inspector, Tobacco Inspector
Le Boutillier, James John	St Brelade. Honorary Parish Inspector, Tobacco Inspector
Le Masurier, Joshua Philip	St Clement. Honorary Parish Inspector
Malzard, Ernest John	St Clement. Honorary Parish Inspector, Tobacco Inspector
Baudains, Philip Lesbirel	St Helier. Honorary Parish Inspector, Tobacco Inspector
Mourant, Philip John	St Helier. Honorary Parish Inspector, Tobacco Inspector
Gartrell, James, Deputy	St John. Honorary Parish Inspector
Le Couteur, Charles.	St John. Honorary Parish Inspector
Ahier, Francis John	St Lawrence. Honorary Parish Inspector
Maillard, Hedley William	St Lawrence. Honorary Parish Inspector, Tobacco Inspector
Pallot, Timothy Alexander	St Lawrence. Honorary Parish Inspector, Tobacco Inspector
Ahier, Philip	St Martin. Honorary Parish Inspector, Tobacco Inspector

NAME	TITLE/POSITION
Le Masurier, George	St Martin. Honorary Parish Inspector, Tobacco Inspector
Le Feuvre, Philip	St Mary. Honorary Parish Inspector
Le Ruez, Ernest John	St Mary. Honorary Parish Inspector
Huelin, George Emile	St Ouen. Honorary Parish Inspector
Vautier, Edward George	St Ouen. Honorary Parish Inspector
Le Rossignol, George	St Peter. Honorary Parish Inspector
Egré, Edward Rive	St Peter. Honorary Parish Inspector, Tobacco Inspector
Le Ruez, Henry Prouings	St Peter. Honorary Parish Inspector, Tobacco Inspector
Perrée, John Arthur	St Saviour. Honorary Parish Inspector
Gallichan, Philip	St Saviour. Honorary Parish Inspector, Tobacco Inspector
Quenault, Charles	St Saviour. Honorary Parish Inspector, Tobacco Inspector
Ahier, Charles Philip	Trinity. Honorary Parish Inspector, Tobacco Inspector
Le Brun, Alfred Renouf	Trinity. Honorary Parish Inspector, Tobacco Inspector

JURATS, CONNÉTABLES, DEPUTIES

By Name

Ahier, Philip, Deputy	St Martin
Amy, John Henry, Deputy	St Helier
Baudains, John William, Connétable	St Lawrence
Baudains, Philip Melmoth, Jurat	
Benest, Snowdon, Connétable	Trinity
Benest, Walter, Connétable	St Brelade
Bertram, William James, Deputy	Grouville
Billot, Charles Philip, Connétable	St Martin
Blampied, Thomas Richard, Deputy	St Clement
Brée, Philip Ernest, Jurat	
Brée, Touzel John, Jurat	
Briard, Philip William Clarence, Connétable	Grouville

NAME	TITLE/POSITION
Crill, Sydney George, Connétable	St Clement
Cuming, Charles James, Connétable	St Helier
Dorey, Edgar Aleck, Jurat	
Du Val, John, Connétable	St Peter
Gallichan, Philip Nicolle, Jurat	
Gartrell, James, Deputy	St John
Gibaut, Edwin Denize, Deputy	Trinity
Hocquard, Stanley, Jurat	
Labey, Ernest George, Jurat	
Le Boutillier, Francis, Connétable	St Ouen
Le Cornu, Philip de Carteret, Jurat	Lieutenant Bailiff
Le Feuvre, Francis Vibert, Jurat	
Le Feuvre, Francis, Deputy	St Ouen
Le Feuvre, Philip, Deputy	St Mary
Le Marquand, John, Deputy	St Helier
Le Masurier, Edwin Philip, Jurat	
Le Masurier, John, Connétable	St John
Le Masurier, William Smythe, Deputy	St Helier
Le Quesne, Edward, Deputy	St Helier
Le Quesne, Philip, Deputy	St Helier
Luxon, Arthur, Jurat	
Mourant, George John, Connétable	St Saviour
Mourant, Thomas Philip, Deputy	St Saviour
Norman, James Messervy, Jurat	
Pallot, Thomas Alexander, Deputy	St Lawrence
Perrée, Francis John, Connétable	St Mary
Richardson, Philip Norman, Deputy	St Helier
Simon, Walter, Deputy	St Peter

JURATS, CONNÉTABLES, DEPUTIES
By Title

Connétable Baudains, John William	St Lawrence
Connétable Benest, Snowdon	Trinity
Connétable Benest, Walter	St Brelade

NAME	TITLE/POSITION
Connétable Billot, Charles Philip	St Martin
Connétable Briard, Philip William Clarence	Grouville
Connétable Crill, Sydney George	St Clement
Connétable Cuming, Charles James	St Helier
Connétable Du Val, John	St Peter
Connétable Le Boutillier, Francis	St Ouen
Connétable Le Masurier, John	St John
Connétable Mourant, George John	St Saviour
Connétable Perrée, Francis John	St Mary
Deputy Ahier, Philip	St Martin
Deputy Amy, John Henry	St Helier
Deputy Bertram, William James	Grouville
Deputy Blampied, Thomas Richard	St Clement
Deputy Gartrell, James	St John
Deputy Gibaut, Edwin Denize	Trinity
Deputy Le Feuvre, Francis	St Ouen
Deputy Le Feuvre, Philip	St Mary
Deputy Le Marquand, John	St Helier
Deputy Le Masurier, William Smythe	St Helier
Deputy Le Quesne, Edward	St Helier
Deputy Le Quesne, Philip	St Helier
Deputy Mourant, Thomas Philip	St Saviour
Deputy Pallot, Thomas Alexander	St Lawrence
Deputy Richardson, Philip Norman	St Helier
Deputy Simon, Walter	St Peter
Jurat Baudains, Philip Melmoth	
Jurat Brée, Philip Ernest	
Jurat Brée, Touzel John	
Jurat Dorey, Edgar Aleck	
Jurat Gallichan, Philip Nicolle	
Jurat Hocquard, Stanley	
Jurat Labey, Ernest George	
Jurat Le Cornu, Philip de Carteret	Lieutenant Bailiff

NAME	TITLE/POSITION
Jurat Le Feuvre, Francis Vibert	
Jurat Le Masurier, Edwin Philip	
Jurat Luxon, Arthur	
Jurat Norman, James Messervy	

■ German Personnel

Name	Position	
Kolb, Lieutenant	Field Command 515, Adjutant	
von Stein, OKVR	Field Command 515, Chief of Administration	Until September 1941. Replaced by Casper
Casper, W., OKVR, Dr	Field Command 515, Chief of Administration	September 1941 to November 1943. Replaced by von Aufsess
von Aufsess, M., KVR, Baron	Field Command 515, Chief of Administration	From November 1943
Heider, Wilhelm, Major	Field Command 515, Chief of Staff	Replaced by von Cleve, March 1944
Schumacher, Colonel	Field Command 515, Field Commander	August 1940 to October 1941. Replaced by Knackfuss
Knackfuss, Freidrich, Oberst	Field Command 515, Field Commander	4th October 1941 to March 1944
Pelz, Hans Egon, KVR	Field Command 515, Food and Agriculture	
Ruhnka, KVR	Field Command 515, Labour Department	
Demmler, Major	Field Command 515, Logistics	
Pokorni, Inspector	Field Command 515, Public Utilities	
Reffler, KVR, Dr	Field Command 515, Supplies	

Name	Position	
Kempt, Dr	Field Command 515, Veterinary Surgeon	
Milkau, KVR	Field Command 722, St Lô	
Frölich, Gustav	Kaiser Wilhem Institute, Dummerstorf	
Lauprecht, Edwin, Dr	Kaiser Wilhem Institute, Dummerstorf	
Löwe, Hans, Dr	Kaiser Wilhem Institute, Dummerstorf	
Schmidt, Jonas	Kaiser Wilhem Institute, Dummerstorf	
Müller, Erich, Lt-General	Military Authority	Kommandant 319 Inf. Div. Befehlshaber from June 1941 to July 1943. Replaced by von Schmettow
Hüffmeier, Frederick, Admiral	Military Authority (Navy), Chief of Staff	Replaces von Schmettow Feb 1945, overall control of Channel Islands
von Cleve, Kurt Corvette Captain	Military Authority (Navy), Chief of Staff	Replaces Heider as Platzkommandant, March 1944
Schmundt, Rudolf, Colonel	Military Authority, Chief Adjutant to Hitler	
Gussek, Erich, Hauptmann	Military Authority, Inselkommandant	Until 19 September 1940. Replaced by Dannenberg
Dannenberg, Dr	Military Authority, Inselkommandant	21 to 27 September 1940. Becomes Kommandant of the 1st Kp. MG Battalion 16, 1940–41
von Schmettow, Rudolf, Oberst, Graf	Military Authority, Inselkommandant	(Later Major-General) Replaces Dannenberg. Replaces Müller as Befehlshaber July 1943

Name	Position
Heine, Siegfried, Oberst	Military Authority, Inselkommandant, then Festungkommandant
Rannecke, Hauptmann, Dr	Military Authority, Ost Battallion
Todt, Fritz, Dr	Organisation Todt

▲ Grain and Potato Control

Cabot, Philip George	Grain and Potato Control, Chief Clerk
Clift, Bertrand Lampard	Petrol Controller
Day, Peter Philip	Mills Supervisor
Gruchy, Charles	JPMA, Vice-President
Malzard, John George	Chief Cereals Inspector
Norman, John Mallet	JPMA, President

THRESHING

Bertram, E. W.	Threshing Inspector
Blanchet, J. F.	Threshing Inspector
Buesnel, R. W.	Threshing Inspector
Buesnel, S. G.	Threshing Inspector
Channing, F. F.	Threshing Inspector
Ching, R.	Threshing Inspector
de la Haye, E.	Threshing Inspector
de la Haye, T.	Threshing Inspector
Du Bois. P. G.	Threshing Inspector
Farrell, W.	Threshing Inspector
Gautier, A.	Threshing Inspector
Gibaut, P.	Threshing Inspector
Gottard, A.	Threshing Inspector
Hamon, O. P.	Threshing Inspector, Eastern District
Huelin Jun., J. A.	Threshing Inspector
Huelin, H. F	Threshing Inspector
Langdon, G. R.	Threshing Inspector

Langlois, J. P.	Threshing Inspector
Le Boutillier, W. J	Threshing Inspector
Le Brocq, E.	Threshing Inspector
Le Maistre, F.	Threshing Inspector, Western District
Melville, G. R.	Threshing Inspector
Pallot, W. A.	Threshing Inspector
Roberts, P. F.	Threshing Inspector
Steel, J. C.	Threshing Inspector
Steel, R. C.	Threshing Inspector
Taylor, A.	Threshing Inspector
Vautier, H.	Threshing Inspector
Wills, C.	Threshing Inspector
Binet, T. R	Threshing Contractor, Trinity
Cabot, S. J. C.	Threshing Contractor, Trinity
Colback Jun, J. E.	Threshing Contractor, St Helier
Farrell, W.	Threshing Contractor, St Helier
Godel, H. P.	Threshing Contractor, St Ouen
Le Cappelain, T. G.	Threshing Contractor, St Peter
Pallot, L. C.	Threshing Contractor, Trinity
Priaulx, J.	Threshing Contractor, St John
Richard, J.	Threshing Contractor, St John

MILLERS

Baxter, William Hunt	Senior Miller
Gilley, Edwin	Senior Miller
Gilley, Ernest Charles	Senior Miller
Gilley, Harold Ernest	Senior Miller
Gilley, Samuel Edwin	Senior Miller
Hawkins, William Henry	Senior Miller
Hervieu, Peter Auguste	Assistant Miller
Horton, Eric	Assistant Miller
Horton, Frederick James	Assistant Miller
Josse, Emile Frederick.	Assistant Miller

Le Marchand	Assistant Miller
Le Mottée, Maurice	Assistant Miller
Lucas, Claude Le Geyt	Assistant Miller
Lucas, W. H.	Assistant Miller

PLOUGHING CONTRACTORS

A'Court, J. F.	Ploughing Contractor, St Peter
Barette, A. F.	Ploughing Contractor, St Mary
Baudains, R.	Ploughing Contractor, Trinity
Baudains, G.	Ploughing Contractor
Bisson, P. F.	Ploughing Contractor
Blake, G.	Ploughing Contractor, St Clement
Blandin, P. J.	Ploughing Contractor
Boucault, J.	Ploughing Contractor
Boutillier & Son, F.	Ploughing Contractor
Buesnel, A.	Ploughing Contractor
Buesnel, C. W.	Ploughing Contractor, St Saviour
Buesnel, F. G.	Ploughing Contractor, Grouville
Burrel, C. W.	Ploughing Contractor
Chevalier, P.	Ploughing Contractor, St Brelade
Colback Junior, J. E.	Ploughing Contractor
Cotillard, A. A.	Ploughing Contractor, St Lawrence
Cotillard, E.	Ploughing Contractor, St John
Daghorn, E.	Ploughing Contractor
Dauny, A. F.	Ploughing Contractor, St Peter
de Caux, J. R.	Ploughing Contractor
de Gruchy, J. W.	Ploughing Contractor
de Gruchy, S. W.	Ploughing Contractor, St John
du Feu, J. W.	Ploughing Contractor
Dupays, E.	Ploughing Contractor
Egré, H. E.	Ploughing Contractor
England, R. G.	Ploughing Contractor
Fullern, W. P.	Ploughing Contractor
Gallichan, E.	Ploughing Contractor, St Peter
Georgelin, J.	Ploughing Contractor

Giot, W. P.	Ploughing Contractor
Godfray, J. P.	Ploughing Contractor, Trinity
Gotel, Y. M.	Ploughing Contractor, Trinity
Hamon, S.	Ploughing Contractor
Helier, S. B.	Ploughing Contractor
Henry, E. L.	Ploughing Contractor
Hervé, A. J.	Ploughing Contractor
Hidrio, E.	Ploughing Contractor
Holmes, L.	Ploughing Contractor
Jarnet, C. H.	Ploughing Contractor
Jean, C. A.	Ploughing Contractor, St Peter
Jean, P. E.	Ploughing Contractor, St Lawrence
Jonny, Y.	Ploughing Contractor
Laisney, W.	Ploughing Contractor, St John
Langlois, A. H.	Ploughing Contractor, St John
Langlois, R. S.	Ploughing Contractor, St Helier
Larose, D. P.	Ploughing Contractor
Le Boutillier, F.	Ploughing Contractor, St Mary
Le Brocq, H. J.	Ploughing Contractor
Le Brun, E. R.	Ploughing Contractor
Le Cappelain, C. G.	Ploughing Contractor
Le Cappelain, T. G.	Ploughing Contractor, St Peter
Le Cornu, C.	Ploughing Contractor, Grouville
Le Cornu, C. H.	Ploughing Contractor, St Lawrence
Le Cornu, E. R.	Ploughing Contractor
Le Gresley, G. R.	Ploughing Contractor, St Clement
Le Gresley, J. C.	Ploughing Contractor
Le Gresley, S.	Ploughing Contractor, St Mary
Le Herissier, C. W.	Ploughing Contractor
Le Masurier, J.	Ploughing Contractor
Le Riche, E.	Ploughing Contractor
Le Seelleur, W. P.	Ploughing Contractor
Le Touzel, E. W.	Ploughing Contractor, Trinity
Lesbirel, H. J.	Ploughing Contractor
Luce, G. A.	Ploughing Contractor, St John
Maletroit, J.	Ploughing Contractor

Mallet, R.	Ploughing Contractor
Michel, J.	Ploughing Contractor, St Brelade
Mundy, A. V.	Ploughing Contractor, St Helier
Nicolle, F. J.	Ploughing Contractor
Noel, E. P.	Ploughing Contractor
Ozouf, F. R.	Ploughing Contractor
Pallot, L. C.	Ploughing Contractor, Trinity
Pallot, T. A.	Ploughing Contractor
Payn, T. G.	Ploughing Contractor, St Peter
Petry, S.	Ploughing Contractor
Pirouet, J. F.	Ploughing Contractor
Pirouet, P.	Ploughing Contractor
Poignard, C. W.	Ploughing Contractor
Prouten, A. E.	Ploughing Contractor
Renouard, W.	Ploughing Contractor
Richardson, K. G.	Ploughing Contractor, St Martin
Rimeur, F. E.	Ploughing Contractor, St Mary
Rondel, C. S.	Ploughing Contractor, St Martin
Rondel, L.	Ploughing Contractor
Sutton, W.	Ploughing Contractor, St Saviour
Vasselin, G.	Ploughing Contractor

◆ Milk Control

Hamon, A. F.	Don Street Dairy, new Manager
Pluck, J.	Don Street Dairy, Engineer
Jensen, Sören	Don Street Dairy, original Manager
Marie, J. Stanley	Jersey Dairies Limited, Managing Director
Tanguy, Cyril	Chairman, Dairymen's Committee
Weeks, Reginald Oswald	Accountant/Secretary, Milk Control Section
Alexander, H. J.	Milk Tester
Baudins, A.C.	Milk Tester
Biddle, C. P.	Milk Tester

Brée, M.	Milk Tester
Buesnel, D.	Milk Tester
Carrel, F. H.	Milk Tester
Carrel, G. A.	Milk Tester
Cary, G.	Milk Tester
Codeaux, C. D.	Milk Tester
Cotillard, P.A.	Milk Tester
Danican, L. (from Guernsey)	Milk Tester
Davy, G.	Milk Tester
de Gruchy, P. E.	Milk Tester
de la Cour, C.	Milk Tester
Gaudin, J. P.	Milk Tester
Gautier, E.	Milk Tester
Gicquel, J. P.	Milk Tester
Gruchy, E. L.	Milk Tester
Hamelin, D.	Milk Tester
Hansford, W.	Milk Tester
Henry, C. W.	Milk Tester
Henwood, P. J.	Milk Tester
Hind, G. J.	Milk Tester
Huelin, G.	Milk Tester
Jones, F. B.	Milk Tester
Le Brocq, C. J.	Milk Tester
Le Cocq, F. P.	Milk Tester
Le Feuvre, A. G.	Milk Tester
Le Feuvre, J. P.	Milk Tester
Le Gros, G.	Milk Tester
Le Gros, S. G.	Milk Tester
Le Lère, A. E.	Milk Tester
Le Masurier, R.	Milk Tester
Le Sueur, G. P.	Milk Tester
Le Sueur, H. F.	Milk Tester
Leonard, S. E.	Milk Tester
Luce, F. G.	Milk Tester
Malzard, J. G.	Chief Milk Tester, Western District
Manning, H. J.	Milk Tester

Mauger, C. R.	Chief Milk Tester, Eastern District
Nicolle, P. A.	Milk Tester
Paulain, G.	Milk Tester
Poignard, J. F.	Milk Tester
Roberts, J. T.	Milk Tester
Talbot, C.	Milk Tester
Tirel, Q. H.	Milk Tester
Yates, R.M.	Milk Tester

❖ Cattle and Livestock

Le Feuvre, Philip	Jersey Farmers Union, President
Journeaux, C. P.	Jersey Farmers Union, Vice President
Le Marinel, T. G.	Jersey Farmers Union, Vice President
Messervy, G. A.	Jersey Farmers Union, Secretary
Le Gallais, Carlyle	RJA&HS, President
Michel, John Buesnel	RJA&HS, Vice President
Le Boutillier, Francis	RJA&HS, Vice President
Shepard, Harold G.	RJA&HS, Secretary
Le Masurier, W. S.	RJA&HS, Solicitor
Journeaux, C. P.	Joint Emergency Committee
Le Boutillier, Francis	Joint Emergency Committee
Le Feuvre, Philip	Joint Emergency Committee
Le Gallais, Carlyle	Joint Emergency Committee
Le Marinel, T. G.	Joint Emergency Committee
Michel, John Buesnel	Joint Emergency Committee
Carson, Robert Wilson	Calf Selection Committee
Godeaux, Claude	Calf Selection Committee
Le Boutillier, Francis	Calf Selection Committee
Le Cornu, Charles	Calf Selection Committee
Le Gallais, Carlyle	Calf Selection Committee

Le Masurier, George	Calf Selection Committee
Michel, John Buesnel	Calf Selection Committee
Mourant, Philip Chevalier	Calf Selection Committee
Shepard, Harold G.	Calf Selection Committee
Le Gallais, Carlyle	Cattle Slaughter Executive Committee
Michel, John Buesnel	Cattle Slaughter Executive Committee
Le Boutillier, Francis	Cattle Slaughter Executive Committee
Perrédès, Eugene C.	Cattle Slaughter Executive Committee
Carson, Robert Wilson	Cattle Slaughter Executive Committee
Romeril, George A.	Cattle Slaughter Executive Committee
Ching, R.	Tattooing Officer, St Mary
Hamon, O. P.	Tattooing Officer, St Brelade
Le Rossignol, G. H.	Tattooing Officer, St Peter
Le Ruez, W. G.	Tattooing Officer, St John
Pallot, W. A.	Tattooing Officer, St Lawrence
Steel, J. C.	Tattooing Officer, St Ouen
Moses, P. L.	Tattooing Assistant, St Mary
Du Bois, P. G.	Tattooing Assistant, St Brelade
Vautier, H.	Tattooing Assistant, St Peter
Marett, J.	Tattooing Assistant, St John
Gautier, A. L.	Tattooing Assistant, St Lawrence
Le Boutillier, W. J.	Tattooing Assistant, St Ouen

Merchants

A. E. Laurens

A. P. Falle and Sons Limited

C. Mossop

C. S. Bailhache

Chas Gruchy and Company Limited

Country Gentlemen's Association (CGA) Limited

de Veulle and Company

E. Becquet

F. Giddens

F. Le Sueur and Son Limited

George Blampied Limited

Guiton and Lucas

J. E. Baudains

J. F. Pirouet and Son

J. Martland Limited

J. Spearman

Jersey Co-operative Wholesale Society Limited

Jersey Farmers (Trading) Union Limited

Jersey Produce Merchants Association (JPMA)

Job and Sons

John Terry Limited.

Le Marquand Brothers

Le Riches Stores Limited

Le Rossignol and Company

Marks and Riches Limited

Normans Limited

O. J. Le Mottée Limited

P. J. de Gruchy

R. P. Amy

Randall's Brewery

Sidney Horman Limited

T. Dorey and Company Limited

T. Mayo and Company Limited

W. Bird and Son Limited

W. Dennis and Sons Limited

W. J. Gaudin

W. Nicolls and Sons Limited

Weights and Measures

	Symbol	Value
Currency		
Reichsmark	RM	varied; 6-8 to £1

Pfennig	Pfg	100 to the Reichsmark 1940–44
Franc	Ff	20 to 1 RM
Pound	£	Pound sterling
Shilling	s	20 shillings to the pound
Penny, pence	d	12 pence to the shilling

Volume

Pint		0.57 litre
Pot		4 pints
Gallon		8 pints
Litre		1.76 pints

Weight

Pound	lb	16 ounces
Quarter	qrt	28 lbs
Cabot		32 lbs
Hundredweight	cwt	4 qrt or 112 lbs
Ton	ton	20 cwt or 2240 lbs
Metric tonne		1,000 kilos or 2,204.6 lbs

Area

Perch	484 imperial sq ft or 576 Jersey sq ft
Vergée	19,360 sq ft or 40 perches or 4/9 of an acre
Acre	2.25 vergées
Hectare	2.47 acres

Meanings – Explanations

Chats	Smallest potato size
Mids	Medium potato size or a later variety

Wares	Large potato size	
Royals	The Jersey variety of potato	
Côtils	Fields on steep slopes	
Gasogene	A fuel made by burning charcoal or wood and used in converted lorries and tractors. Also called "Aniche Gazosse".	
Scarifying	Light harrowing	
Verpflegungausgabestelle	Office issuing rations. Verpflegung = rations	Ausgabestelle = place of issue, issuing counter/office
Vraic	Seaweed used as a fertiliser	

Orders Mentioned in the Book

Order	First Mentioned In	Date Law is Passed (if known)
Agricultural Produce (Crop Control) (Jersey) Order, 1941	Ch. 5	
Cereal Grain (Threshing and Purchase of Crops) (Jersey) Order, 1941	Ch. 6	
Colorado Beetle (Compulsory Spraying) (Jersey) Order, 1943,	Ch. 12	24-Jun-43
Colorado Beetle (Compulsory Spraying) (No 2) (Jersey) Order, 1943,	Ch. 12	
Concentrated Cattle Foods (Jersey) Order, 1940	Ch. 4	
Control of Mills (Jersey) Order, 1944	Ch. 16	25-Oct-44

Order	First Mentioned In	Date Law is Passed (if known)
Cultivation of Lands (Jersey) Order, 1940	Ch. 4	27-Aug-40
Cultivation of Lands (Jersey) Order, 1942	Ch. 11	
Fat Stock (Provisional Prices) (No 7) (Jersey) Order, 1941	Ch. 10	
Fertilisers (Jersey) Order, 1941	Ch. 6	
Fertilisers (Returns) (Jersey) Order, 1940	Ch. 5	26-Sep-40
Glasshouse Potatoes (Jersey) Order, 1942	Ch. 8	
Harvesting of Grain Crops (Fire Precautions) (Jersey) Order, 1941	Ch. 6	23-Jul-41
Home-Grown Hay (Maximum Price) (Jersey) Order 1941	Ch. 15	
Home-Grown Potatoes (1942 Crop) (Maximum Prices) (Jersey) Order, 1942	Ch. 8	
Home-Grown Potatoes (1943 Crop) (Maximum Prices) (Jersey) Order, 1943	Ch. 12	21-May-43
Home-Grown Potatoes (1943 Crop) (Maximum Prices) (Amendment) (Jersey) Order, 1943	Ch. 14	
Home-Grown Potatoes (1944 Crop) (Maximum Prices) (Amendment) (Jersey) Order, 1944	Ch. 16	6-Jun-44
Home-Grown Straw (Maximum Price) (Jersey) Order, 1941	Ch. 12	
Identification of Persons (Jersey) Order, 1940	Ch. 5	2-Jan-41

Order	First Mentioned In	Date Law is Passed (if known)	
Import and Export of Goods (Control) (Jersey) Order, 1941	Ch. 11		
Importation of Livestock (Jersey) Regulations, 1940	Ch. 3		
Livestock (Jersey) Order, 1942	Ch. 9	24-Jul-42	
Livestock (Amendment) (Jersey) Order, 1943	Ch. 12	19-May-43	
Livestock (Amendment No 2) (Jersey) Order, 1944	Ch. 15	24-Jan-44	
Livestock (Amendment No 3) (Jersey) Order, 1945	Ch. 16	24-Apr-45	
Livestock (Restriction on Movement) (Jersey) Order, 1943	Ch. 16		
Livestock (Restriction on Slaughtering) (Jersey) Order, 1940	Ch. 5		
Livestock (Returns) (Jersey) Order, 1943	Ch. 11	4th January 1943	
Livestock (Returns) (Jersey) Order, 1944	Ch. 16	7th June 1944	
Livestock (Sales) (Jersey) Order, 1940	Ch. 9		
Loi (1886) touchant la Falsification des Denrées	Ch. 11		Adulteration of commodities
Loi (1934) sur le Règie et le mode de Perception de L'Impôt sur le Tabac	Ch. 14		Law on the administration and method for collecting tax on tobacco
Meat (Maximum Retail Prices) (Amendment No 5) (Jersey) Order, 1942	Ch. 8		
Meat (Maximum Retail Prices) (Amendment No 6) (Jersey) Order, 1943	Ch. 12	7-Jun-43	

Order	First Mentioned In	Date Law is Passed (if known)
Milk (Registration with Retailers) (Jersey) Order, 1940	Ch. 5	23-Dec-40
Milk (Registration with Retailers) (Jersey) Order, 1941	Ch. 6	9-Jun-41
Milk (Registration with Retailers) (Jersey) Order, 1942	Ch. 7	
Milk (Revocation of Licences) (Jersey) Order, 1942	Ch. 7	
Milk Control (Amendment No 2) (Jersey) Order, 1942	Ch. 7	
Milk Control (Jersey) Order, 1940	Ch. 3	
Milk Control (Prices and Contribution) (No 2) (Amendment No 3) (Jersey) Order, 1940	Ch. 5	1-Nov-40
Milk Control (Prices and Contribution) (No 2) (Amendment No 5) (Jersey) Order, 1941	Ch. 7	8-Nov-41
New Potatoes (Maximum Prices) (Jersey) Order, 1941	Ch. 6	
Newly-Born Calves (Jersey) Order, 1941	Ch. 6	
Pigs (Control) (Jersey) Order, 1941	Ch. 6	
Potato Flour (Manufacture for Sale) (Jersey) Order, 1941	Ch. 9	2-Sep-41
Potatoes (Returns) (Jersey) Order, 1941	Ch. 6	
Potatoes (Sales and Returns) (Amendment) (Jersey) Order, 1941	Ch. 6	

Order	First Mentioned In	Date Law is Passed (if known)
Potatoes (Sales and Returns) (Jersey) Order, 1941	Ch. 7	
Potatoes (Sales) (Jersey) Order, 1940	Ch. 5	19-Aug-40
Potatoes (Sales) (Jersey) Order, 1941	Ch. 5	14-Feb-41
Potatoes and Tomatoes (Maximum Prices) (Jersey) Order 1940	Ch. 5	
Price-Controlled Articles (Auction Sales) (Jersey) Order, 1941	Ch. 12	
Rabies (Jersey) Order, 1940	Ch. 5	
Rationing (Jersey) Order, 1940	Ch. 8	
Rationing (Jersey) Order, 1943	Ch. 16	
Restriction of Legal Proceedings (Jersey) Regulations, 1940	Ch. 4	
Suckling-Pig (Maximum Price) Jersey Order, 1942	Ch. 10	
Tobacco (Rationing) (Jersey) Order, 1940	Ch. 6	
Vegetables (Maximum Prices) (Jersey) Order 1941	Ch. 12	
Warble Fly (Jersey) Order, 1943	Ch. 12	30-Mar-43